Standard Encyclopedia of the World's Oceans and Islands

Contributors

Patrick Anderson
Humphrey Beckett
Oswell Blakeston
Ernle Bradford
Francis Celoria
Ronald W. Clark
Dr A. Classe
Roger P. Coleman
Dr T. F. Gaskell
Geoffrey Grigson
Nicholas Guppy
Dr Martin Holdgate
Peter Hunt
Anthony Huxley
Frank Illingworth
Mrs Barbara Morris
F. Kingdon-Ward
Mrs F. Kingdon-Ward
Sir Harry Luke
Dr A. J. Marshall
Professor N. E. Odell
George Pendle
Richard Scott
John Seymour
E. W. Shanahan
Dr W. T. Stearn
J. C. Stuttard
Paul Tabori
John Usborne
N. M. Wace
Francis Watson

Standard Encyclopedia of the World's

Oceans and Islands

Edited by Anthony Huxley

G. P. Putnam's Sons

New York

This book was designed and produced by George Rainbird Ltd
for G. P. Putnam's Sons, 200 Madison Avenue, New York 16, N.Y.
 Published
simultaneously in Canada by Longmans Canada Ltd
Library of Congress Catalog Card Number: 62-7983
First edition 1962
Printed in the Netherlands by
N.V. Drukkerij Koch & Knuttel, Gouda

Contents

List of Color Plates

Introduction

Water covers some two thirds of the globe. In it, almost certainly, was the beginning of life. Through all the upheavals of our planet – cycle upon cycle of mountain upheaval and volcanic creation, followed by erosion and decay – continents changed their outlines and positions, but always the water remained; and when Earth finally settled into its present pattern great oceans divided the land masses.

Man is basically an inquisitive creature, but it was a very long time before he ventured far on the sea, though in his dugouts and coracles he traveled on rivers and lakes, and probably around the safer coasts. Early literate man supposed that the sea entirely surrounded the land, and many maps, from Babylonian times into the Middle Ages, showed the continents grouped in the center of a circle surrounded by a ring of ocean.

Not surprisingly, it was in the landlocked Mediterranean, the center of early western civilization, that seafaring really began; and seafaring is synonymous with exploration.

The Phoenicians were among the earliest seafarers; from about 1400 B.C. they sailed around and across the Mediterranean, settling and trading. In due course, they sailed out past the Pillars of Hercules (the Strait of Gibraltar) to the Tin Islands (Great Britain) and also south out of the Red Sea right round Africa to re-enter the Mediterranean from the west. Although, in so doing, they must have seen something of that curious phenomenon unknown in the Mediterranean – the tides – nothing is recorded of these till 325 B.C.

In that year Alexander the Great recorded difficulty with these unexpected changes of water level on entering the Indian Ocean from the Indus River. About the same time, another Greek, named Pytheas, followed the Phoenician route to Britain and then sailed farther north to the Shetlands; but when he returned home his description of the large North Sea tides was disbelieved.

Tacitus is the first writer to record storms, met with by the Romans in the North Sea. They must have found these fearsome indeed, in their small vessels: it is amazing to us what risks these early seafarers took. At some time in the sixth century A.D. St Brendan is said to have ventured westwards in the Atlantic for long periods, to reach a never identified and probably mythical island – St Brendan's Isle was long marked on maps, having to be placed farther and farther southwest as explorers failed to discover it. But in 795 A.D. a party of Irish monks sailed from the Hebrides to Iceland, probably in wicker-framed boats covered with hides, not unlike today's curraghs.

An almost insatiable curiosity must have possessed the Vikings, who traveled in the next century all round Scandinavia, to Iceland – where they found the Irish monks – to Greenland, and finally to the west coast of North America. This they did in shallow-draughted open boats. One wonders why their curiosity left them when they reached North America, and what might have happened to history if it had not.

It was not till 1418 that further deliberate sea exploration was carried out. Prince Henry of Portugal launched an era of sea travel among his subjects and those of Spain, which developed after his death into a great age of discovery. In 1486–87 Bartholomew Dias rounded the Cape of Good Hope; in 1492 Christopher Columbus – a Genoese under Spanish patronage – reached Cuba, and in 1503 reached the coast of central America; in 1494–95 Dias piloted Vasco da Gama's fleet to Mozambique and Mombasa. Here they were surprised by the wealth and civilization, and the sailing capacities, of Asiatic traders they met; for these, at least since 1000 A.D., and probably long before, had been traveling in the China seas, the Indian Ocean, the Persian Gulf and the Red Sea, coasting in junks and crossing the open sea in dhows.

Western writers often forget that exploration was not confined to their own countries. The Arabian seafarers Soleyman and Al-Masudi traveled to Ceylon, Malaya and Canton in 850 and 914 A.D. respectively. Polynesian migrations – almost certainly southeast from Asia – are thought to date from the fourteenth century; and they were open-sea journeys in sea-going double canoes – canoes made only with stone tools.

Exploration is not the prerogative of the white, "civilized" man, and the migrations of the stone-age Polynesians were not accompanied by the plunder, rapine and suppression which the Spaniards brought to America, and other nations to Africa and the Pacific in the later centuries of slave-trading and "black-birding."

It is perhaps true that only white explorers — some eastern, more western – were impelled basically by curiosity, a determination to find the continents and islands rumored to exist, even if piracy and loot, or trade, were sometimes other objectives. Think of the Cabots who explored round Labrador between 1497 and 1509; of Cabral who discovered Brazil in 1500; Di Varthema who reached the East Indies in 1519-20; De Saavedra who crossed from Mexico to New Guinea in 1527–28; Xavier who reached China and Japan in 1540–52; Chancellor who visited Moscow by way of Novaya Zemlya in 1553; Drake who circumnavigated the globe in 1577–80; Dampier who discovered Australia on his voyage of 1679–91; and Cook, the greatest scientific explorer of them all, who traveled between 1768 and 1776 in all the southern oceans and to the Antarctic and the Arctic.

The explorers' roll of honor is marked on our maps today, brave men who have left their names on islands and seas in remote places – Barents, Frobisher, Hudson, Baffin, Tasman, Bering, Anson, La Pérouse, Flinders, Humboldt, the Rosses, Franklin, Parry, Weddell, Bellingshausen and so many more.

All this, naturally, was accomplished with steadily improving vessels and navigation instruments – the compass, a Mediterranean invention (though the Chinese appear to have invented it independently); the cross-staff, whose origin is uncertain; the quadrant and the astrolabe, adapted for nautical use by the Portuguese; and the sextant and the really accurate chronometer, both perfected in Britain. In Polynesia some method of measuring latitude must have been known, and extraordinary – to us – "charts" of bamboo strips denoted currents and swells which only the most skilful seaman could recognize. All this time, too, maps and charts progressed, both in the areas they covered and in their accuracy.

So our seas became known, and with them the inhabitants, beasts and vegetation of other continents and islands, their cliffs, bays, sands, shoals, reefs and estuaries. In this volume some of these features are described: the major oceans, seas and islands, bays and straits, currents and depths, capes and coasts.

Under the heading "Land and Sea" a long article outlines the evolution of seas and land masses and the formation of islands, and describes the submarine topography and something of the nature of the ocean itself, much of this information newly acquired during the International Geophysical Year (1959–60). It goes on to show how the position of the seas has affected animal and vegetable development on the islands and continents. This is the "key" article of this volume, and should be read to gain a basic understanding of the whole subject.

There are more than 350 articles in the Encyclopedia, describing the most important seas, islands and other features. To supplement these articles there is a gazetteer with some 2,000 entries. Reference maps show the positions of the principal seas and islands. Numerous photographs demonstrate many aspects of sea and coast and human activities upon them. Finally, there is a comprehensive index. The spelling of place names and the alphabetical order are based on the Columbia Lippincott Gazetteer.

The oceans have impelled innumerable men to face every kind of discomfort and peril in the search for further knowledge and they still have plenty to offer us. Heyerdahl, Bombard and others have made fantastic journeys in impossible-seeming craft; many have traveled the oceans alone in tiny sailing boats; Cousteau has pioneered skin diving; Beebe, Piccard and others have plumbed the depths. Oceanography is beginning to reveal unsuspected submarine features, and its researches may well be vital to man's subsistence in an overpopulated world.

It is not surprising that psychologists often consider the sea as a symbol of our subconscious. Certainly, it has long had a powerful hold on mankind. It is not given to all of us to be explorers; but we may sense something of the ocean's mystique from a liner, more intimately in a sailing vessel, or simply on holiday by the sea's edge. I hope that this volume will add to the reader's knowledge of the myriad fascinating aspects of the world's oceans and islands.

Anthony Huxley

Ardnamurchan Point, on Scotland's Atlantic coast

Land and Sea

The best way to think of the earth's surface is to imagine that the water is removed, laying bare the vast area of ocean floor. This floor is not flat, but is furrowed with ridges and valleys and crossed by great mountain chains. The ocean floor is studded with pimples which are sometimes more than three miles high so that their tops are above water. These are islands; but they are the exception, for most of the volcanic structures that have erupted from the sea-bed either have never reached the surface or have slid back under their own weight to become flat-topped sea-mounts or guyots – their tops having been planed off by wave action. Standing up more than three miles from the ocean floor are the continents, which appear as large plateaus, occupying in all about one third of the earth's surface.

The difference between sea and land, oceans and continents, is often thought of as one of those simple things that every child learns as soon as it is old enough to paddle. Yet the extent to which this distinction is fundamental in terms of the earth's structure and history is a complex problem that has been fiercely argued for years.

It is quite certain that the distribution of land and water over the earth's surface has changed enormously during the several thousand million years that separate our oldest and our youngest rocks. In some places, limestones and shales which were clearly laid down under water, and which preserve within them the remains of marine animals, now cover large areas of land and are raised up in high mountains. Elsewhere, the sandstones formed in ancient deserts now lie below the sea. Further, it is quite common for marine and terrestrial deposits to be piled one on top of the other in long sequences, showing that the processes of uplift and submergence have happened not once but many times.

But, while there is no doubt that the seas have from time to time overspilled the margins of the continents and at other times retreated far beyond present coastlines, this does not mean that the distinction between oceans and continents is unimportant. It simply means that the obvious boundary – the actual shore line – is not the best one to draw. Around most continents today there is a belt of fairly shallow sea – usually less than 600 feet deep – and this deepens only slowly as one passes outwards from the coast. This fringe of shallow sea, which may be several hundred miles wide, is called the continental shelf. Beyond it, the sea bottom falls away more steeply into deep water, until it levels out again in the floor of the main ocean basins, which lie as much as ten or even fifteen thousand feet below the surface. It is quite clear that the true margin of a continent should be drawn not wherever the coastline happens to be at the present moment, but along the lip of the continental shelf, which is a far more prominent and permanent feature.

Once this has been done, the continents become clearly defined as upstanding masses divided by expanses of deep ocean. The various extensions and retreats of sea and land which cause the intermingling of different rocks now fall into place as changes in the pattern of distribution of the shallow seas of the continental shelves. If the land level is raised, or the sea level falls, the coastline may retreat out to the lip of the shelf. If, on the other hand, the land level sinks or the sea rises, shallow waters may invade a large area of the land surface and lay down their deposits there; if the sinking goes on over a long period, these deposits may become very thick indeed. But such changes will in no way affect the major distinction between continental masses and ocean basins.

This distinction is certainly associated with, and is probably due to, important differences in the rocks of the two systems. The continents seem to have a basis of lighter rocks, such as granites, and may be thought of as "floating" on the denser, lower, layers of basaltic material which are exposed in the ocean floors. If this is so, it is clearly unlikely that the two systems could easily be interchanged. To force up a patch of ocean floor into a new continent would mean raising a mass of heavy rock to an unnaturally high level, while to depress a patch of continental material to the level of the ocean floor would be like trying to sink a floating log: there would be a natural tendency for it to bob up again. Both these processes are possible, but it would need force not only to bring them about but to keep them in being.

Consequently, most people now believe that the continents and oceans, despite their many comparatively minor ups and downs, are very ancient features of the world's surface. The chief argument at present is raging over whether their arrangement has remained constant. Some people believe that the broad pattern has always been more or less the same, so that the great basins of the Pacific, Atlantic and Indian oceans are of the same age. Others believe that at one time the world had what amounted to a land hemisphere and a water hemisphere. The latter included the present Pacific basin, but was much larger, while the former comprised all the present continental blocks fitted together in a kind of gigantic jig-saw puzzle. A very quick inspection of a globe shows that the coastline – or, better still, the shelf margin – of Europe and Africa fits snugly into that of the Americas. As for the other parts of the puzzle, the Antarctic fits in between Africa, Madagascar and Australia, and the combination neatly obliterates the Indian Ocean.

This theory, after being generally disbelieved for several decades, has recently been supported by a good deal of evidence, and some of its adherents now hold that the mass may not have split up until about 50,000,000 years ago. The present Indian and Atlantic oceans have been formed, on this theory, by the widening of the cracks between the new continents, which have slowly drifted apart, "floating" on the denser rocks below. But this theory is still controversial, and we cannot pursue it further here. Instead, we must say something about the submarine ridges that lie below some of the oceans, and about the islands that are dotted about them.

The submarine ridges are really mountain ranges, though there is some argument as to whether they are genuine upfoldings of the crust or whether they are thin strips of continental rock, perhaps left behind when the main masses drifted apart, and not "floating" high enough to reach the sea surface. The two biggest and most famous are the Mid-Atlantic and Mid-Indian ridges. The former is one of the longest mountain systems in the world, running down almost the exact center of the Atlantic from Greenland and Iceland to within a thousand miles of the Antarctic. For much of its course it is covered by deep water, though it stands high in relation to the basins on either flank, and only a few volcanic peaks reach the surface in the islands of the Azores, St Paul's Rocks, Ascension, St Helena, Tristan da Cunha and Gough. It may be linked to the Mid-Indian ridge, which runs from India to the Antarctic and supports other islands such as Kerguelen, Heard, St Paul, New Amsterdam and Rodriguez.

The world's islands, as a whole, fall into two classes: continental and oceanic. The former rise on the continental shelves, so that they are mostly close to the main land masses and intermittently linked to them. The British Isles and the islands of northern Indonesia are good examples. A few continental islands, though, such as Madagascar and New Zealand, are not so closely linked to the nearby land masses, and represent small, isolated masses of continental rock which have become separated from the greater blocks. Oceanic islands, on the other hand, rise abruptly from the deep water of the main basins, or from the submarine ridges. They are mostly volcanic and have never been linked by continuous land to any of the continents. All the most famous "lonely islands," such as the Azores, Easter Island, Pitcairn, the Galapagos, Bermuda, Tristan da Cunha and Hawaii, belong to this class.

In most people's minds, the "South Seas" are pictured as studded with coral islands, and these are indeed abundant in the tropical waters of the Pacific and Indian oceans. They have fascinated scientists for over a century, and about ten different contradictory theories have been propounded to account for them. Of course, it is well known that coral itself is the accumulated skeletons of a kind of tiny colonial sea-anemone. The controversy surrounds the manner in which these animals are able to form entire islands, which often lack other visible rocks. This is no place to go into details, but it may be said that Darwin's original theory, put forward in the eighteen-thirties, still holds the field. Darwin pointed out that coral reefs would develop to fringe any stable island in the tropics, and would slowly grow outwards on accumulated debris. If the island subsided, one of two things might happen. If it went rapidly, the upward growth of the coral would be unable to keep pace, and eventually the animals would be carried down into deep, dark water and killed. But if the subsidence was slow, they would be able to grow upwards as fast as the land sank, and eventually the rock base of the island might be entirely covered in a capping of coral. This seems to be the story of the coral atolls, most of which fringe or cap typical volcanic oceanic islands.

There are many discoveries still to be made about the shape of the sea floor. Almost every expedition that goes out into the deep ocean brings back reports of one or two new sea-mounts. During the International Geophysical Year a much better picture was obtained of such features as the long line of islands stretching northwest from Hawaii for nearly 2,000 miles, and of the steep rift valleys that run down the Mid-Atlantic Ridge, not quite continuous, but rather like the cracks in a piece of timber, always parallel to the grain. It will be the turn of the Indian Ocean in coming years. Just as the IGY co-operation yielded a great harvest of results, so the International Indian Ocean Expedition will bring our knowledge of this area, which has been neglected in the past, up to the standard of the Pacific and the Atlantic.

But what of the vast volume of water that fills the ocean to a depth of about three miles and over an area of nearly two thirds of the earth's surface? Until quite recently those few people who gave the subject a moment's thought believed that the waters were still and deep, hiding beneath them a dark and silent world, which received a gentle snowfall of debris from above and became blanketed by a layer of soft mud. We know now that there are complications to this picture. Photographs of the sea-bed show that a whole host of animals live on the sea-bed and their burrowing disturbs the regular pattern of sediment. Ripple marks show on the sea-bed, formed by some kind of water movement, possibly caused by tsunamis, or tidal waves as they are popularly but erroneously called, which speed at five hundred miles an hour from the scene of an underwater earthquake with a wave-length of 100 miles or so. Such a long wave-length means that the water is by comparison shallow, and therefore, unlike the much shorter seawaves, the tsunami can cause movement in the water all the way down.

Everyone knows about the Gulf Stream which moves up the eastern American seaboard before sweeping across the Atlantic as a broad river to circulate warm water to Europe. Careful measurements have shown that this and many other surface currents have a countercurrent moving below them. The great Humboldt Current in the Pacific has its partner, and in fact there is a small movement of water even down to the greatest depths in almost every part of the ocean. There is an obvious importance in this today, because the sea is the traditional dumping ground for rubbish, and modern radioactive rubbish is really safe only if it can be put in a backwater where it will not circulate and spread.

There is another kind of current that alters the face of our sea-bed world. This is the turbidity current, which rushes down the continental slope with the speed of an express train, breaking telegraph cables which are in its path, and carrying a whole mass of material from the continents to form flat pools of sediment. These pools are called abyssal plains and they were at one time supposed to be the primeval sea floor, but the modern echo-sounder, which can distinguish a depth-change of a few feet in 3,000 fathoms, has demonstrated that the plains are not quite flat, but rather slope away from underwater river-beds that have been scoured out by the turbidity currents.

The simultaneous observation of the temperature and salinity of the sea water during the IGY has enabled oceanographers to calculate the main circulation of water in the oceans. Cold water tends to sink in the polar regions and to flow towards the equator, underneath the warmer, lighter water. Where currents meet there tends to be an upwelling of water. The water that had been creeping along the sea-bed brings with it rich nutrients, especially in the form of trace elements such as cobalt and nickel, which it has gathered from the sea-bed. There is often, therefore, abnormal plant and animal growth in these zones of upwelling water, and if ever the exploding world population is to receive a substantial part of its protein requirements by harvesting the sea, a knowledge of currents will be essential so that natural forces can be enlisted to help the sea farmer with his craft.

Although the oceans are of enormous volume, their level is affected considerably by the variation in the amount of ice that is locked up in the polar ice caps. The IGY attack on Antarctica has made possible a fairly accurate assessment of all the world's ice and the quantity is such that, if it all melted, the sea level would rise by nearly 300 feet. The possibility of melting is not so remote as might appear at first sight. A change in the carbon dioxide content of the atmosphere could increase the heating effect of the sun's rays. The balance of carbon dioxide in the air is provided by the amount that dissolves

The eel-like halosaurus, photographed on the deep-sea floor

in sea water, and this amount depends on the rate of mixing of surface water by the ocean currents.

There has been an awakening during the last decade or so to the importance of the study of the oceans, and today this is one of the most rapidly progressing sciences. Deep underwater photography has been developed to a point where it is of the greatest value to the oceanographer, while man himself has already made several descents into the great depths in bathyscaphes, and will doubtless make many more.

Considering their great area and variety of terrain, one would expect the continents to be the starting places for the evolution of most successful new groups and species of land-inhabiting animals and plants. This has, in fact, been the case. From their places of origin, these new forms have spread outwards over the land surface, invading all suitable habitats that they could reach, and replacing their more primitive predecessors. This migration of species has largely taken place overland. It seems difficult for most species, apart from actively flying birds and insects, to cross any expanse of open sea, and quite narrow channels have acted as effective barriers.

Perhaps the best example of such a barrier is the deep-water strait that divides Indonesia, passing between Borneo and Java on the one hand and the Celebes and Timor group on the other. Although the channel is only a few miles wide, the animals and plants on the north and west are mostly "Asiatic" in their affinities, and they differ markedly from the "Australasian" forms to the south and east. Inspection of the relief of the sea-bed in this region helps to explain the difference, for the northwestern section proves to be an extension of the Asiatic continental shelf, and there is no doubt that Borneo, Java and Sumatra were linked to the main mass not very long ago. The Australasian section of the archipelago, on the other hand, rises from deep water, and any land link with Asia probably broke down much earlier.

This link was in existence, however, at the time when Asia was first occupied by the ancestors of the pouched mammals (such as the kangaroos), and consequently these forms were able to migrate overland into Australia. But the land bridge was broken before the later group of mammals – the placentals – reached the region; as a result, these forms have failed to replace the marsupials in Australasia, though they have

A beak-nosed skate, another denizen of the ocean depths

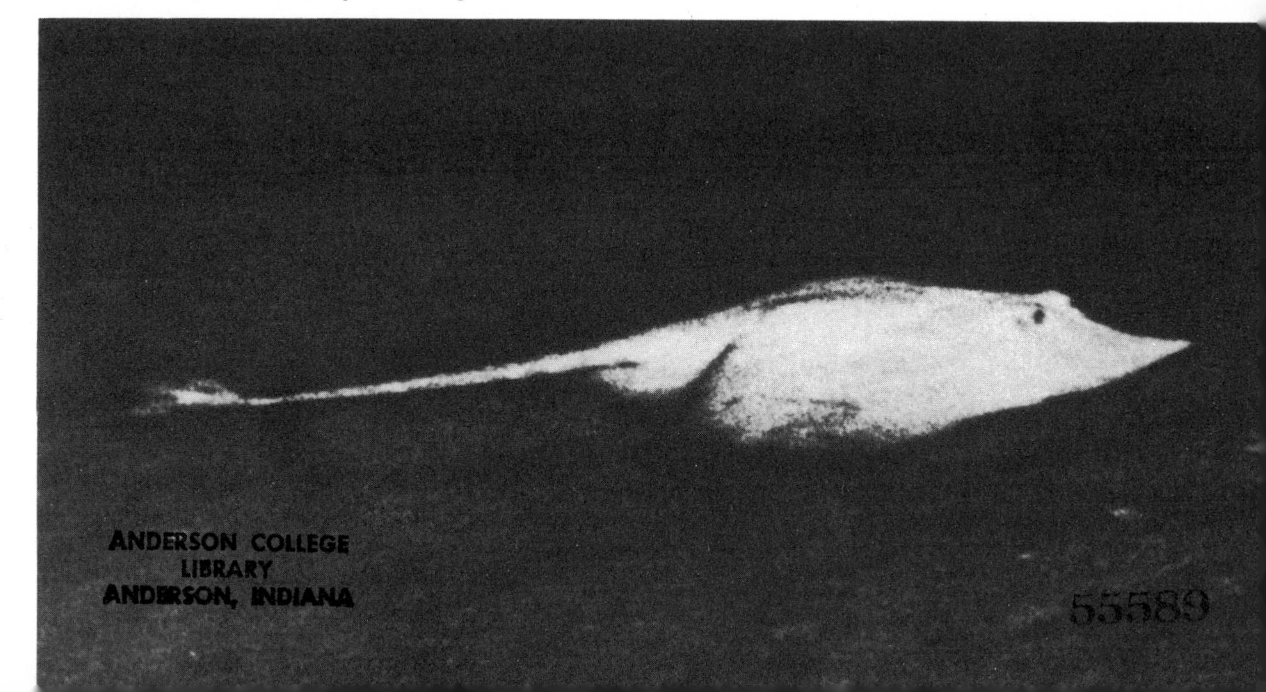

Professor Piccard's bathyscaphe Trieste

become dominant everywhere else in the world.

Evidence of this kind – and there is no doubt that this example could be duplicated for many other groups and regions – shows that the distribution of the oceans has had a profound influence on animal and plant dispersal and on the processes of evolution. It is clear that a new species which evolves on an isolated island, even if it is theoretically capable of spreading all over the world, has little chance of doing so unless a land connection appears to allow it to get there. It is also clear that where two land masses have broadly similar floras and faunas, they were probably once linked, while two areas similar in climate and terrain with very different animals and plants have probably been separated for a long period.

Sometimes these conclusions lead to serious problems. For example, there are many species of animal and plant which occur both in southern South America and in southeastern Australasia, and some people have postulated a direct land bridge across the South Pacific to explain them. But the great age of the Pacific and the structural difficulty of raising a great mountain range across it and then sinking this range into deep water once it had served its purpose militate against such a theory. The alternative view is that the Antarctic must once have been warmer, and perhaps more closely linked to the other two land masses, so acting as a "stepping stone" between them.

Because they are intermittently linked to the greater land masses, continental islands tend to have a rich flora and fauna which closely resembles that of the adjacent mainland. There are very few British animals and plants which do not also occur in the neighboring parts of Europe, though a number of species which migrated into northwestern Europe after the British Isles had become isolated have failed to cross even the narrow gap of the Strait of Dover.

But oceanic islands usually have very poor floras and faunas indeed. Most oceanic islands are volcanic, and while eruptions are in progress they are effectively sterilized. Once quiescence has begun, colonization by animals and plants can take place, but only by long-distance migration across the sea; and, as we have said, this is a difficult process. Obviously, remote islands will not acquire many species, and their floras and faunas will be made up chiefly of forms with an efficient long-range dispersal system. This conclusion is supported by innumerable examples. Henderson Island in the Pacific has only four kinds of land bird; Easter Island has none; in the Atlantic, the Tristan da Cunha group has five land birds and Gough Island only two. Plants show a comparable pattern, and in all the commoner groups species adapted to transport by wind predominate, suggesting air-borne immigration as the chief method of colonization. Land vertebrates – mammals, reptiles and amphibia – are characteristically absent from remote islands.

One result of this poverty of species on islands is that competition – "the struggle for existence" – is less intense. Many forms succeed in living in places from which they would be excluded under the more crowded conditions of continental life. But, because of this, remote island faunas and floras are vulnerable to any sudden influx of species from the outside world. In this sense they are like flower beds, which are also places in which a number of species are enabled to grow because of reduced competition. An influx of species from outside is comparable to the import of weeds, and these may compete so successfully with the original forms that they finally supplant them altogether.

Another consequence of isolation is that evolution may take a peculiar course on remote islands. Once an animal or plant has succeeded in reaching an island, it will be effectively cut off from interbreeding with related stocks outside, unless there is a steady stream of new immigrants of the same species. If new characters appear, as they generally do, on the island, and are favored by selection, they will quickly spread through the small population and this will evolve into a distinct new type. Such a new species will probably be specially adapted to the unique conditions of its place of origin, to which it will in any case be confined by the surrounding ocean. Species of this kind are described as "endemics," and on some islands they may make up the bulk of the flora and fauna. Sometimes an island stock does not just evolve into one, more adapted, species, but divides or radiates into a number of daughter species, each selected because of its success in a particular habitat. The finches of the Galápagos Islands, described by Darwin and more recently by Lack, are the most famous example of this process.

There are other tendencies which affect island species, and one of the most curious is the loss of the power of flight, which is seen in both birds and insects. The extinct dodo of Mauritius is the most famous example, but flightless landrails are still present on several Atlantic and Pacific islands. The beetles of St Helena and Madeira show the same feature. It has been suggested that this change is due to direct natural selection, based on the danger of flight on a small island to which, once an animal has been swept away by the wind, it has little chance of return. On this argument, selection tends to eliminate the strong fliers and preserve the less active forms. But this may not be the whole story.

Islands, then, have a scanty fauna and flora, but a very interesting one. The gaps in terrestrial forms are partly compensated for by the presence in the breeding season of vast numbers of sea-birds and seals. The former nest either directly on the ground or in burrows, the underground habit serving to protect the smaller kinds from birds of prey. All these ground-nesting birds, however, are vulnerable to predatory mammals such as rats, cats and stoats, and once these reach an island the sea-bird population quickly dwindles. The fascinating and peculiar faunas and floras of remote islands thus depend in many ways on their isolation, and when that isolation is broken down, as is happening in many places today through human agency, the days of the original species are numbered.

Maps

The ten maps on the following pages show the positions of the principal seas and islands of the world. The sketch map below indicates the area covered by each map. It should be noted that the maps are drawn to different scales. The ocean depths marked also vary from map to map, and a scale will be found on each map. In the main section of this book – *The World's Oceans and Islands* – the heading to each entry carries a reference to the numbered square on the appropriate map.

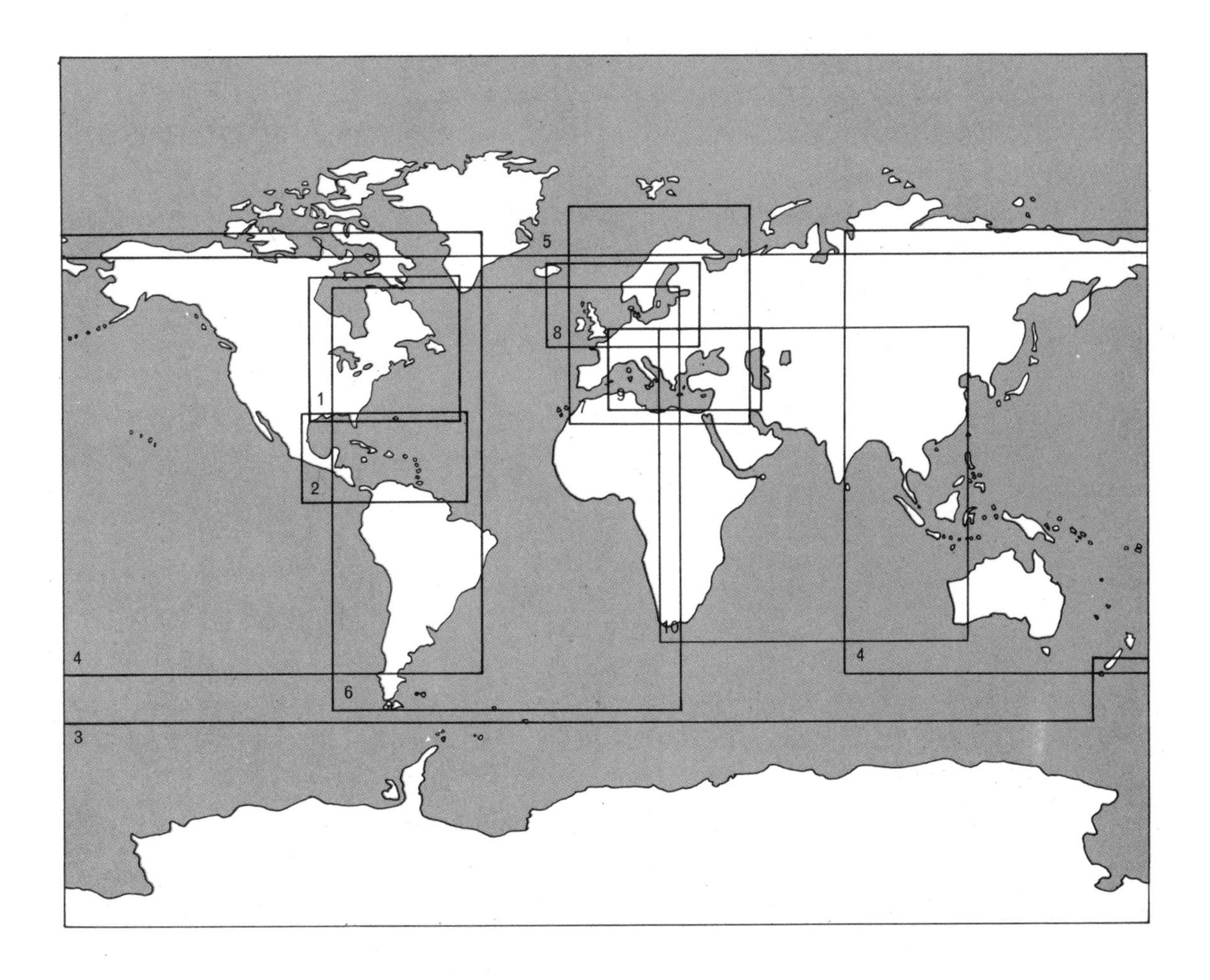

1 North America – east

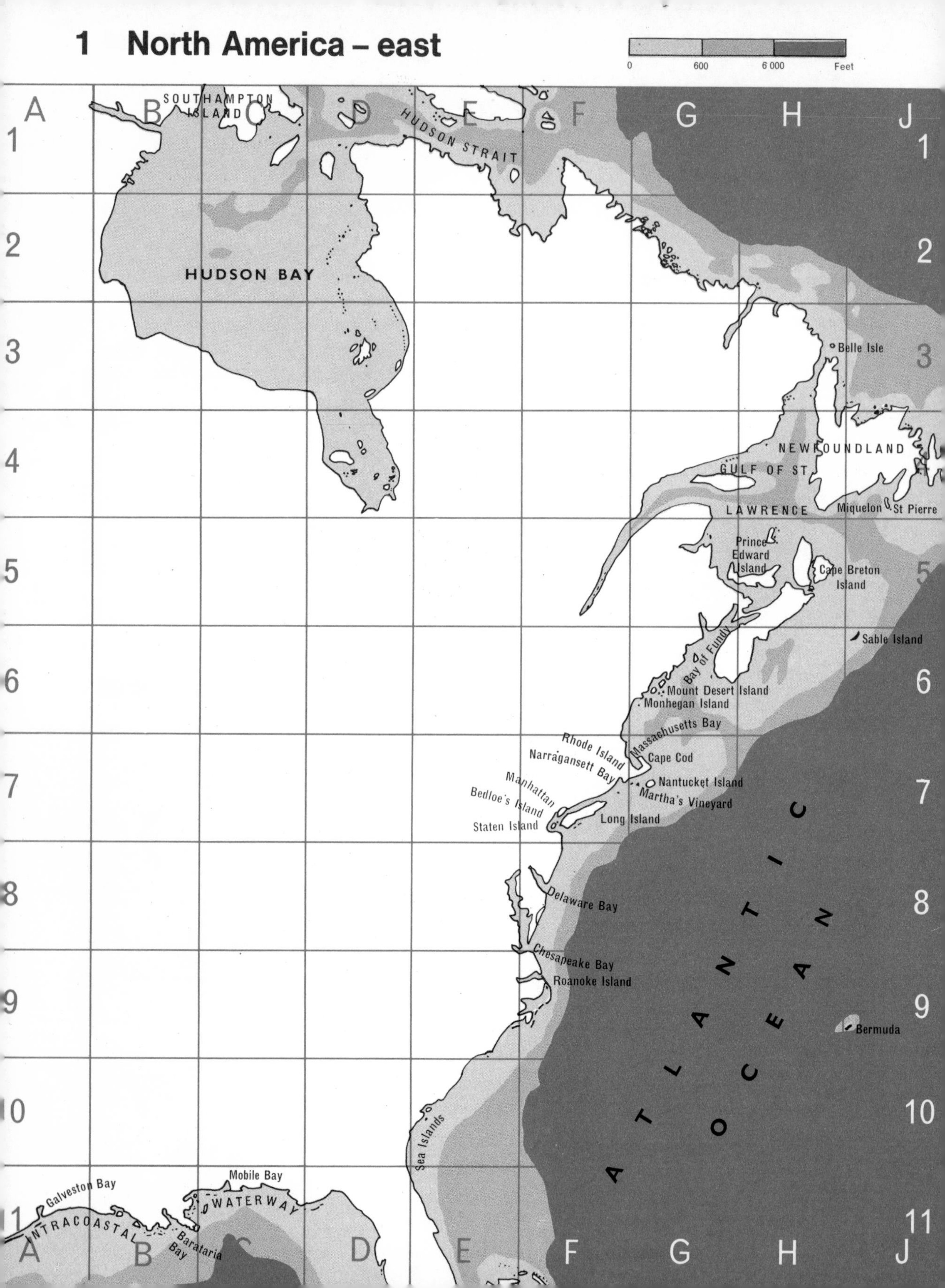

2 The Caribbean

0 | 600 | 6,000 | Feet

GULF OF MEXICO
ATLANTIC OCEAN
CARIBBEAN SEA
PACIFIC OCEAN
Tampa Bay
Palm Beach
Florida Keys
BAHAMA ISLANDS
WEST INDIES
CUBA
Cayman Islands
JAMAICA
Tortuga Island
HISPANIOLA
PUERTO RICO
Virgin Islands
Saba
Montserrat
Guadeloupe
LEEWARD IS.
Rocher du Diamant
Martinique
Barbados
WINDWARD IS.
Tobago
Trinidad
Aruba Island
Curaçao
ANTILLES
SPANISH MAIN
Panama Canal
Mulatas Islands

3 The Antarctic Ocean

0 | 6,000 | 18,000 | Feet

PACIFIC OCEAN
ATLANTIC OCEAN
INDIAN OCEAN
ANTARCTIC OCEAN
South Shetland Islands
Bellingshausen Sea
South Orkney Islands
South Georgia
WEDDELL SEA
Chatham Islands
Bay of Whales
ROSS SEA
McMurdo Sound
NEW ZEALAND
Stewart Island
Auckland Islands
MacQuarie Island
Bouvet Island
Tasmania

4 The Pacific Ocean

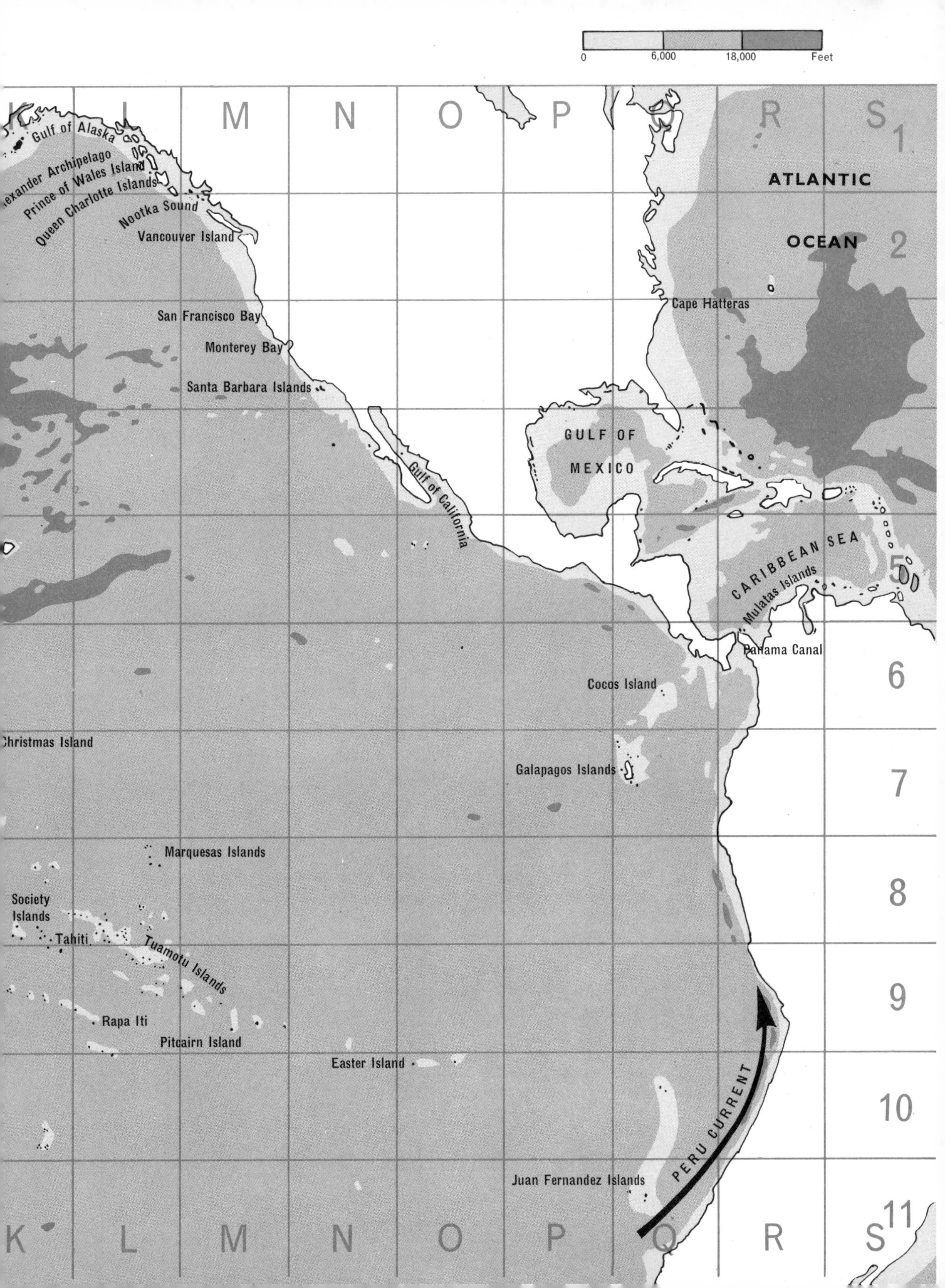
0
6,000
18,000
Feet
K
L
M
N
O
P
Q
R
S
1
2
5
6
7
8
9
10
11
Gulf of Alaska
Alexander Archipelago
Prince of Wales Island
Queen Charlotte Islands
Nootka Sound
Vancouver Island
San Francisco Bay
Monterey Bay
Santa Barbara Islands
Gulf of California
ATLANTIC
OCEAN
Cape Hatteras
GULF OF
MEXICO
CARIBBEAN SEA
Mulatas Islands
Panama Canal
Cocos Island
Christmas Island
Galapagos Islands
Marquesas Islands
Society
Islands
Tahiti
Tuamotu Islands
Rapa Iti
Pitcairn Island
Easter Island
PERU CURRENT
Juan Fernandez Islands

5 The Arctic Ocean

0 3,000 12,000 Feet

Pribilof Islands
BERING SEA
OKHOTSK SEA
Kodiak Island
St Lawrence Island
GULF OF ALASKA
Bering Strait
Diomede Islands
Wrangel Island
BEAUFORT SEA
ARCTIC OCEAN
VICTORIA ISLAND
Viscount Melville Sound
QUEEN ELIZABETH ISLANDS
King William Island
Parry Islands
Ellesmere Island
BAFFIN ISLAND
BAFFIN BAY
Franz Josef Land
Novaya Zemlya
Spitsbergen
GREENLAND
BARENTS SEA
Scoresby Sound
Jan Mayen
Kvaloy
White Sea

C D E F G H J
B C D E F G H J
1 2 3 4 5 6 7 8 9 10 11

6 The Atlantic Ocean

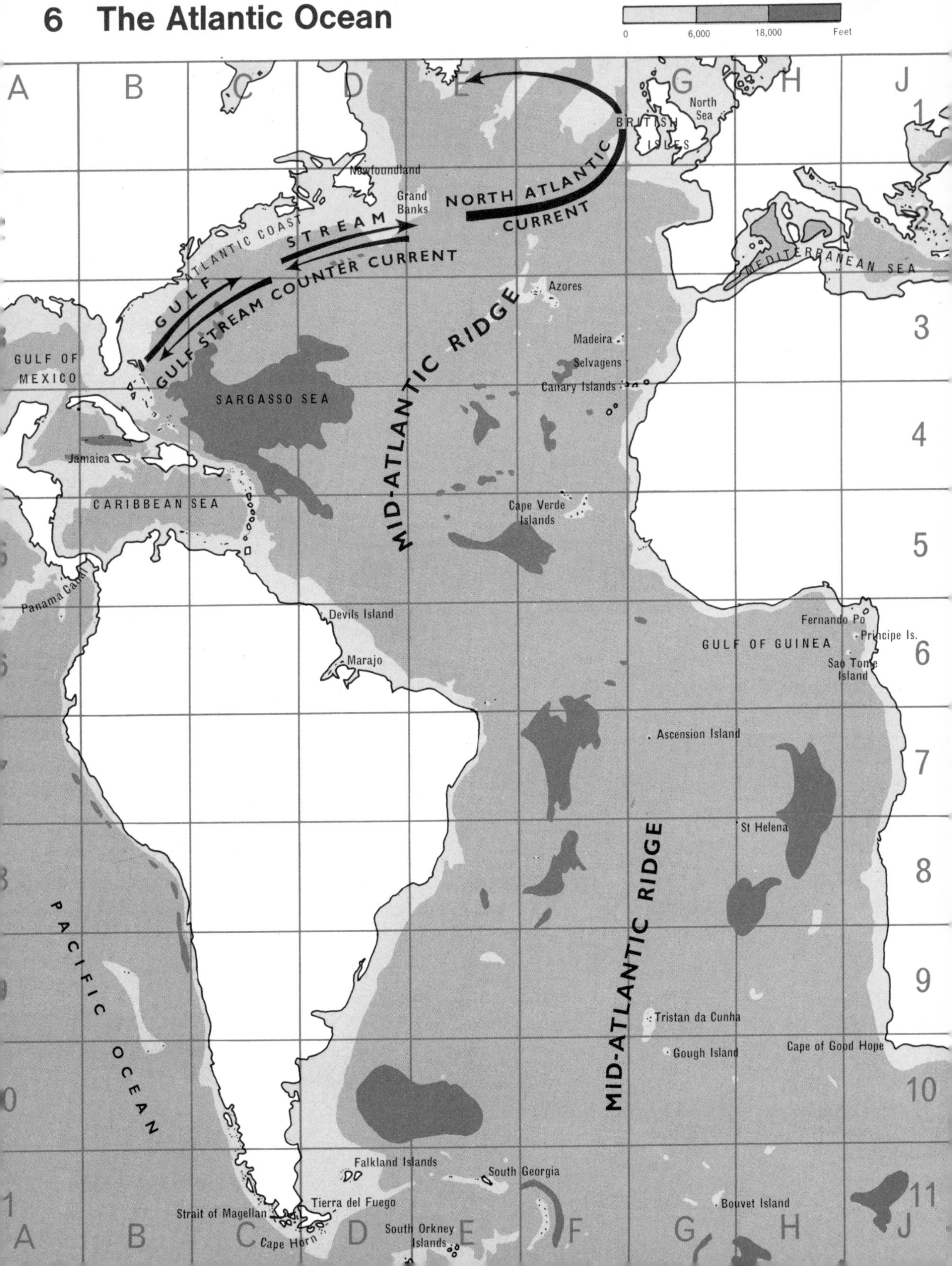

0
6,000
18,000
Feet

A B C D E F G H J
1 2 3 4 5 6 7 8 9 10 11

North Sea
BRITISH ISLES
Newfoundland
Grand Banks
NORTH ATLANTIC CURRENT
ATLANTIC COAST
GULF STREAM
GULF STREAM COUNTER CURRENT
MEDITERRANEAN SEA
Azores
Madeira
Selvagens
Canary Islands
GULF OF MEXICO
SARGASSO SEA
MID-ATLANTIC RIDGE
Jamaica
CARIBBEAN SEA
Cape Verde Islands
Panama Canal
Devils Island
Marajo
Fernando Po
Principe Is.
GULF OF GUINEA
Sao Tome Island
Ascension Island
St Helena
MID-ATLANTIC RIDGE
PACIFIC OCEAN
Tristan da Cunha
Gough Island
Cape of Good Hope
Falkland Islands
South Georgia
Tierra del Fuego
Strait of Magellan
Bouvet Island
South Orkney Islands
Cape Horn

7 Europe

0 | 600 | 6,000 | Feet

ICELAND
ARCTIC OCEAN
Lofoten Islands
Maelstrom
Kvaloy
BARENTS S
Faeroe Islands
Shetland Islands
Sogne Fjord
White Sea
Hebrides
Orkney Islands
ATLANTIC OCEAN
Gulf of Bothnia
BRITISH ISLES
IRELAND
Isle of Man
NORTH SEA
Skagerrak
Gulf of Finland
Kattegat
BALTIC SEA
Land's End
Helgoland
Scilly Islands
ENGLISH CH.
Zuiderzee
Rügen
Zeeland
Mont-Saint-Michel
BAY OF BISCAY
Cape Finisterre
Ile de Ré
Gulf of Lion
Cape St Vincent
Ligurian Sea
CORSICA
Elba
Dalmatian Coast
ADRIATIC SEA
Sea of Azov
Balearic Islands
Monte Cristo
Gibraltar
SARDINIA
BLACK SEA
MEDITERRANEAN SEA
Bay of Naples
TYRRHENIAN SEA
Lipari Islands
Bosporus
Sea of Marmara
SICILY
IONIAN SEA
Dardanelles
AEGEAN SEA
Lesbos
Strait of Messina
Malta
Cyclades
Dodecanese
CRETE
CYPRUS
Suez Canal

8 The British Isles and N. Europe

0 800 3,600 Feet

B C D E F G H J
1 2 3 4 5

Faeroe Islands
Shetland Islands
Sogne-Fjord
Cape Wrath
Fair Isle
Orkney Islands
Gulf of Bothnia
Gulf of Finland
St Kilda
Hebrides
Skye
ATLANTIC OCEAN
Staffa
Iona
Mull
Corryvreckan
BRITISH ISLES
Skagerrak
Kattegat
Gotland
SEA
NORTH SEA
Farne Islands
Galway Bay
Aran Islands
Blasket Islands
IRELAND
Isle of Man
Dogger Bank
BALTIC
Bornholm
Rügen
The Wash
Helgoland
Frisian Is.
Lundy Island
Land's End
Scilly Islands
Eddystone Rocks
Isle of Wight
Goodwin Sands
Zuiderzee
Zeeland
ENGLISH CHANNEL
St. of Dover
Channel Islands
Ushant
Mont-Saint-Michel

9 The Mediterranean

0 600 6,000 Feet

8 9 10 11

Dalmatian Coast
ADRIATIC SEA
BLACK SEA
Gulf of Lion
Ligurian Sea
Iles d'Hyères
Elba
CORSICA
Monte Cristo
Bosporus
Samothrace
Sea of Marmara
Gulf of Salonika
Dardanelles
Ischia
SARDINIA
Bay of Naples
Capri
Lemnos
Balearic Islands
Lesbos
TYRRHENIAN SEA
Corfu
Lipari Islands
AEGEAN SEA
Ithaca
Mykonos
IONIAN SEA
Egadi Islands
Gulf of Corinth
Cephalonia
MEDITERRANEAN SEA
Delos
Naxos
Dodecanese
SICILY
Zante
Corinth Canal
Cyclades
Rhodes
Strait of Messina
Pantelleria
Thera
CRETE
Karpathos
CYPRUS
Gozo
Malta

A B C D E F

10 The Indian Ocean

0 6,000 18,000 Feet

A B C D E F G H J

1 2 3 4 5 6 7 8 9 10 11

BLACK SEA
MEDITERRANEAN SEA
SUEZ CANAL
Gulf of Aqaba
RED SEA
PERSIAN G.
Bahrein
Trucial Coast
Bab El Mandeb
Perim
G. OF ADEN
Socotra
ARABIAN SEA
Elephanta
Laccadive Islands
Maldive Islands
Coromandel Coast
BAY OF BENGAL
Andaman Islands
Nicobar Islands
CEYLON
Mergui Archipelago
Str. of Malacca
Hong K
Hainan
CHINA SEA
Singapore
BORNEO
SUMATRA
Krakatoa
JAVA
Cocos Islands
Seychelles
Zanzibar
Comoro Islands
MOZAMBIQUE CHANNEL
MADAGASCAR
Mauritius
Réunion
INDIAN OCEAN
Cape Agulhas
of Good Hope
Kerguelen Islands

The World's Oceans and Islands

The World's Oceans and Islands

Aden, Gulf of

A long gulf between Africa and Asia. Location *Western arm of the Arabian Sea, between the Somali Republic and southern Arabia.* Dimensions *550 miles long, 300 miles wide at mouth.* Map *10, B5–C4.*

Stretching between the jutting horn of Somalia on the East African coast and the Aden Protectorate on the South Arabian Peninsula, the Gulf of Aden is an arm of the Indian Ocean, or rather, of that section of it known as the Arabian Sea. It is 550 miles long and at its mouth, between Cape Guardafui and Ras Fartak, over 300 miles wide. Bab el Mandeb strait connects it on the west with the Red Sea. The Gulf is part of one of the most important shipping lanes in the world and with its three main ports of Aden, Berbera and Djibouti has played an often decisive part in the history, the economic development and the communications of the Eastern Mediterranean, India and China.

On the Asian side the Gulf's coastline is occupied by the British Crown Colony of Aden and its hinterland, the Aden Protectorate. The Colony, which has been called "a blast-oven in hell," is one of the world's most uncomfortable places to live. Lying 100 miles east of Bab el Mandeb strait, it consists of Aden itself, Perim, the Kamaran Islands (off Yemen) and the Kuria Muria Islands (off the Dhofar coast of Oman). Aden and Little Aden are peninsulas of volcanic origin, joined by a narrow strip of hinterland and enclosing Aden Bay. The town of Aden is on the east side of the peninsula, in the crater of an extinct volcano.

The Romans colonized Aden in the first century A.D. and called it *Arabia Felix*. It was one of the most important bases of Roman trade with the East, then came successively under Portuguese and Turkish rule, and later was under various petty Arab sovereigns. In 1839 Britain acquired it when the East India Company's troops sailed from Bombay to seize the territory in retaliation for the mistreatment of some shipwrecked British sailors two years earlier. For almost 100 years, until 1932, Aden was part of British India. In 1868 Little Aden was acquired; in 1882 and 1888 the coastal strip was added. Aden became a Crown Colony in 1937, but its importance to Britain really began in 1869, with the opening of the Suez Canal. Today it is an important base of the Royal Air Force and a nodal point in civilian air communications.

North of the Gulf of Aden, in southern and southwestern Arabia, lies the Aden Protectorate, a group of independent Arab tribal districts which have given Britain a good deal of trouble and continue to do so. The Protectorate, which fronts on the Gulf for most of its length and stretches 200 miles beyond it, has two main divisions: the Western, composed of 19 sultanates, and the Eastern, consisting of the Hadhramaut.

The Gulf and its coasts have a reasonably cool and pleasant climate during the northeast monsoon, from October to April; but for the rest of the year they are in the grip of a damp, airless heat, except when the southwest monsoon dispels it occasionally in July and August. Though as a naval base Aden has declined in importance since Egypt's expropriation of the Suez Canal, it still is important as a link in aerial defense.

Admiralty Islands

A group of coral islands with a long-established tribal civilization. Location *Bismarck Archipelago, Territory of New Guinea, southwest Pacific.* Area *800 square miles.* Map *4, E7.*

The Admiralty Islands, lying to the north of New Guinea, form part of the Bismarck Archipelago and consist of one large island (Manus) and about 17 smaller ones. Politically they are part of the Manus district of the Australian Territory of New Guinea. Manus island (633 square miles) and Rambutyo island (about 80 square miles) are the only large islands of the group. The leading industries are pearl fishing and coconut growing. The administrative center is Lorengau, at the eastern end of Manus.

The native Islanders are Papuans; there is tension, if not actual hostility, between those living on the coast and the inhabitants of the still little-known interior.

Manus became widely known through the anthropological studies of the eminent American scientist Margaret Mead, who spent several years winning the confidence and exploring the traditions and mores of the islanders. "In this small aquatic world," she wrote, in *Growing up in New Guinea*, "the children are rulers, free to bully their parents, to play all day at swimming, fishing, boating, to do almost anything they wish. For their elders life is stern, harsh, puritanical, ringed round with taboos, an endless, joyless quest for wealth (in dogs teeth, shell money, tobacco) and social advancement... There is no word for *love* in the language. There are no love-songs, no romantic myths, no merely social dances. The village lies fair in the moonlight, the still lagoon holds the shadow of houses and trees' but there is no sound of songs and dancing..."

The Admiralty Islands were discovered by the Dutch in 1616 and mapped and named by Philip Carteret in 1766. In 1885 the Germans annexed the Islands; in 1920, following the German defeat in the First World War, the group was mandated to Australia. In 1942 the Japanese overran the group, but early in 1944 an Allied task force landed and Japanese resistance ended within two months. The Islands functioned as an advanced Allied air and naval base for a time, but when the Allies occupied Hollandia in Dutch New Guinea, they became a staging area and later a rear base. Since then the Admiralty Islands have returned to peaceful and pleasant obscurity.

Adriatic Sea

An arm of the Mediterranean. Location *Between the Italian and Balkan peninsulas.* Dimensions *500 miles long, 60–140 miles wide.* Maximum depth *4,035 feet.* Map *7, E8–F8.*

The Adriatic runs from southeast to northwest, following the line of a structural depression in the earth's surface between the Apennines and the Dinaric Alps. Only 45 miles wide at its entrance by the Strait of Otranto, the Sea opens out to an

Trieste, on the Adriatic Sea

average width of just over 100 miles. It is the shallowest section of the Mediterranean; its greatest depths are south of Ragusa, where over 4,000 feet has been measured.

Set between the Italian and Balkan peninsulas, it has relatively few good harbors on the Italian coast. From Bari and Brindisi in the south to Venice in the north the shore is low and unattractive. In the northwest it slides almost imperceptibly into the mudflats and marshlands surrounding the delta of the Po River. The deposits of the Po have silted up the once flourishing port of Adria after which the Sea is named. On the eastern side the Dalmatian coast is mainly rugged; for long sections it is fringed with beautiful and unusual islands, generally fish-shaped and running parallel to the general line of the Adriatic.

The climate is Mediterranean except for somewhat lower temperatures in the north. This is mainly due to the fierce northeast wind, the *bora*, which blows down from the Austrian and Yugoslav Alps with great violence. Even modern steamships take shelter from it; in the streets of Trieste – the Free City around which so much strife raged between Italy and Yugoslavia after the Second World War – lifelines are sometimes rigged to prevent pedestrians from being blown off their feet. Because it is a shallow sea, the waves become steep whenever the wind is strong. Many of the local boats, even comparatively large coastal motor-schooners, have kept the traditional shape of bluff bows, broad beam and shallow draft.

The famous "Marriage of the Adriatic" was a ceremony carried out by the Doges of Venice on Ascension Day every year from about 1000 A.D. until 1789. The ceremony, originally established to commemorate the Venetian conquest of the Dalmatian coast, came to be regarded as a symbol of the city's mastery of the sea. The Doge in his state galley, the *bucintoro* (Golden Bark) led a procession of gaily decorated boats out into the Adriatic from the Lido. A consecrated ring was then cast into the sea with the words *Desponsamus te, mare* (We wed thee, O Sea). The remains of the last *bucintoro* can still be seen in the Venetian *Museo Civico*.

Many important shipping routes still run through the Adriatic, while the sailors manning the coastal ships are some of the most able in the Mediterranean.

The Dalmatian islands, until subdued by Venice, were for many centuries the haunt of the most ruthless Mediterranean pirates. Today they are part of Yugoslavia.

A large number of civilizations and cultures left their marks upon the Adriatic littoral. Greek colonies were established on both eastern and western seaboards. The Romans took over their cities and harbors. In later centuries Austrians, French and Italians have occupied Adriatic cities and islands. They have left traces of their languages in the dialects or more permanent memorials in the shape of fine architecture. Here, at Rijeka (formerly Fiume), the landlocked country of Hungary had its port. Split (Spalato) is an ancient city that grew up within the ancient palace of Diocletian. Dubrovnik (Ragusa) flourished briefly as a city-republic and many of its patrician houses have survived.

During the First World War some minor naval engagements took place in the Adriatic. During the Second World War Yugoslav partisans fought a bitter campaign from the island bases against the Italian and German occupation. One of the post-1945 international crises was caused by the Albanian mining of the Corfu channel, which led to the loss of two British warships.

Aegean Sea

An arm of the Mediterranean. Location *Between Greece and Asia Minor.* Dimensions *About 400 miles long and 200 miles wide.* Map 7, *G9–10.*

The Aegean, an island-studded sea dividing Greece from Asia Minor, is an arm of the Mediterranean bounded on the north by Macedonia and on the south by the island of Crete. It is linked through the Dardanelles with the Sea of Marmora and the Black Sea; through the Corinth Canal its waters join the Gulf of Corinth. It has a character of its own and no sailor could confuse its wind and weather conditions with those of other parts of the Mediterranean.

The name has been given various derivations: from Aegeus, the father of the hero Theseus, who drowned himself when he thought (mistakenly) that his son had been killed by the Minotaur;

The island of Hydra in the Aegean Sea

from Aegea, a queen of the Amazons, who was also drowned in its waters; and from a town named Aegae. It has also given a word to our language, *archipelago*, a term now applied to any group of islands but originally the Greek name for this sea only.

Irregular in outline, about 400 miles long and 200 miles wide, with numerous gulfs, the unique character of the Aegean is provided by its islands. They lie scattered like stepping stones between Europe and Asia, islands of thyme and olive and wind-swept rock, the home of seamen and one of the cradles of civilization. The two factors which promoted the growth of a rich culture in this area of the world were the closeness of the islands to each other and the seasonal northerly wind which blows during the summer months almost as regularly as the trade winds. This made for easy navigation and developed the skill of seamanship. From Argos on the Greek mainland the Mycenean sailors could run before the wind down to Crete and then, with the same wind still astern of them, as far afield as Egypt.

These strong winds prevail over the Aegean from mid-June until the end of September, particularly in the southern half of the Sea, and they create the characteristic climate of the Aegean summer – the bright, burnished sky and the heat which is tempered even at midday so that the lassitude which afflicts so much of the Mediterranean hardly troubles the islanders.

In winter the Aegean is treacherous, a stormy sea with an iron-bound coast seemingly always lurking somewhere close to hand. While squalls sweep with terrifying suddenness off the high peaks of the islands, and from wave-lashed Cape Matapan in the south to Gallipoli in the north, the small boats are drawn up for safety on the beaches, just as they were in classical times.

The islands which lift their rocky heads out of this sailor's sea are all parts of an old submerged land-block. The sea depth varies greatly; between some islands it is comparatively shallow, while in other places – notably north of Crete – it plunges into deep basins with depths of over 1,000 fathoms.

Fishing for coral and sponges are two of the islanders' main activities; it is likely that European man first learned to dive in these clear waters. Sponge divers can be seen even today diving with no equipment except a heavy rock held to their chests as ballast.

The Aegean is one of the last strongholds of the old-time sailor. Here can be seen a wider variety of sailing craft than perhaps on any other sea of the world, varying from elegant sloops built on the island of Hydra to slab-sided, bluff-bowed trading schooners. They carry men and goods much as in ancient times, with the same hazards and the same dreams.

Agulhas, Cape

A rocky projection, hazardous to navigation. Location *Southwest Cape Province, Union of South Africa.* Map *10, A10.*

Ships rounding the storm-vexed Cape of Good Hope follow the shore southeast in a series of curves, which form shallow bays, until the saw-edged reefs of Cape Agulhas (named by the Portuguese "Needles") appear. Here is the southernmost point of the African continent.

Cape Agulhas, with its jagged, submerged rocks, extending well into the sea, has been for long a danger to navigation and is marked by a lighthouse and a signal station. Off it there are trailing grounds where great quantities of sole are caught. Near to the challenging Cape is the small Bontebok National Park.

Cape Agulhas has also given its name to the Agulhas Current, which sweeps southwest off the eastern and southern shores of the continent and has sufficient force to set up a back drift. This flows northeast, close to the shore, and sailing ships used to take advantage of it on their journeys between Cape Town and Natal. The warm Agulhas Current has some influence on the Cape climate, too; it increases the mean temperatures east of Cape Town.

Alaska, Gulf of

A vast semicircular gulf with precipitous coasts. Location *Southern coast of Alaska.* Area *Over 2,000 square miles.* Map *5, A2–B2.*

Stretching in a huge, broad arc, the Gulf of Alaska is a wide inlet of the Pacific, bounded by the Alaska Peninsula on the west and the Alexander Archipelago on the east. The coast rises steeply into some of the highest mountains in all North America – Mount St Elias, Mount Logan, Mount Baker, the long range of the Chugach Mountains, 5,000–9,000 feet high, rearing up abruptly from the water's edge; deep fjords, gouged out by glaciers descending from their catchment basins far back in the towering ranges, indent the shore. In the northwestern portion, the coast of the Gulf is broken by few rivers and bays of any size, except at Yakutat. Piedmont glaciers, such as the huge Malaspina, calve at the shoreline. The Fairweather and St Elias ranges follow the coast.

The southern central section of the Gulf coastline, from Icy Bay to Controller Bay, is regular, bordered with reefs and usually forested with timber. The Bering Glacier descends from mountains lying a short distance inland. The district around Controller Bay is well timbered and protected by coastal islands and spits. To the west lie the Copper River Flats, a maze of low alluvial islands, about 50 miles wide, deposited by the Copper River after its long course from the Alaska Range to the sea. Prince William Sound is a mountainous, forested area, which is protected from the sea by a belt of islands and carved by many fjords and glaciers. Its western boundary is the Kenai Peninsula, a rugged, mountainous area with marked glaciation on its southern slopes.

Cook Inlet, marking the eastern limits of the Gulf of Alaska, is a body of water with tremendous tides, extending 150 miles northeast from the Gulf, then turning due east into the narrow and rocky Turnagain Arm. Here a plateau 300–400 feet high slopes down from the Kenai Mountains to its eastern shore; a wide gravel plain extends northwest from its upper limits; in the north it is met by the broad flats of the lower Susina. Directly north of Cook Inlet is the fertile Matanuska Valley and the great arc of the Alaska Range.

The climate of this section of the Gulf is extremely varied. West of Cook Inlet the coastal region has no great extremes of heat or cold; the rainfall is heavy and there is more snow than to the southeast. There is a scattering of Sitka spruce along the coast, while the largest stand of timber is centered on Prince William Sound in the Chugach National Forest. The Kenai Peninsula is the largest Alaskan moose preserve and is known to sportsmen the world over for its brown bears, second in size only to those found on Kodiak Island. Salmon run in all the streams reaching salt water, followed by giant trout, which eat their eggs.

There are several oil wells near Cook Inlet and in Controller Bay. The most important island in the Gulf is Kodiak; the main ports are Anchorage, Seward and Valdez. Greater Anchorage, with over 35,000 people, is the largest, fastest growing, most progressive, but perhaps least typically Alaskan town in the whole Gulf area, if not in the whole state of Alaska.

Aleutian Islands

A chain of volcanic islands. Location *Between the North Pacific and the Bering Sea.* Map *4, H2–J2.*

Called in the past the Home of Storms, the Aleutians are a volcanic chain of some 70 islands. They extend 1,100 miles from the tip of the Alaska Peninsula to Kamchatka, separating the North Pacific from the Bering Sea, and forming the partly submerged continuation of the Alaska Range.

Their spring and summer are equally melancholy, frequently shrouded in fog that grows increasingly dense as the raw winter approaches. There is little beauty in their wave-battered cliffs, treeless slopes, sullen mountains and slag-heap volcanic cones, some of which add sulphurous fumes to the fog. The misery of the Aleutian Islands springs from their location. On their north are the cold waters of the Bering Sea into which ice pours from the Arctic Ocean and on their southern shores the North Pacific to which their cliffs slope steeply. Here the "weathers meet": fog in recurring monotony, rain, interminable gray skies, and hurricanes of extraordinary velocity.

Navigation is exceedingly hazardous; not only because of the elements but because of the strong currents and tide-rips running among the reefs and inlets into the caves at the foot of the cliffs.

In the past the Aleuts used their caves as burial grounds, hunching their dead knees-under-chin, wrapping them in grass mats bound with cord and hanging them, like grotesque bats, from the wet walls. The early inhabitants were perhaps settlers from among travelers who used the Islands as stepping stones from Siberia to North America: paddling from Kamchatka towards the Near Islands and the Rat Islands, then passing on to the larger of the four main Aleutian groups, the Andreanof and the Fox islands, under the smoking summit of Shishaldin – at about 10,000 feet the highest peak in the chain – to the Alaska Peninsula. However, Aleut legends tell of a people who came from a land of everlasting sunshine. The aboriginal type is of short stature, with short neck, swarthy complexion, black hair, and a skull and skeletal formation different from other human types. But there has been much intermarriage and mingling of racial strains, and today the inhabitants are mainly a mixed breed of Eskimo, Indian and white.

Apart from Fox and Andreanof islands, the main groups include the Andreanofs, the Rat Islands and Near Islands. The main navigational channels through the chain are Unimak Pass, Umnak Pass, Amukta Pass and Seguam Pass. The volcanic peaks, beside Shishaldin, are Mount Makushin (on Unalaska island), Mount Vsevidof (on Umnak island) and Mount Gareloi (on Gareloi island).

The Aleutians were discovered by Vitus Bering in 1741. Fur traders established themselves a few years later, exploiting the natives cruelly; but later their operations were transferred to Kodiak. In 1867 the United States bought the Aleutians as part of the Alaska purchase. In the Second World War the Japanese attacked Dutch Harbor in June, 1942; two weeks later they occupied Kiska and Attu, deporting all the inhabitants to Japan. The other islands were evacuated by the American Navy, which established bases on Adak and Amchitka islands. From these bases and from Kodiak and Cold Bay the Japanese positions came under heavy attack; later, air and naval bases were established on Shemya and Umnak islands. Attu was recaptured after three weeks of bitter fighting in May, 1943, and the Japanese evacuated Kiska unexpectedly. The natives were returned in 1945. Since the war permanent bases have been established and much expanded on Umnak, Adak, Atka, Amchitka, Shemya and Attu, while Shemya has become an important link on the polar air route between the United States and the Far East.

Alexander Archipelago

A large group of islands. Location *Southeast Alaska, south of Juneau, extending from Icy Strait and Cross Sound to Dixon Entrance.* Area *About 13,000 square miles.* Map *4, L1.*

The Alexander Archipelago is one of the densest and most unusual island systems in the world: over 1,100 islands and islets cover a total area of nearly 13,000 square miles. The archipelago and the coastline facing it represent the most populous area of Alaska.

Running through the islands lies the famous "Inland Passage," by means of which ships bound northward from Seattle avoid the weather and the long ocean swell of the Pacific. Cruise ships favor this route for this reason – quite apart from the fact that the islands themselves, stretching for 300 miles along the southern coast of Alaska, provide superb natural scenery.

The remnant of a submerged chain of mountains, the Alexander Archipelago was discovered by the Russians in 1741 and later explored by the British, Spanish and American pioneers of the Arctic seas. Rising sheer out of the water, the sides of the islands are scarred by glaciation, their peaks and crests densely wooded. They form a natural waterbreak for moisture-laden clouds driving off the Pacific and have a luxuriant vegetation. The still waters of the inland estuaries are deep right up to the cliffs and in many respects the scenery resembles that of the Norwegian fjords, with the same clear air and the same tang of pine trees.

The largest island is Prince of Wales, about 140 miles long by 40 wide; Admiralty, Baranof, Chicagof, Kupreanof, Kuiu, Mitkof, Wrangell and Revillagigedo are other important islands. Sitka (on Baranof) and Ketchikan (on Revillagigedo) are the principal towns. The straits leading between this mountainous maze run up towards the Alaskan shore, where they become fjords leading into the heads of rivers or glaciers. Lynn Canal and Portland Canal are the two most famous; the former with stark mountains rising sheer from its sides, the latter notable for the beauty of its alpine scenery. Lynn Canal is about six miles wide and nearly 100 miles long. On some of the islands gold is mined; there are also lumbering, fishing and fur farming.

Andaman Islands

A group of hilly islands. Location *Bay of Bengal, Indian Ocean.* Area *2,508 squaremiles.* Map *10, G5.*

The Andaman Islands are, like the Nicobars, peaks of the submarine parts of a mountain chain that stretches from the Arakan Yoma in Burma to the islands of Indonesia. The main group stretches for about 160 miles, consisting of the five large islands of the Great Andaman group (North Andaman, Middle Andaman, Baratang, South Andaman and Rutland) and many smaller islands just off their shores. Across the Diligent Strait is Ritchie's Archipelago; across the Duncan Passage, Little Andaman Island.

The Islands are almost all hilly, rising to a maximum of 2,400 feet in Saddle Peak on North Andaman. Jungle covers most of their area, with mangrove swamps on the low-lying parts, especially along the narrow inlets separating the islands of the Great Andaman group. There is much excellent timber, notably *padauk*, and among the successful crops which have been introduced are tea, coffee, cocoa and Manila hemp.

There are few land mammals, but the dugong (a strange aquatic, herbiverous mammal) inhabits the waters of the archipelago, and there is an abundance of turtles. Among Andaman's birds are distinct local species of eagles, parakeets and orioles.

The native peoples of the Andamans are a group of pygmy tribes, settled and virtually isolated since Neolithic times or even earlier. From the late nineteenth century the Negritos of the Islands have been under continual observation by anthropologists. Their numbers have been steadily dwindling and there were less than 100 by the middle of our century. They are round-headed, broad-nosed, averaging less than five feet in height and varying in complexion from black to a reddish brown. They have little social organization and only a few taboos, mostly connected with food. They are nomads and hunters, with no technique for making fire. Their religion is animistic with no organized ritual or priesthood, but men supposed to have visionary powers are regarded with awe. The rest of the inhabitants are mainly ex-convicts of the Port Blair penal colony and recent settlers from the mainland. The common language is Hindustani.

The British rulers of India first became interested in the Islands in the late eighteenth century when a short-lived penal colony was established. This was revived in 1858 for those sentenced after the Indian Mutiny; it remained in operation until 1945. As a territory of the independent Republic of India (administered jointly with the Nicobar Islands), the Andamans have been used for the settlement of refugees from Pakistan and Burma and of Indian emigrants from British Guiana.

The Andaman Islands

An iceberg in the Antarctic Ocean

Antarctic Ocean

A cold and dangerous ocean. Location *The southern parts of the Pacific, Atlantic and Indian oceans.* Maximum depth *28,152 feet (Byrd Deep).* Map *3.*

The home of the wandering albatross, of the eternal west winds, the Antarctic, the harshest and bleakest ocean on our planet, is really the name given to those parts of the Pacific, Indian and Atlantic oceans which surround Antarctica. The Antarctic Ocean proper begins south of the Antarctic Circle and usually includes the vast frozen sea whose drift ice sometimes reaches as far as South Africa. "The Great Southern Ocean," as old-time sailors termed it, is still the most violent and dangerous, with vast seas that run without let or hindrance clean around the world. Nowhere else in the world can the fetch and run of the seas compare with those of Antarctica, for all other oceans are broken at some point by large land masses. In the Antarctic alone, the swell of moving waves runs eternally before the west-to-east air currents which drive with the turning earth.

The great difference between the Antarctic and Arctic regions lies in the fact that, cut off as it is by the most savage ocean in the world, the Antarctic supports no mammalian life other than whales and a few species of seals. Land- and seabirds are fairly common, the penguin, the skua and the snow petrel inhabiting the Antarctic zone, but from the region of the roaring forties to the Antarctic Circle only the wandering albatross circles the seas on the eternal wind currents of the world. The Ocean will always attract the international whaler, for the blue whale, the rorqual and the hump-back which are found in these waters represent a valuable annual catch.

The ancient Greeks forecast the discovery of a south polar region, but when the sea routes around Africa and South America had been found, by 1520, further Antarctic exploration was neglected. For centuries polar adventurers concentrated on trying to find a northwest or northeast passage through the Arctic zone. The Renaissance geographers assumed that there was a large Antarctic continent and James Cook in 1772–75 tried unsuccessfully to find it. He discovered, however, several islands and in 1773 was the first to cross the Antarctic Circle, reaching 71° South in 1774. The Russian expedition under Fabian Bellingshausen in 1819–21 also contributed to the knowledge of the Ocean and its islands. It was Nathaniel B. Palmer, an American sealer, who probably first sighted the Antarctic mainland, in 1820; James Weddell, an English sealer, discovered the sea named after him and reached latitude 74° South in 1823. Dumont d'Urville's French expedition in 1837–40 did not get beyond the Antarctic Circle; but in 1838–40 Charles Wilkes, an American, sailed 1,500 miles along the coast and finally proved that Antarctica was a continent. In 1840–42 the English expedition under James Clark Ross reached latitude 78° South, mapped much of the Antarctic coast, and discovered the two volcanoes Erebus and Terror as well as considerable new territory, including the part of the Antarctic continent now named after Ross, who claimed the whole continent for Queen Victoria. The *Challenger* (1872–76) was the first steamship to cross the Antarctic Circle, in 1874.

The first two expeditions to spend the winter in Antarctica were the Belgica, led by Adrian de Gerlache, and the Southern Cross, headed by the Norwegian C. E. Borchgrevink in 1899. Erich von Drygalski led the German National Expedition in the *Gauss* which discovered Kaiser Wilhelm II Land and wintered off its coast in 1902–03. Robert F. Scott's famous *Discovery* explored and named King Edward VII Land and wintered in McMurdo Sound during 1902–04. Otto Nordenskjöld's Swedish expedition of 1902–03 spent two winters in the American quadrant but did not pass within the Circle. The *Scotia* expedition under Dr W. S. Bruce in 1901–04 was more successful and carried out important oceanographical researches. Jean Charcot explored the coast of Graham Land in 1904 and 1905, first in the *Français* and then in the *Pourquoi Pas*. Sir Ernest Shackleton led a private expedition in the *Nimrod* in 1907; his base was at Cape Royds. Members of his party climbed Erebus while Shackleton and some of his companions advanced to within 97 miles of the South Pole in January, 1909. The Pole was discovered by the Norwegian explorer Roald Amundsen, who hoisted the Norwegian flag on December 14, 1911, naming the area the King Haakon VII Plateau. Amundsen got back safely; but Captain Robert F. Scott and his men, setting an example of truly Spartan heroism, perished on the return trip after reaching the Pole on January 18, 1912, and finding proof of Amundsen's previous presence.

The conquest of the South Pole lessened interest for a while in Antarctic exploration. But Douglas Mawson's expedition in 1911–13 made valuable meteorological observations and the two expeditions of Ernest Shackleton (1914–16 and 1921–22) also contributed valuable geographic and hydrographic data, though they failed in the attempt to cross the continent by way of the Pole.

The most important recent expeditions have been led by the late Admiral Richard E. Byrd. During his first expedition he established a base called Little America in the Bay of Whales which was used as a semi-permanent base for all American explorers. Byrd and his pilot Bernt Balchen made the first flight over the South Pole on November 28, 1929, flying up the Liv Glacier and almost crashing because of the perilous air currents which tossed the plane about. They made a circuit over the Pole. Another flight was made on December 5 east of King Edward VII Land, where Byrd discovered a new mountain range. The second Byrd expedition (1933–35) was notable for the five and a half months which its leader spent alone at an advance base studying weather conditions. This expedition discovered the Edsel Ford Range and identified a large area previously unknown. A third expedition, directed by Admiral Byrd, consisting of 158 men, spent the winter of 1939–40 in the Antarctic and returned in 1941. Lincoln Ellsworth, in his ship

Wyatt Earp, explored the Antarctic coast in 1939 and claimed 77,000 square miles for the United States. At the same time Sir Hubert Wilkins explored the Graham Land sector, confirming on a short flight the discoveries of 1928 and adding some 300 miles of new coastline to the Antarctic continent. In October, 1939, Sir Douglas Mawson, the Australian Antarctic explorer, sailed from Cape Town in *Discovery* for a two-season cruise, reaching Kerguelen Island. A German expedition led by Captain Ritscher claimed for the Reich 231,660 square miles of territory in Crown Princess Martha Land – previously claimed by Norway. Such conflicting claims are still in dispute, more recently between Britain, Chile and Argentina.

The Second World War interrupted Antarctic exploration, but in 1946 Byrd again sailed for Little America with 200 men. They mapped 1,700,000 square miles of land – almost half of which had never before been explored – and 5,400 miles of coastline, 1,900 miles of it unexplored. Another expedition in 1947 was led by Finn Ronne of the United States Navy and included 18 men and two women – the first women to cross the Antarctic Circle.

More recently the Russians have also entered the international lists in Antarctic exploration and the International Geophysical Year (July 1957–December 1958) established no less than 21 stations for observation and research. Among other things, the IGY established important oceanographic principles on currents and the circulation of "cold bottom water," and discovered coal deposits in Antarctica.

Antilles

The main island group of the West Indies. Location *Between Florida and the north coast of Venezuela.* Area *Nearly 100,000 square miles.* Map *2, D2–H4.*

The main island group of the West Indies, the Antilles curve in an arc of 2,500 miles from Florida to the north coast of Venezuela. As a vast natural breakwater they separate the Atlantic from the Gulf of Mexico and the Caribbean.

Politically they consist of three independent republics (Cuba, Haiti and Dominica); the British islands (Jamaica, Trinidad, Tobago, the Leeward and Windward islands, the British Virgin Islands and Barbados); the United States possessions (Puerto Rico and the United States Virgin Islands); the Netherlands islands (Curaçao, Bonaire, St Eustatius, Aruba and the southern half of St Martin); and the French islands (Guadeloupe, Martinique and the northern half of St Martin). Their relationships with the governing home countries vary considerably: some of the islands have a great deal of self-government while others are tied more closely to Europe.

Geographically, the Antilles are divided into two main groups: Greater and Lesser. The Greater Antilles include Cuba, Jamaica, Hispaniola (shared by Haiti and the Dominican Republic) and Puerto Rico; the Lesser Antilles – sometimes called the Caribbees – include the rest, except the Bahamas. Trinidad is really a detached portion of South America.

In the Greater Antilles the mountain ranges run from east to west. The Lesser Antilles are also mountainous and some of the islands are of volcanic origin and contain active volcanoes.

The Antilles lie wholly within the Tropics; their climate is tropical, modified by their maritime position. The annual variations in temperature are very small – within 10° F. In winter there is a little rain, but during the summer months rainfall is heavy. The seasonal differences depend on rainfall rather than on temperature – there is a dry (cool) season and a wet (hot) one. The Antilles are one of the hurricane centers of the world, and these storms usually occur near the end of the rainy season.

The climatic conditions determine the main crops of the Antilles: bananas and sugar cane, which can be grown throughout the year. Sugar is especially widely cultivated: the high temperatures, the heavy annual rainfall (with a drier interval before harvest in which the crops can ripen under the tropical sun), the sea breezes and the alluvial soils all contribute to the successful growing of this crop. The Antilles also produce tobacco, coffee, sponges, cacao, cotton and sisal, and there are some off-shore oil wells between Venezuela and the Antilles.

The population of the Antilles is a mixture of Spanish immigrants, Negroes, Indians and East Indians, with a comparatively small European element.

The Antilles were the first part of the New World reached by Columbus. Today they form an important strategic and economic area with widely varied political and commercial problems – but are at the same time one of the most attractive (though not one of the cheapest) vacation grounds of the world.

Aqaba, Gulf of

A long, narrow gulf, northeast arm of the Red Sea. Location *Between Sinai Peninsula and northernmost Hejaz.* Dimensions *100 miles long, 12–17 miles wide.* Map *10, B3.*

A narrow strip of brilliant blue water, lying between the plateaus of Sinai on the north and of northwestern Arabia on the south, and dominated by the slopes rising abruptly on either side, the Gulf of Aqaba does little to suggest today that it was one of the busiest waterways of antiquity. Despite its uniformly narrow width (between 12 and 17 miles, with dark, steep shores on the north, rich in minerals, and red and barren on the south), the Gulf is more than 600 feet deep from the Red Sea almost up to its head. It forms part of the Great Rift Valley dividing the Middle East from north to south.

For all its great depth, there is little plain sailing in the Gulf. Where it joins the Red Sea the channel is obstructed by small islands and coral reefs; the generally rugged coastline farther north is an additional hazard. The Gulf's position between two mountain masses makes it subject to sudden squalls at all seasons. There are virtually no natural harbors. Dahab on the coast of Sinai is built on a sheltered inlet 30 miles from the mouth of the Gulf, but the larger ports of Elath (developed and ambitiously planned by the new state of Israel) and Aqaba (in Jordan) at its head have become harbors more by necessity than by nature.

The natural disadvantages of the Gulf did not prevent its use in Biblical times for trade and, perhaps, for military purposes. It was at "Ezion-geber, which is beside Eloth," that King Solomon built in the tenth century B.C. the fleet of ships which sailed down the Red Sea to seek the treasures of Ophir (probably in southwestern Arabia) and to disseminate the stories of the king's wisdom that brought the Queen of Sheba to Jerusalem. Another expedition to Ophir was fitted out by Jehoshaphat, but he incurred God's displeasure and the ships were broken, perhaps by one of the Gulf's characteristic squalls, before they left harbor.

Many centuries later the Romans used the Gulf as a base for their trade adventures to the East. They called it Sinus Aelaniticus after their military post Aelana (at what is now Aqaba), a post set up to protect their Palestinian trade routes.

In the early Middle Ages the town at the head of the Gulf declined as a trading port. Nevertheless it survived as a market for the herdsmen of the Hejaz and was considered of sufficient strategic importance to the Crusaders for them to build a fortress there and use the port as a base to repel sea attacks by Saracen galleys. The first Christian king of Jerusalem, Baldwin I, at the beginning of the twelfth century, built his own castle on a small islet near the head of the Gulf which was known as the Isle de Graye but is now called Jezira Firun (Island of Pharaoh). The mainland was sacked by Saladin and its castle later became important as a strongpoint and as a resting place for Egyptian pilgrims traveling to Mecca.

After Israel was founded in 1948 the head of the Gulf of Aqaba grew into a center of political crisis, for Israel's narrow strip of coastline around Elath – her only means of direct sea communication with the east – was sandwiched between Egypt and Jordan, two of her principal enemies, and beyond Jordan's port of Aqaba lay a third enemy, Saudi Arabia. Egyptian and Saudi Arabian possession of all the coast but the head enabled the Arab countries to block the narrow Gulf to Israeli shipping. Both Israel and Jordan devoted much energy to restoring the harbors at the head of the Gulf. As Jordan's only seaport, the importance of Aqaba is obvious. Elath, in Israel, is the center for a region rich in minerals, the southern Negev. Behind the date palms which line the shore (the name of the town means "grove") are mountains containing iron and copper ore. Elath is developing not only as a port but also as a winter resort, hoping for a revival of the prosperity it enjoyed in King Solomon's day.

Arabian Sea

A sea with few islands and several important gulfs. Location *Between India and Arabia.* Width *1,800 miles.* Map *10, C4–E5.*

Bounded on the north by Persia and Baluchistan, on the east by India and on the west by Arabia and the jutting Horn of Africa, the Arabian Sea, a broad arm of the Indian Ocean, divides Africa from India. It is 1,800 miles wide between Cape Guardafui (at the Horn of Africa) and Cape Comorin (at the southern tip of India), and is crossed by many shipping routes. Bombay, Karachi, Cochin and Aden are its main ports.

The Sea runs out into two prongs or gulfs: the Gulf of Aden connecting through Bab el Mandeb strait with the Red Sea, and the Gulf of Oman leading into the Persian Gulf. It has few islands – the scattered Laccadives towards the Indian coast, Socotra, and the Kuria Muria Islands off Arabia. Socotra was for centuries a haunt of pirates.

The Arabian Sea remains one of the last areas of the world where trade is still carried on in sailing boats – the famous Arab dhows, the design of which has changed little over the centuries. These distinctive vessels of 150–200 tons, with their stems rising in a graceful slope from the water and their single masts carrying a lateen sail with a huge yard, still trade between Africa, Arabia and India. The sailors are dependent on the half-yearly monsoons which blow from the southwest in summer and the northeast in winter.

The monsoons are the prevailing feature of the Arabian Sea, creating the Monsoon Drift in a clockwise direction during the summer. Those from the southwest can be extremely violent, dangerous even for modern steam ships. Hurricanes are rare, occurring only during the change-over periods between the monsoons.

Aran Islands

Three islands with historic remains. Location *Off the southwest coast of County Galway, Ireland.* Area *18.1 square miles.* Map *8, B3.*

Looking westward from Black Head on the southern shore of Galway Bay, the three islands of the group lie like whales basking on the surface. The largest of them, Inishmore, has an elevation of no more than 350 feet. Beyond them runs the long surge of the Atlantic, and they provide a natural breakwater to the long, deep sound of Galway Bay.

Today, the Islands are almost uninhabited. The harsh conditions of life and the constant battle with the elements have driven away all but a handful of the old fisher families. Yet time was when these islands supported a considerable number of people – several thousand at least – for they were a place of pilgrimage and one of the most famous havens for hermits and ascetics. *Aran na naomh*, Aran of the Saints, was the name given to Inishmore on account of its many religious teachers, holy wells and sacred shrines. Here, also, are the remains of a large circular tower called *Dun-Aengus*, supposed to be the work of Aengus, the great hero of Irish legend who came to the Islands in the first century A.D. Other early remains – among them seven similar towers – testify to the importance that the Arans once held. These bleak and rocky outposts have also inspired much Irish poetry and one great play – J. M. Synge's *Riders to the Sea.*

Arctic Ocean

A virtually landlocked sea at the top of the world. Location *Extending from North Pole to Atlantic Ocean.* Area *5,440,000 square miles.* Maximum depth *17,850 feet.* Map *5.*

A vast, more or less land-locked sea, the Arctic Ocean's main features are the ice with which it is laden, the major islands of its continental shelf and the Polar Basin, a deep depression lying roughly at its center. The greatest depth recorded – by Sir Hubert Wilkins in 1927, 400 miles north of Herald Island – is 17,850 feet.

Bounded by Norway, the U S S R, Alaska, Canada and Greenland, the Arctic Ocean communicates with the Atlantic through Baffin Bay, Davis Strait and the Labrador Sea on the west side of Greenland and by the Greenland Sea and the Norwegian Sea on the east side. Bering Strait connects it with the Pacific. The main islands flanking it are the Queen Elizabeth Islands, the Spitsbergen and Franz Josef archi-

pelagos, Novaya Zemlya, Severnaya Zemlya and the New Siberian Islands.

The shelf seas are the Barents Sea, Kara Sea, Laptev Sea, East Siberian Sea and Chukchi Sea; the Beaufort Sea is marginal, part of the deep basin. The Kara Sea is off the USSR, bounded on the north by a line running from Cape Kohlsaat to Cape Molotov, containing the estuaries of the Ob, Yenisei, Pyasina and Taimyra rivers; it is a comparatively shallow sea which is navigable for only two months – August and September – in each year. The river mouths are rich in fish; the main ports are Dickson Harbor and Novy Port. The Laptev Sea extends between the East Siberian coast and the continental shelf, receiving the Anabar, Khatanga, Olenek, Lena and Yana rivers; shallower than the Kara, it is also icebound for ten months in each year. Named after the eighteenth-century Russian navigators Khariton and Dmitri Laptev, its main ports are Nordvik and Tiksi.

During the short summer the coasts of the Arctic Ocean are bright with a variety of small flowering plants over large areas, and the often glaring white of ice floe and iceberg is relieved by shades from pale green to purple; during the long winter night the scene is one of blizzard, with the ice heavily laden with new snow.

With the Greenland and the Barents seas, the area commonly known as the Arctic Ocean exceeds 5,400,000 square miles. The ice floes are often piled by pressure into hummocks 50 feet or more above sea level. The noise of this piling up, or "rafting," and the colliding of moving floes has been described as terrifying.

The surface waters of the Arctic Ocean, laden with ice, overflow into the North Atlantic and the North Pacific through gaps in the Arctic Ocean's retaining walls. The reasons for this are fourfold: the constant flow into the Arctic Ocean from major rivers; a low evaporation rate; the prevailing winds; and the impact of the northward flow of the Gulf Stream. The combined effect of these produces the great trans-polar drift which moves across the Arctic Ocean from Siberia and Alaska towards Spitsbergen and Greenland.

Most of this surface overspill moves into the Greenland Sea between Spitsbergen and Greenland and then down the Greenland coast towards the North Atlantic. Part of it then possibly travels south from Greenland into the North Atlantic. Most of it rounds Cape Farewell and travels up the west coast of Greenland, some of it crossing Davis Strait to return to the Atlantic as the Labrador Current. Smaller quantities of water flow southwards along Robertson Channel between Greenland and Ellesmere Island and southwards through the contorted straits of the Queen Elizabeth Islands, reaching the North Atlantic via Foxe Basin, Hudson Strait and Baffin Bay.

A major body of water deflects from the main trans-polar drift, curves away to the west, skirts the bleak north coast of Greenland, where it deposits timber carried thousands of miles from Siberia, and continues into the Beaufort Sea. The rest merges into the main trans-polar drift again to continue a tireless journey back across the Polar Basin, carrying the sleek forms of several species of seal, and walrus, whales and polar bear in unknown numbers, with quantities of ice, grinding with movement, often tinted with pastel shades; while ice-free areas here and there are tinged bright green with diatoms and pink with plankton.

Arctic exploration properly began with Sebastian Cabot's discovery of Newfoundland and Labrador in 1497. Sir Hugh Willoughby's ill-fated expedition of 1553 sighted Novaya Zemlya but he and his men perished on the coast of Lapland. In 1607 Henry Hudson succeeded in reaching the latitude of Spitsbergen. Sir Martin Frobisher first sailed in 1576 to explore the Arctic parts of America; John Davis, the great navigator, in 1585–88 sailed up the strait now bearing his name and along the coast of Greenland. Hudson – like so many others, seeking the Northwest Passage – discovered the strait and bay named after him in 1610. In 1615–16 William Baffin – as skilful a navigator as Davis – found the great northern outlet to Baffin Bay.

Russia joined the quest under Peter the Great. Vitus Bering discovered the strait called after him. A Russian expedition in 1742 found the northernmost point of Siberia, named Chelyuskin after its discoverer. In 1765 Tchitsakoff sailed to Spitsbergen. Baron Ferdinand Petrovich von Wrangel explored the Siberian coast between Cape Chelagskoi and the Kolyma River in 1820–23.

In 1818 the British Admiralty sent out Sir

4 Canadian supply ship cracking pack ice n the Arctic Ocean

John Ross and William Edward Parry who explored part of Lancaster Sound; the next year Parry discovered Prince Regent Inlet, Barrow Strait and Melville Sound. In 1826–27 Sir John Franklin traced the North American coast from the Mackenzie River to Cape Beechey for 860 miles; in 1838 Peter Warren Dease and Thomas Simpson extended this survey.

The Arctic claimed its victims, staged its tragedies. Sir John Franklin and his men perished – though not before discovering the long-sought Northwest Passage. Commander George Washington De Long's *Jeannette* expedition, sent out by the *New York Herald* in 1879 to push north of the Bering Strait, also ended in disaster. But Sir Robert McClure, sent out to find Franklin in 1850, actually traversed the Northwest Passage from ocean to ocean – partly by sledge – before he was rescued in the spring of 1851 by Sir Edward Belcher. It was Sir F. L. McClintock, sent out by Lady Franklin in 1857, who found a cairn at Point Victory which told the tragic tale of the Franklin expedition.

In 1827 Parry, seeking the Northeast Passage, reached latitude 82° 40′ North. About 1855 Sweden entered Arctic exploration under the leadership of Baron Nordenskjöld who, in 1878, rounded Cape Chelyuskin and, after wintering near the Bering Strait, sailed into the Pacific, reaching Yokohama in September, 1879. Three-and-a-quarter centuries after Willoughby's attempt, the Northeast Passage was at last completed. The Lady Franklin Bay Expedition of 1881–84, led by Lieutenant Greely, approached the Pole closer than anyone before; of the expedition only seven men survived.

Fridtjof Nansen crossed the icy plateau of Greenland in 1888; Robert Edwin Peary did excellent work in the same area in 1886–1900. He sailed again in the summer of 1905 and got within 174 nautical miles of the Pole. Nansen entered the ice with his *Fram* near the New Siberian Islands in 1893, spent two winters drifting towards the Pole and with Frederic Hjalmer Johansen marched to latitude 86° 14′. Roald Amundsen completed the first journey by ship through the Northwest Passage in 1903–06. On April 6, 1909, Peary finally reached the North Pole by a sledge journey over the sea ice from the north coast of Grant Land. It seemed that the High North had at long last been conquered.

But much remained to be done and men like Vilhjalmur Stefansson, Dr R. M. Anderson, Sir Hubert Wilkins, Dr S. Horn, Ivan Papanin and his Russian companions and Captain Robert A. Bartlett have contributed decisive chapters to the history of Arctic exploration. In 1926 successful flights in the Arctic began: Richard Evelyn Byrd flew a plane to the North Pole and returned to his base in 15½ hours. The Amundsen-Ellsworth-Nobile Trans-Polar Expedition of 1926 completed a 71-hour flight in the dirigible *Norge* from Kings Bay, Spitsbergen, across the North Pole to Teller, Alaska. In 1927 Sir George Hubert Wilkins and Carl Ben Eielson made another polar flight. The much-publicized dirigible *Italia* under General Nobile made three polar flights in May, 1928; the third ended in a crash and a rescue operation in which Finnish, French, Italian, Norwegian, Soviet and Swedish units took part. Roald Amundsen and Dr Finn Malmgren lost their lives in this large-scale international polar action, but Nobile was rescued by the Russian aviator Chukhnovsky and his men were saved by the Soviet icebreaker *Krassin.*

In 1936 the whole length of the Arctic coastline was traced for the first time by V. S. Molokof, who flew 15,625 miles. Papanin's Soviet expedition (1937–38) studied the drift of polar ice and pioneered the Moscow-United States polar air route. In 1939 the American Captain Robert A. Bartlett made his fifteenth Arctic voyage; D. B. MacMillan conducted scientific observations in Labrador, Baffin Island and along western Greenland.

Though the war brought some interruptions, by 1940 Soviet airmen had flown over 1,000,000 arctic miles and by 1958 had established 81 semi-permanent research stations. Today, flights over the North Pole by commercial airlines are commonplace. The Arctic is studded with military and scientific installations. The two American submarines, *Nautilus* and *Skate,* have passed under the Polar icecap, the former discovering a depth of 13,140 feet under the Pole. Another interesting discovery is the Lomonosov Ridge, located by Soviet oceanographers, and the ridge discovered by the Lamont Geographical Survey in 1957. Slowly the Arctic Ocean yields its secrets, but there is still much left to explore.

Aruba

A tropical island. Location *Dutch West Indies.* Area *67.56 square miles.* Map *2, G4.*

Aruba, owned by the Netherlands since the Dutch West India Company established itself in the Antilles in 1634–35, is only one third the size of its neighbor Curaçao, 45 miles west of it. It is closer to the South American mainland, as only 20 miles divide it from the Paraguaná Peninsula of Venezuela, and this geographic position has given it very considerable economic advantages. For it is to Aruba that Venezuela sends the yield of its immensely rich oil wells – or at least, a large part of it – for refining and transshipment.

Oranjestad, the chief town of Aruba, is the center of the oil installations. It is oil that has increased the population of Aruba from about 8,000 before the First World War to over 50,000 today. The island is only 19 miles long and about 4 miles wide but within its 60-odd square miles more industrial plant is concentrated than anywhere else in the West Indies. Besides oil there is a lucrative exploitation of "leached guano," the richest fertilizer in the world, and phosphates are exported to the tune of more than half a million tons annually. With its tropical, semi-arid climate, Aruba also grows sisal and raises goats and sheep: but since the oil industry was introduced in 1925, the "black gold" has been the lifeblood of the island's economy.

Ascension Island

An isolated volcanic island. Location *South Atlantic, 700 miles northwest of St Helena.* Area *34 square miles.* Map *6, G7.*

A rugged, semi-barren volcanic island, 7½ miles long and about 6 miles wide, Ascension lies in the South Atlantic, about midway between South America and Africa. The chief settlement is Georgetown, locally known as Garrison. The Island is of volcanic rock and rises to 2,870 feet in Green Mountain. The climate is tropical but healthy, with the heat moderated by the southeastern trade winds, and its uplands – conical, smooth hills – have sufficient rainfall for some agriculture and for cattle and sheep raising.

The population varies, moving for the most part between Ascension and St Helena, 700 miles away; in 1940 it was 169, in 1956, 416. Ascension is the site of an international cable station and boasts a golf-course and a swimming pool – sharks and a strong undertow make sea-bathing dangerous.

The Island was discovered by the Portuguese João de Nova on Ascension Day, 1501. Two hundred years later the British explorer William Dampier was wrecked here; his ship foundered in the harbor with the loss of practically all Dampier's papers and sketches. The crew managed to struggle ashore and had to camp out until two months later a British man-of-war rescued them. When Napoleon was exiled to St Helena, the British maintained a naval station on the otherwise uninhabited Island. Charles Darwin visited it during his voyage on the *Beagle* and described it graphically – including the strange invasion every year, between January and May, of thousands of sea-turtles which crawl up the beaches and dig holes in which they lay their eggs.

Atlantic Coast, United States

Location *From Canada to the Gulf of Mexico.* Length *5,565 miles.* Map *1.*

The Atlantic Coast stretches for 5,565 miles, framing the Atlantic coastal plain of the United States. It is, like the Gulf coast, basically a coastline of submergence, with a great many sharply edged embayments, sandspits – like Cape Cod or Sandy Hook – and occasional barrier beaches which are backed by lagoons. The northeastern coast has many fine bays, but from the great capes – Fear, Hatteras, Lookout – southward there are few large bays.

It is the coast along which the Great Lakes drain into the Atlantic through the St Lawrence River, as do the rivers from the eastern slopes of the Appalachians and the eastern coastal region, including the Hudson, Delaware, Penobscot, Connecticut, Susquehanna, Potomac, James, Savannah and Saint Johns. The climate here is that of the warm-summer continental belt with humid subtropical variations at the southern extremity; the mid-Atlantic states have generally more rainfall and higher temperatures than the humid-continental climate of the Great Lakes and New England. The hinterland of the Atlantic coastline is the important agricultural area for truck crops, peanuts, poultry and fruit; just as the most important manufacturing belt of the States extends from New England and the middle Atlantic States as far south as the Potomac. The coast and its immediate vicinity is the most thickly populated area – especially in the northeast, mainly because of its proximity to the Atlantic seaboard.

But of course the Atlantic Coast is most famous and most important because of the cities that have grown and flourished along it. Portland, Maine and Boston, the great city of New York, the thriving communities of Massachusetts and New Jersey, of Delaware and Virginia, right down to the Carolinas, Georgia and Florida, prove the importance of the Atlantic Coast both in the north, middle Atlantic and southeastern regions of the United States. As widely varied as Nantucket and the Florida Keys, Atlantic City or Bar Harbor, the eastern seaboard, facing Europe across the Atlantic, is the major gateway of the New World.

Atlantic Ocean

The second largest ocean of the world. Location *From the Arctic to the Antarctic, between the Americas and Europe and Africa.* Area *31,830,000 square miles.* Maximum depth *30,246 feet (Milwaukee Deep).* Map *6.*

Dividing the continents of Africa and Europe from the Americas, this huge ocean covers nearly 32,000,000 square miles – or 41,000,000, if we include the adjoining seas. Stretching from the Bering Strait in the Arctic to the Weddell Sea in the Antarctic, the Atlantic, though slightly less than half the size of the Pacific, receives half the drainage of the world – four times as much as the Pacific.

Taking its name from the legendary lost continent of Atlantis (though another theory ascribes it to the Greeks' speaking of the "sea beyond Mount Atlas"), the vast S-shaped Atlantic Ocean is limited at both ends by the pack ice of the poles. For geographical convenience it is divided into the North and South Atlantic; the line between them is about 300 miles north of the equator. The character of the two sections is very different. The North Atlantic is an ocean of immense variety, with many islands in it, including in its area the Mediterranean on the east and the Caribbean, the Gulf of Mexico and the Gulf of St Lawrence on the west. The South Atlantic is predominantly a barren waste of water with only a scattering of small islands – the Falklands, St Helena and Ascension – breaking its monotonous surge and sweep.

The scientific explanation which to some extent accounts for the existence of the Atlantic Ocean is based on the theory of "Continental Drift" – the theory that the hard land masses of the continents have broken apart from one another by the rotation of the earth and "drifted" in the soft magma beneath the earth's crust until they took up their present positions. One of the most convincing arguments for this theory is the shape of the continents surrounding the Atlantic; the pieces dovetail into one another with an almost perfect regularity. Running more or less parallel to the coasts of the land masses is the great Mid-Atlantic Ridge (formerly known as Telegraph Ridge), the longest mountain range in the world, extending 7,000 miles, and mostly rising about 6,000 feet above the ocean floor, itself an average of 13,000 feet down. The only points of this ridge above water are St Helena, Ascension, Tristan da Cunha, St Paul's Rocks and the Azores.

The winds that govern the North Atlantic are the northeast trade winds and the westerlies. The trade winds blow permanently and with little variation in direction, throughout the year, from approximately the latitude of the Canary Islands. These were the winds that drove Columbus and all the early explorers steadily westward, and until the close of the nineteenth century the merchant shipping of Europe ran down their westing for the Americas, the Caribbean and Panama. Today the trade wind routes are almost deserted. The modern steamer can lay a more direct course between her ports of call, and only an occasional yachtsman westward-bound now knows the flying-fish weather and the trade wind swell, where once tall clippers in their hundreds lifted white clouds of canvas out of the sea.

On the northern side of the region of high pressure that divides the wind and weather systems of the North Atlantic, the prevailing winds are the westerlies. The main feature in this area is the variable weather – periods of overcast skies and rain (or snow in winter) alternating with fairer intervals. Fine weather is seldom prolonged, at least in winter, and clouded skies are the rule. It is the westerlies together with the Western Current, or Gulf Stream, that largely determine the climate of the British Isles.

North of the equator and dividing the weather systems of the North and South Atlantic lies the Doldrums, a belt of variable winds and calms, broken only by sudden electrical storms and squalls. Off the coast of Africa violent rain storms descend – so heavy that visibility can be reduced to zero as if by fog. South of the Doldrums there is again a trade wind area, the southeast trades.

The wind systems of the two halves of the ocean are similar, except that in the North Atlantic the wind blows clockwise around an area of high pressure and in the south it moves anti-clockwise around a similar area. Roughly off the Cape of Good Hope, the roaring forties begin. Here the winds are overwhelmingly westerly and blow without let or hindrance clean around the world. Massive long seas are set up; seas without rival, for their steadily marching battalions have vast depths of oceans beneath them and the thrust of an eternal wind behind them. Before the Panama Canal was cut, all shipping bound for the Pacific or the west coast of America had necessarily to pass round Cape Horn – where a ship might hang for day after day in the teeth of an unrelenting westerly and facing giant seas.

In the western half of the Atlantic, during certain seasons of the year, the dreaded tropical storms or hurricanes occur which can overwhelm large liners and devastate islands. Today the United States Weather Bureau, the "hurricane hunter" planes of the United States Navy and Coast Guard, keep a close track of such storms – usually given a feminine name – from the moment of their inception, and issue regular warning of their advance. Under the full fury of an Atlantic hurricane few ships can survive and when the storm heads inland, even brick buildings sometimes dissolve like packs of cards.

Auckland Islands

An uninhabited group famous for its fur seals. Location *South Pacific.* Area *234 square miles.* Map *3, A10.*

One of the outlying island groups of New Zealand, these volcanic islands lie 300 miles south of Invercargill and are part of the Dominion politically. They consist of six islands of which the largest is 27 miles long and 15 miles wide and rises to 2,000 feet.

The group was discovered in 1806 by Captain Abraham Bristow of the English whaler *Ocean.* He found the soil extremely fertile and the slopes of the volcanic hills covered with thick forest. In 1849, the British government granted the Islands to a London firm for a whaling station, but by 1852 this was abandoned and the Islands are now uninhabited, in spite of their favorable climate and agricultural possibilities.

Azores

A beautiful archipelago of nine islands. Location *North Atlantic, 900–1,200 miles west of Lisbon.* Area *888 square miles.* Map *6, F3.*

The Azores, three widely separated groups of islands, rise almost sheer out of the Atlantic sea bed, peaks of immense volcanic mountains, and they are the most remote from the mainland of any islands in the Atlantic. The water around them is about two and a half miles deep, yet the highest point of the archipelago, Mount Pico, is 7,611 feet high. The island of Pico – one of the central group which includes Terceira, Graciosa, São Jorge and Faial islands – is in fact the summit of a mountain that rears, over four miles high, out of the ocean floor. On a clear day Pico can be seen from miles away at sea, a high-pointed cone that might be the prototype of all volcanoes. Pico is still active and, on days when cloud does not hide the summit, a lazy trail of smoke is always visible. Across the channel from Pico lies Faial where in 1957 volcanic activity caused a new mountain to rise out of the sea bed close to the coast.

The port of Horta in Faial is the only real harbor in the islands; the others are just open roadsteads, unsafe for vessels to anchor in at all

Whale-fishing in the Azores

times of the year. Southwesterly winds, in particular, make navigation around the islands extremely dangerous and when the winds are at all westerly in direction only Horta is safe for shipping.

Faial is the whaling center of the islands and the inhabitants, who are a mixture of Portuguese and Flemish, are born seamen. The sea off the Azores is possibly the last area in the world in which organized whale-hunting in open boats is still carried on. The boats are of shallow draught, narrow-beamed and extremely fast; with the wind astern they are reported to be able to do up to 14 knots. Apart from fishing, the main occupation of the islanders is agriculture. There is little industry, but the soil is fertile and many varieties of fruit are grown; oranges, lemons, apricots, bananas and pineapples are exported and so is the local wine.

The islands of the central group are all similar in character, rising steeply from the sea but – unlike many volcanic islands – they are far from barren. Rich in vegetation, they have many trees, most of them imported from Europe.

One of the most beautiful of the islands is Flores which, with Corvo, forms the northwestern group. Flores is criss-crossed by deep ravines in which small lakes sparkle surrounded by a rich variety of wild and cultivated flowers.

The third group of islands, the southeastern,

is composed of St Michael's, St Mary's and Formigas. St Michael's (San Miguel) is the largest of the archipelago.

All the Azores are particularly fortunate in their climate, which is temperate with no great degrees of heat or cold, ranging on the average between 48° F. in winter and 80° F. in midsummer. The "Azores High," a region of high pressure usually situated in summer slightly to the north of the islands, has a great effect on the climate of Britain during the summer months.

Coins found on Corvo show that the Carthaginians probably reached the Azores in the fourth century B.C. The islands first appeared on an Italian map in 1351. Portuguese navigators (Lisbon is 900 miles away) visited them in 1427–31; Gonçalo Velho Cabral landed on Santa Maria shortly afterwards. The Portuguese settlement began in 1450 and within 20 years many Flemish immigrants arrived when Faial was presented as a gift to Isabella of Burgundy. For centuries the Azores served as a place of exile for rebels and malcontents and played an important part in Portuguese history. Here was the center of resistance to the accession of Philip II of Spain to the throne of Portugal and in 1830–31 Dom Pedro's supporters against Dom Miguel made the islands their headquarters.

In the late sixteenth century Flores island was a station for the British fleet and it was from here that Sir Richard Grenville in the *Revenge* sailed out to do battle with the Spanish fleet. In 1812 an American privateer engaged a British flotilla off Faial and caused such havoc that the ships were delayed in joining the rest of the fleet at Jamaica – a delay which had a considerable influence on the assault against New Orleans in the Anglo-American war.

The Azores have played an important part in transatlantic aviation history; they were used as fueling stops on important flights. In 1943 they became an Allied air base and two major airports were built at Lajes on Terceira Island and on Santa Maria Island; Ponta Delgada and Horta became Allied naval and seaplane bases. Today, with Portugal a member of NATO, they continue to serve as important links in the defense of the west. They have also developed into a center of submarine cable communications while remaining a popular winter resort.

Azov, Sea of

A shallow sea receiving some of the principal rivers of the USSR. Location *Northern arm of Black Sea, USSR.* Area *14,000 square miles.* Maximum depth *49 feet.* Map *7, J8.*

The Romans called it *Palus Maeotis*, after the neighboring tribes, to whom it was known as *Temarenda*, Mother of Waters. Surrounding swamps and labyrinthine water-courses supported the belief for a long time that it was directly connected with the Northern Ocean. There was, indeed, a connection in prehistoric times with the Caspian Sea; but since the earliest historical times not much has changed in its character or relations. Today, however, the completion of the great Don-Volga Canal has made it possible for ships to travel not only between the Baltic and White seas and the Caspian, but also – by river and canal – to continue to the Sea of Azov and the Black Sea. However, these waterways are all frozen in winter for between three and six months.

The Sea of Azov is connected with the Black Sea by the Strait of Kerch. About 230 miles long from southwest to northeast with a maximum breadth of 110 miles, it is a very shallow sea – only 3–49 feet in depth. It freezes over generally from November to the middle of April. Because of the great volume of water which its affluents – the mighty Don, the Mius and Kalmius on the north, the Yeya and Kuban on the east – contribute, its waters have little salinity. The Turks used to call it *Baluk Deniz* (Fish Sea) because of the great abundance of fish in its waters, including the great sturgeon.

During July and August there are fierce, continuous winds from the east which can make navigation hazardous. The counter-clockwise currents have created fantastic sandspits on the northern and eastern coasts, and built up the long Arabat Tongue in the west which separates the Sea of Azov from the area of lagoons and marshes known as the Sivash, or Putrid Sea, where the water is intensely salt.

Roughly triangular in shape, the Sea of Azov narrows at its northeastern end to form the Gulf of Taganrog. Its main ports are Rostov (actually on the Don, just above the river mouth), Taganrog, Zhdanov, Osipenko (all on the northern coast), and Kerch inside the Strait. The fishing centers of Yeisk and Temryuk which process the large catches of pike, carp and herring are on the east coast. Kerch and Zhdanov are also important metallurgical centers and iron ore and coal are transported between them.

Bab el Mandeb

An important shipping lane. Location *Between the Red Sea and the Gulf of Aden (Arabian Sea).* Dimensions *17 miles wide, about 20 miles long.* Maximum depth *1,020 feet.* Map *10, B4–5.*

Bab el Mandeb received its name ("Gate of Tears" in Arabic) because of its unfriendliness to mariners. At its narrowest point the strait is divided by the rocky island of Perim into two channels. The eastern channel, two miles wide and everywhere less than 100 feet deep, is complicated by a swift northward-flowing current. West of Perim is a much deeper channel with a southward undercurrent. To sailing vessels and to the early steamships high and conflicting winds from the Ethiopian mountains on the west and from the Indian Ocean on the east presented an additional hazard.

Despite its miserable reputation, however, the strait has had great importance throughout history as a gateway. It has provided a connecting link for seaborne traffic between the countries bordering the southern Mediterranean and the Orient; it is the point at which the continent of Africa comes closest to the fertile and well-populated southwestern quarter of Arabia, and in consequence migrations between the two land masses have passed across it.

The movement in both directions between Africa and Arabia is of far greater antiquity than the incidental use of the strait for long-distance sea voyages. The ancestors of the Semitic peoples who, some 2,000 years before Christ, spread throughout the lands of the eastern and southern Mediterranean were probably Hamitic peoples of eastern Africa who passed through the Gate of Tears on to the fertile shores of Arabia and later moved northwards. Later expansion took some of these Semitic folk who had remained in southern Arabia back across Bab el Mandeb to found the empire of Ethiopia, also before the beginning of the Christian era. A Greek traveler of the first century A.D. recorded the existence of substantial trading across the strait and in the seventh century it was one route by which Mohammedanism was carried into Africa.

There is no certain evidence of the use of Bab el Mandeb as a sea route to the east before classical times. Greek and Roman traders passed through the strait on the way to India and later it was a dangerous stage in the voyages of pilgrim vessels plying between East Africa and Jiddah. The Portuguese, who first came to the Indian Ocean by way of the Cape of Good Hope in the sixteenth century, realized the strategic importance of Bab el Mandeb; later, France, Britain and Italy each sought to gain control of the strait. Since the opening of the Suez Canal the traffic passing through Bab el Mandeb has greatly increased. Today, Ethiopia and the Somali Republic lie on its African shores with Yemen and the Aden Protectorate opposite.

Baffin Bay and Island

An Arctic sea and an island, named after the explorer William Baffin. Location *Arctic Ocean.* Dimensions *(Bay) 700 miles long, 70–400 miles wide.* Area *(Island) 231,000 square miles.* Maximum depth *(Bay) 9,000 feet.* Map *(Bay) 5, B9; (Island) 5, A9.*

The days of exploration and discovery are apparently not yet ended in Baffin Island and its polar waters, although they began nearly three centuries ago. Indeed, in 1948 a large island, provisionally named New Island, was discovered in Baffin Bay where once it was thought there was nothing but polar pack ice. Lying between Greenland, the north of Quebec province and the Northwest Territories of Canada, with Baffin Bay touching its northern flank, Baffin Island was probably seen by Norsemen who sailed Baffin Bay. Both Bay and Island returned to the limbo of fog that so often hangs over polar seas, until the great age of Elizabethan Arctic exploration when Sir Martin Frobisher, William Baffin, Luke Fox and John Davis with many others set sail to discover a sea route to the Far East via the Far North, penetrated deep into the Bay and reached the Island, giving it such names as Fox Land and Cockburn Land – "land" meaning *terra incognita*.

Baffin Island's shores are so indented that the early explorers considered it to be an archipelago. They found no certain end to Admiralty Inlet, the fjord that curves deeply into northern Baffin, one of the largest fjords in the world with many smaller inlets branching from it. Its neighbor to the northeast, Eclipse Sound, is a maze of indentations filled with ice. Cumberland Sound, too, is a miniature sea that penetrates far into the Island, the sea ice merging into the white of the land, so that early explorers could not always distinguish land from water. The Eskimos, who decoyed away five of Frobisher's men, could have told him that the deep indentation he had discovered in 1576, which now carries his name, was not the beginning of the Northwest Passage but a blind alley that ended deep in a polar island. And for many years after the discovery that Baffin Bay was really an arm of the Arctic Ocean connected with it by narrow, ice-filled straits between Greenland and Ellesmere Island, Baffin Island still remained unexplored. Nor did the discovery that a way to the Far East lay along its northern shores, or perhaps through narrow Fury and Hecla Strait at the end of Foxe Basin, advance the exploration of its interior.

Baffin Island

Today, much is known of both Bay and Island. Military radar sites sit atop some of the peaks that rise from glaciers and icefields to about 8,000 feet. There is a major airport at Frobisher Bay; aircraft operate the length of Baffin Island and ono ranspolar schedules across Baffin Bay. Geologists probe among the frost-split rocks and naturalists make surveys of the walruses, polar bears, foxes, and the birds of the several large lakes. The little red-roofed trading settlements of Arctic Bay, Pond Inlet and Pangnirtung are firmly established deep in inlets that defeated the early explorers. The Eskimos go to school and many speak English. Yet so long as the glaciers of Baffin Island pour into the ice of Baffin Bay, both Bay and Island will retain something of the mysterious qualities that first caused them to be dubbed *incognita.*

Bahama Islands

A large archipelago. Location *West Indies.* Area *4,403.5 square miles.* Map *2, E1–F2.*

Rising barely 100 feet above the ocean and unprotected from the fury of seasonal hurricanes, the islands of this huge archipelago – 20 inhabited islands, about 700 uninhabited islands and islets and more than 2,000 rocks, reefs and cays – are the exposed portions of the crest of a 900-mile-long submarine cliff. An awe-inspiring barrier between the Gulf of Mexico and the Atlantic Ocean, stretching from within 50 miles of southeast Florida, generally parallel with Cuba, to within 70 miles of Haiti, the cliff sinks in a line of titanic precipices into the sea, culminating in a deep of 27,972 feet off the Navidad Bank in the southeast. (The deepest point of the Atlantic Ocean, 30,246 feet, off the northeast coast of Hispaniola, is only a short distance farther east.)

The older portion of this cliff, in the area of the great Bahama Bank to the north, is a foreland of Cuba, its rocks part of that island's continental shelf. To the southeast – separated from the northern section by the 9,000-foot-deep Crooked Island Passage through which sail ships bound for Panama and the Gulf – lies a 500-mile arc of islands, formed by deposition on the peaks of long-extinct volcanoes and separated by troughs up to 12,000 feet deep. Like icebergs, only a tiny part is visible of this vast submerged limestone plateau upon which shells and corals have deposited their calcareous matter. In Eocene times, however, these massive mountains stood high above the surface. Eroded by wind, weather and pounding surf into shallow banks, they were colonized by corals and became the sites of gigantic atolls, up to 200 miles long and 80 miles across. Then in turn these atolls were submerged – only a few thousand years ago – by the rising ocean level as the glaciers of the great Ice Age melted.

Corals still grow on their remains and the milky lime-precipitate rains gently down. This ever-increasing vast limestone plateau's most important sections are the Great Bahama Bank and Little Bahama Bank. The portions above sea level are low, riverless, pitted and honeycombed, with many mangrove swamps and ponds. The principal islands from north to south are: Grand Bahama, Great Araco, Bimini, Berry, New Providence (with Nassau, the capital), Andros (the largest), Eleuthera, Cat Island (which rises highest, though only to 400 feet), Great Exuma, San Salvador or Watling (the traditional landing-place of Columbus), Long Island, Crooked Island, Acklins, Mayaguana, Little Inagua and Great Inagua.

The climate is subtropical with mild winters; the hurricanes at the end of the rainy season (May-October) often cause considerable damage but the Gulf Stream's closeness keeps frosts away. Today frogmen pick their way among the shallow reefs and winding channels, pausing to peer into the black, mysterious depths of the great inter-island troughs, studying the fantastically colored and shaped fish. Deepsea fishermen go after sailfish, kingfish, amberjack and barracuda, while local people scoop tortoises, crawfish, shells and sponges from the depths. Above, surf-riders and water-skiers furrow the Gulf Stream's warm waters and many thousands of sun-seekers come to vacation or to settle down, though land prices have rocketed and there is now little left to buy.

The original inhabitants of the Bahamas were the Lucayos, a gentle and primitive people who disappeared within 20 years of the coming of the Spaniards – probably deported to Cuba. Columbus made his first landfall here on October 12,

Turtle-fishing in the Bahamas

1492, on the island then called Guanahani. There was no permanent Spanish settlement; but early in the seventeenth century British colonists arrived from Bermuda.

In 1647 the Company of Eleutherian Adventurers was formed in London and two years later Cromwell made them proprietors of the Islands, though there had been a previous grant to Sir Robert Heath. Charles II presented them to six of the Lords Proprietors of Carolina and these gentlemen relinquished their claim only in 1787. Blackbeard, perhaps the most famous of the West Indian pirates, had made the Bahamas his main base and had to be driven off by the British Navy under the first royal governor, appointed in 1717. The vast group was frequently under Spanish and French attack; in 1776 there was a brief American occupation of Nassau, and the Islands capitulated to the Spaniards in 1787, only to be retaken by the British. After the American Revolution they became the home of many loyalists, but when slavery was abolished in 1833 the plantations declined. During the Civil War the Bahamas were used as bases by blockade runners from the South; and the Prohibition Era made them equally lucrative bases for bootleggers.

In 1940 the United States leased bases in the Bahamas; during the war years the Duke of Windsor (the former Edward VIII) was governor, and developed many plans for the economic future of the Islands. Some of the inhabitants moved to Florida to work in war plants. Now the Bahamas have their own House of Assembly and Legislative Council with definite autonomous functions. The great majority of the population is Negro and the universal language is English.

Bahrein

A small archipelago. Location *Gulf of Bahrein, Persian Gulf.* Area *231 square miles.* Map *10, C3.*

Though mystery envelops the earliest history of Bahrein and its sister islands of Muharraq, Sitra and Umm Nasan, they were certainly known and peopled not long after the beginning of recorded time. Early settlers were attracted to Bahrein by its unexpected fertility, which is due to the presence of a number of fresh water springs. An Arab writer of the eleventh century describing Muharraq, the second largest island of the archipelago, referred to cascades of sweet water sufficient to turn mill-wheels. This abundance is still something of a mystery, for the annual rainfall never exceeds five inches a year. The springs are said to originate in the highlands of Nejd, in Central Arabia, and to flow underground for hundreds of miles, finally emerging at the Persian Gulf. In places fresh water is found coming from the bed of the Gulf itself. With this water supply the people of Bahrein are able to grow dates in abundance, as well as cereals and citrus fruits. They are also active as herdsmen and fishermen; pearling is a long-standing local occupation and some 250 vessels still leave Bahrein each year between May and September to visit the pearl banks off the western coast of the Gulf.

Since the late nineteen-thirties these industries have been overshadowed by the development of the oil resources lying under Bahrein and the adjoining sea, although these are not so rich or extensive as some on the Arabian mainland. A small refinery on Bahrein processes both the local crude oil and some carried by pipeline from the mainland.

The islands are in general low and sandy, except for a cluster of barren rocky hills, the Jebel Dukham (Hills of Smoke) in the center of Bahrein island. The north is especially favored by spring water; here are the richest date groves. Between Bahrein and Muharraq there is a good deepwater harbor known as Khor Khaliya.

There is considerable speculation about Bahrein's early history. An Akkadian tablet of about 2870 B.C. is said to refer to the place as the seaport of Niduk-ki on the "lower sea" taken by the conqueror Sargon. An archeological curiosity is a vast necropolis some miles southwest of Manama, the capital of Bahrein island. Scattered over a large area are two-storey sepulchral buildings, each one built along an east-west axis in the manner of the burial chambers erected by the ancient Phoenicians. From the entrance a passage, roofed over with roughly plastered stone blocks, extends the length of the building. The passage is flanked by small niches or chambers large enough to accommodate stone tombs. Dr Theodore Bent, who examined these curious buildings in the eighteen-eighties, set them down as Phoenician; other archeologists rejected this idea, while some say that ancestors of the Phoenicians built the tombs before migrating to the Mediterranean.

The importance of Bahrein grew as the Persian Gulf became an avenue of sea traffic from Mesopotamia to the east in classical times. In the time of Mohammed it was under Persian domination and remained for many years the seat of the Abbasside governors of the region. When European influences first began to be felt in the Persian Gulf in the early sixteenth century, Bahrein became a subject of contention between the Persians and the Portuguese, who built a fort there in 1507, the ruins of which are still visible. Sargon was probably not the first conqueror to have cast a greedy eye upon the islands and he was by no means the last. In the seventeenth and eighteenth centuries a series of bloody wars was fought over them between the Persians and the Arabs until in 1783 the Arabian tribe of the Athubis triumphed, and the present ruling family, the Sunni Khalifah, came to power. They are descended from the same ancestors as the ruling houses of Kuwait and Saudi Arabia. In 1820, after having been in direct relations with Britain since 1805, the sheik entered into treaty relations with the East India Company and in 1861 claimed the full benefits of British protection. An oil concession was granted to an American company in 1925 and renewed in 1940 and large-scale production began in 1934. The Bahrein government has British advisers and there is a British political agent. Iran has intermittently made claims to the islands without any success. During the Persian oil crisis after the Second World War, Bahrein's importance increased considerably and today it is one of the important sources of Western Europe's, and especially Britain's, oil supplies.

Balearic Islands

A popular vacation area. Location *Western Mediterranean, 190 miles off the eastern coast of Spain.* Area *1,936 square miles.* Map *7, C8.*

Within easy distance of Barcelona by sea, or by air from most European airports, the Balearics have within recent years become one of the most popular resorts in the Mediterranean. They owe their enviable reputation largely to their climate, which is mild and humid, with a long, rainless summer and a short, temperate winter. Majorca, largest of the Islands (430 square miles), is perhaps the most beautiful, a typical example of limestone scenery with craggy peaks covered with conifers and fertile valleys full of almond, olive and carob. Few sights in the Mediterranean can equal a Majorcan valley in early spring when the almond blossom is out and when the wind passes like a wave of the sea.

Majorca, Minorca and the islet of Cabrera form the eastern group of islands. Palma, Majorca's capital and the principal city and port in the Balearics, is situated on a large bay in the southwest. The city shows traces of Moorish architecture, for the Balearics were held by the Moors for nearly 200 years until their conquest by James I of Aragon in 1232. But the archipelago's cultural antiquity is attested by many prehistoric remains and it had been in the possession of Iberians, Phoenicians, Greeks, Carthaginians, Romans and Byzantines before the Moors conquered it in the eighth century. The independent Moorish kingdom, established in the Islands 300 years later, became the headquarters of marauding, well-armed pirates who were a scourge of Mediterranean trade and provoked the campaign of James I which regained the archipelago for Christendom.

Palma has expanded considerably in recent years and its old character has been somewhat swamped by modern buildings and port extensions. Even so, working class areas, such as that behind the Plaza Ataranzanes, reveal the ancient pattern of the city. Narrow alleys with tall houses shade the streets even at midday and the houses lean so close together that it is possible to shake hands across the street with one's opposite neighbor.

The southern and southeastern parts of the island are comparatively low-lying but towards the north and northwest it rises into high limestone peaks culminating in Silla de Torrellas (5,154 feet). On the west coast lies Soller, the most important harbor, a beautiful land-locked bay that opens out on to the sea through a narrow, bottleneck entrance. At the northeastern end of the island lie the bays of Pollensa and

Aloudia, a picturesque and fertile area but lacking the grandeur of the west coast.

The Majorcans are nearly all engaged in agriculture. The export of almonds, olives and fruit is considerable, while the local wine is the best in the Balearics – that of Binisalem is outstanding. The language is a dialect of Catalan with a number of French importations dating from the French occupation of the Islands during the eighteenth century. The people are cheerful and peaceable with less of the Spanish "fire" than the mainlanders – though politics can inflame them. During the Spanish Civil War Majorca and Iviza went over to the Nationalists in 1936 while Minorca held out on the Loyalist side until 1939. Their pleasant, indolent climate has suggested to some scholars that the Balearics were the Homeric "Isles of the Lotus-Eaters."

Minorca, to the northeast, is flatter and less obviously attractive than Majorca, but is distinguished by one of the finest harbors in the Mediterranean. "June, July, August and Port Mahon are the finest harbors in the sea," runs an old Spanish saying, and Port Mahon with its large, land-locked bay scattered with small islets is a sailor's paradise. Minorca was occupied by the British for over 50 years – which accounts for the English Georgian architecture in the town and the manufacture, to an eighteenth-century formula, of English gin. (It was for losing Port Mahon to the French in 1756 that Admiral Byng was condemned to death – as Voltaire remarked: "to encourage the others.") The other harbor and town of Minorca, Ciudadela, lies at the far end of a narrow, rock-bound creek, and is one of the oldest cities of the Balearics, having been founded by the Carthaginians.

Iviza (Ibitza) and Formentera, like the other Islands, are principally agricultural, with sheep and pig raising as sidelines. La Ciudad, the capital of Iviza and the only important town in the two islands, hangs over the small harbor, its thirteenth-century Gothic cathedral dominating the fortified town. In the narrow straits between Iviza and Formentera the remains of many Roman trading ships have been found with their cargoes intact. The island also boasts a special breed of dog – somewhat like a greyhound – of supposedly Carthaginian origin and nowhere else to be found in the Mediterranean.

Bali

An island famous for the beauty of its people. Location *Lesser Sundas, Indonesia.* Area *2,243 square miles.* Map *4, B8.*

Bali, formerly a Dutch possession and now part of the Indonesian Republic, has captured the imagination of artists, poets and enthusiasts for a "Pacific paradise." The Balinese, by their innocence and charm, have become the twentieth-century successors to the "Noble Savages" of America, Hawaii and Tahiti. Dutch sailors, passing the island in the seventeenth century, leaped overboard in their anxiety to reach so enchanting a shore and were never seen again.

One of the Lesser Sunda islands, lying between the Java Sea and the Indian Ocean, just east of Java across the Bali Strait, Bali owes its attractiveness partly to the careful isolation in which it was kept by the Dutch, who refused entry to Christian and Mohammedan missionaries alike, so that its people could preserve in peace their *adat* or customs (an intricate mixture of Hindu animism and art), while devoting only part of a tranquil day to the leisurely cultivation of rice, maize, coffee and coconuts. Although not large – 90 miles long and 55 miles wide, with a population of a little over 1,000,000 – Bali is culturally and economically one of the most important islands of Indonesia. It has remained unspoiled – except by wealthy tourists and eccentrics.

On the north coast there is little rainfall; in the south, where a large plain extends, there is a good deal of rain during the monsoon period. Beside small forests of teak there are groves of the giant waringin trees, worshipped as sacred by the Balinese. Tigers still roam the forests. The main products of the island are coffee, copra, livestock, rice and tobacco; there is much home industry, still unspoiled by the demands of the tourist trade, with exquisite weaving, wood carving and metalwork. The main towns are Singaraja, near the port of Buleleng, and Denpasar.

Bali embraced Hinduism as a religion in the seventh century but with important local modifications; large numbers of Javanese Hindus emigrated to the island in the ninth and tenth centuries – much as the Huguenots left France in the

A fishing village on Bali

seventeenth. The first Dutch ship called at Bali in 1597 and the Dutch East India Company began trading early in the sixteenth century. From 1811 to 1816 the island was under British rule; it was not until 1908 that the Dutch firmly established their sovereignty.

Today the Indonesian Republic, of which Bali is part, faces something of a quandary. Its officials, who are mostly Javanese, have resented the fame of this comparatively unimportant island, seeing its "primitiveness" as reactionary. Bali's first Indonesian governor, Major Salim, distributed 2,000 long-sleeved blouses among the women free of charge, in order to discourage (without much success) their "immodest bearing." On the other hand, it has been found necessary to send future diplomats of Indonesia on a short fact-finding tour of the island, so importunate are the questions about it from abroad. The situation remains precarious. Already an airplane has replaced Garuda – the eagle ridden by the god Vishnu – on the sculptured *tufa* of a modern temple, while life-size gunmen with stone revolvers have appeared on another. But this adaptability is characteristic of the Balinese and, since it is usually gracious and artistic, may be a virtue rather than a defect.

Baltic Sea

A shallow sea, an arm of the Atlantic. Location *Northern Europe.* Area *163,000 square miles (including Kattegat).* Maximum depth *1,519 feet.* Map *7, F5–G4.*

The ancient *Mare Suevicum* which the Germans call *Ostsee* is an arm of the Atlantic bordered by Denmark, Sweden, Finland, the USSR, Poland and Germany. It is connected with the North Sea by the Danish Oresund strait, the Great Belt and the Little Belt; then by the Kattegat and the Skagerrak; or by the Kiel Canal across northern Germany. It is a shallow sea with a mean depth of only 180 feet; its greatest depth (1,519 feet) is off the Swedish island of Gotland. Oland, the Danish islands, Fehmarn, the German Rügen, the Russian Saare and Hiiumaa and the Finnish Alands are the other main islands.

The coasts of the Baltic are generally low and in the south often backed by dunes. They are rocky only at the top of the Baltic basin itself where the ships leaving Stockholm pass through an archipelago of granitic fir-crowned islands, dodging floes of broken ice in winter before reaching Turku on the Finnish coast. Higher up the Gulf of Bothnia – between Finland and Sweden – the eastern coast is rising year by year. Today few ships can use the ports of Vaasa, Nykarleby and Jakobstad; the little wooden churches and ocher-painted houses of some of these ancient ports look out upon a shallow river now. The shallowness of the Baltic, together with the low salt-content of the water (the Neva, the Narva, the Western Dvina, the Neman, the Vistula, the Oder, the Dal, Angerman, Ume and Torne all pour their fresh waters into it), causes it to freeze over readily in many parts during the winter.

The Norsemen were almost the first to exploit the waters of the Baltic and the rivers to the south for trade, plunder and profit. It was through the Varangians of Kiev and Novgorod who controlled an empire along the great Russian waterways that the products of the north (and its people taken in slavery) were exchanged for the gold, luxuries and ornaments of the East. Ever since ancient times the Baltic has been famous as the source of amber which was found around the Samland peninsula, in former East Prussia. The insignificant tides made navigation fairly easy, though the sudden, vicious storms often claimed victims; they could bring about considerable changes in the water level.

From the twelfth century onwards the Knights of the Sword and the Teutonic Order established German rule over the primitive scattered tribes of the forests and marshes south of the Baltic. Traders followed in their wake. Towns were built and trading establishments were set up around the shores of the North and Baltic seas, until the powerful Hanseatic League arose – Hamburg, Riga, Bergen, Bruges, Danzig and above all Lübeck, where the members met in conference – monopolizing commerce in furs, herrings, timber, pitch, metals, cereals and amber from the surrounding countries.

But the Baltic, from the sixteenth century onwards, became the cockpit of the conflicting ambitions of eastern and western Europe. After 100 years and more of Swedish and Polish domination, the Baltic provinces were absorbed by the Russian Empire in the eighteenth century. Finland, too, after a war of epic battles by the shores of the Gulf of Bothnia, passed from Sweden to Russia in 1809. Today, after the brief years of independence from 1920 to 1940, Estonia, Latvia and Lithuania are Soviet federal republics and the larger part of the Baltic coastline is under Communist domination. Only Finland has kept the independence won in 1918 by a precarious compromise with her powerful neighbor.

Banda Islands and Sea

A part of Indonesia. Location *Eastern Indonesia, Pacific Ocean.* Area *(Islands) About 40 square miles; (Sea) 285,000 square miles.* Maximum depth *(Sea) More than 21,000 feet.* Map *4, C7.*

A group of several islands in the Southern Moluccas, Indonesia, the Bandas lie south of Ceram. The large island of Bandalontar is surrounded by about ten islets, including Gunung Api (an active volcano) and Bandanaira. The total area of the group is about 40 square miles with a population of just over 13,000. The chief products are copra, fish, nutmeg and sago. Dutch vessels visited the Bandas in 1599 and gained control of them 20 years later; today they are part of the Indonesian Republic, attached to Amboina.

The Banda Sea, part of the Pacific, with an area of 285,000 square miles, is bounded by the vast semi-circular arc of the Southern Moluccas including Buru, Ceram, Tanimbar, Babar and Wetar. It merges with the Flores Sea on the southwest, the Molucca Sea on the northwest, the Ceram Sea on the north, the Arafura Sea on the southeast and the Timor Sea on the south. Its greatest depth – more than 21,000 feet – is west of Kai Island.

A. R. Wallace, the great naturalist, visited the Bandas in the eighteen-sixties. He found them covered with dense green vegetation and called Banda "a lovely little spot." Its three islands enclosed a secure harbor "with water so transparent that living corals and even the minutest of objects are plainly seen on the volcanic sand at a depth of seven or eight fathoms."

Wallace explored the little town with its neat, red-tiled white houses and thatched cottages, bounded on one side by an old Portuguese fort. "Beyond, about half a mile distant," he wrote, "lies the larger island in the shape of a horseshoe, formed of a range of abrupt hills covered with fine forest and nutmeg gardens; while close opposite the town is the volcano, forming a nearly perfect cone, the lower part only covered with a light green bushy vegetation."

Wallace found traces of the widespread devastation caused by the earthquake of 1852, during which the sea broke over the larger island and destroyed all vegetation on the lowlands. Earthquakes are still frequent; some of them very severe, throwing down houses and carrying ships out of the harbor bodily into the streets, and the explosions of Gunung Api can be extremely violent.

Barataria Bay

One of the centers of picturesque bayou country. Location *Southeast Louisiana.* Dimensions *About 12 miles by 15 miles.* Map *1, B11.*

Lying 35 miles south of New Orleans, Barataria Bay is separated from the Gulf of Mexico by Grand and Grand Terre islands, flanking Barataria Pass, the channel leading from the Gulf. The Bay's shores are much indented and its waters are dotted with innumerable marshy islands. Here is the center of the Barataria country, a huge low-lying region criss-crossed by tortuous waterways, west of the great Mississippi Delta. It is famous as the home of Louisiana's shrimp industry and has many picturesque villages built on stilts over the water. Muskrat trappers still go after their small but valuable prey and there are many oil and natural gas wells. The navigation channel from Barataria Pass leads through the Bay and the many connecting waterways (including Bayou Barataria) into the Gulf Intracoastal Waterway system.

In the early nineteenth century this was "Lafitte Country," the home and operational base of Jean and Pierre Lafitte, the French smugglers and pirate leaders. Their headquarters were divided between the Barataria region and the island site of present-day Galveston, Texas. During the war of 1812 the British tried to enlist Lafitte and his men on their side. But the brothers refused to participate in the attack on New Orleans and even turned over the papers containing the proposal to the American authorities. A naval force was first dispatched against them but later Andrew Jackson accepted the aid of Lafitte in the Battle of New Orleans, giving them and their men a free pardon for their services. After the war the Lafittes resumed their piratical operations in Texas but when another naval force was sent against them, they departed peaceably. Their final fate is not definitely known and many folk legends grew up around their adventures and alleged buried treasures.

Barbados

A popular tourist resort. Location *West Indies, 175 miles north-northeast of Trinidad.* Area *166.33 square miles.* Map *2, J3.*

Most easterly of the Lesser Antilles, Barbados lies directly in the path of the northeast trade winds – a fact which made the island one of the main ports of call for ships bound from Europe for America in the days of sail. The trade winds are also responsible for the pleasant climate; even when other West Indian islands are hot and humid in the tropical summer, Barbados is tempered by cooling breezes.

Encircled by coral reefs, the island is comparatively flat with the exception of Mount Hillaby (1,104 feet) in the center. Its main composition is of limestone and sandstone, with some red clay. There is a top layer of sandstone which, being volcanic in origin, provides a fertile soil. From Mount Hillaby the land slopes gently away on all sides in a rich expanse of plantations. Sugar cane has been cultivated since the mid-seventeenth century and the island is still basically dependent on a single-crop economy. Cotton and tobacco have also been introduced and rum is distilled – among the best in the West Indies.

Barbados is unlike most other West Indian islands in its history, which has been almost without incident ever since it was first occupied in 1605. The original inhabitants were the Arawak Indians; the Portuguese were the first Europeans to visit it, naming it Los Barbados after the bearded fig trees they found. Although threatened several times during the Napoleonic wars, it has never been a battlefield as have most of the islands in the Caribbean. The capital, Bridgetown, on the southwest coast, has an attractive eighteenth-century atmosphere blending with a colorful market and fishing port. The small harbor, known as the Careenage, has been enlarged to take larger vessels. Bridgetown is also the last place in the world where the costume of Nelson's sailors is still a regular feature of the daily scene – as the uniform of the harbor police.

Lacking the mountains of Dominica or the rich tropical interior of St Lucia, Barbados has more of a domesticated air than most of the Lesser Antilles. On the eastern coast, where the Atlantic swell rolls in, the land is rocky and inhospitable. On this side is the district of Scotland, so-called because of its resemblance to parts of the Scottish Highlands – a Scotland mellowed in sunshine, sugar cane and flowers. On the western side of the island mile after mile of beaches run down to the blue Caribbean.

The population density is extremely high, about 1,160 per square mile. About 90 per cent of the people are colored; a good-humored, hard-working people speaking a dialect that has something in common with the intonations of the English west country. Barbados is one of the few islands in the West Indies with a small community of "poor whites," known locally as the "redshanks" and reputed to be descended from the unfortunate followers of the Duke of Monmouth's insurrection against James II in 1683. At the "Bloody Assizes" in 1685 some 800 of the rebels were sentenced by Judge Jeffreys to be transported to the West Indies, the majority of them being sent to Barbados.

Agriculture engages most of the population although many of the inhabitants are fishermen – the flying-fish caught off the island is a local delicacy. Barbados is occasionally visited by hurricanes, which have caused great damage and some loss of life.

Barents Sea

A shallow sea. Location *Arctic Ocean, north of Norway and European USSR.* Dimensions *800 miles long, 650 miles wide.* Maximum depth *About 600 feet.* Map *5, G10*

Lying between latitudes 70° and 80° North, the Barents Sea takes its name from the Dutch sailor William Barendz, who navigated these waters in the last years of the sixteenth century. He discovered Spitsbergen in the course of his voyages and died on the coast of Novaya Zemlya.

The Barents Sea is part of the Arctic Ocean and is bordered by Russia, Finland and Norway

A Russian ice-breaker in the Barents Sea

on the south, by Franz Josef Land on the north, by Novaya Zemlya on the east and by Spitsbergen and Bear Island on the west. It is extremely cold at all seasons of the year: the summer temperature is about 40° F. and in winter it sometimes falls below zero. During the Second World War it became a familiar sea to British and American sailors. The Arctic convoys routed to Kola Inlet in Russia passed through it in the region of Bear Island, more often than not running the gauntlet of German planes and U-boats. Today the Barents Sea forms the westernmost part of the 5,000-mile seaway established by the U S S R, leading from Murmansk to Vladivostok.

The water temperatures are slightly less cold than the air, for the tail end of the Gulf Stream which washes the west coast of Norway enters the Sea. The Murmansk coast is thus kept relatively ice-free, which has made it of considerable importance to Russia. The northern end of the Sea from the region of Bear Island is polar, and ice is constantly to be met with. The juxtaposition of this cold polar air and water with the warmer water of the southern area adds another danger to the Sea, as dense fogs form where the two meet, especially when the wind is blowing from the south.

Apart from its navigational importance to Russia, the Barents Sea is an increasingly popular area with deep-sea fishermen. Cod, haddock and plaice abound. Even in midsummer, ice may be encountered between Spitsbergen and Bear Island and in winter only the southern part of the Sea is safely navigable.

Bathurst Island and Melville Island

Two large islands, an Australian aboriginal reservation. Location *Timor Sea.* Area *Bathurst: 786 square miles; Melville: 2,400 square miles.* Map *4, C8.*

These two large islands lie close together, 40 miles off Darwin on the northern coast of Australia. Bathurst Island is covered largely with mangrove forests. Melville is more than three times its size and its coasts form the western shores of Dundas Strait and the northwestern coast of Van Diemen Gulf. Both islands are aboriginal reserves – Melville has been deeded in perpetuity to the Tiwi tribe by the Australian government – and both are interesting for their fauna and flora.

It was in the eighteen-twenties that Britain established a convict settlement at Fort Dundas on Melville; but the settlement did not last long, and until 50 years ago the Tiwis' knowledge of the outside world was practically nil, their only contact being with occasional Malay fishermen in search of sea-cucumbers.

Missionaries and the presence of an air force base, protecting Darwin in the Second World War, have changed things to some extent. The Islanders now speak a sort of pidgin English and are very avid learners. There are about 180 aborigines at the Government Station, housed, fed and provided with western clothing, employed around the houses or gathering oysters and crabs for sale on the mainland. But from time to time they "go walkabout" – return to the mangrove bush for a few weeks. Every year they organize a great hunt when they burn off the tail grass to see their prey – lizards, snakes, opossums, wallabies – more clearly. Their spears and armlong sticks are believed to be blessed by the fire. The Tiwis belong to about 24 different totem groups; exceptionally, and as a mark of the highest honor, they admit a white person to them. For all these groups fire is the most important part of ritual – singeing the hair by passing through flames is supposed to cleanse a man of evil spirits and to protect him from misfortune.

The aborigines of Bathurst and Melville are taller and darker than their mainland cousins and their hair is curlier; but they share the common practice of decorating themselves with welted scars in angular patterns. Separated from the mainland by the turbulent, swift-running waters of the Clarence Strait, they have remained in their isolation at a cultural level of almost 50,000 years ago. Their frail craft could never survive such seas and we do not know how long ago they reached the islands.

Rare and curious forms of wild life have also survived in this isolation – perhaps the most curious is the brush turkey, the megapode, which piles huge mounds of leaves and dirt together (often 12 or 15 feet high) to provide the warmth to hatch its eggs, which are hidden three feet below the top of the heap.

Beaufort Sea

A sea without islands. Location *Arctic Ocean, between northern Alaska and the Arctic Archipelago of Canada.* Average depth *More than 10,000 feet.* Map *5, C5.*

Named after Admiral Sir Francis Beaufort (1774–1857), who in 1805 established the Beaufort Scale to measure the strength of wind, the Beaufort Sea is part of the deep Arctic basin and differs in many respects from the Siberian shelf seas. It is a large expanse of water, usually frozen over, which is unbroken by any land.

It was during the Canadian Arctic Expedition of 1913–18 that Vilhjalmur Stefansson made his long journey between northern Alaska and Banks Island in a wide arc which more or less enclosed the Beaufort Sea. The main result of this expedition was to establish that the waters of the ice-covered Arctic Ocean are far from being devoid of life; Stefansson was able to "live off" these inhospitable frozen wastes. His journey in 1914 took from March 28 to June 30 and he did not encounter any serious shortage of food. Following the shore lead of the Arctic Ocean pack ice, it was on this journey that Stefansson filled in the last gaps in our knowledge of the Canadian Arctic Archipelago with the discovery of Borden Island and Meighen Island.

In 1918 Storkensen crossed the Beaufort Sea but almost 50 years later it is still partly unexplored.

Bedloe's Island

The site of the largest statue in the world. Location *Upper New York Bay.* Area *About ten acres.* Map *1, F7.*

Bedloe's is a small island, just off busy, towering Manhattan, under the authority of the United States National Park Service. It was part of New York City until it was ceded to the United States Government in 1800. Bedloe's Island, or Liberty Island, as it is often called, owes its fame to the great Statue of Liberty, raising her torch to welcome travelers from Europe approaching New York.

This gigantic bronze statue was a gift of the French people to commemorate the centenary of American independence. It was a project conceived by the eminent French sculptor, Frédéric Auguste Bartholdi, who had to overcome immense difficulties to realize it. His dream was to create a 150-foot-high statue to be erected in New York harbor as a lasting monument to Franco-American friendship. The French, remembering the aid they had received from the fledgling republic during their Revolution, subscribed generously; but eminent engineers on both sides of the Atlantic told Bartholdi that the idea was impossible. The violent, gusty winds of New York Bay, they said, would soon topple such a lofty statue into the sea, and there was no way of bracing it.

Bartholdi took his problem to Alexandre Gustave Eiffel, whose great tower is still a major landmark in Paris. Eiffel designed a fragile-looking frame of steel girders and braces which he claimed would be light enough to stand on the statue's pedestal yet strong enough to withstand a hurricane. Both he and Bartholdi were derided; yet the Statue of Liberty was placed on its 155-foot pedestal in 1885 and has stood remarkably firm ever since. The total height of pedestal and statue is 305 feet 6 inches, the loftiest in the world. Entitled "Liberty Enlightening the World," the immense female figure holds a book representing the law in her left hand and a torch raised aloft in her right. Whittier, Stedman, Hovey and others have written poems about the statue, but it was a sonnet by Emma Lazarus that was selected to be placed on the pedestal itself.

Belle Isle

A small, rocky island inhabited only in the fishing season. Location *Off Newfoundland.* Area *20 square miles.* Map *1, H3.*

When the traveler approaches North America from Europe by the northerly route, Belle Isle is the first piece of land he sights. A barren block of granitic rock rising to 660 feet and bordered by steep sea-cliffs, the island is geologically a detached portion of the rolling rocky plateau of Labrador. It is inhabited only in the summer fishing season, apart from a wireless station and the Misery Point lighthouse. Belle Isle Strait, separating Newfoundland from the Labrador coast, is blocked by ice throughout the winter and is often very difficult to navigate even in summer – particularly in the early weeks – owing to fog. Drift ice begins to accumulate round the island and in the Strait in mid-December, increasing in thickness through the winter. Then in spring the icebergs float in, mostly hugging the northern shores of the Strait. These fantastic ice-monsters, originating in the great glacier-fronts of the west coast of Greenland, often assume the most eccentric shapes, and with their beautiful translucent green and blue-green coloring provide an unforgettable sight.

Historically, Belle Isle and its Strait first appear about 1000 A.D. when, as related in the Sagas, "Vinland" (i.e. grass or pastureland, not wine-land) – probably modern Newfoundland – and "Markland" (i.e. forested land) – to be plausibly identified with Labrador – were separated by "Staumerfjord," the Strait of Belle Isle. In the earlier part of the sixteenth century the French navigator Jacques Cartier, after several attempts and having missed the alternative passage of Cabot Strait, first sailed in 1534 through Belle Isle Strait into the Gulf of St Lawrence.

Bellingshausen Sea

Part of the South Pacific. Location *Antarctica.* Width *700 miles.* Map *3, E7.*

The Bellingshausen Sea borders Antarctica, west of the base of the Palmer Peninsula, between Alexander I Island and the Thurston Peninsula. To the northeast of it stretches Tierra del Fuego. Its mean depth is only 300 feet and it is obstructed throughout the year by ice floes.

The Sea is named after its discoverer, Thaddeus von Bellingshausen, an Estonian, who was appointed by Tsar Alexander I in the spring of 1819 to command the first South Polar Expedition after Cook's pioneering voyage of 1774–75. He sailed on July 15, with the masts and spars of his flagship, the *Vostok*, and of the sloop *Ladoga*, specially shortened to withstand the rigors of the Southern Ocean.

By January 13, 1820, Bellingshausen had crossed the sixtieth parallel south. He had studied Cook's career with care and admiration but he did not merely follow Cook; he always tried to strike out in new directions. Six times he forced his way across the Antarctic Circle, but was on each occasion driven back by storms that encrusted his ships with thick ice, and by the continuous floes. Only poor visibility prevented Bellingshausen from sighting the Antarctic mainland, discovered a few days later by Edward Bransfield at a point much farther north, outside the Antarctic Circle at Graham Land.

After sailing half way round the world Bellingshausen found temporary relief in a cruise among the Society and Tuamotu islands, then little known. Bellingshausen Island, a tiny uninhabited atoll northwest of Tahiti, commemorates this part of the cruise, during which he discovered and named 17 islands.

After a refit at Sydney, Bellingshausen sailed to complete his circumnavigation. This time he succeeded in covering one third of the circumference of the globe south of the sixtieth parallel. On January 22, 1821, he made the first landfall within the Antarctic Circle. He named the small island Peter I, after the founder of the Russian Navy. A week later he found and named the far larger Alexander I Island.

He landed at Kronstadt, after a voyage of two years and ten days, over 500 days of which had been spent under sail. His voyage confirmed the existence of a continuous passage south of the sixtieth parallel – an achievement which fully justified the commemoration of his name in an Antarctic sea called after him.

Bengal, Bay of

A broad arm of the Indian Ocean, including the Ganges-Brahmaputra delta. Location *Between India and Ceylon on the west and the Andaman and Nicobar islands on the east.* Width *1,000 miles.* Depth *More than 3,000 feet.* Map *10, F4–G5.*

With the great port of Calcutta to the north, Madras to the west and Rangoon on the east, the Bay of Bengal, the broad arm of the Indian Ocean between India, Ceylon and the Andaman and Nicobar islands, is crossed by many shipping lines and has been an important area for navigation over the centuries. Vizagapatnam, Chittagong and Akyab are other ports lying on its shores. Climatically the Bay has a great influence on the Indian province of Bengal; the moist winds coming from it produce the high humidity which is a feature of the area. At times this may be as high as 90 per cent. The Bay is also renowned for the violence of its cyclones, the tropical revolving storms which can bring disaster even to large ships and can devastate land areas. In 1876 one of the worst of these, accompanied by a vast tidal wave, killed 100,000 people. In 1919 a similar cyclone, besides killing 3,000 people, destroyed 40,000 cattle and caused havoc throughout the province.

A number of large rivers flow into the Bay, the sacred Ganges and the Brahmaputra on the north, the Irrawaddy on the east and the Godavari and the Kistna, among others, on the west. The finest harbors lie on the low-level eastern coast, with Rangoon, Moulmein and Akyab the most important. Hot and humid, alternating between cloudless days and the violence of typhoon weather, with the spice islands of Andaman and Nicobar and exotic Ceylon at its southwestern end, the Bay is Janusfaced.

Bering Sea and Strait

An Arctic region of the Pacific. Location *Between Siberia and Alaska.* Area *(Sea) 878,000 square miles.* Maximum depth *(Sea) 13,422 feet; (Strait) 170 feet.* Map *4, H1–J1.*

The man who gave his name to a sea, a strait, an island and a glacier in the Arctic was born in

A settlement on the Komandorski Islands in the Bering Sea

Jutland, Denmark, in 1680 and baptized Vitus Bering. He served in the Danish Navy and visited the East Indies; then, however, hoping for more rapid promotion in Russia, he served in the Russo-Swedish war as captain of a Russian frigate. In 1724 Peter the Great gave him what must have been one of the most remarkable orders issued to any man: Bering was to cross Siberia, build himself a vessel and find out whether America and Asia were one continent or whether the Dutch and English of the sixteenth century were right in predicting the existence of a gap which would make it possible to sail from the Pacific to the Atlantic by way of Novaya Zemlya and Cape Chelyuskin.

Bering *walked* across Siberia to the coast of Kamchatka, built himself a small boat and then sailed along the Asiatic coast from the mouth of the Kamchatka River to the Gulf of Anadyr. As he found no land in the east, he deduced that the two continents must be separated. He walked back to St Petersburg and reported that Russia could never conquer the northern part of America without a fleet.

In 1733 Bering was once again sent to Kamchatka, by the Empress Anna Ivanovna, Peter the Great's successor. Most of his subordinates were Slavs and there were innumerable quarrels and drunken fights. It was not until 1740 that he was able to sail with two small boats, the St Peter and St Paul, revisiting the waters he had first explored in 1729. He followed an easterly course which took him past the Aleutians – but they were wrapped in their eternal fog and he never saw them. He must have reached the American mainland, for he discovered and named Mount St Elias, the great volcano near the present frontier of Alaska and British Columbia.

His undisciplined and quarrelsome Russian crew and the approach of winter forced him to turn back before he had the chance to explore the great land mass. Heavy fog dogged him and he was forced to go into winter quarters on one of the Komandorski islands. It was uninhabited and treeless. His crew were finally rescued after six months of terrible privations – but Bering died, whether of scurvy or maltreatment by his own men, we do not know.

The Sea is part of the Pacific, bounded by the Aleutians and the Komandorski Islands, with an area of 878,000 square miles. The Bering Strait connects it with the Chukchi Sea of the Arctic Ocean. Its affluents are the Yukon and Anadyr rivers; it is indented by the large Anadyr, Bristol and Norton gulfs and is dotted by Pribilof, St Lawrence, Nunivak and St Matthew islands. Its deepest point is at the western end of the Aleutian chain (13,422 feet) but generally it is shallow and its extremely severe climate is little softened by the warm Japan Current so that its northern sections are frozen from October to June. Anadyr, Nome (in Alaska) and Provideniya are its main ports and it provides riches for the whaler, the fisherman and the fur-seal hunter. It was over the seal fisheries that the Bering Sea Fur-Seal Controversy arose between Britain and the United States; the dispute was finally referred to an Anglo-American Commission which decided, in 1893, in Great Britain's favor. It took an international treaty (1911) to stop the wholesale destruction of seals in the area, when pelagic (deep-sea) sealing was abolished.

The Bering Strait separates the Chukchi Peninsula of northeast Siberia from the Seward Peninsula of Alaska; it is 55 miles wide and has a maximum depth of 170 feet. Like the northern parts of the Sea, it freezes from October to June. The International Date Line runs through the Diomede Islands in the center of the Strait.

The Bering Glacier is part of the St Elias Range glacier system; after a course of 45 miles it drains into the Gulf of Alaska. Bering Island is the largest of the Komandorski Islands off the Kamchatka Peninsula – it is the island where the great navigator died in 1741.

Bermuda

A famous pleasure resort. Location *North Atlantic.* Area *21 square miles.* Map *1, J9.*

Just like the "Fortunate Isles" of the ancients or the "Hy Brasil" of the Cornish, the Bermudas have come to represent something beautiful and remote. But for the early navigators, these coral islands of the North Atlantic, only 580 nautical miles from Cape Hatteras and 670 from New York City, were not only remote and difficult to find but – once found – extremely dangerous. The 300 coral islands (of which only about 20 are

St George's Harbour, Bermuda

inhabited) are encircled by murderous reefs and an early seventeenth-century chart shows them surrounded by the topmasts of ships – a graphic illustration of the many vessels which had been lost in the approaches.

Great Bermuda or Main Island is, like the other islets around it, of coral formation on top of limestone. The soil is fertile and indulgent to plants and trees, though in recent years, unfortunately, the famous "Bermuda pines" have become infected by blight.

The Bermudas take their name from a Spanish seaman, Juan de Bermúdez, who discovered them in 1515. The islands remained uninhabited until a group of colonists under Sir George Somers were wrecked on them in 1609. From Sir George the islands took their alternative English name of the Summer (or Somers) Islands. Shortly afterwards they came under the control of the Virginia Company who were the first to establish a regular settlement on them. In the early days the capital was located on St George Island but at the end of the eighteenth century it was removed to Hamilton (or Hambleton as it is called on the old maps). The modern capital is situated on the inner part of the Great Sound in a magnificent moon-shaped bay that provides a secure port and anchorage for modern shipping. In recent years Bermuda's importance as a fleet and military base has declined (a naval base was established in 1767), but the islands' economy has become extremely prosperous, largely through American tourism. The eastern seaboard of the United States is only three hours away by jet-plane and the islands are most popular with every class of vacationer.

The climate is mild; lemon trees, limes and all varieties of flowers thrive and a large trade in cut flowers is done with New York. Fish are plentiful in the surrounding waters and the green turtle is common on the island beaches. Coffee, tobacco and cotton are grown and the descendants of the colored slaves who were introduced by early settlers to work the plantations form 60 per cent of the island's population.

The magnificent coral-sand beaches of Main Island and the blue waters inside the reefs make this a swimmer's and a small boat sailor's paradise. The Bermuda Rig which has revolutionized modern yacht design took its name from the rig used by the small local craft on the islands. The famous biennial yacht race from the New England coast of the United States ends at Bermuda in mid-July. In some years almost 100 sailing yachts approach the island within a few hours of each other.

Bikini

An uninhabited atoll, site of atom bomb tests. Location *Ralik Chain, Marshall Islands, Pacific Ocean.* Area *2 square miles.* Map *4, F6.*

In February, 1946, a gray ship anchored beyond the reef of crescent-shaped Bikini atoll, which consists of some 36 islets clinging to the coral ridge 25 miles long. Amphibious craft swept up to the sandy beach. "King Juda," the chief of

The world's first underwater atomic explosion, in the lagoon of Bikini Atoll

the islets (which included Bikini, Enyu and Namu), was summoned by the commanding officer. A great undertaking was about to begin for which this distant spot in the Marshall Islands, 225 miles north of Kwajalein, had been chosen. The co-operation of every islander was needed – for they would have to leave forever the ancient home their forebears had discovered centuries ago in their eastward voyage across the wide Pacific in their long canoes. Coconut palms along the shore, breadfruit, yams, and fish from the giant lagoon had provided these isolated people with a sparse living; with copra they traded for a few luxuries – kerosene lamps to light their matted palm-thatch huts, printed textiles for clothing, fish-hooks and water tanks to hold the precious fresh water which passing showers produced. Now they were offered a new home, for the whole atoll, which possessed one of the largest lagoons in the world (280 square miles), must be abandoned. They were to move to Rongerik, 125 miles to the east, where the soil was richer, where hibiscus and taro grew and the coconuts were bigger.

In the following weeks the islanders watched the arrival of masses of equipment, listened spellbound to the clattering of typewriters and posed for cameramen. The women exchanged their bracelets and necklaces of woven palm and sea shells for ones made of cast-off G.I. dog-tags; their husbands added jack-knives to their few metal tools.

On March 4, 1946, a last short service was held at the island's cemetery. Two days later the men and women loaded 100-pound bundles on their backs and boarded the waiting "Ducks." There were songs of farewell as the island vanished below the horizon. During the short voyage to Rongerik they repainted canoes or watched movies, while their children played with disinfectant sprays. The first stage of *Operation Crossroads* was complete.

The stillness of the deserted atoll was shattered on July 1. From 30,000 feet a B29 plane dropped the first atomic bomb since Nagasaki. Far larger than those used in the war, it exploded with tremendous force; at its center the temperature approached the 20,000,000 degrees Celsius of the sun; a pressure-wave, advancing faster than sound, shattered the swaying palms. Within two seconds a fog two miles in diameter had hidden Bikini and within five minutes a mushroom cloud had reared 25,000 feet into the sky.

Some three weeks later the first underwater atomic explosion took place. In one second 10,000,000 tons of water were hurled into the air in a vast central mass surrounded by spouting 4,000-foot-high columns. All the water was radioactive. The downward blast pounded the lagoon's coral floor to mud, poisoning the area with the equivalent of hundreds of tons of radium.

King Juda's people were moved in 1949 from Rongerik to Kili, where they still live. And ten years after their evacuation, on May 21, 1956, the first aerial drop of a hydrogen bomb took place over Namu Islet, with an atomic bomb used as a detonator. The force released this time was equivalent to 10,000,000 tons of T.N.T. and the sea boiled over many square miles.

Biscay, Bay of

A storm-swept sea with dangerous currents. Location *Atlantic Ocean, from Ushant in France to Cape Ortegal, Spain.* Maximum depth *1,200 feet.* Map *7, B6–C6.*

A corruption of the Spanish *Viscaya* – the name of the northern province from which it takes its name – the Bay of Biscay, an inlet of the Atlantic bounded by Spain and France, has inspired awe among seamen ever since the first ships navigated its waters. To the south, the Spanish coast holds few harbors between Corunna, Santander and Bilbao; to the east there are only the estuaries of the Loire and the Garonne breaking the long, barren coast of Bordeaux; and to the north lie the islands, the tide-rips and dangerous races of the inhospitable Brittany coast. A ship caught in this area during the days of sail was liable to find nothing but rocks under her lee. What gave (and still gives) the Bay its unenviable reputation is that the full sweep of westerly and southwesterly Atlantic gales pours into the inlet. The movement of the sea is considerably increased by the fact that the long swell of a full Atlantic gale becomes worsened and tends to break as it runs on to the continental shelf of Europe. The tides, up to 40 feet, are among the biggest in the world. Byron's comment: ". . . And winds are rude in Biscay's sleepless bay," was only too accurate. The Bay *is*

Heavy weather in the Bay of Biscay

sleepless – in the sense that, even on fair days, there is nearly always a swell running. After a southeasterly gale the indraft of the Atlantic into the Bay is considerable.

The Charente, Adour, Gironde, Loire and Vilaine all end their long courses in the Bay of Biscay. Of its islands Belle-Île, Île de Noirmoutier, Île d'Yeu, Île de Ré and Île d'Oléron (all off the French coast) are the most important. The principal ports, either on the Bay itself or on various inlets, are Brest, Arcachon, Bayonne, La Rochelle, Rochefort and Saint-Nazaire in France and Pasajes and San Sebastián on the Spanish shore. Up the estuaries of the Loire and the Garonne lie Nantes and Bordeaux respectively, accessible for ocean-going ships. The popular resorts of Biarritz, La Baule and Saint-Jean-de-Luz are along the French coast.

On a fair day with a northeasterly wind, and the fishing boats of Bordeaux and Bilbao rocking in the swell, the Bay has a sparkling clarity, and one might think that its reputation has been exaggerated. A full southeasterly gale in spring, however, presents a very different picture. The sea that roars in then, hammering the coastline of Europe, has the full sweep of the Atlantic behind it – from Cape Hatteras in Carolina unobstructed all the way to Bordeaux. The fishermen of France and Spain who are born and bred on the Bay's hard coastline have for centuries provided their countries with their finest seamen.

Bismarck Archipelago

A volcanic, mountainous group. Location *Southwest Pacific, Territory of New Guinea.* Area *19,200 square miles.* Map *4, E7.*

The Bismarck Archipelago includes two fairly large, mountainous islands, New Britain (the largest) and New Ireland, with a considerable number of smaller islands and islets – among them Lavongai, the Admiralty Islands, Duke of York Islands, Mussau and the Vitu Islands. These encircle the Bismarck Sea on the south, east and northeast. New Britain and New Ireland are long and relatively narrow; they swing away from each other at their eastern ends, having approached within a few miles. Off north New Britain are a number of isolated volcanic cones, roughly circular; off northwestern New Ireland are a number of low, irregularly shaped coral islands and reefs which stretch westward toward the Admiralty group. A pepperpot scatter of small islands, some volcanic, some marine in origin, completes the Archipelago.

The volcanoes of New Britain march from the westernmost part of the island to the northeastern promontories close to Rabaul. They rise to 7,000–9,000 feet; the insular divide, with some exceptions, stands above 4,000 feet. In the northeast recently-active volcanoes ring the wonderful natural harbor of Rabaul and the city of Rabaul. Until it was completely destroyed in the early phases of the Second World War, this was the finest port and the largest city of northern Melanesia and the capital of the Mandated Territory of New Guinea. The Japanese destruction was the second disaster to strike Rabaul within ten years, for it had been devastated by volcanic explosions in the nineteen-thirties.

New Britain's lowlands are small and generally along the coast, except in the eastern part where a few valleys thrust into the interior. The climate in the higher parts of the interior is wet and humid; the majority of the population lives along the coast or within a short distance in a few scattered villages. Plantations have also avoided the unfavorable climate and the steep slopes of the interior; except in the east, where the topography is a little more favorable for cultivation.

New Ireland is in general lower and along the coasts drier and flatter. Instead of the isolated, massive volcanic cones the crestline consists of metamorphosed sedimentary and igneous rocks. The coastal plains are narrow, especially in the west, and well suited for plantations of coconut, the principal product of the islands.

The climate, with some exceptions, does not encourage agriculture and human settlement in the Bismarck Archipelago. The southern slopes of New Britain are extremely wet; the annual rainfall at Gasmata in the southern central area averages 250 inches a year. The coast is fully exposed to the southeast monsoon for six months and gets a considerable amount of rainfall from the northern half of the island during the northwest monsoon the other half of the year. The eastern shores of New Ireland are less wet because during both monsoons the winds' direction is more or less parallel to the coastline. The normally exposed coasts are breezy places, especially at the height of the monsoons – and are therefore much more comfortable to live in, but the rainfall is higher and this does not help cultivation.

The volcanic soils are highly fertile if properly handled, but some are extremely poor as they are little more than thick layers of recent volcanic ash. The higher the rainfall, some experts say, the poorer the soils. The rain forest of the Archipelago spreads to the summits of most of the higher mountain peaks. It consists of tall, buttressed forest trees of many varieties; the giant liana vines grow to the very tops of the forest, strangle their hosts and become trees themselves.

The natives are similar to their Melanesian cousins in New Guinea; their dialects, tribal customs and traditions vary somewhat, as does their life, but these differences are not very great. The most important product is copra though there have been experiments to introduce coffee, tea, derris root and a new variety of sisal; experiments, however, interrupted by the Second World War.

The Bismarck Archipelago became a German protectorate in 1884. Australian forces occupied it in 1914 and in 1920 it was made an Australian mandated territory. The Japanese established their chief naval and air base at Rabaul – but this and their other island bases were put out of action in 1943–44. In 1947 the United Nations approved the Australian trusteeship over the group.

Black Sea

A large inland sea with two layers of water of different density. Location *Between Europe and Asia, bounded by the USSR, Turkey, Bulgaria and Rumania.* Area *159,000 square miles (with Sea of Azov, 173,000).* Maximum depth *About 7,360 feet.* Map *7, H8–J8.*

Known to the ancient Greeks as the Euxine (the sea "friendly to strangers"), the Black Sea was first navigated by Greek colonists who settled around its shores. According to legend, Jason sailed across it to Colchis in search of the Golden Fleece. But it is the golden grain of southern Russia (as well as the oil of the Caspian) which prompts most modern shipping.

The Black Sea is one of the most unusual bodies of water in the world. It is unique because over the greater part of its depth – from below about 500 feet to its maximum depth of 7,360 feet – there is no organic life of any kind, although the surface waters harbor the normal Mediterranean fish. The reason for this is that the Black Sea receives the flow of so many large rivers – the Danube, whose delta is by-passed by the Danube-Black Sea Canal, the Dniester, the Southern Bug, the Dnieper with the lesser Coruh, Irmak, Kizil, Rion and Sakarya rivers – that the salt content of the surface is very low, the Sea taking in more fresh water than it loses by evaporation. (In addition to the above rivers it also receives, through the Sea of Azov, the Don and the Kuban.) Meanwhile a deep underwater current flows in from the Mediterranean through the Bosporus and this salt water is trapped below the warmer and fresher surface water. The Sea is accordingly divided into two layers, the deeper and saltier layer making no contact with the atmosphere and receiving no oxygen to support life. It was often assumed that the deeper parts were virtually stagnant, consisting of foetid water charged with hydrogen sulphide, and this led to suggestions that the Black Sea might be a suitable depository for atomic waste. Recent Russian research, however, shows that there are almost certainly convection currents which in fact produce some vertical water circulation.

The strange, dead world below the surface is matched by a harsh climate above and only the southern coast of the Crimea has anything approaching a Mediterranean climate. In winter the Sea is cold and dangerous, whipped by fierce gales that rage down from Russia and the north. Even in spring and summer northerly winds prevail and these are violent and strong near the source of their origin though they soften by the time they reach the Aegean. The Strait of Kerch, which connects the Black Sea and the Sea of Azov, while the Crimean Peninsula separates the Karkinit Gulf from the latter, is often obstructed by ice in the winter months.

For all practical purposes the Black Sea is tideless, although there is a fairly marked surface current which flows counter-clockwise round the shores.

After the Greek colonists came Romans, and the Sea became of great importance: through it was carried most of Constantinople's trade with Persia and the East. The Genoese established colonies in the thirteenth century. From the fifteenth to the eighteenth centuries the Black Sea was practically a Turkish lake, being closed to foreign ships for almost 300 years. In 1783 Russia became a riparian nation with the annexation of the Crimea and later, as the Ottoman Empire fell, the dominant power on the Black Sea shores; a domination which she has retained since the defeat of the Axis Powers. Recently the Black Sea has again become important for the shipment of Rumanian and Russian corn, wheat and oil.

Blasket Islands

A group of rocky islands, important in Irish history. Location *Atlantic Ocean, west of Ireland.* Area *1,132 acres (Great Blasket).* Map *8, B4.*

The Blaskets represent the westernmost inhabited point of Europe, apart from Iceland, offering a bleak welcome to the traveler from America and an equally bleak farewell to those leaving Europe. Great Blasket, the only inhabited member of the group (though there is a lighthouse on Tearaght

Island, nine miles west of Slea Head), presents a long hump, four miles long and rising to 937 feet, at the end of the Dingle Peninsula, a fairly narrow and tidally dangerous strait separating it from Dunmore Head. Here the best and purest Irish was spoken in this century; Celtic scholars came to the small village, now almost depopulated, which crouches under the eastern end of Blasket's lofty hump or hogback. Here, too, was the castle of Piaras Ferriter, the last of the Irish chieftains to defy Cromwell.

In the nineteen-thirties there were 200 islanders, including 40 or 50 schoolchildren. By 1949 numbers were down to 28. The desks in the schoolroom were empty, the island had one child and only just enough men for the crew of a curragh or canvas boat. The black Kerry cattle still grazed against the green of the hump, smoke was still blown from a few houses from the turf fires tended by old women and old men.

Now, almost the last of the islanders have left for the mainland, in that progress of depopulation which has emptied so many Atlantic islands from Ireland to Scotland.

Borneo

The third largest island in the world. Location *Between Sulu Sea, Java Sea, South China Sea and Macassar Strait.* Area *286,969 square miles.* Map *10, J6.*

The third largest island in the world is also the largest of the Greater Sundas and the Malay Archipelago and is equally famous for the former head-hunting activities of its Dyaks and for the orangutans, or "men of the woods," those immense apes which roam its uplands.

Borneo is largely jungle with extensive swampy lowlands in the southern and southwestern coastal areas. In the center there is a ring of mountains which rise to 13,455 feet in Mount Kinabalu. It has large, navigable rivers, notably the Barito, the Kapuas and the Rajang. With a hot and humid climate – the average annual rainfall is about 100 inches – it possesses immense timber resources which are renewed constantly by the long monsoon seasons. Camphor, sandalwood, sago, coconut and mangrove provide the setting for the varied fauna, including elephants, tapirs, rhinoceroses, gibbons, deer and lemurs.

The Dyaks of Borneo are not aboriginals but have drifted in from the Philippines and Indochina. Their communities are based upon remarkable long-houses, anything from 30 to 1,000 feet long. They cultivate sago and rice, hunt with enormous blowpipes and practise many handicrafts. An amulet of hen's feathers sprinkled with blood, a bronze gong from China or Japan, china plates and earthenware pots of great age, also imported, for their wine, basketwork, calabashes and bamboo water-tubes with perhaps a few dried and shriveled heads from not so long ago, form the setting of these hospitable people.

Borneo has not advanced like the islands around it: up to 1944 its conditions were similar to those which, perhaps five centuries ago, must have been general in the East Indies. Recent archeological explorations found an extensive series of caves in Niah, Sarawak, with cultures extending unbroken from Paleolithic to historical times. Paintings, too, have been found on the cave walls. A group of inscriptions from Kutei date from about the sixth century A.D. and large remnants of iron slags show that iron was one of the principal exports of the island in its trade with China. The Chinese visited Borneo a very long time ago for pearls and bird's nests like those of the Cave of Niah; Hindu traders came up some of the rivers over 1,000 years ago. But Borneo was off the main trading routes of southeast Asia; the rivers have shifting bars at their mouths and the coasts are often impeded by coral reefs; there were no early discoveries of outstanding minerals or other attractions. Yet Borneo's resources are prodigious: large oil fields, iron, copper, diamonds, coal, gold, silver, lead and antimony are all abundant.

Six hundred years after the Hindus came the Portuguese (in 1521), followed by the Dutch in 1600 and the English in 1665. The island was finally divided into four political sections: North Borneo and Sarawak, which are British crown colonies; the British protectorate of Brunei; and the Indonesian section, the former Dutch Borneo, which occupies about three-quarters of the island. Sarawak, until it was ceded to Britain in July, 1946, was practically owned and completely run by the Brooke family, the "white rajahs," who interfered very little with native traditions.

Within the central ring of mountains, almost

isolated from the exterior, lived the Kelabits, a strong, intelligent, laughter-loving people with an elaborate ritual of politeness surrounding the consumption of much rice wine. They specialized in megalithic erections in huge clearings on mountain ridges as monuments to their dead; they believed that mockery of any animal would result in the turning to stone of the entire long-house. It was these tribes who formed the core of guerilla forces built up during the Second World War under the inspiration and leadership of Tom Harrisson, the British anthropologist and sociologist. The Japanese had invaded and occupied the island by February, 1942; but they were constantly harassed and finally destroyed or captured by this effective resistance – without their ever realizing that an organized force a hundred thousand strong had come into being.

The war completely changed the habits and outlook of the natives, especially as to their social units. All the tribes, previously often on feuding terms, submerged their differences during the war. Unfortunately the Dutch restored the rigid demarcation line after 1945 and today Indonesian Borneo or Kalimantan is again separated from the British areas. The autonomous states of West Borneo, Great Dayak, East Borneo, South-east Borneo and Banjar lasted only five years and were absorbed in 1950 by the Republic of Indonesia.

On the coast, where the Malays, Javanese and Chinese live, as mineral and oil resources are tapped, civilization has begun to seep in, bringing missionaries, political parties and other outside influences. But there is still virtually no means of penetrating the interior except along the rivers or by insignificant jungle tracks, so that most of Borneo is still isolated and unspoiled.

Bornholm

A largely granitic island with important home industries. Location *Baltic Sea.* Area *227 square miles.* Map *8, G4.*

The peaceful, chiefly agricultural life of Bornholm, an island in the southern Baltic Sea, today gives scarcely any hint of its importance in the earliest years of western and northern European history.

The rocky coast of Bornholm

It was about the time of Christ that according to legend overpopulation caused the emigration of a large number of people from Bornholm (Borgundarholmr in Old Icelandic) to north-eastern Germany. At the beginning of the fifth century these emigrants had grown into a tribe of many thousands and were living around Worms on the Rhine. Having suffered from the Hun invaders, they migrated southwest and established the kingdom of Burgundy in eastern France; the name of the new kingdom preserved a record of their ancient home.

By the time the Burgundians had settled in France, the pressure of population in the 227-square-mile island, coupled with other factors, was again driving the inhabitants of Bornholm abroad, in common with other Baltic peoples, to join the many Viking expeditions ravaging the shores of western Europe and the British Isles. An indication of the importance of the island in the second half of the ninth century is given in King Alfred's account of the voyages of Othere and Wulfstan. Bornholm (*Burgenda land*) is described as having a king of its own while most of the other southern Baltic islands were tributary to Denmark.

Danish influence extended to the island in the twelfth century, when it came under the control of the Archbishop of Lund in Sweden, then Danish territory. Apart from brief periods in the hands of the Hanseatic League and of the city of Lübeck, in the sixteenth century, and of Sweden in the seventeenth, Bornholm has remained Danish until the present day.

The larger part of the island is an ancient granite mass forming a ridge of undulating grassy country scattered with boulders and suitable only for grazing cattle (a small local breed). The density of this cattle population is greater than on any other Danish island. The highest part of the ridge, Rytterknaegten (520 feet), is covered by oaks and hornbeams in the forest of Almindingen. The only arable part of the island is a narrow apron of sandy soil lying on the more recent sedimentary rocks of the southern coast, where potatoes and cereal crops are grown.

Bornholm's 48,000 inhabitants have several important industries. The island's granite is quarried for use as building material both on Bornholm itself and on the mainland. It was an ideal material for constructing Bornholm's characteristic whitewashed round churches (notably that at Osterlars with its massive buttresses and conical roof) which had at times to serve for defence as well as worship. Another mining industry is the production of kaolin for pottery. There are small weaving and clockmaking industries and many tourists visit the island. Most important, however, are the fishing and fish-salting. From half a dozen small ports on the east and north coasts, the modern descendants of the Bornholm Vikings operate an efficient herring fleet in some of the best stocked waters of the Baltic.

Bosporus, *or* Bosphorus

A strait of great historic and strategic importance. Location *Between the Black Sea and the Sea of Marmara.* Dimensions *17 miles long, ½–1½ miles wide.* Maximum depth *396 feet.* Map *9, H8.*

The Bosporus is more like a winding river than a strait, since it is everywhere narrow, with steep shores, and its water is swift-flowing with frequent changes of direction. It links the Sea of Marmara with the Black Sea, and separates Turkish Thrace from Anatolia. The city of Istanbul stands at its southern entrance, with Uskudar (Scutari) on the Asiatic shore; but its northern entrance from the Black Sea is marked mainly by forts and fishing villages. The scenery is striking and varied, with village-dotted bays, bizarre palaces, unusual wooden residences, romantic tumble-down castles, rich pasturelands and picturesque hamlets.

The ferry-boats start from the Galata Bridge at the busy heart of Istanbul and carry their passengers northwards, criss-crossing from Asia to Europe, first to Uskudar, then paying a succession of short visits to little quays and landing stages with ever-changing scenery; for the first few miles sailing along the incomparable skyline with its mosques and graceful minarets. As the boats struggle against the strong southerly current, the slopes on both sides are steep, yet well settled, cultivated in parts and forested. Sandstones, marls and limestones of various kinds predominate in the southerly sections, changing to volcanic granite and dolerite as the

Black Sea is approached, rising to a rougher, bleaker landscape. At the northern entrance of the Bosporus there are rocky capes marked by lighthouses.

At Scutari, near the cypress-shrouded Moslem cemeteries, are the barracks and hospital where Florence Nightingale nursed during the Crimean War. A few miles away, also on the Asiatic shore, is the Beylerbey Palace where the Empress Eugenie stayed in 1869; on the opposite shore the two palaces of Dolma Batche and Yildiz stand, the over-ornate residences of the late nineteenth-century Sultans. Kemal Ataturk died at Dolma Batche. At Beylerbey is the medieval fortress of Rumeli Hisar, built by Mohammed II, the conqueror of Constantinople, in the mid-fifteenth century; even in ruins it gives an impression of its original character. It commands one of the narrowest parts of the Bosporus – only 1,000 yards across – and on the Asiatic shore opposite there is another ruined castle, Anatoli Hisar. The massive walls and towers of these castles contrast with the many timber residences, dark with age, some of which are still used as summer houses. As the Black Sea is approached, the fishing villages become more numerous; the Bosporus is indeed a rich source of fish, including the much-prized swordfish.

The palaces, castles and other buildings along the Bosporus serve as a reminder of the historical importance of this strait. Its name is the Greek word for "ox-ford"; this was one of the straits traditionally crossed by the white heifer, Io. From ancient times the Bosporus has been a channel of communication between Europe and Asia. At its southern entrance the Emperor Constantine founded Byzantium (Constantinople). In the Middle Ages the Bosporus carried the fleets of the Crusaders, the Genoese and the Venetians and saw the coming of Ottoman supremacy, even before the fall of Constantinople in 1453. In modern times it has maintained its importance as a strategic waterway and an international trade route. The Montreux Convention of 1936 (which Turkey has refused to amend under repeated Russian pressure) gives the Turks the right to fortify its shores and forbids the passage of warships of belligerent states unless they are going to the assistance of victims of aggression.

Botany Bay

An inlet of the Tasman Sea. Location *New South Wales, Australia.* Dimensions *Roughly circular; one mile wide at mouth, five miles in diameter.* Map *4, E10.*

Botany Bay, just south of the great city of Sydney, has two claims to fame: it was the place where Captain Cook proclaimed British sovereignty over the east coast of Australia; and it gave its name to a penal colony nearby.

It was on Sunday, April 29, 1770, that Captain James Cook's ship the *Endeavour* reached a wide bay on the Australian coast where an anchorage was found about half a mile from the shore.

Cook landed with three of his officers and a native Tahitian, who had joined his crew be-

The Captain Cook Memorial on the shore of Botany Bay

cause "he wanted to see the world," to take possession of the new continent on behalf of his king. The natives attacked the landing party with spears and stones but the firing of a few muskets sent them off in headlong flight; they were not seen again while the *Endeavour* stayed in port. The first white man actually to set foot on the east coast of Australia was the midshipman Isaac Smith, a cousin of Cook's wife. Today the spot is marked by a monument on Inscription Point.

Joseph Banks (after whom one of the capes is named) was Cook's shipmate and an eminent botanist. It was probably because of his discovery of unknown species of flowers and shrubs in the area that the Bay received its name. After Captain Cook was murdered by natives in Hawaii, Dr Banks became a champion of Australia as a new and delightful place of settlement. He first tried to persuade the American loyalists to move to what was then called New Holland; next, he suggested that Chinese should be imported to cultivate the empty land. Only when this, too, failed, was the decision made to turn the region around Botany Bay into a penal colony. The colony was actually at Sydney, five miles north from the Bay, at Port Jackson, but was known as Botany Bay. The transportation of criminals to New South Wales ended in 1840.

Today Botany is a suburb of Sydney and a not very attractive one. "Perhaps the flowers have died," wrote Hendrik van Loon, "for when I set foot on this historic spot it looked about as exciting as the harbor of New London or Bridgeport, Conn... A road, cars, gas-stations and a number of those nondescript little houses which are to be found all over Australia and New Zealand... The commonplace character of the place is further enhanced by a few factory chimneys and the remnants of hoardings, giving the dates of last year's race meetings in Sydney..."

Bothnia, Gulf of

A shallow sea with many islands. Location *Northern arm of Baltic Sea, between Sweden and Finland.* Dimensions *415 miles long, 93–149 miles wide.* Maximum depth *330 feet.* Map *7, G3–4.*

The Gulf of Bothnia is a "Scandinavian lake" and, indeed, it has several peculiarities which belong more to a fresh-water than to a salt-water sea. It is frozen for anything up to five months every year, and can then be crossed by sledge. The Gulf has very low salinity and its shores have been rising steadily – at the rate of

Timber rafts at a sawmill in the Gulf of Bothnia

about five feet every 100 years – so that since the middle of the eighteenth century its ports have become more and more shallow, in spite of being repeatedly dredged. These ports include Oulu, Pori and Vasaa in Finland, Gavle, Harnosand, Lulea and Sundsvall in Sweden.

The Angerman, Kemi, Lule, Oulu, Torne and Ume rivers flow into the Gulf, which is dotted with innumerable small islands, both along its shores and in the middle, not to mention sandbanks, rocks and cliffs called *skaers*, which make navigation difficult.

The Gulf was named after its former riparian region of Bothnia (*Botten* in Swedish); a name which still survives in the two Swedish counties of Norbotten and Vasterbotten on its northwestern shore. This shore is lined with sawmills which process the valuable and extensive lumber of the Swedish forests.

Bouvet Island

The most isolated island on earth. Location *South Atlantic, 1,500 miles from southwestern tip of South Africa.* Area *22 square miles.* Map *3, H9.*

The famous explorer Sir James Clark Ross returned from his last Antarctic voyage in 1843 disappointed in his failure "to locate that child of the mist, Bouvet Island," and for over a century after its discovery, the Island's position and very existence were in doubt. First sighted by the Frenchman Lozier Bouvet on January 1, 1739, and thought to be the lofty headland of an unknown continent, it was marked on the charts (in the wrong position) as "Cape Circumcision." Twice sought in vain by Captain Cook (who thought that Lozier Bouvet must have seen an enormous iceberg), Bouvet Island was not rediscovered until 1808 and nobody landed there until 1825, when Captain Norris took possession in the name of King George IV. When the Island's position was accurately determined by a German expedition in 1898, it was found to be 200 miles west of Bouvet's plot.

A dispute between Britain and Norway in 1928 as to who owned it was settled in Norway's favor, but the Island remains uninhabited. The South Africans intended to set up a weather station there in 1955 but were unable to land. Ice-cliffs fall straight into the sea around most of the coast and it is difficult to get ashore, except on the rocky headlands which are covered by penguin rockeries and seals. The best site for a weather station would seem to be on top of the icecap but nobody has ever been there and without a helicopter such a station would be impossible to supply.

Bouvet is the most isolated point of land on the surface of the earth: no other land is found for 1,000 miles in any direction. It is also one of the most inhospitable islands round the Antarctic and lies in the tracks of the stormiest weather. It is often blocked for miles around by heavy pack ice, so that no ships can get near.

British Isles

Two large islands and several smaller ones, off the northwest coast of Europe. Location *Between the Atlantic Ocean and the North Sea.* Area *88,745 square miles.* Map *7, C5–D2.*

The British Isles consist of England, Wales, Scotland and Ireland. All but the southern, and larger, part of Ireland – Eire – constitute the United Kingdom. There are also a great many much smaller islands, including the Isle of Man, in the Irish Sea; the Channel Islands, off the French coast; the Isle of Wight, on the English side of the Channel; the Outer and Inner Hebrides; and the Orkney and Shetland islands.

Highland and lowland each have their characteristic scenery. The former includes most of Scotland, Northern Ireland, Wales and the parts of England lying north and west of a line from the mouth of the River Tees to the Bristol Channel. The area to the south and east constitutes lowland Britain.

There are high tablelands with rolling country, cut by wide and deep valleys in the eastern Grampians, in southeastern Scotland; in the Pennines, the "backbone" of England; and in the Mourne Mountains and other hills of Northern Ireland. More rugged is the scenery of the western Grampians, the northwest Highlands and southwestern Scotland. Here are many freshwater lochs and deep, U-shaped valleys. The English Lake District, shaped like a dome, has radiating valleys framing many lakes, including Derwentwater, Ullswater and Windermere. North Wales has its Snowdon mountain area, with lakes and deep, rounded hollows and sharp ridges formed by glaciation.

The highest peak in the British Isles is Ben Nevis (4,406 feet) in Scotland, while the Cairngorms (also in Scotland) average 4,000 feet and Snowdon rises to 3,560 feet. Southwestern England is mainly a series of low tablelands; it reaches 2,000 feet only in the granite mass of Dartmoor. In the central Lowlands of Scotland there is a line of volcanic hills reaching about 2,000 feet.

Along the coasts one finds the cliffs and fjords of western Scotland, the drowned valleys of southwest Ireland and the cliffs and rock stacks of Wales and southwest England, some of them of spectacular beauty.

Lowland Britain offers a landscape of limestone and chalk hills, broad clay valleys, with steep north and west slopes to the hills, which seldom rise above 1,000 feet. The hills have their regional names – Chilterns, Cotswolds, North and South Downs, York and Lincoln Wolds.

Britain's climate has no great extremes of cold or heat, though snow is fairly regular in the Highland winters. The meteorologists speak of rainfall being "plentiful at all seasons," which is something of a British understatement. But while the Lake District and North Wales might average 200 inches a year, eastern England and Scotland do not get more than 20 or 30 inches – even if to the foreign visitor there appears to be considerably more. Gales are severe in the winter and though the notorious London pea-souper fog is nowadays more rarely encountered, there is still plenty of mist during the late autumn and the winter in various parts of the country.

The British Isles have heathland, moorland and woodland as their main types of vegetation. The trees are largely oak, beech, elm and chestnut in the south and Scots pine, larch and fir in the north. The fauna is restricted to birds and small animals such as fox, hedgehog, otter and rabbit; wild deer roam Exmoor and the Scottish Highlands. There are many preserves for game birds such as grouse and partridge.

In prehistoric times a short, dark people from southern Europe invaded the British Isles; they were later driven by newcomers into the hills of the north and west, where they peopled Cornwall, Ireland, Scotland and Wales, keeping a distinctive Celtic language and culture. Rome ruled from 43 A.D. to the beginning of the fifth century, but held only the lowlands and left little mark. Angles and Saxons were followed by Danes and these strains form the basis of the present-day population. In 1066 the Norman Conquest brought political and military feudalism and a thin layer of French culture. English authority was established in Wales by 1284; the Act of Union with Scotland was not passed until 1707.

Throughout the Middle Ages Britain was on the fringe of the civilized world. With the discovery of America in 1492 the position changed. Colonial and commercial rivalry brought England into conflict with Spain in the sixteenth, with the Low Countries in the seventeenth and with France in the eighteenth centuries. Newfoundland, England's first colony, was established in 1583 and by the eve of the First World War Britain ruled a quarter of the world's inhabitants – a rule that has been gradually, though in the last few years far more rapidly, transformed into a partnership, with the majority of the former "subject peoples" being loosely connected with or entirely outside the Commonwealth. There are, however, still many British dependencies in Africa, the Far East, the Indian and Atlantic oceans and the Mediterranean.

English is the dominant language in the British Isles, with Welsh also spoken by 29 per cent of the Welsh population and Gaelic by about 100,000 people in northwest Scotland and the Outer Hebrides. There are many local dialects of English.

Four fifths of the area of the British Isles is still used for agriculture. Cereals, root and fodder crops, vegetables, fruit and temporary grasses are the main crops. Livestock farming is important; stock-raising the mainstay of most farmers, with truck farming around the major towns.

Coal is the main mining industry, employing over 700,000 men and producing about 222,000,000 tons a year, most of it deep-mined. The chief coal fields are in Yorkshire, Derby and Nottingham. Iron-ore – insufficient for Britain's needs – is found close to the surface in northeastern and central England. Tin, lead and zinc are obtained in very small quantities and there are small oil wells in Nottinghamshire and near Edinburgh. The most important industry in the British Isles is the manufacture of all kinds of metal products; the engineering, shipbuilding and electrical goods industries represent almost a quarter of the country's industrial output. Aircraft and automobiles, textiles, chemicals, food, drink and cigarettes come next. Light industries are of immense variety and widely scattered. Atomic energy is utilized at Calder Hall where the first full-scale nuclear power station in the world was built.

California, Gulf of

An arm of the Pacific Ocean, originally known as the Sea of Cortés.

Location *Between Lower California and the rest of Mexico.*
Area *62,500 square miles.*
Maximum depth *Over 6,000 feet.*
Map *4, O4.*

The Gulf of California extends about 700 miles southeast from the mouth of the Colorado River; it is about 100 miles wide, broadening to 150 miles at its mouth and narrowing towards its head. It is indented by many bays and dotted with numerous islands, particularly in its upper part. The largest are Angel de la Guarda and Tiburón, with Cerralvo, Montague and San José among the others. Apart from the Colorado, the Gulf receives several Mexican rivers – the Altar, Fuerte, Mayo, Sonora and Yaqui are the most important – and its major ports are La Paz (in Lower California), Guaymas (Sonora), Mazatlán (Sinaloa), San Felipe and San José. But the Gulf's greatest claims to fame are the excellent deep-sea fishing it offers and, above all, its beautiful pearls. Navigation in the Gulf is hazardous because of sudden strong winds and a pronounced tidal bore.

Cortés was the first to discover the Gulf and in 1539 sent an expedition along it under Francisco de Ulloa; Hernando de Alarcón ascended the Colorado River in 1540. The Spanish chronicler Obregon paid a visit to the west coast of the Gulf in 1504.

Adventurers, impoverished sons of noble families, had flocked to the New World from Spain throughout the sixteenth century, seeking a quick fortune from its fabulous riches – and usually disguising their true intentions with proclamations of zeal to propagate the true faith. When rumors of pearl beds in the "Sea of Cortés" reached Mexico, an expedition was hurriedly mounted and a frigate built – but the ship was destroyed in a raid by the English captain Thomas Cavendish and interest lapsed. In 1596, however, Sebastian Vinczano sailed north with three ships and 230 men, including several friars – who deserted with many soldiers at an early stage, rather than face the reported hardships ahead.

Entering the treacherous, uncharted waters of the Gulf, Vinczano found the land barren. In return for corn, wine and beads, the coast's primitive, shellfish-eating inhabitants at first offered the Spaniards only lizards and dead snakes but then added a few misshapen pearls, discolored by the fires on which they flung their oysters, clams and mussels to open them. Having established a settlement, La Paz, near the tip of the Lower California peninsula and leaving his seven-year-old son with his mutinous followers as a hostage to guarantee his return, Vinczano sailed on among unknown reefs and arid islands. Eventually thirst forced him to abandon the search for pearls. Indians led him to a large freshwater lake where he and his men filled their casks – until an accidental blow sparked off a native attack. The Spaniards were forced to retreat under a hail of arrows and 18 were drowned in their hurried re-embarkment. The survivors insisted upon returning to La Paz. The whole temporary colony was taken on board ship. The empty-handed voyage to the mainland was marked by violent storms which drove the ships far up the Gulf and the flag-ship was nearly lost. The only large pearl brought back by the expedition was one given to a Negro servant by the Indians in tribute to his "extraordinary irremovable blackness" – and then only after repeated attempts by the entire tribe to rub it off with their hands.

The actual pearl fisheries were not discovered until 1632; Jesuit missionaries established themselves on the peninsula in 1697 but it was only in 1746 that Father Consac made a large-scale survey of the area. Today the pearl-fishers of Mexico carry on the work along the southwestern coast of the Gulf.

Canary Islands

An archipelago of seven large islands. Location *Atlantic Ocean, off North Africa.* Area *2,912 square miles.* Map *6, G3–4.*

Those who visit the Canary Islands for the first time find beautiful scenery, a splendid, dramatic variety of light and color. The Islands – or any single one of them – appear as striking and fantastic surprises. From 50 or 60 miles away a faint cone gathers shape in the sky, rootless, floating, aerial. This is the Pico de Teide, the peak of Tenerife, rising more than 12,000 feet above the Atlantic, which here is a halcyon blue and full of flying fish. The apparition of this great mountain has always excited wonder and inspired poets.

The Canaries are volcanic and always exposed to new volcanic uprush. Peaks, craters, cinder-heaps and snakes of cold, ancient lava, across the countryside or down the mountainsides, sometimes suggest a vast rubbish dump. But towards the Atlantic the Canaries are brilliantly lush, and towards Africa they are glaringly naked. A cap of ocean cloud may turn the rich lower slopes and lands sullen and gray. Above the clouds, a floor of cotton-wool, pierced in the distance by the blue peak of Tenerife, will be a high world of infinite quiet and calm and the clearest definition in which hoopoes speak gently to each other out of the scattered chestnut trees. A gap opens in the cotton-wool flooring and thousands of feet below a ship appears very small on a black ocean surface.

Lanzarote, Fuerteventura, Grand Canary (forming Las Palmas province), Tenerife, Palma, Gomera and Hierro (in Santa Cruz de Tenerife province) all have their individual attractions. Around and above the coastal towns the gardens have a subtropical brilliance. Fields are a warm brown, roads are edged with pelagoniums. Valleys are dull green with banana plantations, cochineal insects are picked from a silky webbing on the leaves of the prickly pear. Vineyards clamber round the lower peaks and in the drier valleys, the vines growing sometimes out of broken lava. Toward the higher summits, cultivation thins out.

The port towns – Santa Cruz on Tenerife, Las Palmas on Gran Canaria, La Laguna (bishopric and university), La Orotava and Icod (all on Tenerife), and Arrecife on Lanzarote – have a cosmopolitan air, with international hotels, food and bougainvillea to match. Children pursue the visitor, begging for pennies. In the high valleys and above the cloud levels, grave Canarians (mixtures of Spanish and aboriginal Guanche, probably of Berber stock) emerge from their cave houses and greet the visitor with a severe courtesy.

The difference between the Atlantic and the African sides is the difference between the clothed and the naked, the luscious and the barren, the gentle and the savage. The diversity of the Islands is not only that of flowers and trees and vineyards, but that of plains where camels draw ploughs through the dust and tomatoes are raised for faraway grocers' shops; it is also that of smooth, towering slopes, of savage, enormous and profound valleys, of peaks and crests and a surrounding sea of immense depth lapping on beaches which are often of black volcanic sand. The temperature is remarkably constant, day and night, winter and summer, an equably delicious warmth. Rain is restricted to three or four days a year, when the wild valleys become torrential.

If chroniclers are to be trusted, the original inhabitants, the Guanches, were a most peaceable race. They preferred games and pleasure to religion (of which they were ignorant) and fighting. They had no weapons with which to resist invasion. The Islands were known to the Phoenicians, Greeks, Romans and Moors; but it was only at the beginning of the fifteenth century that the Norman Jean de Béthencourt began their conquest. His expedition sailed from La Rochelle; but he possessed himself only of some of the smaller islands. Pedro de Vera took Canaria for Spain in 1483; soon after, Tenerife and Palma were taken by Alonson Fernández de Lugo. It was from Las Palmas in the newly conquered Gran Canaria that Columbus set out in the autumn of 1492 on his voyage to the New World. In the city they show the small chapel, lined in red silk, in which he is supposed to have attended Mass before his departure. Later the French, Dutch and British tried to take the Islands from Spain but they were all repelled;

Nelson lost his arm in a vain attempt in 1797. For nearly five centuries the Canaries have remained the secure possessions of Spain.

Cape Breton Island

A large island close to the Canadian mainland. Location *Northeast Nova Scotia.* Area *3,975 square miles.* Map *1, H5.*

The two-mile strait separating Cape Breton from Nova Scotia is known as the Gut of Canceau or Canso; the Island itself juts out so far into the Atlantic that it has been called "the long wharf of Canada." It is a large island, some 110 miles long and up to 80 miles wide. Its extremities are Cape St Lawrence in the north, Cape Linzee in the west, Bear Head in the south and Cape Breton in the east – said by some to be the first land that John Cabot sighted on his voyage in 1497–98.

The central part of the Island is covered by the large, irregularly shaped, tidal salt-water lakes of Bras d'Or, which communicate with the sea by two channels on the northeast; a short ship canal connects them with St Peter's Bay on the south, dividing the Island into two. Except on the northwest, the coastline is extremely rugged and irregular, with many bays which form excellent harbors – Aspy, St Ann's, Sydney, Mira, Louisburg, Gabarus, St Peter's and Mabou are the most important; Sydney Harbor, with Sydney and North Sydney towns around it, is one of the finest in North America. The largest rivers are the Baddeck, the Denys, the Margaree and the Myra, mostly rapid hill streams, not navigable for any distance. Lake Ainslie in the west is the biggest of several fresh-water lakes. There are moderate hills, well-wooded, with many picturesque gorges and glens; the highest point is in the Cape Breton National Park, which occupies 390 square miles in the center of the Island and which rises to 1,747 feet.

The geology of Cape Breton is a mixed one. In the north there is a plateau of Laurentian gneiss bordered by carboniferous rocks; south of this extends a Cambrian belt, continuing a similar formation on the Atlantic coast of Nova Scotia. There are extremely valuable coal deposits in the Sydney area which have been worked continuously for more than two centuries and were greatly expanded in 1893, supporting the local steel industry. Several of these mines protrude under the ocean and have been drilled deeply under water. Slate, marble, gypsum and limestone are also quarried; there are minor copper and iron deposits.

Though Cape Breton's forests have been exploited almost since its first settlement, it still exports pine, oak, beech, maple and ash. Agriculture and dairy-farming flourish, with exports of butter and cheese; the Bras d'Or Lakes and the surrounding seas supply cod, mackerel, herring and whitefish in abundance; salmon and trout are caught in almost every stream, attracting fishermen from all over Canada and the United States. The Intercolonial railroad crosses the Island and there is a train ferry at Point Tupper connecting Cape Breton with Mulgrave on the mainland. A railway also runs up to Inverness on the west coast and there are a number of other lines controlled by the mining companies.

The people of Cape Breton are mostly of Highland Scottish descent and Gaelic has not yet disappeared from the country districts. Several hundred Mic Mac Indians, mostly of mixed blood, work in the lumber trade and other industries. Along the south and west coasts, descendants of the original French settlers and of the Acadian exiles still live. Divided between the Catholic and the Presbyterian churches, the different races and religions live in perfect amity.

Until 1820, Cape Breton Island had a very varied and stormy history. Leif Ericson, the Viking, probably visited it about 1000 A.D.; John and Sebastian Cabot probably landed on its shores in 1497. In the sixteenth century it became the main North American base for fishermen, mainly Bretons. In 1629 a Scottish settlement was made, but the French captured it and in 1632, by the peace of St Germain, the Island was formally assigned to France, becoming part of French Acadia. In 1713 the Treaty of Utrecht reaffirmed this and Cape Breton was renamed Île Royale, absorbing part of the Acadian (French) population of Nova Scotia, which had become British. France built up a military and naval base at Louisburg. The British again took the Island in 1745 but four years later it was restored to France. In 1758 the British conquered it once again and by the Treaty of Paris in 1763 it was formally ceded, together with Canada, to Britain. In 1784 it was made into a separate province with Sydney as capital; in 1820, not without strong opposition from the Islanders, it was reincorporated in Nova Scotia.

Cape Cod

A historic peninsula with many summer resorts and fishing towns. Location *Southeast Massachusetts.* Dimensions *65 miles long, 1–20 miles wide.* Map *1, G7.*

Cape Cod is a low and sandy peninsula, curling northwards in a semicircular hook from the southeast corner of Massachusetts. Its base is crossed by the eight-mile-long Cape Cod Canal which connects it with Buzzards Bay. Its height seldom exceeds 200 feet and it has many fine beaches.

The shores of Cape Cod Bay are the Pilgrim Fathers' Land. Their tall, turreted monument stands sentinel above Provincetown – a picturesque place at the very tip of the peninsula, a favorite haven for artists and the former home of the Provincetown Players, perhaps the most important "little theater" in American history, which contributed decisively to the establishment of Eugene O'Neill as America's greatest modern dramatist. It was here that the Pilgrim Fathers landed in 1620. Eastwards, on the outside of this often marshy, sea-moulded cape, is the Atlantic Ocean, and these low dunes and hills were once the first land sighted by voyagers from Europe, in the days before New York replaced Boston as the great trans-ocean terminal.

It was the incredible number of codfish in the seas around that led Bartholomew Gasnold, the English explorer who discovered Cape Cod in 1602, to give it its name and induced English and French to establish colonies here. Salted down, barrels of cod were shipped to Europe or to the West Indies in exchange for rum, sugar and molasses. Then came the great days of whaling when it was the duty of every citizen on sighting a whale to inform the fishermen. These were days of high prosperity but the whales were driven into deeper waters, beyond the reach of small shore-based boats, such as the Cape provided, and the industry moved to Nantucket, Martha's Vineyard and New Bedford.

Meanwhile the countryside was being shaped by a steadily increasing population, with scattered farms, village greens, mill-ponds, elm trees and towns, like Chatham, Barnstable, Falmouth, Bourne, Dennis and Truro, full of stately mansions, graceful churches and monuments to local notables. The villages of Hyannis, Buzzards Bay and Woods Hole grew into popular summer resorts – Hyannis can boast of being the summer home of President John F. Kennedy – and every year many thousands of visitors from Boston, New York and farther afield flocked, and still flock, to the Cape.

Today, apart from fishing, the year-round Cape dwellers either commute to work in Boston and other New England towns or are engaged in the growing of cranberries (of which huge quantities are produced) and asparagus. Dennis has the oldest summer theater in America; Provincetown one of the largest and safest harbors on the Atlantic seaboard. There are a number of lighthouses along the outer coast, including Nobska Light (Woods Hole), Chatham Light, Cape Cod Light (North Truro), Race Point, Wood End and Long Point (Provincetown). Coast Guard stations are spaced along the same coastline.

Cape Verde Islands

An archipelago of ten inhabited and several small uninhabited islands. Location *Atlantic Ocean, off West Africa.* Area *1,557 square miles.* Map *6, F5.*

Gaunt and seemingly barren, the Cape Verdes raise their heads out of the long Atlantic swell, 450 miles west of Senegal. They lie just on the track of the northeasterly trade winds, a fact which made them a regular port of call in the days of sail. Later, when steam had taken over and the clippers no longer called at them for water and vegetables, the Islands became a coaling port. Today, when oil in its turn has superseded coal, they are rarely visited and lie outside most shipping routes.

The Islands were first discovered in 1456 by either the Venetian sea captain Alvise Luigi da

Cadamosto or by Antonio de Nola, both in the service of Prince Henry the Navigator. They were uninhabited until the Portuguese settled on them and imported Negro slaves from the mainland. Today there are few white inhabitants, and Negroes and mulattoes who speak a dialect of Portuguese form the greater part of the population. Not all the Islands are barren, although that is the first impression they give. The flora is tropical, most of it identical with that on the neighboring African coast. On Santo Antão, one of the more important islands, coffee-growing has been introduced; sugar cane, tobacco, wheat, oranges and sweet potatoes are the other main products.

The climate is characterized by a certain haziness, so that the sailor will often fail to see the Islands until he is nearly on top of them, especially in summer, when the trade winds are slightly weaker than in autumn. The dry east wind, the Harmattan, which blows off Africa, occasionally reaches as far as the Cape Verdes. While it is blowing, the temperature soars to the nineties.

Quail abound on all the Islands and the sea is rich with fish. Dolphin, tunny and whale are all caught in their waters and the local inhabitants are excellent seamen and fishermen. The Cape Verdes are one of the few places left in the world where large schooners still operate entirely under sail.

The capital is Praia on São Tiago Island; the rest of the archipelago consists of Santo Antão, São Vicente, São Nicolau, Sal and Boa Vista in the Windward group and Maio, São Tiago, Fogo and Brava in the Leeward group. Santa Luzia, Branco, Razo and Secos are deserted. The commercial center is São Vicente with its fine natural harbor of Pôrto Grande. At one time an important coaling center, São Vicente has declined of recent years. Its capital, Mindêlo, is a curious mixture of Portuguese architecture and African shanty town. A few steps beyond the main street – which might be anywhere in Portugal – one is in West Africa, with simple shanties, open air markets and old colored women trudging in from the country with fruit and vegetables slung in wicker baskets on their backs.

All the Islands are the peaks of vast volcanoes rising out of the depths of the Atlantic. Fogo (Fire Island) is still active and a regular landmark for navigators. Rising sheer out of the sea to a height of 10,000 feet, it is often visible from a distance of 80 to 100 miles.

Though Britain has coveted the Cape Verdes, they have remained in Portuguese possession ever since their discovery. Recently the population has been decreasing because of emigration to the western hemisphere.

Capri

A famous beauty spot with many historical associations.

Location *Campania, southern Italy, near the Bay of Naples.* Area *Four square miles.* Map *9, D9.*

An island dear to exiles and expatriates, Capri, a small, rocky piece of land, only 4 miles long and nowhere more than 1½ miles wide, has been immortalized by numerous writers from Suetonius to Norman Douglas. It may seem curious that such a small island has exercised such a fascination and that tens of thousands of tourists visit it annually; its attraction is perhaps the fact that it is the ideal window from which to look into the Bay of Naples. Gazing from the small piazza of the town of Capri, Sorrento lies on the mainland to one's right; north of it Torre Annunziata is backed by the long vine-clad shoulders of Vesuvius; Naples lies in the far right corner; and across the Bay to the left Ischia is visible on a clear day. The minute shapes of fishing boats move over the water like insects on a pond. The sea is so clear that at the base of the island's cliffs one can define, deep below its surface, the blue veins of rocks and the changing violet colors where the water shelves in towards the shore. The famous Blue Grotto is only one of many caves in the steep cliffs.

The Emperor Tiberius – who died on Capri in 37 A.D. – is credited with having built 12 villas on the island. The ruins of some of them – in particular the Villa Jovis – are still preserved. Since that time the number of villas has increased by thousands and the prosperity of the islanders is now dependent on the residents of these as well as on the annual tourists. The days are long past when it was only fishing and the tending of vines that supported the island economy. The wine is still excellent (though most of

Rock formations on the coast of Capri

what is sold during the summer as the famous Capri wine comes from the mainland). The volcanic ash which various eruptions of Vesuvius have laid over the top-soil has made the ground very fertile. During the most recent eruption it covered parts of the streets in Capri and the surrounding fields to the depth of three feet.

The town of Capri is on the northern side of the island, some 400 feet above the main harbor, Marina Grande, with a funicular railway connecting the two. The ancient town was here on the waterfront, but the inhabitants moved up the hill for security from Moorish pirates during the fifteenth century. At the same time the other town on the island, Anacapri, was founded. It is nearly 1,000 feet above the sea and still possesses more of the quiet charm that commerce and tourism have tended to drive away from Capri itself. From its high vantage point, Anacapri looks both northward over the Bay of Naples and southward towards the Lipari Islands and Sicily. On this southern side of the island lies the other harbor, Marina Piccola. It is occupied only by small local boats, except when a strong northerly wind makes Marina Grande unsafe.

The island's beauty stems from its limestone peaks to the west and east, with sheltered gardens, vineyards, orange orchards and olive groves lying between. Capri is justifiably renowned for its beauty spots – the Blue Grotto, the stark needle-like splinters of the famous rocks I Faraglioni and San Michele, and the villa built by Axel Munthe, the Swedish physician and writer, which hangs like an eagle's nest over a sheer cliff on the northern face of the island. On a summer night, when the Bay of Naples is twinkling with the lights of fishing boats and soft operatic songs sound across the water, the beauty of Capri seems to hang like the scent of its flowers on the warm air.

Caribbean Sea

A warm, beautiful sea with low salinity, situated entirely in the tropics. Location *Part of the Atlantic Ocean, between the north coast of South America, the West Indies archipelago and Central America.* Area *About 750,000 square miles.* Average depth *8,400 feet.* Maximum depth *22,788 feet (Bartlett Trough).* Map *2.*

When Columbus sailed along the coasts of Cuba, Jamaica and Hispaniola in 1492, he believed he had reached the fabled East described by Marco Polo. Though he had miscalculated by half the circumference of the globe, the gold of these new "West Indies," as he called them, proved tangible enough to launch the greatest territorial scramble in history. By a declaration of the Pope in 1493 and the Treaty of Tordesillas of 1494, everything west of a point fixed 370 leagues west of the Cape Verde Islands was agreed to be the possession of Spain, while everything to the east of this point was given to Portugal (which just enabled her later to claim Brazil). But other powers were not slow to demand their share of the New World and soon the shark-infested Caribbean became a theater of conquest and exploitation, piracy and plunder, where many of the great naval and land battles, decisive for the course of European history, were fought.

First to suffer were the indigenous inhabitants. Before long the Arawaks and Ciboneys, enslaved, massacred, overwhelmed by new diseases to which they had no resistance, were extinct. Even the fierce and warlike Caribs – who gave their name to the whole region – were reduced to a few small scattered communities. To work the mines and the sugar plantations, their European owners brought in Negro slaves from West Africa – an infamous practice that continued sporadically until less than a century ago. As a result the island population is today overwhelmingly colored while that of the more recently exploited Central and South American shores remains predominantly Amerindian.

Few regions on earth have crammed so colorful and turbulent a history into so short a time and few vary so extremely within themselves. Each island represents a separate and distinct civilization which seems to have developed largely by accident and chance circumstances.

Except for the British Honduras, the countries around the Caribbean's western and southern rim, together with Cuba, the Dominican Republic and Puerto Rico (although the latter is politically attached to the United States), form, culturally and racially, part of Latin America; the remaining islands bear the stamp of Britain, France, Holland, Denmark and the United States. The Caribbean is developing more and more into a cockpit of conflicting interests with dictators falling and rising, and with practically all the world powers trying to gain or maintain a foothold in the area. Fidel Castro's Cuban revolution, the assassination of General Trujillo, for so many years master of the Dominican Republic, the mass emigration of Puerto Ricans to the continental United States, the almost monthly upheavals in this or that Latin or Central American republic have time and again made the Caribbean front-page news. So many nations, races, clashing cultures – this is the Mediterranean of the New World.

Its constantly changing and developing civilization expresses itself not only in political conflicts and economic aspirations but also in a bewildering variety of ecstatic dances and rhythms; calypso, tango, meringue, beguine, rumba, conga, mambo. There is much poverty, with crowded millions living marginally on farming and fishing, riches for the few, ruined castles, crumbling cathedrals – but over and around all this the trade winds blow their galleon clouds along, combing the heads of the palm trees, swaying the forests, ruffling the silver miles of sugar cane and of the blue, rolling sea.

Caroline Islands

A large archipelago. Location *Western Pacific.* Area *461 square miles.* Map *4, E6–F6.*

Truk, Yap, Palau – these exotic names became headline news during the Second World War when the Carolines were in the Pacific front line. Scattered over an area of 1,300,000 square miles, they number altogether 936 islands, islets and atolls, but all these add up to very little dry land. Tiny dots across an immense expanse of water, their total population is only about 33,000 and communications over the vast distances are a major problem.

The Caroline Islands have been called New Philippines and Carolinas in the past; as for the individual islands, almost every one of them has had half-a-dozen names according to the explorers who discovered or rediscovered them. Politically, they are divided into the eastern and western Carolines; the former are subdivided into the Truk and Ponape districts while the latter have been formed into the Palau district, which includes Yap.

The major islands of the western Carolines are the tops of submerged mountain ranges rising above the surface of the sea. The Palau islands – or at least most of them – consist of the elevated portions of great ridges, representing wrinkles in the continental shelf, similar in origin to Japan and the Ryukyus. The islands of the eastern Carolines stand on a great submarine shelf that is fairly stable; the western ones are still rising, as earthquakes and recently emerging marine terraces show. Generally, there are three types: high volcanic islands, low coral atolls and raised atolls. There are five in the first group: the Palaus, Yap, Truk, Ponape and Kusaie. The Palaus and Yap consist of recent volcanic lavas and ancient metamorphic rock; Truk, Ponape and Kusaie are composed chiefly of basaltic lavas. Some of these volcanic islands rise more than 2,000 feet above sea level; the low coral atolls are seldom higher than six or eight feet; the partly raised ones – such as Fais and Angaur – have elevations of up to 60 feet and mostly contain phosphate deposits.

The climate of the Carolines is tropical with an average of 25 typhoons every year – some of which do considerable damage. They occur at all times of the year, though they are most common in September. Rainfall is as high as 255 inches in the mountains of Kusaie, though the low coral atolls are much drier. The soil of the coral isles is thin and not suitable for prolonged cultivation; the volcanic islands vary a good deal, but are generally much more fertile. The eastern islands of Kusaie, Ponape and Truk contain forest areas, while Yap and Palau are mostly covered with savanna grass. The natives of the Carolines have long practised burning off the sword grass in order to produce tender shoots for grazing cattle, which has often led to large areas being burned. American agricultural experts have taught them to use other, less destructive methods. The fauna is not very varied; dogs, deer and cattle were introduced in the early nineteenth century, there are crocodiles in the Palau swamps, and a species of iguana lives on Yap. Lizards, toads, two species of snakes, centipedes, scorpions and spiders are more numerous. Bauxite is the most important mineral, while the Angaur phosphate deposits rank as one of the most important sources of phosphate in the Pacific.

The Carolines were discovered in 1526 by the Spaniards in a series of voyages following Magellan's Pacific crossing. As little wealth was found, they were neglected – and as they were a hazard to navigation, they were even avoided as much as possible during the sixteenth and seventeenth centuries. Early in the eighteenth century Spanish missionaries made a few, completely unsuccessful, attempts to convert some of the natives.

When New England whalers began to follow the sperm whale into the Marshalls and the eastern Carolines in the eighteen-forties, they brought the outside world to the natives of Kusaie, Ponape and Truk. But the traders and whalers also brought smallpox and other disastrous diseases to the entire area. In 1852 American missionaries established bases on Kusaie and Ponape; Hawaiian missionaries followed and they branched out into various sections of the Islands.

In the eighteen-seventies Germany began a commercial offensive in the Pacific. Spain claimed sovereignty and came into conflict with German and British claims. The Pope was asked to arbitrate and in 1885 he ruled in favor of Spain. Spanish rule, however, lasted only 14 years. In 1898 Spain, after her defeat by the United States, ceded Guam to the Americans and next year sold the rest of her Micronesian possessions to Germany. In 1914 Japan took over the German possessions under military government until, in 1922, a civilian administration came into being. In the Second World War, Yap, Palau, Truk and Ponape became Japanese air bases.

By 1944 the Allied counter-attack in the Pacific had reached the Marshalls and the Marianas. In the fall of that year, Palau and Ulithi were taken by the American forces and later played an important part in the operations against the Philippines and the Ryukyus. The other islands, which had been bypassed though repeatedly attacked by air, surrendered after the defeat of Japan and were occupied by the American Navy. In April, 1947, the Carolines were handed to the United States as a Trust Territory.

Carpentaria, Gulf of

A large arm of the Arafura Sea, generally shallow. Location *North coast of Australia.* Dimensions *370 miles long, 350 miles wide.* Map *4, D8.*

The Gulf of Carpentaria lies off the largely uninhabited Northern Territory of Australia, and is connected with the Coral Sea by the Torres Strait. Its islands are Groote Eylandt, Sir Edward Pellew and Wellesley. Its coastline is a romantically wild, hot and healthy countryside. The climate alternates sharply between the wet and the dry seasons. Into the Gulf flow a series of swift-running rivers – the Albert, the Flinders, the Limmen Bight, the McArthur, the Mitchell, the Leichhardt, the Roper and others – which overflow during the rainy season and convert vast areas of the coastal country into a quagmire. During one wet season 60,000 head of cattle were washed out into the Gulf. In recent years the country has become increasingly traversed because of the post-war mineral boom.

The Gulf country is one of prolific wild life, including fish, marsupials and the dugong, or sea-cow. Vast flocks of geese, duck and other waterbirds enjoy a relatively unmolested existence. It is a place of lonely, unfenced cattle stations, several of which are bigger than some small European countries. Worked by a handful of whites and a large number of aboriginal stockmen, the remote stations are connected by radio-telephone and most of them have their own private airfields.

It was Jan Carstensz, when on a voyage of discovery in this part of the world in 1623, who named a small river near Cape Duyfhen Peter Carpentier, in honor of the governor-general of the Dutch East Indies at that time. After the second voyage of Abel Tasman in 1644, the Gulf which he had successfully explored began to appear on charts under its present name.

Cayman Islands

An archipelago of three Caribbean islands – Grand Cayman, Cayman Brac and Little Cayman. Location *British West Indies, about 150 miles west-northwest of Jamaica.* Area *92.81 square miles.* Map *2, D2.*

The Caymans are raised beds of coral which act like gigantic sponges, soaking up and holding the water that falls on them or surrounds them, so that inland they have numerous swampy, peaty lagoons of varying degrees of freshness or saltness, enclosed in a dense, thorny and often poisonous vegetation of trees and shrubs. Large caverns extend beneath the sea; and on Grand Cayman there is a huge natural tank of deliciously fresh spring water – which turns cloudy, however, and emits a foul smell on the approach of storms. Serious hurricanes occasionally cause great loss of life and damage to property.

When Columbus, returning from Central America to Hispaniola in 1503, discovered these islands, he was astonished at the number of turtles in their waters and named them Las Tortugas. Later visitors were equally amazed at the swarms of alligators in the lagoons of the smaller islands and gave them their present name, the local word for alligator. Nonetheless, turtles have had the day, for world gastronomic opinion admits no equal to a Cayman Island turtle. Indeed, until the tourists began to swarm of recent years (they swim, spear-fish, ride, explore, hunt treasure, sail and deep-sea fish; there are now several hotels, including a luxury one), turtles were the mainstay of the economy.

The Islands' boats, made from the local hardwoods, are famous. Beautiful, sturdy, swift, gaily-painted, they contribute greatly to the liveliness of the scene, not merely here but everywhere in the Caribbean. Cayman boys are taught from the age of 14 not merely how to handle but how to *build* a boat.

In such locally-built boats, specially constructed for the purpose, the turtles are hunted, quite a distance from the Islands, among the sandy cays along the coast of Nicaragua. Hawksbills – whose shell is "tortoise-shell" – are killed at once and their shells removed, but the magnificent green turtles, up to six feet long and weighing 700–800 pounds, from which turtle-soup is made, are captured alive. The initials of their owners are carved on their backs and they are brought back to the Cayman Islands where they are turned loose into "crawls" – areas of shallow water enclosed by fencing – where they live until ready for shipping. In these crawls they never breed, not even at the appropriate season – proof of the depression of their spirits. Yet, fed with basic food and kept fairly inactive, they put on weight. Then comes their great ordeal – shipment to Europe or America. Turned on their backs, lashed through pierced flippers to the decks (to prevent them beating themselves to death), with a bucket of salt water occasionally thrown over them to revive them, they may lie there for two or three weeks until they reach their destination and are killed.

Celebes

One of the largest islands of Indonesia, with a population of almost 4,000,000. Location *90 miles east of Borneo.* Area *69,277 square miles.* Map *4, B7.*

Celebes, a mountainous and thickly forested island, has the oddest of shapes – like a gigantic octopus sprawling with its tentacles over the tropical seas of Indonesia. It has four high and narrow peninsulas, pointing eastwards and southwards from a small central backbone of mountains and plateaus which rise to 11,286 feet in Mount Rantemario. Precipitous shores emphasize the line of these peninsulas, and the contrast of the mainly flat coasts of Borneo, eastern Sumatra and northern Java with the rugged grandeur of the Celebes coast and hinterland is quite dramatic. There are exceptions to this, (for example, around Macassar), as might be expected in a coastline nearly 3,000 miles long, but steep, forest-clad shores are the most common. The sea generally shelves quickly close off shore and soon reaches great depths, especially in the Celebes Sea to the north of the island. Picturesque sailing craft ply along the coast and much of the local trade of Celebes still depends on them. The people of the island, especially the Buginese and Macassarese, have a well-deserved reputation for seafaring and shipbuilding.

Celebes is particularly interesting to the naturalist since many of its plants and animals have Australian rather than Asiatic affinities. Among the animals are the pouched opossum, the sapiutan or anos, an unusual creature looking like a small cow, the tailless baboon and the babirusa, a pig-like beast with enormous tusks. Although most of the trees are tropical evergreens, in some mountain areas there is a conifer related to the

Native fishing boats, Celebes

Kauri pine of Australasia, and the eucalyptus is also seen, not to mention oak, teak, cedar, sandalwood, bamboo and the upas with its poisonous juice.

To the anthropologist Celebes has more than usual attraction because the population has enormous variety. There are three types of peoples, each differing in their ways of life. In the south are the Buginese and Macassarese, a community of seafarers and agriculturists, professing Islam as their religion. An equally distinctive group are the Minahasans of the north, who have adopted Christianity and in appearance are the most "European" in clothes and manners. The third group, those of the hills, generally referred to as the Toradjans, are the most backward culturally; they revere local spirits (though some have been converted to Christianity), and carry on a primitive form of agriculture, while several families live together in enormous houses built on piles.

The forests and mountains which dominate so great a part of Celebes have made its economic development slow. Paradoxically, the island was one of the very first on which Europeans landed and was used by them as a springboard for commerce. The Portuguese discovered it in 1512 and settled in 1625 in Macassar. The Dutch ousted them in 1660 and made Celebes their chief trading base in the eastern half of the archipelago. But it was a long time before Dutch influence on the island extended much beyond the Macassar area in the south and the Minahasa area in the north – not only because of the inherent difficulties of access, which make the island still one of the least known in the whole of Indonesia, but also because of the fierce opposition of the local peoples. Celebes is now part of the Indonesian Republic.

Cephalonia

The largest of the Ionian Islands. Location *Ionian Sea, off the Gulf of Patras.* Area *289.4 square miles.* Map *9, E9.*

Cephalonia lies like a sentinel outside the Gulf of Patras; hence its importance in classical and medieval history. To the east of the island lies rocky Ithaca, separated from it by a narrow channel; to the south is Zante, across a wider channel through which the main shipping route to Patras and the Corinth Canal passes.

Like most of the Ionian Islands, Cephalonia is mountainous but with fertile valleys and it lies on the same fault in the earth's crust, which has several times caused earthquake disasters in this region. The main range of hills runs from northwest to southeast and the mountains are conspicuous landmarks for the sailor approaching the Gulf of Patras across the Ionian Sea. The highest, Elato (ancient Mount Aenos), is nearly 5,500 feet and its peak dominates the island, frequently snow-covered when all below is green and luxuriant.

Apart from its commanding position, the island's importance was long ago determined by its magnificent natural harbor, formed by a deep gulf that runs up from the south for a distance of seven miles. On the shores of the gulf are the two principal cities, Argostoli on the east and Lixouri or Lexourion on the west. Both are busy in the export and marketing of the excellent local currants, some of the best in Greece, while olives and olive oil, wine and cotton are the next most important products.

Cephalonia is very typically Greek. It seems to have absorbed little of the Italian influences so noticeable in Corfu, and even less from its occupation in the nineteenth century by the British – although certain aspects of the island's material prosperity, such as roads and water supply, are still traceable to the work of British engineers.

In classical times the island sided with Athens during the Peloponnesian War; in 189 B.C. the Romans conquered it after the chief town, Same (the remains of which are still to be seen in Same Bay), had been reduced in a famous four-month siege. Byzantium inherited Cephalonia from Rome until it was captured in the eleventh century by the Normans of Sicily. Afterwards the island was ruled by various Italian families – including the Tocchi of Naples – and passed in 1479 to the Turks. Twenty years later the Venetians took it. Some traces of the Venetian occupation can still be found in the architecture as well as in the local dialect and in the names of some of the principal families. Venetian rule ended in 1797, after which Cephalonia shared the history of the other Ionian Islands.

Ceylon

A large and beautiful island. Location *Indian Ocean, off the southeast coast of India.* Area *25,332 square miles.* Map *10, F5.*

Ceylon, one of the most beautiful islands in the world, is separated from India by the Palk Strait and the Gulf of Mannar; but a giant could easily stride from it to the mainland along the chain of rocky islets connecting Mannar Island with Rameswaram Island off Madras. This line of "stepping stones," 18 miles long, is known as Adam's Bridge or Rama's Bridge; the legendary site of the causeway built by the hero of the great Ramayana epic. The India-Ceylon ferry route passes between Dhanuskodi on Rameswaram Island and Talaimannar on Mannar Island, providing a fast and convenient route between Ceylon and the huge subcontinent.

Pear-shaped, 270 miles long and about 140 miles across at its widest point, Ceylon consists basically of a central mountain mass of pre-Cambrian crystalline rocks ringed by a broad coastal plain. There are many sand bars along its coast – the Jaffna Peninsula, the Kalpitiya Peninsula and Manner Island are the chief formations – hugging shallow lagoons and marshes. Pidurutalagala (8,291 feet), Kirigalpotta (7,857 feet) and Adam's Peak (7,360 feet) are its loftiest points; here a great many rivers and streams rise, of which the Mahaweli Ganga, flowing 206 miles to Keddiyar Bay, is the longest. The plains are fairly level in the north, but the extensive soft limestone deposits are broken elsewhere by outcrops of the main rock core.

The climate is hot and tropical, tempered somewhat by the sea breezes; the variations of temperature are small but rainfall is heavy, brought by the southwest and northeast monsoons. About one fifth of the island is covered by forests – mainly ebony, halmalille, rubber and satinwood trees. Of the 7,000,000 people the majority live in villages and are engaged in agriculture. Ceylon produces over 12 per cent of the world's tea; on its 4,000,000 cultivated acres rice, coconut, rubber, millet, cinnamon, tobacco, cacao and fibers are produced in abundance. Oxen and buffaloes are raised primarily as draft animals; there are many elephants, leopards, deer and monkeys. Sapphires, rubies and moonstones are mined, and so are graphite, iron ore, kaolin and mica. Colombo, Kandy, Trincomalee, Jaffna, Galle, Matara, Anuradhapura and Nuwara Eliya are the principal centers; there is a good railway system and many airlines serve the island.

From the earliest times travelers have given vivid reports of Ceylon. In the fifth century a Chinese Buddhist priest admired its piety and the richness of its gems. The Franciscan Friar Odoric, passing through in 1321, also admired its jewel industry, and its cinnamon and elephants, but was alarmed by its "infinite number of serpents." The British sailor Robert Knox, who was a prisoner there from 1660 to 1679, found the people "proper and well favored beyond all people that I have seen in India." His picture of the small whitewashed mud huts, crouching under their thatch, with their owners in the nearby fields naked except for a string round their middles, would be recognizable by anyone passing today through the paddy-fields and up the vapor-blue gorges to the Shrine of Buddha's Tooth.

Channel Islands

An archipelago of considerable scenic and historical interest. Location *Southern side of English Channel, west of Cotentin Peninsula, Normandy.* Area *75.1 square miles.* Map *8, C5.*

Mild in climate, for the Gulf Stream warms their coastlines, the Channel or Norman Islands are rich in flowers and indulgent to fruit. From the tenth century onwards they belonged to the Dukedom of Normandy and became incorporated with the English crown after the Norman conquest. When Normandy and England became separate kingdoms the Islands were attached to Britain.

The principal islands of the group are Alderney, Guernsey, Jersey and Sark; Alderney lying in the northern group, which also includes Burhou, Ortach and the Casquets; Guernsey to the west with a few unimportant islets; Sark, with Herm and Jethou, to the east; and Jersey (the largest island with an area of 45 square miles), together with a few islets, southeast of Guernsey. In recent years, because of their pleasant summers, as well as their low taxation and customs duties, the Islands have become increasingly popular not only as a summer resort but as a permanent place of residence for many British people.

The fine coastal scenery of the Islands, with steep cliffs and pleasant bays, gives them a special character of their own. Geologically, they originated as part of a long peninsula projecting from the French coast, and their rocks consist mainly of granites and gneisses similar to those of Normandy. Granite quarrying is carried on in some of the Islands but market gardening and fishing remain two of the main occupations of the inhabitants. Dairy farming is also important; Guernsey, Jersey and Alderney have given their names to famous breeds of cattle. English has recently become the main language for all business and the Norman-French patois has almost died out; but modern French remains the common language of the Islands.

The concentration of the tidal wave as it races up the Channel makes navigation hazardous in the area. There are tidal races of exceptional violence and an almost unparalleled rise and fall of tide. The hardihood of the local fishermen and sailors can only be matched by that of their cousins on the Atlantic coast of Brittany. Apart from the dangers of the swift tidal races and the vast surge of the Atlantic when westerly gales are blowing, thick sea fogs are often experienced in late spring and early summer. In the main, though, as their flora shows, the Islands have an exceptionally mild climate. Grapes and peaches ripen without artificial heat, the tomato is a field crop, and the arbutus, the myrtle and the famed Guernsey lily are grown.

Chatham Islands

A group of volcanic islands with several uninhabited islets. Location *South Pacific, 422 miles east-southeast of Wellington, New Zealand.* Area *373 square miles.* Map *4, H11.*

The Chatham Islands form a county of New Zealand, though they are quite a distance from their "mother country." They consist of two main islands – Chatham (347 square miles, of which nearly one fifth is occupied by an enormous lake or lagoon) and Pitt (24 square miles) – and a scattering of small rocky islets with attractive names such as Star Keys and The Sisters. Their population is about 530.

Although the climate is bleak and cold, with much low cloud and damp winds from the southwest, frosts are rare and cultivation is comparatively easy. At one time forest covered the low hills and scrub and swamp vegetation occupied the sandhills and edges of the lagoons, but now four fifths of the total area has been cleared for grazing, and a grassy or ferny sward extends in all directions.

In spite of the difficulty of marketing wool and animals in New Zealand proper, sheep rearing remains the principal economic activity of the Islands, with fishing (blue cod is abundant) in second place.

In 1832 or 1835 an English vessel put in to Chatham to purchase food; not the least curious of its crew regarding the inhabitants was a Maori from Taranaki in the North Island of New Zealand. Strolling round the village he noted how prosperous, plump and peaceful the Islanders were; Polynesians who had arrived here in the fifteenth century, smaller in stature than his own people but undubitably stronger and more robust, with fine features and distinctive aquiline noses. Returning to New Zealand, he spoke long and forcefully about the islands he had seen and his report was followed by an invasion during which the Maoris conquered, killed and ate practically all the inhabitants, reducing them in numbers from about 1,500 to 36, whom they allowed to live practically as slaves. Today the Maoris themselves have become mixed with other races – the last pure-blooded Chatham Island Maori died in 1936.

Chesapeake Bay

The largest embayment on the Atlantic Coast of the United States. Location *Atlantic Ocean, between Maryland and Virginia.* Dimensions *195 miles long, 3–30 miles wide.* Map *1, F8.*

On April 26, 1607, the first Europeans to catch sight of the great bay that cuts deeply into present-day Virginia and Maryland anchored off Cape Henry. They were the English who settled on Jamestown Island, Virginia, 17 days later. Next year, the redoubtable Captain John Smith, who performed such prodigious feats both in the New World and in Transylvania, explored the Bay; and in 1631 the first permanent English settlement was made on Kent Island. Certainly, Chesapeake Bay has played a part in American history that perhaps no other body of water can equal.

Separated from the Atlantic by the Delmarva Peninsula (which is called the Eastern Shore along the Bay), the Chesapeake is the submerged lower valley of the Susquehanna River, which enters the sea at its head. Delaware Bay and the Delaware River are on its eastern limits. The entrance from the Atlantic Ocean – 13 miles wide – is between Cape Charles and Cape Henry. On the western side of the Bay are the estuaries of the Patapsco (Baltimore's port), the Severn (which leads to the approaches of the Annapolis Naval Academy), the Patuxent, the Potomac (leading on to Washington, a favorite stretch for presidential cruises), the Rappahannock, the York and the James rivers. On the northeast the estuary of the Elk River is linked to the Delaware River by the Chesapeake and Delaware Canal, a waterway which provides shipping with a short route to and from the Camden-Philadelphia port area. The chief ports on the Bay – navigable by deep-water vessels throughout its length – are Newport News, Norfolk and Portsmouth in Virginia, and Baltimore in Maryland. The estuary of the James River, together with the mouths of the Nansemond and Elizabeth rivers, debouches into the great Hampton Roads anchorage at the southern end of the Bay. There are many islands along the eastern shore, with the sheltered Pocomoke and Tangier sounds; along here, too, are the estuaries of the Elk, Chester, Choptank,

Miles, Nanticoke, Northeast, Pocomoke and Sassafras rivers, with numberless inlets leading to a good many shipping centers used by the huge seafood industry of the Bay – crabs, finfish and oysters are the most important catches. Cambridge, Crisfield and Salisbury are some of these centers.

The Bay has given its name to a great variety of things. The Chesapeake Formation is the geological term for the combination of clays, marls and sands that outcrops within the Atlantic coastal plain of the United States, comprising the entire Miocene series of that region. In Maryland the formation is 400 feet thick; here, as in Virginia, it contains deposits of diatomaceous earth – known in industry as *kieselguhr*, the fossilized form of algae with a high content of silicates – which have considerable value.

The Battle of Chesapeake Cape was an important naval engagement in the American War of Independence, fought at the mouth of the James River on September 5, 1781, which led to the surrender of Cornwallis at Yorktown on October 19. In the War of 1812 it was across the Bay that the British forces invaded the young republic. There is a Chesapeake Bay retriever, and the frigate *Chesapeake* is a memorable name in United States naval history. It was on her deck that Captain Lawrence, as he lay dying, spoke the famous words "Don't give up the ship!" which became the American watchword during the War of 1812.

On the isles of the Bay, especially on Tangier and Smith and along the Eastern Shore, the fisher folk have kept their old ways and customs remarkably intact, in spite of the completion of the Chesapeake Bay Bridge – about seven miles long, of which four miles are entirely over water – which has linked Sandy Point and Kent Island, both in Maryland.

The Chesapeake Bay bridge

China Sea

A vast section of the Pacific Ocean. Location *Western Pacific, bordering on China.* Area *East China Sea: 480,000 square miles; South China Sea: 895,000 square miles.* Maximum depth *East China Sea: 8,920 feet; South China Sea: over 15,000 feet.* Map *4, A6–D3.*

Tung Hai, as the Chinese call the eastern part of the China Sea, extends between the east China coast and Kyushu and the Ryukyu Islands. The Formosa Strait connects it with the South China Sea and the Korea Strait with the Sea of Japan, while on the north it merges into the Yellow Sea. Its coasts are indented by the estuaries of the Yangtze, the Tsientang, the Wu and the Min rivers; its main ports are Foochow, Hangchow, Ningpo, Shanghai and Wenchow on the Chinese mainland and Keelung on Formosa.

Nan Hai, the South China Sea, lies between the southeast Asian mainland and the Malay Archipelago, bordered by southern China, Vietnam, Cambodia, Thailand, Malaya, Borneo and the Philippine Islands. The Luzon Strait connects it with the Philippine Sea, the Mindoro and Balabac straits with the Sulu Sea, the Karimata Strait with the Java Sea and the Malacca Strait with the Andaman Sea. It cuts deeply into Asia through the gulfs of Siam and Tonkin. The most important rivers flowing into the South China Sea are the West River of China, the Mekong and Red rivers of Vietnam and the Chao Phraya of Thailand. A series of great ports are scattered along its coasts – Bangkok and Canton, Haiphong and Hong Kong, Saigon and Singapore on the mainland, with Kaosiung on Formosa and Manila in the Philippines. It has many groups of islands, the most important being Anambas, Lingga, Natuna, Riouw and Tambelan of Indonesia and Nansha, Sisha, Pratas and Hainan of China. The Sea's depth varies from the shallows of the Sunda platform to the great deeps of its northern part.

Throughout history, until quite recently, the China Sea has been notorious for its pirates. In 1846 Richard Glasspoole wrote that it was ". . . the only part of the globe in which pirates are still a menace." The savage cut-throats of the China Sea would mark down a likely prize while she was still in port and board her there under various disguises – some as coolies, others as fare-paying passengers, deceptively neat in Western clothes and horn-rimmed spectacles. Then, at a signal, the bridge would be stormed, the crew and poorer passengers massacred, the richer held to ransom and the cargo looted. The pirates, for all their up-to-date methods of attack, still rejoiced in picturesque names – "Scourge of the Seven Seas," "Jewel of the Whole Crew" and similar epithets.

Today the greatest of the China Sea's ports is Hong Kong, eclipsing the former glory of Shanghai. A British colony, rich because of its thriving manufacturing industries, Hong Kong has recovered rapidly from the Japanese occupation during the Second World War. But Manila, Bangkok and Saigon are also important in China Sea shipping and commerce.

Christmas Island

I: An isolated island with important phosphate deposits; II: The largest atoll in the Pacific. Location *I: Indian Ocean, 260 miles south of Java Head; II: Line Islands, central Pacific.* Area *I: 60 square miles; II: 222.6 square miles.* Map *I: 4, A8; II: 4, K7.*

There are two Christmas islands. The first is part of the Singapore Crown Colony, under British authority – an island about 11 miles long and 4½ miles wide. Surrounded by high cliffs of coral limestone, it was uninhabited when discovered in 1666. It was not annexed and settled until 1888, and was then placed under the Straits Settlements administration. Now the Island is inhabited by about 1,500 Malays who work the extremely rich phosphate deposits. Here the enormous and ill-reputed robber or account crab *(Birgus latro)* – one of a group of crabs which has forsaken the sea – is found in abundance even in the densest part of the forest of the central plateau. The Island rises over 6,000 feet from the ocean bottom with precipitous sides and is heavily forested. It was leased in 1897 to a phosphate company, whose production was interrupted only by the Japanese occupation during the Second World War.

The second Christmas Island was discovered by Captain Cook in 1777. It is a highly irregular atoll, as far as shape is concerned. Its main products are coconuts and pandanus fruit. Though the United States claimed it under the Guano Act of 1856, it was included in 1919 in the Gilbert and Ellice Islands colony. This was questioned by the United States in 1936, but British ownership has not been challenged since. The British have imported several hundred people from the Gilberts to work as contract laborers on the copra plantations, which are extensive.

Cocos Island

A small, uninhabited island, a favorite haunt of treasure-hunters. Location *Pacific, about 300 miles southwest of Costa Rica.* Area *10.4 square miles.* Map *4, Q6.*

Cocos Island, a Costa Rican dependency, lies about 100 miles off the west coast of Panama. Almost impenetrably forested, some 5½ miles long and 3½ miles wide, it has two good natural harbors, Wafer and Chatham bays, on its north coast. Geologically, it is an outlier of the Galápagos group.

The main interest of Cocos, however, is the treasure estimated to be worth at least $20,000,000 that is believed to be buried there. The Island, being off the main trade routes, had been a favorite haunt of pirates for more than a century when in 1822 Benito, one of the most savage and bloodthirsty of pirates, buried on Cocos the fruit of many years of successful high seas banditry, estimated to be worth millions of dollars. His ship was sunk shortly after with all her crew, and only two men, Thompson and Chapelle, survived.

Later that same year, when Peru was in the throes of a civil war, a vast treasure was sent to the fort of Callao and there transferred for safe keeping to the British sloop *Mary Dyer*, commanded by a Captain Thompson – according to some, the same man who had escaped from Benito's ship. The crew of the sloop murdered the Peruvian guards and set sail with the treasure, hotly pursued by Peruvian gun boats. Arrived at Cocos, the treasure (which took ten journeys in a long boat to unload) was buried above Chatham Bay and the *Mary Dyer* put out to sea again – only to be caught by the Peruvians. The whole crew was hanged except Captain Thompson and his mate who were spared on condition that they led their captors to the treasure. Taking them on a wild goose chase to the Galápagos Islands, both men jumped ship. Swimming towards a British whaler, the mate was killed by sharks but Thompson escaped and stowed away. He died in a London hospital in 1844, leaving his charts of the treasure to his friend Keating, whom he had met on the whaler and later lodged with at his home in Newfoundland. The happy heir, an illiterate fisherman, made three trips to the Island and brought back some $500,000 worth of treasure. The mutiny of his crew on one voyage and the disappearance of one of his companions (which led to his being tried for murder) made him a marked man whom other would-be treasure seekers avoided or fawned upon. He died on his third trip, leaving various charts – perhaps none authentic.

Towards the end of the nineteenth century several expeditions went to look for the treasure. The most famous was that of August Gissler in 1888. Gissler had made an agreement with the Costa Rican government that he should found a penal settlement on Cocos of which he would be resident governor and part owner. The penal settlement was soon abandoned but Gissler lived on the Island for 20 years and wrote a book which contains the most complete account of the treasure. He was convinced he knew where it lay but had not the equipment to move a landslide that covered it.

Adventurers, businessmen, two elderly spinsters, an eccentric peer, even a crew of the British Navy have been among the many subsequent treasure-seekers – but of the two main hoards not an ounce has been found since Keating died.

Cocos Islands

An isolated group of 27 coral islands. Location *Indian Ocean.* Area *11.5 square miles.* Map *10, G7.*

The Cocos or Keeling Islands lie about 600 miles southwest of Sumatra and were discovered in 1609 by Captain William Keeling. They became a British possession in 1857, were attached in turn to Ceylon in 1878, to the Straits Settlements in 1882 and to Singapore in 1903 until, in 1951, they were transferred to Australia for development as civil aviation bases. The largest of the group, West Island, about 5 miles long and a quarter of a mile wide, has an airstrip; there is a cable station on Direction Island.

When Charles Darwin visited the Islands in 1836 he made the observations upon which he based his theory of the formation of coral reefs. The land is entirely composed of rounded fragments of coral, loosened from the reef by the continuous pounding of the waves along its edge and slowly sorted and piled until made firm by the growth of plants.

The Islands have luxuriant vegetation; beside coconut palms and sugar canes, there are bananas, fruit trees and vegetables cultivated by the settlers, half-a-dozen kinds of trees, several herbs, a moss, a lichen and a fungus – all of which must have reached the Islands by sea, or as seeds carried by birds. In the reefs there are many kinds of multi-colored tropical fish, and frigate birds, boobies, snipes, rails and several species of terns nest there; but by far the most interesting creature is the enormous coconut-eating crab, *Birgus latro*. Fiber by fiber, it removes the husk at the end where the three eye-holes of the coconut are situated, then, hammering with its heavy front pincers, it pierces one of these. Turning round, it inserts its slender hind legs and scoops out the meat with its claws.

The Cocos Islands are famous for their "white kings" of the Clunies-Ross family, to whom in 1886 Queen Victoria granted the Islands in perpetuity. The present "white king," Mr John Clunies-Ross, is the great-great-grandson of the original John Clunies-Ross who settled there in 1827. Many people have been tempted to go and live in this primitive Eden but the population is strictly controlled by its owners and new settlers are not allowed.

Comoro Islands

A volcanic archipelago of four main islands. Location *Indian Ocean, at northern entrance of Mozambique Channel.* Area *650 square miles.* Map *10, B7.*

The Comoro Islands lie between the African mainland and the northern end of Madagascar, of which they are a dependency. The main islands, Mayotte, Anjouan (Anjuan or Johanna) and Grande Comore, are surrounded by a number of coral islets.

The Comoros are of volcanic origin and mountainous; the highest peak, Kartola or Karthala, on Grande Comore, rises to 8,500 feet and is still active. Grande Comore is the largest island of the group, 40 miles long and about 18 miles wide, but is also the least fertile, though it contains a forest which provides timber for building. The other islands produce coconuts, corn, coffee, cacao, cotton, aloes, cloves, sisal, sugar cane, rice, sweet potatoes, perfume plants, yams and tropical fruit. Maroni, the principal town, on Grande Comore, has a population of about 2,000.

The Comoro Islanders are of mixed Malagasy, Negro and Arab descent, most of them Moslems. They are skilled farmers, cattle-breeders, fishermen and sailors. The refining of sugar, lumbering and the distilling of rum are the main industries. Exports consist mainly of copra, sisal, sugar and vanilla.

Europeans visited the Comoro Islands for the first time in the sixteenth century, but for a long while the group remained under the rule of native sultans. France turned Mayotte into a colony in 1843; in 1886 the other islands came under French protection and were first attached to Réunion and later to Madagascar. In 1912 they were declared French colonies and in January 1947 became a French overseas territory with a representative in the French parliament. When the independent Malagasy (Madagascar) Republic was formed in 1960, the Comoro archipelago was incorporated in it.

The Comoros' most interesting claim to fame has been the capture of nine or ten coelacanths in their waters. The first, caught in December, 1938, near the port of East London in South Africa, came as a shock to biologists all over the world, for its race was believed to have been extinct for at least 50,000,000 years. Moreover, its paired fins were limb-like and apparently used for crawling, which gave the fish a curious four-legged appearance. The coelacanth, in fact, was one of the fishes that first crawled out of the water on to dry land 300,000,000 years ago.

The second coelacanth was caught by a native only 200 yards off the coast of Anjouan. Professor J. L. B. Smith, a South African ichthyologist, flew by special plane to the Comoros and brought it back for study. Since then some seven or eight more coelacanths have been caught in the area, and goggle fishermen claim to have seen and photographed them alive. It is interesting that coelacanth fossils are notably abundant in nearby Madagascar; apparently, the line has survived in a region where its remote ancestors were common and where conditions were perhaps not so different from those obtaining today.

Cook Islands

Two widely scattered groups of islands in central Polynesia. Location *South Pacific.* Area *84 square miles.* Map *4, J9.*

When Captain Cook discovered the islands now named after him, in 1773, he seems to have sighted only the southern group, which is hilly and volcanic; the northern group – mostly low-lying coral atolls – was discovered by the English missionary, John Williams, 50 years later.

A short way inland from the sandy shores of Mangaia – the second largest island of the group – a sheer perpendicular wall of dead coral rises for more than 100 feet. Its upper surface is flat and its width varies between a few hundred yards and a mile. This weird, encircling rampart is an ancient coral reef, now elevated above the sea. Its surface is largely covered with rich red soil, in which the natives make their gardens and plant citrus fruit. Here and there the bare rock is exposed, so sharp and jagged as to make walking virtually impossible. Vast stone staircases have been constructed by the natives from the upper to the lower levels and the entire formation is riddled with caves and crevices of every shape and size, full of stalactites and stalagmites, and used in ancient times as burial places and for storage. The interior face of this rampart – called the "Makatea" – slopes gently down into the low swamp lands – the former lagoon – which are largely planted with taro. The very center of the island, "the Crown of Mangaia," is a cluster of low, rounded hills and plateaus, nowhere rising above 550 feet but well-watered by streams which filter out to sea through the porous coral limestone of the Makatea. Surrounding the whole island is a narrow new reef of living coral.

The largest and most important island of the group is Rarotonga, the administrative center of the whole Cook Islands Territory, which has been part of New Zealand since 1901. Rarotonga's rugged, richly-forested mountains rise to 2,110 feet. It has luxuriant valleys, wide, fertile plains watered by innumerable streams and broad, palm-fringed beaches. For many years – because of diseases introduced by the white man, together with the effects of alcohol and poor administration – the natives seemed a dying race; large numbers emigrated to New Zealand or left the countryside (the interior is still almost uninhabited) to work in the capital or the coastal villages. But today the population is increasing. New gardens and groves are being planted – oranges, bananas, coconuts, tomatoes and vanilla are the chief crops – and everywhere there is a feeling of prosperity and progress.

Coral Sea

Southwest arm of the Pacific Ocean, east of Australia and New Guinea, west of New Hebrides and New Caledonia. Map *4, E8.*

The boundaries of the Coral Sea are indefinite; it is generally considered that it extends from the Australian coast to the irregular line of islands comprising the western Solomons, New Hebrides, New Caledonia and the Louisiade Archipelago. The Sea's area and its maximum depth have not been decided. It owes its name to the coral growths of the Great Barrier Reef, which lies along its western edge.

In 1897, Captain Joshua Slocum, on his lonely journey around the world, wrote of his passage through the Coral Sea that it seemed "smooth indeed but coral rocks are always rough, sharp and dangerous. I trusted now to the mercies of the Maker of all reefs, keeping a good lookout at the same time for perils on every hand. . ."

Forty-five years after the brave captain's solo voyage, the Coral Sea was the scene of a great naval and air battle, which marked the high tide of Japanese conquest in the southwest Pacific.

It took place in early May, 1942, just six months after Pearl Harbor, when the Japanese were about to move into position for the invasion of Australia, and it saved Port Moresby – and possibly Australia – from imminent invasion.

Islets off Corfu

Corfu

A Greek island with a long and varied history. Location *Ionian Islands, Greece.* Area *229 square miles.* Map *9, E9.*

Within its 40-mile length Corfu displays considerable changes of scenery and even of climate. In the north, white chapels and monasteries gleam on silver peaks; farther south, the center of the island opens out in valleys rich with olive and fruit trees; south again, and Corfu spreads itself in low-lying plains broken by picturesque hummocks of limestone outcrops and scented with thick undergrowth, in which myrtle, bay and ilex predominate.

The town of Corfu is on the east coast, with a fine natural harbor guarded against the northerly winds by the neighboring islet of Vido. It is overshadowed by the ancient citadel, which rises high overhead on steep twin peaks; the fortifications themselves were largely destroyed during the British occupation of the Ionian Islands from 1815 to 1864. Architecturally, the town is a blend of French and Italian styles, with occasional reminders of British taste in buildings such as the Palace, which was constructed in stone brought from Malta. In St Spiridion's church lies the mummified body of the island's patron saint, credited with innumerable miraculous cures and with having warded off from the island many misfortunes, wars and epidemics which have from time to time afflicted the mainland of Greece.

Apart from the olive and the vine, Corfu is

rich in almost every variety of fruit tree. Plum brandy, a sparkling red wine and a liqueur made from lemons are local products worth the connoisseur's attention – as are the excellent Corfu lobsters.

Traditionally, Corfu has been credited with having been the home of the seafaring Phaeacians who were unwise enough to incur Poseidon's wrath by restoring Odysseus to his homeland; it has been identified with Scheria in the *Odyssey*. The island was colonized by Corinth in 734 B.C.; the alliance that the Corfu colony (called Corcyra) formed with Athens was a cause of the Peloponnesian War.

In 229 B.C. Corfu came under Roman rule and the rise of Nicopolis eclipsed its glory for a while. Later, the Byzantines held the island until the Normans of Sicily took it in 1080; 70 years later the Venetians seized it, and later the island was under the rule of Epirus and of the Angevin kings of Naples. The Venetians regained their hold in 1386, and their rule lasted until the destruction of the Venetian Republic in 1797. Twice the Turks besieged it – in 1537 and in 1716 – and twice Corfu withstood the Moslem attack.

In 1864 Corfu passed to Greece, together with the other Ionian Islands. During the First World War the island gave refuge to the sadly battered remnants of the Serbian army which was evacuated from the mainland; French troops landed in 1916 to give the Serbians support. It was on Corfu that the present Yugoslavia, the union of Serbs, Croats and Slovenes, was proclaimed in 1917. In 1923 Mussolini sent his warships to shell Corfu because of the killing of some Italian officers; the incident was settled by the Council of Ambassadors in Paris. In the Second World War the Italians bombed and occupied the island until it was liberated in 1943.

Corinth, Gulf of

An inlet of the Ionian Sea. Location *Between the Peloponnesus and central Greece.* Dimensions *3–20 miles wide, 80 miles long.* Map *9, F9.*

As the narrows of Patras are left behind, the Gulf of Corinth opens to the view. On the right hand the fertile coastal plains of the Peloponnesus run back to distant mountains, on the left the silver and blue peaks of Greece culminate in the craggy, eagle-haunted heights of Delphi. Mount Parnassus dominates the Gulf north of Ites, while just behind Corinth the strange bald head of Mount Acrocorinthus looms over the modern city.

The Gulf seems to have receded since classical times, for the ancient city of Corinth is now about a mile and a half from the shore, and its western harbor whence the Corinthian fleets once sailed is now inland. Another famous port in the Gulf which has altered in the course of centuries is Naupaktos – better known to history as Lepanto, the scene of the great sea battle of 1571. Just inside the Gulf of Corinth, Naupaktos is today no more than a shallow-water port suitable only for fishing boats, although the fine old ramparts of the harbor and town remain.

Fishing and local trading still occupy most of the men who live on the Gulf and every type of Greek fishing boat and trading schooner can be seen in the course of a day. Although motor craft are becoming more and more common, the Gulf is still one of the last great strongholds of sail, and caiques of 10–100 tons run up and down between the coastal villages and the towns of Corinth and Patras. The beauty of the scenery is enhanced by the rocks and islets lining the shores of the Gulf, many of them capped by small, white-washed chapels.

Corinth Canal

An important channel in Aegean navigation. Location *Northeast Peloponnesus, Greece, joining Gulf of Corinth with Saronic Gulf.* Dimensions *4 miles long, 72 feet wide.* Maximum depth *26 feet.* Map *9, F9.*

Viewed from the Gulf of Corinth, the Corinth Canal opens ahead like a dark wound in the sandstone-colored shore. To the south, the modern city of Corinth sprawls along the water's edge, with the peak of Acrocorinthus dominating the port, while to the north, the approaches are guarded by the blue-shadowed heights of Parnassus.

Work on the Canal began in 1881 and took 12 years to complete. Cut through almost solid rock, and with no intervening lakes or shallow depressions like the Suez Canal, it was costly to build; almost every yard had to be blasted. It was the

The Corinth Canal

difficult nature of the terrain which had led to the abandonment of a canal begun during the reign of the Emperor Nero. Nero, a devotee of Greek culture, had visited Greece in 66 B.C. and had been so flattered by the reception the astute Greeks gave him that he agreed to divert part of the Imperial finances towards the construction of a canal. The difficulties encountered and the death of Nero two years later put an end to the project.

The Canal's importance lies in the fact that it shortens the route between the Adriatic and the Aegean by 200 miles and enables shipping to avoid the stormy water round Cape Matapan at the southern end of the Peloponnesus. Pending widening and further dredging, though, the largest types of modern ships, such as oil tankers, are still compelled to round the Peloponnesus.

Today the Canal is used mainly by Adriatic shipping bound for the Piraeus or Istanbul and by westward-bound Aegean ships. The strangest assortment of craft follow one another through the narrow, moat-like waters – cruise ships and cargo vessels, fishing boats and coastal schooners. Behind an old steam yacht (now converted to inter-island trade) may come a modern diesel coaster, with a graceful caique towed by a motor boat hard on her heels. In mid-summer, when the sun stands high over the Isthmus of Corinth, the Canal is torrid and airless and the traveler longs for the fresh breezes of the open gulfs at either end.

Coromandel Coast

A monsoon-beaten shore with several important towns and ports. Location *East coast of Madras, India, between Point Calimere and the Kistna River.* Length *About 450 miles.* Map *10, F4–5.*

The Coromandel Coast, battered by cyclones during the northeast monsoon from October to April, has no natural harbors but several bustling commercial ports – of which Cuddalone, Negapatam, Pondicherry and Madras are the most important. Facing the northern tip of Ceylon, it contains the delta of the Cauvery River and the mouths of the Palar, Penner and Ponnaiyar rivers. Its name is supposed to have been derived from *Cholamandalam*, the country of the Cholas – a great seafaring dynasty that flourished from the early Christian era to the middle of the eleventh century.

Along this low coast and among the hills inland, the India of ancient times survives as perhaps nowhere else. Southern India escaped the invasions and upsets of the north of the subcontinent, and its largely Dravidian peoples have a continuity of tradition that is amazing even in this ancient land. It can be seen in the great crowds thronging the temples at festival times; in the temples themselves, so piously ornamented and kept in repair by the local men of wealth; in the living sanctity of such places as Tiruvanna Malai, a short way from the Coast, where the great saint Sri Ramanz Makarshi died in 1950, surrounded by his disciples, indifferent to the gold and diamonds heaped upon him by the faithful.

Corryvreckan

Straits with a large and famous whirlpool. Location *Between Jura and Scarba islands, Inner Hebrides, Scotland.* Dimensions *Two miles long and one mile wide.* Maximum depth *900 feet.* Map *8, D3.*

During spring flood tides, when the whirlpool of Corryvreckan (also known as Corrievreckan or Corrievrekin) whips itself into its greatest fury and several subsidiary vortices are created, the hoarse roar can be heard for miles around. Caused by tidal movement of water over a bottom varying greatly in depth, it is the greatest overfall round the coasts of Britain and one of the greatest potential sources of power in Europe. Martin Martin called it, around 1695, "an impetuous current not to be matched anywhere about the isle of Britain."

The current race in the straits varies in speed according to tide and season, but on an average flows at about ten knots. Though the whirlpool is dangerous, experienced local people have been known to cross it in small motor boats and deer have often been seen to swim it. Among the local Gaelic-speaking population it is known as Cailleach the Hag – and when the straits are particularly rough and foam-capped, the Hag is said to have donned a white kerchief to give warning that she is in no mood to be trifled with.

Corsica

A large, leaf-shaped island with a population of over 270,000. Location *Mediterranean, south of the Gulf of Genoa, separated from Sardinia by the Strait of Bonifacio.* Area *3,367 square miles.* Map *7, D8.*

Corsica's history is almost as harsh as the granite spurs of its great northern mountains. While other Mediterranean islands – between their periods of war, revolution and conquest – have enjoyed long intervals of comparative prosperity, Corsica for many centuries seems to have been doomed to figure as the scene of eternal strife. It was perhaps fitting that a land with such a background should have been the birthplace of the Emperor Napoleon I.

Corsica's first civilized inhabitants were Greek colonists from Ionia; they were driven out by the Etruscans, who were quickly dispossessed, in their turn, by the Romans. After the collapse of the Roman Empire, Corsica's unhappy history reads like a roll call of all the nations who ever aspired to power in the Mediterranean. The island was occupied successively by Vandals, Goths, Lombards, Moslems, the Counts of Tuscany, the Genoese and the Pisans. For most of these powers the island's importance was not only strategic and agricultural, for here they also found a vast supply of timber for building and maintaining their fleets. The indiscriminate cutting down of trees over the centuries left many of the mountainsides in an appalling condition – barren screes with patches of tangled brushwood and scant pasturage.

Corsica's worst period was in the sixteenth and seventeenth centuries, when the island was administered by the Genoese Bank of San Giorgio, a company which had no interest except for the profits they could wring out of the people. The wild, fierce and intractable character of modern Corsicans has been shaped to a certain extent by their unhappy past and not least by their cruel and ruthless exploitation at the hands of the Genoese. Just as in Sicily the Mafia was the outcome of a complete lack of normal justice, in Corsica the vendetta or blood feud became the established code by which the inhabitants settled their own rights and wrongs. Even today violence lies close beneath the surface and a man may shoot his enemy or rival and then "take to the maquis." The maquis, the tangled, sweet-smelling scrub that covers the mountainsides, has added a word to our language. In the Second World War the French Resistance forces came to be known by this name because their way of life was similar to that of the Corsican bandits.

In the eighteenth century the British and the French became involved over Corsica; for a short time the British occupied the island. It was during these years that Pasquale Paoli, one of the few noble, disinterested and genuine patriots in the whole of Corsica's history, rose to fame. Paoli made so great an impression on James Boswell, Dr Johnson's friend and biographer, during his tour of the island that on his return to London Boswell became an almost fanatical supporter of Corsican independence, but – as Lord Holland

The town of Bonifacio, Corsica

remarked – "we cannot be so foolish as to go to war because Mr Boswell has been to Corsica." The island was finally restored to the French crown in 1815.

In 1942 Italian and German troops occupied the island; but a little over a year later the Corsicans revolted and seized Ajaccio. A Free French task force came to their aid and the island was finally liberated in October, 1943, after which Corsica became a very useful Allied base for operations against Italy and Southern France. In 1960 Corsica was in the news again when the French Government, in anticipation of Nikita Krushchev's state visit, sent several hundred well-known anti-communists on an enforced vacation to the island.

The chief towns and ports of Corsica are Bastia, Ajaccio, Calvi and L'Île-Rousse. In all of them the influences of Corsica's successive invaders are reflected in the architecture and in the pattern of life. Bastia, the former capital, on the northeast coast, possesses a noble harbor surrounded by old buildings, behind which the long, maquis-covered slopes rise to high granite peaks (the highest, Monte Cinto, reaching 8,891 feet). Ajaccio, the present capital and main shipping center, has little of architectural interest except for its Napoleonic associations, which include the house where the Emperor was born.

Bonifacio, though not important commercially, is among the most interesting of the island's towns. Commanding the Bonifacio Strait, it is a perfect example of a fortified walled town; the nucleus is tenth-century in origin. On the seaward side the town hangs over precipitous cliffs. The only entrance to its harbor is through a narrow inlet, almost a mile long and dominated on both sides by the surrounding heights. Overhead the walls and embrasures scowl down and navigation is difficult, for the channel is both narrow and tortuous.

The island has a wide variety of scenery: mountain-girt inlets on the western coast; vineyards, olive groves, tobacco and mulberry fields in the fertile plains. Mountain torrents drop from high peaks and the rivers, though short, have excellent freshwater fishing. Around the coast, tunny, pilchard, mullet and anchovy abound. The people are handsome, temperamentally a mixture between French and Italian, with something of the Spaniard's rigid sense of personal honor. French is spoken throughout, but in most places it is a *patois* with many Italian importations. The unforgettable thing about Corsica is the scent of the maquis. "Once a man has known it," the Corsicans say, "he can never return to the towns."

Crete

The largest island of the Greek Archipelago, cradle of an ancient civilization. Location *The Mediterranean.* Area *3,207 square miles.* Map *7, G10.*

Crete lies in the southern part of the Aegean, known as the Sea of Candia. This rugged island, 140 miles long with an average width of less than 30 miles, has played an important part in mythology and legend. It was famous even in pre-Homeric times for its "90 cities" and its mixed nationalities. Its king Minos was revered as the island's first law-giver and in later mythology became one of the three Judges of the Dead.

The plains of Candia, Canea and Mesara, the deeply indented rocky coasts, the gulfs of Kisamos, Canea, Suda, Almyros, Candia and Mirabella have witnessed (so legend says) the story of Theseus and Ariadne, of the labyrinth of Minos and the Minotaur. Whether Sir Arthur Evans, the explorer of Knossos, really found the actual labyrinth in his excavations, is disputed by scholars. But he certainly found a civilization that was previously almost unknown to history. The Crete of Knossos and the other sites of Minoan culture are most important, and in many ways still tantalizing, treasure-troves of art and archeology: pictographic and linear scripts, not yet fully deciphered, thin-waisted pottery statues with that curiously modern air resulting from the combination of naturalistic and expressionistic features, jars boldly decorated with flowers and cuttle-fish, frescoes of elegant long-nosed youths, the recurrent decorative themes of double axes and acrobatic games with bulls.

Cretan civilization flourished about 1500 B.C. and merged, after about five centuries, with that of the Dorian Greeks. Knossos (or Cnossus), Gortyna and Cydonia (the modern Canea) were the most important city states. Yet Crete remained largely outside the mainstream of Greek history. Three centuries before Christ it accepted the not very trustworthy protection of Macedon and was turned into a nest of ruthless pirates. The Romans conquered it in 68–67 B.C.; in 395 A.D. it came under Byzantine rule. The Saracens invested it for almost 140 years (from 823 to 961) and after the Fourth Crusade the island came under Venetian rule in 1204, when it was renamed Candia – after the residence of the ruling duke. The Turks conquered it in 1669 – the last important victory of the Turkish empire.

There were a series of revolts against the Turks in the nineteenth century: the insurrection of 1896–97 led to a Turco-Greek war, ending in Greek defeat, but leading to the liberation of Crete under pressure of the European powers. In 1898 an autonomous Cretan state was formed under Turkish sovereignty but governed by a high commissioner appointed jointly by England, France, Italy and Russia as the occupying Great Powers. Ten years later, however, following the Young Turks' revolution, the Cretans proclaimed their union with Greece and a year later the foreign troops were withdrawn. The Cretans revolted several times against the Greek central government, too, – notably in 1935 and 1938 – but these revolts were suppressed.

The island has a population of about 440,000; the relatively small cultivated areas produce olive oil, wine, grapefruit, oranges, lemons, almonds, carobs and potatoes. An excellent goat cheese is manufactured. The climate is generally mild with comparatively little rainfall; the mineral resources include iron ore, gypsum, limestone and lignite. But Crete is perhaps proudest of one human "export" – for El Greco, one of the great painters of all time, was a native of the island, even though he made his career in Spain.

Cuba

The largest West Indian island. Location *Greater Antilles, West Indies, at the entrance to the Gulf of Mexico.* Area *44,218 square miles.* Map *2, D2–E2.*

Cuba lies south of the Florida Peninsula (only 90 miles south of Key West) and east of the Yucatán Peninsula of Mexico, commanding the two entrances to the Gulf of Mexico – the Florida Strait and the Yucatán Channel. On the east it is separated from Hispaniola by the Windward Passage, the principal shipping route between the North Atlantic and the Caribbean Sea.

From Cape San Antonio to Cape Maisí, the crescent-shaped island's western and eastern extremities, is almost 760 miles. Cuba's average width is about 50 miles, with 160 miles as its greatest width and 22 miles as its narrowest. Its total area includes the 1,350 square miles of the Isle of Pines and some other islands; the population is close to 5,000,000.

The republic is divided into the six provinces of Havana, Camagüey, Matanzas, Oriente, Pinar del Rio and Santa Clara. The capital, Havana, is also the largest city and chief port, with Holguin the second in importance. Camagüey, Ciego de Avila, Cienfuegos, Guantánamo, Matanzas, Pinar del Rio, Santa Clara, Sancti Spiritus, Santiago de Cuba and Trinidad are other important cities and towns.

More than half of Cuba's surface is mountainous or hilly; the mountains are scattered over the island and do not form a central massif. The Cordilleras de los Organos in Pinar del Rio (the westernmost province), the Guamuhaya Range in central Cuba, and the Sierra Maestra in the easternmost Oriente province are the principal ranges. The first two do not rise above 3,000 feet; the Sierra Maestra – which includes the Sierra del Cobre and Macaca subranges – is both the highest and the largest in area, and contains Turquino Pico, at 7,870 feet the highest point in the island.

Among the most striking natural features of Cuba are the sub-surface limestone caves – those of Cotilla, the best-known, are near Havana. Cuba's rivers are mostly short and unnavigable; the chief stream is the Cauto. The coastline is much broken and irregular, with many gulfs and bays to make its total length about 2,500 miles. There are excellent harbors, most of them almost entirely landlocked. Of these, Cárdenas, Bahia Honda, Havana, Matanzas and Nuevitas on the north coast and Cienfuegos, Guantánamo, Santiago de Cuba and Trinidad on the south are the most notable.

Cuba's semi-tropical climate is tempered by the northeast trade winds; more than 60 per cent of the rainfall occurs during the wet season, from May to October. August, September and October are the hurricane months, and these storms are often of extreme violence. The royal palm is the commonest tree, with cottonwood, cedar, ácana, ebony, mahogany, lignum vitae, logwood, rosewood and pine flourishing. Among the animals the hutia rat and the rare, insect-eating solenodon are the indigenous mammals; bats are numerous and there are nearly 300 species of birds, varying from vultures, wild turkeys and macaws to quails, gulls, and hummingbirds. Cuban boa constrictors can grow to 12 feet; there are over 700 species of fish, together with tortoises, caymans, sharks, eels and crabs.

Cuba was conquered by Spain in 1511, and Spanish colonization was a thorough-going affair from the beginning. A few campaigns destroyed the power of the native Arawak and Ciboney Indians, then the work of building up a purely Iberian civilization began. As in Spain, Church and State were almost one and the highest ideals were tainted by the most terrible corruption. The Inquisition appeared and stately arcaded piazzas, vast baroque cathedrals and governors' palaces, immense castles (the Morro Castles at Havana and Santiago and Jagua Castle at Cienfuegos among others) were built, all proclaiming the proud spirit of Spain.

The first capital of the island was Santiago de Cuba, in the extreme southeast, and its first mayor was Hernán Cortés, conqueror of Mexico. Cuba, easily and strongly controlled, its cities heavily fortified, became the springboard for further Spanish conquests in Central and North America. But Santiago was gradually displaced by Havana, founded on its present site in 1519 above one of the best natural harbors in the New World. Here each year the two great Spanish treasure fleets – one from Vera Cruz, loaded with Mexican silver and Philippine merchandise, the other from Cartagena and Puerto Bello, laden with pearls from the Margharita Isles and gold from Peru – met for the homeward voyage. Offshore, numerous freebooters lurked, waiting to pounce on any ship that straggled.

The island's own products grew in importance. Spacious haciendas were laid out, worked by Negro slaves. The "barracoons" round the harbor in Havana, where the slaves were brought back to life after the ghastly ordeal of their journey from Africa, were crowded. Yet the Negroes never outnumbered the whites and today 73 per cent of the population are white, 14 per cent mulattoes and only 12 per cent Negroes – the remainder consisting of Chinese, Indians and other immigrants.

Sugar became king (to be rivalled later by tobacco and the famous Havana cigar) and the richness of a West Indian sugar planter became proverbial. Life was easy, civilized, elegant, with a wealth of slaves and flunkeys, and long avenues of royal palms leading to the magnificent estate houses – and only an occasional alarm of war or civil strife. In 1762 Havana was captured by the English, but was exchanged a year later for Florida. From that time, perhaps, date the beginnings of Cuban disaffection with the mother country, though Cuba, the most Spanish of Spanish possessions, was the last Latin American country to achieve independence – and then only through American intervention.

For four years following the Spanish-American War of 1898 (precipitated by the mysterious blowing up of the United States battleship *Maine* in Havana harbor) the island was under American military rule – until May 20, 1902, when it became an independent republic, though the Platt Amendment, effective until 1934, did limit Cuban sovereignty. For the last 60 years the United States has leased a naval base in Guantánamo Bay.

In 1917 Cuba entered the First World War on the side of the Allies and had a short-lived, fantastic period of prosperity which is still remembered as the "Dance of the Millions," based on the high price of sugar. When this bubble burst, there was a long series of revolutions and dictatorships. Gerardo Machado ruled from 1923 to 1935, then came Fulgencio Batista who, with some interruptions, remained in power until January, 1959, when Fidel Castro's bearded men swept down from the hills and the dictatorship disintegrated like a piece of rotten sugar cane. Batista fled to the Dominican Republic; there were mass executions, and bulldozers dug huge graves for the dead. Castro's revolution had undeniably wide popular support but his subsequent policies and his acceptance of Russian and Chinese aid have created opposition. An attempted invasion by anti-Castro exiles from Miami in 1961 proved a failure, but did not erase the causes of discontent and resistance. Cuba's future is as much in the balance as it has been several times during the past centuries.

Curaçao

Principal island of the Dutch West Indies. Location *Dutch Antilles, 40 miles north of Venezuela.* Area *174.13 square miles.* Map *2, G4.*

When Alonzo de Ojeda discovered Curaçao in 1499, he found a barren, cactus-covered island with a few Arawaks, Caribs and Tupis living on it – soon to be expelled by the Spanish colonists, who came in 1527. In 1624 the island was captured by the Dutch in their long war with Spain, and Dutch it has remained ever since, with a brief interlude of British control in the Napoleonic wars. From 1651 onwards, Portuguese Sephardic Jews arrived in large numbers from Amsterdam or Brazil (where they had fled in the first instance from Portugal) and they and their descendants have made an important contribution to the island's prosperity. There have been English, French, Syrians and Chinese since; and many African Negroes, mostly from the British West Indies, have come to work in the oil refineries. Today there are about 100,000 inhabitants, four out of five being Negroes or mulattoes.

The island's history is one of shrewd business sense bringing wealth. Starting with no resources except a fine harbor, some phosphate of lime, salt, and wild divi-divi (the dried pods of *Caesalpinia coriaria*, used in tanning), the islanders set to work to establish their home as the chief commercial market of the Spanish Main. This, under the liberal and politically stable government of Holland, they were able to do. Smuggling, slave trading and – more recently, during the American Prohibition – bootlegging, grew to be important, sometimes dominant, sidelines. From 1827 the island was a free port, with no customs duties on imported goods (even today there is only a flat three per cent duty on all goods, except tobacco and alcohol), which therefore could be bought here more cheaply than anywhere else in the region. The islanders invented the famous liqueur, Curaçao, a rich, golden-brown syrupy liquid compounded of rum and the dried rind of a special variety of orange, large groves of which soon covered the island, until a year of disastrous drought killed most of them.

Then came the greatest stroke of luck: enormous oil fields were discovered under and around Lake Maracaibo, a vast, shallow inlet of the sea, 6,300 square miles in extent, between Venezuela and Colombia. Drilling was started in the shallow water – but a huge sand bar blocked the entrance, and no ship with a draught of more than 13 feet could enter. The nearest suitable harbor for ocean vessels was in Curaçao, and here, or on the neighboring Dutch island of Aruba, the refineries were built – now among the largest in the world.

Today, 100,000 tons of shipping pass each day through the center of the capital, Willemstad, along the narrow, canal-like channel which leads from the sea into the vast inner harbor. The channel is lined with picturesque, eighteenth-century brick houses; with their stepped or curvilinear gables and red-tiled roofs, they might be in Haarlem or Delft – except that they are painted bright pink, green or yellow, and have vivid tropical flowers in their gardens. As the ships pass, a pontoon bridge opens and closes to let them through; a moment of great excitement, of scurrying pedestrians, cyclists, automobiles – for it is ten miles round to the other side. No architect could have designed the layout better, for the sterile, efficient industrial center is completely separated and immunized from the charm and bustle of the picturesque old town.

Cyclades

A group of over 50 islands in the Greek Archipelago. Location *Aegean Sea, extending southeast from Attica and Euboea.* Area *1,023 square miles.* Map *7, G10.*

Rugged and barren to the seaward view, the Cyclades often conceal sheltered valleys with green acres, backed by shining silver peaks, recalling classical landscapes as imagined by eighteenth-century painters. Each island has a distinctive quality that sets it apart from its neighbors. Syros, the most important, was until this century the main trading port of the Aegean and has a land-locked harbor with a twin-breasted mountain rising behind it. The island delicacy – and one of its major exports – is Louloumia, or Turkish delight. Naxos, on the other hand, is extremely fertile and rich in lemon groves. (It was of Naxos Byron used to dream when he thought of retiring to the Aegean.) The peak of Zia, the highest mountain in Naxos and in the Cyclades, gleams across the narrow straits between Naxos and Paros and forms a landmark for sailors. The famous marble of Paros is still mined. Different again is Thera, an island formed around an active volcano, Nea Kaumoni, whose smoking cone reminds one that only recently it erupted, causing damage and loss of life. Tiny Delos, the sacred island, lies almost at the geographical center of the Cyclades.

Many traces can be found of the days when the Cyclades were under the rule of Venice in the later Middle Ages – families with Venetian names, Italian churches and architecture, Italian phrases mingled in the Greek speech and even, as in Syra, two distinct divisions of the town: one with its houses built around the peak on which the Roman Catholic cathedral stands and the other clustered under the shadow of the Greek Orthodox cathedral.

Cyprus

The third largest Mediterranean island. Location *Eastern Mediterranean, 40 miles south of Turkey.* Area *3,572 square miles.* Map *7, H10.*

Cyprus, 140 miles long and 60 miles across at its widest point, with a population of about 544,000, is an island of contrasts; in history a rich panoply of the ages, in culture a dichotomy of Greek and Turkish life. Hatchet-shaped, it lies close to the Turkish and Syrian coasts, the handle represented by the narrow Karpas Peninsula, pointing towards the Gulf of Iskenderun. Behind a coast of rocky headlands and long, sandy beaches are steep and craggy limestone hills in the north, forested mountains in the south, and between them the broad, central plain of Messaoris. From Nicosia, the capital, in the center of this plain, the jagged crest of the northern hills is clearly seen; the broken pinnacles of white limestone pierce like fingers into the sky. Perched on their slopes are the picturesque ruins of the medieval castle of St Hilarion and the abbey of Bellapais. On a clear day the Turkish coast can be seen from these ruins and immediately below them is the richly colored coastal plain round Kyrenial.

Far away to the southwest are the Troodos Mountains; a massif of steep valleys and peaks clothed in forests of dark pine with the highest point, Mount Olympus, rising 6,403 feet above sea level. Here in summer are tree-shadowed retreats from the sun-scorched lowlands, and in winter there is excellent skiing. On the northern slopes of Troodos is the famous monastery of Kykko. The summer sun bakes the central plains of Cyprus a dun drab color, but in spring, after the heavy winter rain, the green of the fields and the flowers by the wayside add brightness and color to the landscape.

Cyprus has had a long history, rich in legend and from the earliest times influenced and controlled by the changing pattern of civilization in the countries close to it. It is famous as the island which, according to Greek legend, gave birth to Aphrodite, the goddess of love: the supposed site is near Paphos on the west coast. Paphos is also renowned as the place where St Paul and Barnabas made their first important conversions to Christianity. In the early Christian era Lazarus, after his resurrection in Bethany, is said to have visited Cyprus and at Larnaca, where he died, there is a church dedicated to him.

Politically, Cyprus has had many masters: Egyptian, Roman, Byzantine, Crusader, Levantine, Turk and British. One of the most remarkable periods of its history began with the Crusade led by Richard Coeur de Lion who for a short time occupied the island after marrying his Queen, Berengaria, at Limassol in 1191. Soon afterwards Richard set up Guy de Lusignan, the former king of Jerusalem, as ruler of the island and the Lusignan dynasty survived for nearly three centuries. It was succeeded by the Venetians, who built the fortifications still standing at Nicosia and Famagusta; and it was in their period of rule that Shakespeare set his tragedy *Othello*. Many of the outward signs of Cypriot history today are connected with the long Turkish rule (from 1571 onwards), such as the castle at Larnaca and the mosques at Nicosia. In 1878 the island was leased to Britain, while nominally remaining Turkish, but when in 1914 Turkey entered the Great War against the Allies, Cyprus was annexed and was formally recognized as a colony in 1925. Since then there has been a constant movement for union with Greece (*Enosis*), which came to a climax after the Second World War. Britain, trying to keep an uneasy balance between the Greek and Turkish Cypriots, became involved in a costly and unpopular conflict which led to much loss of life. Archbishop Makarios, the Greek leader, was deported to the Seychelles; in the mountains Colonel Grivas organized an efficient and elusive guerilla force. Finally, in 1960, an agreement was reached and Cyprus became an independent republic, with Britain retaining some military and air bases, while the administration was shared by Greeks and Turks.

Out of the total population of over half a million, the Greek Cypriots number 80 per cent and the Turks 18 per cent. Some villages are exclusively Greek or Turkish, others are inhabited by both nationalities. The Cypriot branch of the Orthodox Church has for long been powerful and the privileged position of its archbishop dates from the discovery of the remains of St Barnabas in the fifth century. The importance of Islam in Cyprus is associated especially with the sacred shrine of Umm el Haram (a relative of the Prophet) near Larnaca. There are separate Greek and Turkish quarters in Nicosia, the capital and largest town. Although there are few other towns – Famagusta, Limassol, Larnaca, Paphos and Kyrenia are the most important – about two thirds of the population live in villages widely scattered through the island.

Copper ores are mined on the northern slopes of the Troodos Mountains, as they were in Roman times, and some salt is obtained near Larnaca and Limassol. High quality lace-making is a traditional village industry, while the rich, sweet Commanderia wine of Cyprus has been prized since the time of the Crusades.

The Dalmatian coast

Dalmatian Coast

The coastline of Yugoslavia, with many offshore islands. Location *From Velebit Channel to the Gulf of Kotor, along the Adriatic.* Map 7, *F8.*

One of the most fascinating coastlines in the Mediterranean, if not in the world, the island-strewn Riviera of Yugoslavia stretches from Fiume in the north to the frontiers of Albania in the south. Not all parts of the coast are equally attractive – some are arid and barren – but these stretches serve only to intensify the beauty of such sections as the Seven Castles between Trogir and Split. Here a fertile coastal plain is backed by stark, shining limestone hills from which brisk mountain streams pour down into the Adriatic. Olives, wine, sage, laurel and rosemary grow in profusion. There are few trees along this part of the coast but the shoreline and the islands are covered with flowering shrubs and aromatic herbs.

The history of the coast begins with the ancient kingdom of Illyria, conquered by the Romans in 168 B.C. but not finally subdued until a century later. Then, as now, the tough peasants from the interior and the hardy fishermen of the seaboard were a proud people and difficult to tame. Greek colonies had already existed on some of the islands and most of these, in due course, became flourishing Roman towns. The most famous Roman to be born in Illyria was the Emperor Diocletian, whose ruined palace still forms the center of the town of Split, or Spalato.

In the fifth century A.D. Dalmatia was overrun by the Ostrogoths, but was soon reconquered by Byzantium. In the seventh century it was settled mainly by Slavs with the exception of the coastal cities. By the tenth century, it was split between the kingdoms of Serbia and Croatia, with Venice in possession of several ports and islands. Great seamen and pirates, preying upon the Adriatic trade routes, the inhabitants inevitably clashed with the power of the Queen of the Sea; after centuries of struggle between Croatia, Hungary and Venice, Venice emerged victorious and in 1420 gained complete control, which was later to be extended by the Turkish cession of some interior districts. Dalmatia provided Venice with many fine sailors and shipbuilders. It was during the fifteenth and sixteenth centuries that so many of the architectural masterpieces which now decorate the small fishing villages and harbors were built. Ragusa (Dubrovnik), perhaps the most perfect example of the Mediterranean small city state, remained a center for the arts and for science throughout the Venetian occupation.

The Napoleonic era brought a series of changes and upheavals; in 1797 Dalmatia became Austrian, in 1805 Italian, and in 1809 was made part of the Illyrian Provinces. The Congress of Vienna restored it to Austria; it became a province and one of the titular crownlands of the Habsburg Emperors. When Ragusa's independence ended, the patrician families committed genetic suicide by refusing to have any children. During the Austrian control some characteristic Austrian baroque was added to the architectural mixture.

In 1919 the entire coastline became Yugoslav with the exception of the enclaves of Zara, Cazza, Lagosta and Pelagosa. In 1947 these, too, became Yugoslav. During the Second World War there was an Italian occupation up to 1943 when the Germans took over; from 1941 onwards the coastline and the islands were almost uninterruptedly battlefields in the guerrilla war the Yugoslav partisans waged against the foreign invaders.

In many respects the Dalmatian coastline is a small boat sailor's paradise. It has beautiful harbors and well-sheltered islets; there is practically no tide and in summer the water in the sheltered island bays is always warm. Land and sea breezes alternate by day and night and numerous local fishing boats still work the winds just as their ancestors have done for thousands of years. In winter, however, the area can be extremely dangerous, with white squalls hurling suddenly from the mountains and islets. The *bora*, a northeasterly wind, blows in winter – one of the most dangerous in the Mediterranean, sometimes attaining speeds of 100 miles an hour.

Dampier Archipelago

A rocky archipelago of six main and many smaller islands. Location *Indian Ocean, off the northwest coast of Western Australia.* Area *About 30 square miles.* Map *4, B9.*

"I had a strong suspicion that here there might be an archipelago of islands and a passage possibly to the south of New Holland and New Guinea into the great South Sea eastward," wrote William Dampier, the great English navigator, when he sighted the first of the group of islands which now bears his name.

Dampier was a remarkable man in every way. Buccaneer, navigator, hydrogapher and teller of tall stories, he discovered the passage between New Britain and New Guinea which also bears his name – as does another strait in the South Pacific, not to mention a mountain in New Zealand and several townships. He was also indirectly responsible for the birth of "Robinson Crusoe" – for it was on one of his voyages that Alexander Selkirk, the original Crusoe, was marooned on an uninhabited island, from which, however, he was collected and returned to England after five years. The accounts Dampier published not only provided much detailed information about new places, peoples and creatures, in remarkably vivid prose, but led directly to the great French and English scientific voyages of the nineteenth century.

At the age of 47, Dampier was commissioned by the British Admiralty to find out what he could about New Holland, as Australia was then called. He sailed on January 14, 1699, from the Downs in command of the *Roebuck*, specially fitted out as a discovery vessel, with 20 months' provisions aboard and a seasoned crew. In June he reached the Cape of Good Hope, passed into the Indian Ocean, and sailed towards Shark's Bay, an inlet on the west coast of Australia, where he hoped he would find an anchorage. Sailing within sight of the red and white cliffs of the mainland, he began his long search for fresh water, food and a safe harbor, a search which finally drove him northeastwards around the coast some 400 miles or so to "his" archipelago, which he reached in late August.

He explored the first island, hoping to discover rich minerals and "ambergreece" and, above all, fresh water. But all he found was two varieties of shrub.

Dampier examined each island carefully, navigating the shoals, sandbanks and reefs lying in the narrow channels between them. The largest of the group, 6 miles long by 2 miles wide, which he named Enderby Island, was rocky and dry like Rosemary, with little hope of water. Dampier did not mention any mammals on it though it is possible that there were wallabies, as there are today – sheep on Enderby and on Lewis, another of the larger islands, are a fairly recent addition to the fauna of the archipelago. The most interesting animals were the water snakes – some of them the thickness of a man's wrist, four feet long with a flat tail, and of a rusty yellow color, while others, shorter, were spotted black and yellow.

Dampier stayed in the Archipelago as long as he could, about a month in all, until – giving up hope of finding any form of wealth and anxious for the health of his men, who were beginning to suffer through lack of fresh water – he sailed eastward for New Guinea.

Today the islands are sparsely inhabited and mostly devoted to sheep raising.

Dardanelles

A narrow strait of great strategic importance. Location *Northwest Turkey, connecting the Sea of Marmara and the Aegean Sea.* Dimensions *37 miles long, 1–4 miles wide.* Map *7, G9.*

The strait of the Dardanelles has been of strategic and commercial significance ever since ancient times because of its position at the crossroads between the Mediterranean and the Black Sea, between Europe and Asia. Many legends refer either to passage through it or to events near its shores. Among the oldest is the legend of the Golden Fleece, a part of which relates how Helle, a Boeotian princess, was drowned in the strait when being carried eastwards by the ram with the Golden Fleece. The name Hellespont is derived from this legend. In the later quest for the Fleece, Jason and his Argonauts passed through the strait. A blend of legend and fact concerns the land immediately south of the Dardanelles, where the ruins of ancient Troy stand today. Another legend tells the tragic love story of Leander, who used nightly to swim across the strait to meet Hero, but one night was drowned. In 1810 Byron emulated Leander by swimming across from Europe to Asia, in the Narrows close to Canakkale.

Historical events connected with the Dardanelles are as numerous as legends. Herodotus, the Greek historian and geographer, describes how in 480 B.C. Xerxes, the Persian king, constructed a bridge of boats across the narrowest part of the strait to carry his army on to the invasion of Greece. It took a full week for the soldiers and baggage-trains to pass. In 334 B.C. Alexander the Great crossed the Dardanelles at the start of his invasion of Asia. Some centuries later when the Emperor Constantine was looking for a site on which to establish a capital for the Eastern Roman Empire, he gave serious consideration to the site of ancient Troy, at the entrance to the Dardanelles, before deciding on Byzantium.

The strategic importance of the Dardanelles was early recognized and fortresses were built by the Byzantine Emperor Justinian, by the Genoese and the Venetians and also the Ottoman Turks. The Dardanelles were indeed a strong bulwark to Turkish power, freeing their fleets for overseas ventures to extend their empire. Control of the strait (with the Bosporus) remained important on the decline of Ottoman strength and the increase of Russian interest in the region from about the eighteenth century onwards, and it has remained so in international politics to this day. In 1936 the Montreux Convention gave Turkey formal permission to fortify the Dardanelles, after it had been a demilitarized zone for the previous 16 years. Warships of belligerent states cannot pass through unless "going to assist the victims of aggression" – a somewhat loose definition which depends on Turkish interpretation.

During the early part of the First World War, in 1915, the Dardanelles were the scene of Allied landings on the Gallipoli Peninsula. This borders the strait on the north and the Allied aim was to establish a foothold here against the Turks. The famous "Anzac" Beach, where the Australian and New Zealand brigade landed, is on the northern shore of the Peninsula, facing the Aegean Sea. Turkish resistance was strong and after heavy losses the Allies were forced to withdraw.

The Dardanelles have little to offer in scenery. Both the northern and southern shores are rather bare and monotonous; the only vegetation is scrub, thickets and occasional clumps of pine. The northern, European, shore, forming part of the Gallipoli Peninsula, is steeper than the southern, though the hills are neither particularly high nor impressive on either side. If one views the Dardanelles from the Aegean Sea, the headland of Cape Helles rises prominently, but apart from this there is little striking scenery until about halfway through, in the so-called Narrows. Beyond here a few high bluffs and sandy beaches are passed, then, near the town of Gallipoli, the Dardanelles open out into the Sea of Marmara.

Delaware Bay

An inlet of the Atlantic, receiving the Delaware River. Location *Between New Jersey and Delaware.* Dimensions *52 miles long, about 12 miles wide.* Map *1, F8.*

Long and narrow, Delaware Bay stretches from the mouth of the Delaware River, just below the mouth of Alloway Creek, to the entrance to the Atlantic between Cape May (New Jersey) and Cape Henlopen (Delaware).

The Bay has played a very important part in American history. The natural harbors of the Atlantic coast gave easy access to the colonizers and helped to decide where they settled. Delaware Bay was one of the readily accessible areas (like Cape Cod, the regions protected by Long Island and Staten Island, Chesapeake Bay and the vicinity of Charleston). From the Bay, too, the great navigable river of the same name flowed directly into the Atlantic and its bank furnished good locations for early settlements.

Henry Hudson, in 1609, entered Delaware Bay, seeking a passage through America, but quickly realized that this was not the right entrance and went on to discover the "great river of the mountains" which today bears his name. Charles I, in 1632, granted George Calvert, the first Lord Baltimore, a "precinct of land" between Delaware and Chesapeake bays, which Calvert called "Terra Mariae," Mary's Land. When Charles II made his grant to his brother James, Duke of York, in 1664, it included all the area from Delaware Bay to the Connecticut River, the region embraced by New Netherland. Eighteen years later the grant was transferred to William Penn and in 1703 "the lower counties of Pennsylvania" were given the right to elect a separate assembly. Delaware became a sovereign state in 1776.

Today the Chesapeake and Delaware Canal links the Bay with the inland navigational system of the eastern seaboard and inland states.

Delos

A small Greek island with many religious and historical associations. Location *Cyclades, Aegean Sea, Greece.* Area *1.2 square miles.* Map *9, G9.*

Delos lies almost in the center of the Aegean Sea, and the other islands of the Cyclades radiate round it like spokes of a wheel. It is easy to see why the ancient Greeks attached a mystical importance to its position, for Delos, though small, is still the center around which the Aegean world revolves.

It was known as "the wandering island" for it was supposed to have drifted erratically since the beginning of time; then, one day, Zeus sighted it sailing through the Aegean and anchored it in the center of the Cyclades. Here, on Delos, Apollo and his sister Artemis were born and the island became the center of their worship. Apollo's altar was so widely revered that even the pillaging Persians respected it.

The island is a low bone of rock, crested by the austere, barren peak of Mount Cynthus. Once the richest island in the Aegean, Delos is now visited only by summer tourists, who are ferried over from neighboring Mykonos. During the winter it is uninhabited, except for shepherds and goatherds.

The ruins of temples, granaries and houses straggle down to the tideless water's edge. Boats are still moored alongside the ancient mole where once ships came from Athens, from Asia Minor and from the most distant Greek islands. Giant lizards of a type peculiar to Delos confront the visitor and bull-frogs boom from the dank mouths of old cisterns and underground cellars. In the sixth century B.C. the island was declared "sacred ground" and no one save priests and priestesses was allowed to live there, nor were dogs allowed. Neither birth nor death was allowed to contaminate the holy place and women nearing childbirth or old pilgrims in danger of dying were hastily ferried across to one of the neighboring islands. At one stage the Athenians disinterred all who had been buried there and reburied them on other islands. Delos was supposed to be "outside of time's creatures," and something of this feeling still haunts it.

Devils Island

A small rocky islet famous as a penal settlement. Location *Off the Atlantic coast of French Guiana.* Map *6, D6.*

Devils Island is the smallest of the three Guiana islets formerly used by the French as a penal settlement. The others are Île Royale and St Joseph. Devils Island itself was uninhabited until Alfred Dreyfus, the hero of the famous *affaire*, was confined there from 1894 to 1899; it was subsequently reserved for political offenders, an "élite" compared to the cut-throats herded or kept in solitary confinement in the awful prisons of Île Royale, or the overspill of prisoners driven mad in captivity who ended their days on St Joseph. The name Devils Island has, in fact, acquired an evil repute that properly belonged to the other two islands.

The three were known as the Îles du Salut because of their freedom from malaria; the anopheles mosquito could not cross the strait that separates them from the mainland. Apart from this, the "Health Islands" have nothing to recommend them. Situated within six degrees of the equator, they have a monotonous, humid climate, and their vegetation consists mainly of coconut palms. Cut off from the mainland and from one another by shark-infested waters, they were natural prisons. Their smallness contributed to the atmosphere of confinement; the largest of them, Île Royale, is barely a mile from end to end and it is possible to walk round Devils Island in about half an hour.

It is difficult to conceive of more dispiriting or more effective places of imprisonment. Escape to the mainland was extremely difficult and the few prisoners who managed to reach it nearly all perished in the jungles and swamps of the interior if they were not recaptured. Human contrivances were added to the natural obstacles; there were frequent musters of prisoners for checking and warning signals were given by cannon firing and red lights if anyone was missing; the most desperate criminals were held by chains secured to their ankles with iron bands welded round them.

Devils Island itself is merely an elongated rocky islet rising to less than 100 feet at its highest point, but for five years it was the center of world interest. The Dreyfus case had split France from top to bottom. Emile Zola, Anatole France, Georges Clemenceau and many others had rallied to the side of the innocent man who had been caught up in a web of intrigue, fear and bigotry. The *affaire Dreyfus* was such a violent upheaval in French political and intellectual life that its effects have still not completely disappeared, more than 60 years later. After Dreyfus was brought back to France (though the long fight for his rehabilitation took another six years), Devils Island remained uninhabited for nine years. The next prisoner, Lieutenant Ullmo, who had been condemned for treason, arrived in

1909 and spent the first eight of his fourteen years' confinement alone. When war broke out in 1914, others convicted of having had connections with the enemy were sent there; but later on, as the war fever died down, fewer and fewer prisoners were allocated on the Island. The whole penal settlement was gradually liquidated between 1938 and 1946.

Diamant, Rocher du

A small islet near Martinique. Location *Windward Islands.* Area *About one square mile.* Map *2, J3.*

For 17 months this small, precipitous hump of rock was commissioned as a ship of the Royal Navy, H.M.S. *Diamond Rock.* This was in 1803–05, during the Napoleonic wars, when Admiral Hood found that many French ships escaped British pursuit through the channel between the Rock and Pointe du Diamant. At the one possible landing place he brought his ship, the *Centaur,* alongside. Somehow, his men clambered to the top of the inaccessible-looking stone pyramid, taking ropes and tackle with them which, firmly fixed above, they lowered on to the frigate's decks. By this aerial route five guns, kegs of powder, shot, victuals and water were hauled to the summit. Then 120 men and boys, under the command of a naval lieutenant, were landed as garrison and Hood sailed away, leaving them to harass the enemy's merchant shipping and defy his navy – which they did with great success.

It was only when powder had run out and the water casks were dry that H.M.S. *Diamond Rock* surrendered at long last. Even so, the final assault took a French squadron of 16 ships, of which three were lost, while 70 men were wounded. The total British losses were two men killed and one wounded.

Diomede Islands

An island group between Siberia and Alaska. Location *Bering Strait.* Map *5, D2–3.*

Vitus Bering discovered these two small islands on St Diomede's Day, 1728, and named them accordingly. Here, the United States and Russia are only a mile apart – for Little Diomede Island is an American possession, while Ratmanov Island, to the west, belongs to the Soviet Union. Another boundary that divides them is the International Date Line.

The Islands are inhabited chiefly by Chukchi, a hunting people closely related to the Eskimos. From very early times these have been middlemen between Asia and America, though in more recent days the populations on the two sides of the border have had little communication with each other. Their barren granite homes are often enveloped in haze and fog, so that Nunárbrook and Ignálook – the native names of the western and eastern Diomedes – are often invisible even to each other.

Dodecanese

An archipelago of 14 islands and about 40 islets and reefs. Location *Southern Aegean Sea, between Turkey and Greece.* Area *1,044 square miles.* Map *7, G10.*

Less famous in history than the Cyclades to their west, and off the track of most travelers, the Dodecanese hang like a crescent off the southwestern coast of Turkey. They are stark and mostly barren, yet reveal with great force of contrast sudden vistas of green vines, almonds and carobs in their hidden valleys. The total population is over 120,000 and most of the inhabitants are seamen and fishermen; many of them are away from the islands for long months on end, employed in the Greek mercantile marines. Sponge fishing is another island activity, and some coral is found.

Though called the Twelve Islands, the Dodecanese really consist of 14 – Astypalaia, Chalke, Kalymnos, Karpathos, Kasos, Kos, Leros, Leipsos, Nisyros, Patmos, Rhodes (the biggest), Syme, Telos and the tiny Kastellorizo, separated from the rest at the easternmost end of the crescent. Leros and Patmos have two of the best harbors; that of Leros is a fine sheltered inlet on each side of which the white-washed Greek houses shine like icing sugar in the sun. In the summer the prevailing northerly winds keep the islands cool, although the east wind when it blows off the mainland of Turkey comes as though from an oven, with all the withering qualities of the North African khamseen.

The port of Kalymnos island in the Dodecanese

In 1522–23 the Turks wrested control of the island group from the Knights Hospitallers, and Turkish rule continued until the Italo-Turkish war of 1911–12, when the Italians occupied the group (with the exception of Kastellorizo). The Treaty of Sèvres, in 1920, confirmed by the Treaty of Lausanne three years later, awarded the Dodecanese to the Italians. When Italy surrendered in 1943, the Germans took over the islands, until in May, 1945, their garrisons also surrendered to the Allies. By the peace treaty of 1947 they were awarded to Greece, on the basis of their overwhelmingly Greek population, and in 1948 a formal transfer was made from temporary British military government.

Dogger Bank

An extensive shoal, with a depth of water of only 10–20 fathoms. Location *Central North Sea, between England and Denmark.* Map *8, E4.*

The name Dogger is probably Dutch in origin, meaning a trawling vessel, generally applied in the past to a type of two-masted fishing boat working in North Sea waters. For centuries the Dogger Bank has been famous as a fishing ground. It lies in the middle latitudes of the North Sea and extends over roughly one third of the distance between England and the Jutland Peninsula.

The North Sea, itself part of the continental

bed on which the British Isles stand, is shallow throughout, but nowhere more so than in the vicinity of Dogger. In places there are as little as six fathoms over the Bank, and the area is notorious for its dangerous breaking seas which occur whenever the wind is strong. At times the water is so shallow that the sea actually breaks in surf and the whole bottom is stirred up. The characteristic drab brown color of the North Sea after a period of bad weather is largely due to these stirred-up deposits being held in suspension in the water. In winter the Dogger is a favorite trawling ground. At times, there is nothing as far as the eye can see but a circle of fishing boats rising and dipping in the swell. Cod, haddock, herring, plaice, mackerel and whiting are caught in the area; for the sea here is rich in the organisms on which these fish thrive.

Dover, Strait of

A narrow channel separating the British Isles from the continent of Europe. Location *Between England and France, connecting the English Channel with the North Sea.* Dimensions *About 22 miles long, 21 miles wide (at narrowest point).* Maximum depth *180 feet.* Map *8, D5.*

For centuries the Strait of Dover has been a busy waterway, an effective barrier between England and Europe, and a frequent battleground – not to mention the various sporting activities for which it has served. Every season dozens of swimmers grease their bodies to brave the choppy waves and the strong currents in order to cross it; recently there have been attempts by a couple named Baldessare to swim it underwater and in 1961 an eccentric crossed it on a brass bedstead with an outboard motor.

The chief ports of the Strait are Dover and Folkestone in England and Calais and Boulogne in France. Calais was the last English possession in France – until 1558 – and seems to be securely linked to England today by cross-Channel ferry. Though the crossing takes only an hour, it can be a severe ordeal, for the tides of the North Sea and the English Channel meet in Dover Strait, frequently causing choppy waters. In 1960 an old project was revived – the building of a cross-Channel tunnel which, after having been shelved for 50 years, was once again seriously discussed; though there is still argument as to whether it should contain a railroad or a motorway.

In the First World War there were several minor naval clashes in the Strait – but it came into its own as a frontline in the defense of Britain after the fall of France in 1940.

Easter Island

An isolated volcanic island with remarkable monolithic statues and undeciphered inscriptions. Location *South Pacific, about 2,350 miles west of Chile.* Area *45.5 square miles.* Map *4, O10.*

The Dutch navigator Jacob Roggeveen saw an island on Easter Day, 1722, and named it accordingly. Generally known to its Polynesian inhabitants as Rapa-Nui (Big Rapa), to differentiate it from Rapa-Ita (Little Rapa) in the Austral group, it is over 2,300 miles out in the Pacific from Chile (to which it has belonged since 1888), and about the same distance east of Tahiti. It is of volcanic origin, although all its volcanoes are now extinct, and rises to 1,765 feet. Its 600 gigantic stone statues, its other remarkable archeological monuments and its so far undeciphered *rongo-rongo* writing, or petroglyphs, have posed many still unsolved problems. A ship calls at Easter Island about once a year; it is both one of the most isolated and one of the most talked-about small islands in the world.

Most of the statues – all quarried from the tufa of the Rano-Raraku volcano – have low brows, narrow heads, and large, square jaws. The lobes of the ears are generally much elongated; the noses are long, outward-curving and tip-tilted; the thin lips are pursed in a scornful, supercilious sneer. These *moais*, as the Polynesian vernacular calls them, are half-length figures, with arms against the sides of their greatly prolonged trunk and their long, thin fingers with elongated nails meeting under the stomach, but with no legs. They range from 15 to 33 feet in height and weigh up to 30 tons.

A hundred and fifty of the statues still lie unfinished in their quarry but the others are scattered throughout the Island, about 60 of them upright inside the crater or at the foot of the volcano from which they were quarried; the others

Some of the giant statues on Easter Island

thrown on the ground all round the coast, cast down during a succession of inter-tribal wars from the funeral platforms (*ahus*) on which they originally stood. Lying beside them are the "top hats" by which they were surmounted, great cylinders taken from a quarry of red stones in quite another part of the Island. These are thought to represent top-knots – the original inhabitants are traditionally red-haired. Thor Heyerdahl, the explorer of *Kon-Tiki* fame, discovered statues of an entirely different kind, built into the megalithic walls and statue-platforms, suggesting a culture earlier than that represented by the others.

Why is it that the Easter Islanders of today do not know who made their bizarre gallery of statues, unique in the world, or how long ago, or for what purpose? Why is it that they cannot read the writing of their forefathers?

It is because in the middle of the nineteenth century the Peruvians discovered the commercial value of guano on some bleak islets off their coasts and scoured the Pacific to seize defenceless islanders as forced labor to work on those sun-scorched, waterless pieces of rock. Easter Island was then a no-man's-land, with no one to protect it. The unscrupulous press-gangs had no difficulty in transporting all the able-bodied men, including the king, princes and all the learned elders, to Peru, where within a year most of them died of ill-treatment and privations. When the British and French governments learned of this scandalous state of affairs, they protested to the Peruvian authorities, who finally agreed to repatriate the survivors. By then exactly 100 were still alive; of this pitiful remnant 85 died of smallpox on the journey home. The 15 who lived to see their island again introduced the smallpox to a population with no immunity against the disease and most of those who had escaped the clutches of the press-gang lost their lives in the epidemic. Only 111 remained alive, none of them able to transmit to the next generation the names and dates and motives of the statue-makers and the interpretation of the writings. The cultural lifeline had been cut. However, one of the Islanders was able in 1957 to demonstrate to Thor Heyerdahl how the statues had been carved, transported and erected; and the traditional belief in the battle of "Long-ears" and "Short-ears" was supported by excavation of the ditch that had traditionally been a defence work for the Long-ears. Charcoal from fire-sites in the bottom dated its original digging to about 400 A.D.

Almost as remarkable as the enigmatic statues were the small tomb objects discovered by Heyerdahl in caves with secret openings; representing, among other things, ships and animals not known on the Island today.

In the 70-odd years since the establishment of Chilean rule the population has slowly increased, though to nothing like the numbers of the days when the great statues were made. The Islanders live by tending the 35,000 merino sheep for which their country's gently rolling, grassy slopes provide excellent grazing. They are devout adherents of the Roman Catholic Church; though a number are extremely superstitious and claim to be in thrall to "guardian spirits" or *aku-aku*.

Undoubted affinities exist with South American cultures – the megalithic stone walling, the *balsas* or reed boats, the stone ship carvings are all part of a common tradition. On the other hand, megalithic stonework and huge statuary are also known in other, isolated Pacific islands. The tradition is that the "Long-ears" came from the east – America, where the Spaniards did record a race which artificially lengthened the ears – after a 60-day voyage; and that the Short-ears who finally overcame the Long-ears came from the west – Melanesia. This is a reasonable theory, but one still debated by ethnologists.

Eddystone Rocks

A rocky islet with a famous lighthouse. Location *Southeast Cornwall, 14 miles south-southwest of Plymouth, English Channel.* Map *8, C5.*

In 1695 Henry Winstanley began work on a tower upon the dangerous Eddystone Rocks which, covered only at flood tides and fully exposed to the southwest gales, represented a serious hazard to the approach to Plymouth, then one of England's chief ports, and were the cause of many wrecks and lost lives. A polygonal framework of wood, nearly 120 feet high, far in advance of its time in design and execution, his tower was completed in 1700; but three years later, the great storm of November 1703 swept it away. The next tower upon the site, Henry Rudyerd's, begun in 1706 and completed in 1709, was a massive construction 92 feet high, made of oak timbers securely bolted together and with its base filled with stone. Fire destroyed it in 1755. Then came John Smeaton's tower, begun the following year and finished in 1759 – the model upon which all later lighthouses have been based. It was a circular, conical stone tower 85 feet high, with each stone elaborately dovetailed into the surrounding ones to form a rigid structure.

In 1877 the Corporation of Trinity House (which had been granted control of all British lighthouses in 1837) decided to pull it down, because a higher tower was thought necessary and the rock on which it stood had been undermined. The new tower, designed by Sir J. N. Douglass, stands on Eddystone Rocks today, while Smeaton's tower was re-erected on Plymouth Hoe as a monument. The design of Douglass was at first much criticized, but time has amply proved its worth, for even the heaviest sea cannot damage it. Upon a solid, vertical-walled cylinder 22 feet high and 44 feet across stands the tower, 149 feet high; its walls, built of dovetailed granite blocks, curve upwards concavely. The domed lantern gives two quick flashes of 292,000 candle power every half-minute. In fog, a compressed-air whistle, like a giant ship's siren, bellows its warning.

It is a lonely station: each principal keeper alternately serves one month at the light and one ashore; each assistant – of whom there are two –

serves two months at the light and one ashore. But there is no shortage of applicants – even though reliefs are sometimes delayed by mountainous seas.

Egadi Islands

A group of islands famous for their tunny fisheries and a classic naval battle. Location *Mediterranean, off western Sicily.* Area *15 square miles.* Map *9, C9.*

The Egadi Islands, also called Aegadian or Aegadean Islands, known to the ancients as the Aegates, are spread in a long, broken circle from the western tip of Sicily. They have a population of over 6,000.

Favignana, the largest of the group (though only 7½ square miles in area) is 6 miles long and 3 miles wide; its steep hills rise to 991 feet. The inhabitants are engaged in tunny fishing – there are a number of canneries along the coast – and the cultivation of vineyards and citrus fruits. Part of the island is reserved for a penal colony. Marettimo or Marittimo is higher (its maximum elevation is 2,244 feet) and farther from Sicily than Favignana; apart from tunny, its people also fish for coral. Levanzo, closest to Sicily, is the smallest of the three and the lowest (912 feet); it also owes its livelihood mainly to the tunny fish.

It was off these islands that the Carthaginian fleet was defeated by C. Lutatius Catulus in 241 B.C. – a victory for the Romans which put an end to the First Punic War.

The entire group was the property of the ancient Pallavicini family of Genoa until 1874, when it was sold to a Signor Florio of Palermo. Today the Islands are no longer private property, and the Egadians have formed several fishermen's co-operatives.

Elba

A mountainous island, with ancient iron ore mines. Location *Tuscan Archipelago, Tyrrhenian Sea.* Area *86 square miles.* Map *9, C8.*

"Able was I ere I saw Elba" is a catchphrase that almost every schoolboy knows. And for most people Elba springs to mind as the home of Napoleon during his exile from 1814 to 1815. The ex-emperor's palace and a villa that belonged to him still exist; the palace rises above the harbor of Portoferraio, the capital and chief port of the island.

Elba, part of a sunken mountain range which extends towards Corsica and Sardinia, lies lengthwise east to west off the Italian coast, seven miles from the mining town and port of Piombino on the mainland. Both Elba and the coastal district adjacent to it are rich in iron ore, and the mines, which were worked as early as the Etruscan period, are still active. Tools, instruments and relics of every period of history have been uncovered in the ancient mine-workings. Despite the fact that the Greeks called it "Soot Island," Elba remains totally unlike similar mining areas to the north. Large areas are fertile, and terraced slopes of vines climb the hills and soften the dark outlines of the mine buildings.

Portoferraio is in the center of the north coast, surrounded by an amphitheater of hills, their peaks shining silver and their sides rich in vegetation. The only other harbor of any consequence is the long bottleneck of Porto Azzuro, a perfect natural shelter on the east coast, with a small village lying at its head and an old fortress dominating the entrance. The narrow strait between Elba and the mainland is always alive with fishing boats under sail, for the coastal waters are rich in sardines. Many tunny fish are also taken during the months when they approach the coast to spawn.

The wealth of Etruscan civilization was largely drawn from the mines of Elba and Piombino and the island's importance was recognized right up to the sixteenth century when the Medicis of Florence found in it an important source of revenue. Captured by Philip III in 1596, Elba remained under Spanish rule until 1709, when it was ceded to Naples. In 1802 the peace of Amiens gave it to France. Napoleon, on his deposition, received it as his domain with full sovereign rights – but the fallen emperor lived there only from May, 1814, to February, 1815, when the Hundred Days began. After Napoleon's final defeat at Waterloo, Elba was restored to the Grand Duke of Tuscany and the island was incorporated in the kingdom of Italy when this was established in 1860.

Elephanta

An island with famous sculptured caves. Location *Bombay Harbor, India.* Dimensions *1½ miles long, 1 mile wide.* Map *10, E4.*

Boats and launches plying from the Gateway of India, where formerly British viceroys landed and departed, ferry sightseers and picnic parties to the island of Elephanta, five miles east of Bombay. The famous Brahmanic caves, which date from the eighth century A.D., are carved in the side of a hill 250 feet above sea level. The great cave – there are five smaller ones in another part of the island, which are seldom visited – is hewn out of the hard rock of the hillside and is reached by a modern flight of steps. Formerly, a monolithic carving of an elephant (which may have given its name to the island, which is also called Gharapuri), stood on the right of the lowest flight of steps; its remains are now in the Victoria Gardens of Bombay. There has been much damage to the cave-sculptures since Carstens Niebuhr first described them in 1764. The most impressive that remains is the great *Trimurti*, 19 feet in height, the three-faced image of Brahma, Vishnu and Siva. This is carved behind the small central shrine and looks towards the northern entrance. Other figures, some 16 feet high, represent Siva and his consort Parvati in various manifestations.

Elephanta is a purely Brahmanical and Sivite shrine, one of perhaps 1,000 separate excavations in 40 or 50 groups in western India, the majority of which are Buddhist. Relatively small and uncomplicated, it serves as an introduction not only to Hindu mythology but also to that craft which combined architecture with sculpture and made cave-dwelling a high form of civilization.

The island, right up to the two hillocks which crown it, is covered with scrub, bushes and flowering trees, beautiful in their season.

Ellesmere Island

The northernmost island of America. Location *Arctic Ocean.* Area *77,392 square miles.* Map *5, C8.*

A large island, 500 miles long, 25 to 300 miles wide, grimly mountainous and mainly covered in ice. Ellesmere is the northernmost island of the Arctic Archipelago.

The first to explore it was Commander Sir E. A. Inglefield, who in 1852 led a party in search of the lost Franklin expedition. Inglefield was followed by the Grinnel expedition the following year, and by C. F. Hall in 1871–73, Sir G. S. Nares in 1875–76 and A. W. Greely and

Polar bears on Ellesmere Island

R. E. Peary in the early years of the twentieth century. Otto Sverdrup explored the west coast between 1898 and 1902.

These various expeditions mapped the coastline, which is deeply carved by numerous fjords, and climbed the United States Range in the north, which rises to over 11,000 feet. Gradually the main divisions of the Island – King Oscar Land in the southwest, Ellesmere Land in the southeast, Grinnell Land in the center and Grant Land in the north – were established and explored. Somewhat to the explorers' surprise, considerable vegetation was found in the ice-free districts, where large musk-ox herds are able to survive and even thrive. Today there are small settlements at Craig Harbor in the southeast and Buchanan Bay on the east and on Eureka Sound there is a weather station run jointly by the United States and Canada.

Ellice Islands

A group of nine coral atolls north of Fiji. Location *Southwest Pacific.* Area *9.5 square miles.* Map *4, G7–H8.*

Discovered by Captain Byron in 1764, the scattered Ellice atolls lie so close to the Pacific waves that their green pandanus groves and fringing palms seem from a distance to grow from the water. There are neither cliffs to break the violence of surf or sudden tidal waves nor valleys sheltered from typhoons.

The nine atolls are named Funafuti (the administrative center and main port of the group), Nanumanga, Nanumea, Nui, Niutao, Vaitupu, Nukufetau, Nukulaelae and Nurakita.

Apart from the pandanus, coconut palms and their copra provide the main livelihood of the Polynesian inhabitants and their sole export. In 1897 a British expedition visited the group to plumb the coral depth of Funafuti. In 1898 they reached a depth of 1,184 feet in the coral without touching bedrock. The scientists concluded that Funafuti was like a gigantic fortress wall of coral crowning a submerged conical mountain, some 750 square miles in area, rising from a depth of 6,000 feet.

The Islands became a British protectorate in 1892, and were incorporated in the Gilbert and Ellice Islands colony in 1915.

English Channel

An arm of the Atlantic. Location *Between England and France.* Area *30,000 square miles.* Maximum depth *564 feet.* Map *7, C5–D5.*

Originally no more than a narrow inlet of the North Sea, the Channel came into being in Pleistocene times when the sea broke through the neck of land that joined Dover to Calais, flooding a long valley that lay on the far side and joining up with the waters of the Atlantic.

It is its remarkable tidal system that especially distinguishes the Channel from other similar straits in the world. The tides owe their origin to the gravitational pull of the moon on the large expanse of the Atlantic Ocean. At new and full moon, when this influence is at its height, an undulating motion is set up in the Atlantic and a large tidal wave occurs. (Low tides occur at the half phases of the waxing and waning moon, when its influence is weakest.) The free tidal wave of the Atlantic meets the continental shelf on which Britain and Europe stand and becomes a directional movement of water – or what is called a wave of translation. This body of moving water is then forced through the bottleneck of the Channel, setting up tidal streams that are varied by the shape and contour of the coastline and of the sea bottom. In places the water moves at great speed; in the strait between Alderney island and the French coast at Cap de la Hague it reaches as much as seven or eight knots. One of the most dangerous races on the English coast is off Portland Bill. In general, the speed of the Channel stream – apart from the races – is about three to three-and-a-half knots, although in certain areas, such as the ill-famed Goodwin Sands, scene of many shipwrecks, it reaches four or five.

Westerly winds prevail in the Channel area and, in the days of sail, "waiting off the Downs" became a phrase which sailors throughout the world knew. While the westerlies were blowing, there was little chance of a square-rigged ship beating her way down the Channel. Homeward-bound ships, on the other hand, racing for London with their tea, spices and perishable goods, had only one thing to fear – that the Atlantic westerlies would drop as they neared the Channel and that a cold easterly would delay them. The importance of these winds – now largely unknown to sailors of the steam and diesel age – is brilliantly described by Joseph Conrad in his *Mirror of the Sea*.

Few sights can equal a full southwesterly gale blowing up the Channel. With the whole sweep of the Atlantic behind them, the seas reach the continental shelf and begin to shorten and break. As they near the Channel mouth between Ushant and the Scillies, the rollers feel the constraint of the land and immense breakers are formed, together with a backwash along all the capes and headlands of England and France. When the southwest cone is hoisted on the Cornish coast and the maroons go off to summon the lifeboats, even modern Leviathans like the *Queen Mary* or the *United States* delay their sailing.

This is a stretch of water of perpetual change. Even when it is calm, there remains another hazard – the Channel fog. More dangerous perhaps even than gales, it settles like a heavy curtain over the water, while the blinded sailor hears all round him the melancholy and alarming sound of the sirens of other ships. Even with modern radar, Channel fogs still take their toll of shipping. They are commonest in winter, whenever the warm air of an anticyclone moves over the colder waters of the sea.

A branch of the Gulf Stream or Western Current enters the Channel from the Atlantic and this warms the south and west coasts of Britain. With this warm water come the pilchards which are caught off the Cornish coast and, following the pilchards, numerous blue sharks. The character of the Channel is largely determined by the fact that on one side lies the comparatively warm Atlantic, and on the other the cold North Sea. In its western approaches the water may be quite blue and friendly, but the farther east one goes the more dour the aspect becomes.

From the first crossing by Caesar's legions to the threatened invasions of Napoleon and Hitler, the history of England has been written on this narrow strait. Jean Pierre Blanchard and Dr John Jeffries crossed it by balloon in 1785, the first man to swim across it was Captain Matthew Webb in 1875, and Louis Bleriot made the first airplane crossing in 1909. Now, modern weapons have made it useless as a defense, but the Channel is still the main approach to England's chief ports and her principal link with Europe.

Equatorial Current

A vast system of oceanic drift. Location *Atlantic Ocean, Indian Ocean and Pacific Ocean.*

It is more accurate to speak of the Equatorial "currents," for this great surface drift, moving west in the oceans along the equator, has clearly marked divisions and branches.

All surface currents of the oceans are due largely to the prevailing winds, and in the equatorial regions these are the trade winds. Generally speaking, in each hemisphere great swirls are formed by the agency of the trades and westerlies, centered near the tropics of Cancer and Capricorn; in the northern hemisphere their direction is clockwise, in the southern it is anticlockwise. Along the equator minor countercurrents are induced by them, generally separating the two main currents.

In the Atlantic, the Southern Equatorial Current divides into two parts at Cape St Roque: one branch, the Brazil Current, is deflected southwards and follows the coast as a true stream current at least as far as the River Plate; the second branch moves northwestwards towards the West Indies, where it joins the waters of the Northern Equatorial Current. The two drifts, blocked by the wedge shape of the land, contribute to raising the level of the surface in the Gulf of Mexico, the Caribbean Sea and the entire area outside the West Indies. The Northern Equatorial is joined by the greater part of the Canaries Current, which moves southwards along the northwest coast of Africa; the rest of the Canaries Current unites with the equatorial return currents and penetrates into the Gulf of Guinea. Again, in the South Atlantic, the cold Benguela Current moves northwards along the west coast of South Africa and rejoins the Equatorial Current.

In the Indian Ocean, the Equatorial Current is controlled by the monsoons. Along the line of the equator, the Indian Counter-Current flows eastwards all the year round, acting as compensation to the main Equatorial Current itself, which here moves westwards. The two currents, meeting at the northern end of Madagascar, send a branch southwards, along the east coast of the island, which is sometimes called the Mascarene Current. Reaching the African coast, the main Equatorial Current sends another minor stream to the source of the Indian Counter-Current; the discharge is mainly by the Mozambique Current. South of Cape Corrientes this becomes the Agulhas Current, one of the most powerful on the globe.

Finally, in the Pacific, we find the North Equatorial Current, caused and directed by the northeast trade winds. It divides in two east of the Philippines; one branch flows northwards as the Kuro Siwo, or Black Stream, feeding a drift circulation which follows the winds of the North Pacific, and finally becomes the California Current, flowing southwards along the coast of America. Part of this rejoins the North Equatorial Current and part forms the fitful Mexican Current close to the coasts of Mexico and California. The Equatorial Counter-Current in the Pacific, flowing eastwards, is largely created by the southwest monsoons; from July to October it is further strengthened by the southwest winds. The South Equatorial Current is produced by the southeast trades and is more vigorous than the North. When it reaches the western Pacific, one section of it passes southwards towards New Zealand; east of Australia, as the East Australia Current, it flows south along the southeast coast of the continent. The other section moves northwards to join the Equatorial Counter-Current, and this section makes its way during the northeast monsoon at least in part through the China Sea towards the Indian Ocean. During the southwest monsoon this last branch is reversed and the surface waters of the China Sea are united with the Kuro Siwo, completing the circle that spans the whole globe along and around the equator.

The influence of the equatorial currents is immense in determining the climate of the oceanic land margins; it is due to them that, in the latitudes of the great swirls, the western margins of the oceans, the eastern continental regions, are warm, wet and humid, while the eastern shores of the oceans are inclined to desert conditions. The warm and cold branches produce such contrasts in climate of the same latitude as Europe and Labrador display. Climate in turn determines agriculture and almost every other human activity, so that the equatorial currents can justly be said to influence the life and prosperity of the vast majority of mankind.

Espiritu Santo

A volcanic island, the largest and westernmost in the New Hebrides group. Location *Southwest Pacific.* Area *1,485 square miles.* Map *4, F8.*

In 1606, Pedro Fernandez de Queirós found and named Austrailia del Spiritu Santo, the Southern Land of the Holy Ghost. He sailed his fleet into Big Bay (he called it Bayu do S Philippe y S Santiago), and planned a marble city (New Jerusalem) and a cathedral to rival St Peter's of Rome. He proposed to import "3,000 friars to plant the holy faith" among the heathen inhabitants of the supposedly enormous hinterland. But the island turned out to be much smaller than he expected and the inhabitants were hardley welcoming, so after a brief stay the Spaniards sailed away and never returned.

Rising to 6,195 feet, Santo's malarious jungle shores are today largely depopulated: the original Melanesians have been decimated by European diseases introduced by whalers and slave-merchants, sandalwood traders and missionaries. Yet each bay has its lonely coconut plantations; a little coffee and cocoa is grown as well. The population is just over 4,000.

Formerly served only by a six-weekly steamer from Sydney and an even less frequent connection with France, Santo is now regularly accessible by an Australian airline. European settlers are governed by French or British law, according to their nationality; administration is by an Anglo-French condominium of which the British center is at Hog Harbor and the French at Segond Canal, on the south coast.

Faeroe Islands

A group of 21 volcanic islands under Danish sovereignty. Location *North Atlantic Ocean, between Iceland and the Shetlands.* Area *540 square miles.* Map *7, D2–3.*

Rising with sheer flanks from the long, narrow inlets that divide them, shrouded in fog by summer and beaten by storms in winter, the Faeroes carry into the twentieth century much of the raw contact with nature which is a basic element of their Nordic past.

Here, one can tell when spring is coming, for the turf which forms the house-roofs turns to green. The staple occupations are fishing and the capture of birds which swarm on the cliffs. Finance of the fishing fleet, international negotiations on offshore limits – these link the Faeroes with the modern world; but their day-to-day existence is still firmly rooted in the elements.

Seventeen of the 21 islands are inhabited; their narrow dividing sea-trenches suggest the flooding of one much bigger land-mass. High, rugged, treeless, and comparatively small in area, they manage to support some 70,000 sheep and a population that has grown to six times the 1850 figure, totalling over 30,000 today. The approach to the group provides a magnificent panorama of fantastic islands – peaked, sharp, precipitous rocks with angular bases, rising sheer from the sea. The large-sized islands are regularly terraced in two or more grades of columnar rock. Some of them are straight along the top like the ridge of a house and a slope down on either side to the sea, at a steep angle. In some places boats are still launched by lowering them down the cliff-side with ropes.

Stromo and Ostero are the largest of the group. Thorshavn, the capital, is a fishing port with a population of some 3,600; although the Faeroes are so far north, the influence of the Gulf Stream usually makes their harbors ice-free even in winter.

The Islands, first colonized by Norsemen about 800 A.D., were converted to Christianity in the eleventh century. Norway ruled them until 1380, after which they were governed jointly by Norway and Denmark. In 1815 the Peace of Kiel gave Denmark sole possession. In April, 1940, following the German invasion of Denmark, the Islands passed under British military control. In September, 1946, after a plebiscite had given a narrow majority in favor, the Faeroes *Lagting* (parliament) declared the Islands independent of Denmark – the culmination of a long fight by local patriots who demanded, above all, the recognition of the Faeroese language, an old Germanic tongue akin to Icelandic. But Sudero, the third largest island, still held out for union with Denmark; King Christian of Denmark dissolved the *Lagting*, declaring the ballot inconclusive, and a new assembly was elected. Finally, the Faeroes were given considerable autonomy within the Kingdom of Denmark; there is a Danish governor, but the *Lagting* has the right of local legislation.

Fair Isle

The southernmost Shetland island. Location *Halfway between the main group of the Shetlands and the Orkneys.* Dimensions *Three miles long, two miles wide.* Map *8, D2.*

Fair Isle, a bleak, rocky islet with a population of barely 100, is famous throughout the world as the home of "Fair Isle" sweaters.

Its rocky promontories, rearing up into formidable sea-cliffs that reach 480 feet in Sheep Craig, were seen by the battered relics of the Armada in 1588 as they returned to Spain round the north of Scotland, and at least one ship, reputedly the flagship of the Duke of Medina Sidonia, was wrecked in Stromceiler Creek. Legend claims that the native inhabitants were taught by the survivors the art of knitting parti-colored woolens of pseudo-Moorish design.

Fair Isle is an important bird migration station and has a hostel for bird-watchers.

Falkland Islands

Two islands and about 200 islets and rocks. Location *South Atlantic, east of the Strait of Magellan.* Area *4,618 square miles.* Map *6, D11.*

The Falkland Islands, a small British colony, are situated in South Atlantic waters seldom frequented, since the opening of the Panama Canal, by ships other than whalers. Their remoteness, inhospitable climate and poor soil have unavoidably restricted settlement, and the present population is little more than 2,000.

The Islands were discovered by John Davis in 1592 but remained uninhabited for more than a century until the Spaniards planted a settlement which they called Soledad. In the turmoil of eighteenth-century colonial rivalries and of the

Napoleonic wars, Britain established a claim to occupation which, however, she did not implement until 1833 – though Spain had abandoned the Soledad settlement earlier in the nineteenth century. The repeated claims by Argentina that the Falkland Islands were rightfully part of her territory were based upon her title as heir to all the former Spanish dominions in that part of the continent, and upon the foundation by Louis Vernet, in the name of the newly established Republic of Buenos Aires, of a short-lived colony upon the Islands in 1829. Most of the population, however, is of British origin.

The Islands are composed of hard, old rocks similar to those of Patagonia, of which they are an outlier. From ridges which rise to over 2,000 feet in both the larger islands, former glaciation has stripped the soil; it has also shaped the Islands into their present fretted outlines with numerous fjords. On the lower ground, ridges and "stone runs" of white quartzite rocks break the surface.

The climate is bleak and sunless though fairly equable. Prevailing westerly winds, often of gale force, sweep over the Islands, bringing rain or drizzle for almost nine months a year. In such a setting trees cannot survive, except in a few sheltered valleys. The vegetation, where soil exists, is grassy moorland on the better drained areas and marshland in the depressions.

The land can be used for little but sheep farming and the extraction of peat, the chief source of local fuel supplies. There are some 600,000 sheep on the Islands; their wool, together with whale and seal oil, furnishes the main export. Contact with the outside world is provided by a vessel plying between Stanley, the capital, and Montevideo. The colony is ruled by a governor and executive and legislative councils.

Farne Islands

A group of 26 islets 1½–6 miles off the coast of England. Location *North Sea.* Area *About 50 acres.* Map *8, D3.*

The Farne Islands – also called Fearne, Ferne or The Staples – are the eastern tip of the Whin Sill, a hard dolerite shelf that runs 70-80 miles

Sea birds on the Farne Islands

across the north of England. The Islands and the rocks and reefs that surround them have always been a peril to shipping. Yet this cluster of small dots of rock, isolated by the fierce North Sea more than by the distance from land, has long been a refuge for men and birds alike. To protect and encourage the many species of birds that nest on the Islands or stop there briefly while migrating, the Farne Islands were purchased by public subscription and handed over to the British National Trust in 1925 to be preserved as a bird sanctuary.

For seven years, until his death in 687, St Cuthbert lived on the inner Farne with little more company than the birds and seals of the North Sea. In the anonymous life of the saint there is talk of the devils that beset him and how he "fearlessly put them to flight and, digging almost a cubit of a man into the earth through very hard and stony rock, he made a space to dwell in."

St Aidan and other hermits succeeded him, and in 1255 the Benedictines of Durham established a house that lasted until the Reformation. Their chapel still stands in front of a stout tower built by Prior Thomas Castell of Durham in 1500, and the ruins of their guest house can be seen along the path leading to the jetty.

In 1673 a beacon was erected on Thomas Castell's tower. A lighthouse was built on the inner Farne in 1809 and another was built on Longstone Island in 1826. From this lighthouse, in 1838, Grace Darling and her father rowed out to rescue nine survivors from the wreck of the *Forfarshire* – an exploit that won Grace enduring fame.

Fernando Po

A large volcanic island. Location *Gulf of Guinea.* Area *779 square miles.* Map *6, J6.*

Fernando Po is the largest and most beautiful island off West Africa – a fertile, well-wooded, roughly rectangular piece of land, about 35 miles long and 20–25 miles wide. Of volcanic origin, it rises to 9,350 feet (or 9,449 feet – the estimates differ) in Santa Isabel Peak, an extinct volcano which occupies the northern half of the island. In a broken, steep and rocky coast, the only sheltered bays are at Santa Isabel and San Carlos. The climate is unhealthy, with a rainy season lasting from May to November; until 50 or 60 years ago, Fernando Po shared with the rest of tropical West Africa a notorious reputation as "the white man's grave." Only when malaria, blackwater fever, dysentery and other endemic diseases were brought under control could its extraordinarily rich volcanic soil be exploited in earnest. The annual rainfall is over 80 inches and gets heavier at the higher altitudes. The first commercial crop of the island in the last century was sugar cane; but today the chief export is cocoa, with coffee, bananas, palm oil, copra, kola nuts, citrus fruit and cabinet woods as other important products.

The Portuguese explorers who discovered the island in 1471 included one Fernão do Po, after whom the island was named. Portugal ceded it to Spain in 1778; in 1827 it came under British occupation, during which Clarencetown (now Santa Isabel) was founded; but in 1843 it became Spanish again.

Tradition asserts that the Bubis, the indigenous people of Fernando Po, came originally from the mainland. Anthropologists, noting their customs, which resemble those of the Bantus, are inclined to accept this. Another popular legend says that the first Bubis emerged from the crater of Santa Isabel Peak – and O Wassa, as it is called, is still an object of Bubi veneration.

Unlike coastal West Africans, Bubis care little for trade. They prefer forest life, hunting monkeys, porcupines, pigs and gazelles and stoutly resisting the lures of the white man's religion and culture. They grow yams and produce on their own lands a fair share of the palm oil which is one of the island's chief exports – but nothing will induce them to work on the European-owned plantations, which is the reason they are now outnumbered three to one by Ibos and other coastal West Africans brought over as laborers. These later arrivals they call "Portos" and the Spanish governor of the island is regarded as the Chief of the Portos, for the idea of a non-Bubi ruling over them is quite inconceivable. To everyone's surprise, the Bubis continue to flourish in spite of modern civilization's inroads and they make up a growing proportion of the 34,000 inhabitants of Fernando Po.

Fiji

A group of 250 islands, 80 of them inhabited. Location *Southwest Pacific, in Melanesia.* Area *7,056 square miles.* Map *4, G8–H9.*

Fiji, the most important British Crown Colony in the Pacific, has been called the "insular hub and crossroads" of the southwestern part of that ocean, the equivalent of Hawaii in the North Pacific. With a fertile soil, it is both an important producer and market, an essential link in trans-Pacific air and sea travel, an advanced strategic air base and a popular winter tourist resort. Fiji stands third among the island territories of the Pacific in the size of its population – over 320,000 – and provides a melting-pot of Melanesian and Polynesian civilizations and cultures.

Geologically, Fiji represents a "continental" island, lying on two partly submerged platforms, joined northeast of Taveuni; the various islands are composed of continental sedimentary and volcanic rocks and of coral limestone and basaltic lava. The larger islands of Viti Levu (Viti is the former, local name of Fiji), Vanua Levu, Taveuni, Kandavu, the islands of Lomaiviti (Ngau, Ovalau and Koro) and the Yasawas stand on the broad northern shelf. The eastern shelf, more narrow, elongated and running almost straight north and south, carries the Lau group, scores of small volcanic, limestone and coral islands. Between the two shelves are the deeper waters of the Koro Sea, while east of the 300-mile stretch of the Lau islands, the ocean floor dips rapidly to considerable depths.

Viti Levu and Vanua Levu are large "high" islands, mostly of ancient volcanic and more recent andesitic rocks mixed in a jumble with sedimentary rocks. Their interiors are elevated, rugged, cut by deep valleys, wet and forest-covered. There are many "thumbs" or "spikes," the remnant necks or plugs of volcanoes which have been eroded away. Several rivers, fed by heavy tropical rains, have built up deltas around the coasts – on Viti Levu the lower valleys of the Rewa, Navua and Mba have created cultivable land, though large areas are still swampy, undrained and overgrown with mangrove thickets. On Vanua Leva the lowlands are mostly on the dry, northwestern side.

Ovalau and Taveuni are also both high volcanic islands. Ovalau is roughly circular, with its outer slopes rising steeply to a concentric series of peaks 2,000 feet high which overlook the deep crater of an old andesite volcano. Taveuni has a backbone 3,000–4,000 feet high consisting of a ridge of volcanic cones of recent origin and activity.

The scores of smaller islands have an almost endless variety of form and structure and are scattered over a quarter of a million square miles of ocean, together with a maze of coral reefs which line the sea lanes closely and leave only a few approaches to the center of the group. This explains why both Tasman and Cook, who touched at the islands, failed to investigate and chart them and why the redoubtable Captain Bligh, after the mutiny of the *Bounty* in 1789, became the first European to penetrate deeply among them when he explored the group in an open rowing boat with only six oars. The lesser islands of Lau consist of volcanic materials or of uplifted bedded limestones, carved into fantastic shapes by rain and waves.

The climate of the Fijis is governed by the steady trade winds with more variable air currents from November to March or April – the season of intense tropical storms.

Fiji presents a striking variety of landscape – from the reef-fringed shores with their dark foliage and golden strands, the blue lagoons and the vivid white surf of the reef, to the deep, quiet valleys of the wet zone, with the rain-drenched forests covering the yellow clay soil of the hillsides; from the gray-green mangrove thickets to the brown, sun-drenched hills of the dry zone; from the coral islets thick with palms but no drinking water to the fantastic shapes and eroded surfaces of the low limestone islands.

The indigenous culture of Fiji is equally varied. Besides the Melanesian and Polynesian contribution there is also the more recent Asiatic element, represented by a large number of Indians and a small group of Chinese, and an influential minority of Europeans. Suva and Lautoka on Viti Levu are the main ports, with Suva as the capital. The idyllic inland life is contrasted with the bustle of the Indian bazaars, the busy sugar-mills, the patterns of the European plantations, the massive machinery of the

Australian-operated gold mine and the isolated government outposts.

After Tasman discovered Fiji in 1643, more than two centuries went by before the native chiefs ceded it to Britain in 1874. The missionaries had arrived in 1835 and were largely instrumental in ending tribal wars and – a far more stubborn tradition – cannibalism.

In the seventeenth century, the islands were occupied by tall, dark-skinned negroid Melanesians; but a mixture of Polynesian blood was already evident in the eastern islands and even on Viti Levu. The villages were compact communities of closely related families, and feuds were chronic among rival chiefs and groups of villages. Settlements were built as fortresses, many of them on offshore islands like Mbau and Serua or on hilltops and moated sites. Transport was mostly by water with rafts and dug-out or outrigger canoes. There were three dominant traditional concepts of economy and social life: *lala* stood for mutual aid and communal work which all fit members of the community had to perform; *kerekere* meant sharing of food and goods and hospitality; the third concept was the right of the chiefs to extract tribute, especially when outsiders settled on communal land.

Much of this triple tradition still survives on the outlying islands or inland on the larger ones; especially as British colonial policy tried to preserve the ancient way of life. Though the Indians have introduced commerce, and sugar and copra plantations have been established, the tribal structure and its customs have been kept alive in many ways and to a large extent. Today, Fiji's economy is based on the export of sugar, copra, coconut oil and gold and the production of domestic foodstuffs such as butter and canned pineapple. The islands are connected by a small fleet of copra boats.

Finisterre, Cape

A cape on the Atlantic coast of Spain. Location *Galicia, northwest Spain.* Map *7, B6.*

A high promontory at the northwestern tip of the Iberian peninsula, Finisterre shares with Cape Toriñana (to the north) the westernmost longitude in Spain.

In 1747, a large-scale naval action was fought off the Cape when the British channel fleet, commanded by Admiral George Anson, scattered a big French convoy bound for the East and the West Indies. Several men-of-war and armed French Indiamen were captured, though the battle was somewhat one-sided because of the great superiority of Lord Anson's forces which included 14 men-of-war.

On July 22, 1805, another naval battle was fought off Cape Finisterre in which the British forces were commanded by Admiral Sir Robert Calder and the French and Spanish combined fleet by Admiral Villeneuve. Two of the French ships of the line were captured by the inferior British forces – but Admiral Calder was court-martialled and severely reprimanded for breaking off the action before he had won a complete victory.

Finland, Gulf of

An arm of the Baltic with many islands and important ports. Location *Between Finland and the USSR.* Dimensions *About 250 miles long, up to 80 miles wide.* Maximum depth *Over 300 feet.* Map *7, G4–H4.*

The Gulf of Finland extends about 250 miles between Finland on the north and the Estonian SSR and the Russian SFSR on the south. At its far eastern end is the Karelian Isthmus which separates it from Lake Ladoga. The larger portion of the isthmus – the scene of bitter fighting in the two Finno-Russian wars of 1940–44 – now comprises the Karelo-Finnish SSR, while the smaller is part of the Leningrad Region of the Russian Soviet Republic. The Gulf varies in width from 12 to over 80 miles; the narrowest point is at its eastern end. It is generally shallow (the minimum depth is only 26 feet) and of low salinity, and it freezes over for 3–5 months in the year. On it are the estuaries of the Neva River, the terminus of the Saimaa Canal (the outlet of the Finnish Saimaa Lake system) and the mouth of the Narva River, which connects it with Lake Peipus. The Neva and the Ladoga Canal link it with the big Ladoga and Onega lakes.

Apart from its immobilization during the winter months, the Gulf has many sand bars and rocks which make navigation extremely difficult.

The south harbor, Helsinki,
in the Gulf of Finland

Where it narrows towards Leningrad at the mouth of the Neva, it contains the fortified islands of Sursaari, Lavansaari and Kotlin, the last with the famous naval base of Kronstadt; on the northern shore are the Finnish ports of Kotka, Helsinki (the capital) and the Soviet naval base of Porkkala, leased from Finland. Other Russian ports are Vyborg, Tallinn (the former capital of Estonia) and the naval base of Paldiski.

Florida Keys

A chain of coral limestone islands arching southwest around the tip of the Florida Peninsula. Location *Southern Florida, from Miami Beach to Key West (Dry Tortugas in Gulf of Mexico, off southern Florida.)* Length *About 150 miles (215 with Dry Tortugas).* Map *2, D1.*

The Florida Keys are a sort of extended barrier, separating the shallow waters of Biscayne and Florida bays from the greater depths of the Straits of Florida. Man's ingenuity and deeply ingrained longing for the trinity of sun, sand and water, have turned them into delightful and popular playgrounds for the rich and the not-so-rich, but above all for the impassioned race of fishermen.

Separated by shorter or longer stretches of water, narrow and generally covered by thickets of low trees and shrubs with mangrove swamps on the landward side, the Keys were first linked by a railroad, with long and repeated sections bridging the ocean. The great hurricane of 1935, which is still recalled with awe by the people of the Keys, destroyed this railroad; but three years later it was replaced by a motor highway which extends from Soldier Key, several miles south of Miami, to Key West, more than 90 miles north-northeast of Havana, Cuba.

Key Largo – 28½ miles long – is the largest of the Keys, with the villages of Rock Harbor, Tavernier and Key Largo itself: a center of commercial and sport fishing and an important link in the over-ocean highway that links the Keys with the mainland.

Key West is the westernmost of the group and the southernmost city of the United States, lying about 130 miles south-southwest of Miami. Here is a port of entry of the United States, a delightful and highly popular resort, a center for sponge-fishing and a United States Coast Guard base, housed in Fort Taylor – a venerable building, erected in 1844–46. There is also an important naval and naval air station. Key West, with a population of over 26,000, has tried its hand at many industries. It was once a center for salvaging and repairing ships, and then built up cigar-making as a major occupation. Today the giant turtles of the seas around the Keys end up at Key West and are made into turtle soup. Apart from an old lighthouse, two Civil War forts and an aquarium which attracts tourists by its well-trained dolphins and other animals, Key West is also the terminus of the new motor highway.

The other principal islands are Virginia Key, Key Biscayne, Sands Key, Elliott Key, Old Rhodes Key, Plantation Key, Upper Matecumbe Key (with Islamorada village), Lower Matecumbe Key (Craig village), Long Key, Grassy Key, Vaca Key (Marathon village), Pigeon Key, West Summerland Key, Big Pine Key, Torch Keys, Ramrod Key, Summerland Key, Cudjoe Key, Sugarloaf Key, Saddlebunch Key and Boca Chica Key.

The Dry Tortugas are usually included in the Florida Keys, though they are 65 miles west of Key West. A small island group of which Loggerhead Key, the largest, is only a mile long, it is included in the Fort Jefferson National Monument. Old Fort Jefferson is on Garden Key and is the largest masonry fortification in the western hemisphere. During the Civil War and afterwards it served as a military prison; its most notable inmate was Dr Samuel A. Mudd, the physician who set the broken leg of John Wilkes Booth after the fanatic and deranged actor had assassinated President Lincoln. There is a lighthouse on Loggerhead Key and a large sea-bird sanctuary on Bush Key.

Another coral atoll, the Marquessas Key, about 19 miles west of Key West, is also usually included in the group. About five miles across, the island is a national wildlife refuge.

Formosa

A large, mountainous island, the refuge of the Nationalist China government and armed forces. Location *Pacific Ocean, separated by Formosa Strait from Fukien coast of China.* Area *13,808 square miles.* Map *4, C4.*

The Portuguese called it "Formosa" – "The Beautiful" – which was a somewhat euphemistic appellation. The Chinese call it Taiwan. It is one of the high chain of volcanic islands of the western Pacific, with the eastern coast rising sheer from the sea and sloping gently westward to a narrow coastal plain which is nowhere more than 25 miles wide. The mountain chain occupies most of the island's surface; there are almost 50 peaks above 10,000 feet. Less than a quarter of the land is arable – yet it supports a population of 10,000,000.

The Portuguese reached Formosa in 1590 and gave it its European name. Chinese began to settle on the island in the middle of the seventeenth century, when large numbers of Ming refugees from the Manchu invasion fled there from the mainland. The original inhabitants were primitive Malayan aborigines who now number 200,000 and occupy the undeveloped mountainous interior, while the Chinese immigrants from Fukien and Kwantung live in the fertile plains and lowlands. In 1624 the Dutch established forts at the present-day Tainan and at Anping, its port, while the Spaniards gained a foothold in the north, at Tanshui and Keelung. In 1641 the Dutch expelled the Spaniards and gained control of the whole island. But 21 years later they, in turn, were forced out by Koxinga, a Ming general who established an independent kingdom. Another 21 years went by before the Manchus overthrew Koxinga's kingdom in 1683. The Chinese influx increased and soon the immigrants outnumbered the aboriginal inhabitants, who were driven into their present home in the interior.

The real economic development and population growth of Formosa took place in the 50-year period of Japanese occupation between 1895 and 1945. The island supplied a million tons of sugar and two thirds of a million tons of rice every year for Japan. In 1941 the Japanese used it as a base for the invasion of the Philippines; when the war ended with their defeat, Formosa was returned to Chinese sovereignty. In 1949 it became the fortress home of the exiled Nationalist Government of China, its armed forces and a large refugee population from the mainland. In 1957 its population was estimated at 10,000,000, plus the armed forces of Generalissimo Chiang Kai-shek.

The climate is varied. From October to March the northeast winds bring heavy rainfall to the northeast part of the island but the southwest has clear skies. From May to September southwest winds prevail; the south and southwest are then very wet and the north has a lower rainfall. Northeast winds during the winter often rise to gale force and the exposed fields must be protected by bamboo fences or tree shelters. Typhoons can be especially destructive during the summer in the south. Disastrous floods sometimes bury parts of the fertile alluvial plains with cobblestones, gravels and sands, especially on the precipitous east coast.

The main crops during the Japanese occupation were sugar and rice; in the last decade or so a more balanced agriculture has been established including sweet potatoes, tea, tropical fruit and essential oils to make Formosa self-sufficient in foodstuffs. More than 100,000 people are employed in fishing; the leading animal industry is hog raising.

About 70 per cent of the mountains are covered with forests, which provide about three-quarters of the world's natural camphor. Industry is still rudimentary, with food processing the most important branch, followed by ceramics, textiles, chemicals and machinery. Coal is the chief mineral product; there are a petroleum and an aluminium refinery, dependent on imported raw materials. The Japanese developed hydro-electric power extensively and by the end of 1957 this had been further increased to about 800,000 kilowatts to provide support for the new and expanding industries.

The only good natural harbor is the port of Chi-lung, which also has shipyards. While American aid has made a large contribution to Formosan economy, by 1950 Japan had regained her former position as chief customer and supplier of the island.

Franz Josef Land

The most northerly land of the eastern hemisphere. Location *Arctic Ocean.* Area *8,000 square miles.* Map *5, G8–9.*

Discovered in 1873 by the Austro-Hungarian Arctic Expedition under Julius Payer and Karl Weyprecht, this large archipelago was named after Francis Joseph, Emperor of Austria. In 1926 it was claimed by Russia, and four years later the Soviet Academy of Science proposed that it should be renamed Fridtjof Nansen Land in honor of the great Arctic explorer. This was never officially adopted, though occasionally the second name is used for the islands.

The archipelago is east of Spitsbergen and north of Novaya Zemlya. Its ice-covered mountains of volcanic origin consist of basalt formations, and rise to about 2,410 feet on Wilczek Land. There are about 100 small islands, separated by bays, fjords and straits. There are three main sections, separated by the deep British Channel on the west and the Austrian Sound on the east. The principal islands are Alexandra, Graham Bell, Prince George, Prince Rudolf, Wilczek, MacClintock, Hooker and Northbrook. The vegetation, because of the extremely low mean temperature (about 6.5° F.) and the ice-covered soil, is scarce, and is limited to lichens, mosses and some varieties of flowering plants. But there is a rich and varied animal life – polar bears, foxes, walruses, ringed seals and many sea-birds, including the ivory gull. There are only about six species of insects. There are observation stations and permanent settlements at Tikhaya and Teplitz bays. Dense fogs and violent gales are frequent; but the weather is often clear and produces magnificent displays of the Aurora Borealis.

"To the southwest lay the blue ice-cliffs and white snow uplands of Bruce Island," wrote F. A. Worsley in 1927, describing the strange beauty of this archipelago, "south and southeast lay Northbrook with two black basalt fortresses breaking through its icecap. North and east were vistas through the drifting mists, with masterpieces, by Nature, of dim, mysterious, snowclad lands, black rocky bastions and ice-choked sounds. The sea was studded with beautiful, stately bergs and littered with growlers, hummocks and broken-up floes. The sun swept low in a golden mist along the northern horizon and threw a radiant glory over sea and ice. The soft blue shadows of the ice, the golden, rosy mist over all and the sun's glowing path broken by lines of drift ice and hummocks of fantastic shape, made a scene so exquisitely beautiful and fairylike as to seem unreal. . ."

After Payer and Weyprecht, the exploration of the archipelago was completed by a number of expeditions – among them Leigh Smith's in 1880–82, the Frederick George Jackson and Alfred Harmsworth expedition of 1895–96, Nansen's in 1896, the Duke of Abruzzi's in 1899–1900, Evelyn Briggs Baldwin's and William Ziegler's in 1901–02 and Anthony Fiala's and Ziegler's in 1903–05.

Frisian Islands

A long eroded island chain divided into three main groups. Location *North Sea, off the coasts of Holland, Germany and Denmark.* Area *About 320 square miles.* Map *8, E4.*

"Who will not build dikes must go away," runs the old Frisian proverb, and it still holds good for these islands, lying at a distance of 3–20 miles from the mainland of Europe and constantly battered by the ruthless waves. About 1250 A.D., the area of the North Frisian Islands alone was estimated at about 1,065 square miles. By 1850 this was reduced to only 105 square miles. In spite of the protection of sand dunes and earthen embankments backed by stones and timber, the Frisian Islands were slowly but surely crumbling away. There are innumerable Frisian legends and folksongs about the submerged villages and hamlets swallowed by the treacherous waters of the Wadden. Heinrich Heine incorporated some of these legends in his famous *Nordseebilder*, which he wrote during a visit to Norderney in 1825. Though the shore facing tidal waters has gradually been expanded since the nineteenth century by diking, the Frisians must always be ready for floods and storms. In 1362, in 1570 and in 1634 there were disastrous assaults by the sea which changed the shape of most of the Islands and devoured great chunks of land.

The population, largely Frisian, was mostly engaged in fishing and shipping throughout the Middle Ages. With the discovery of the sea as a tonic and healing force, in the early nineteenth century, the fine sandy beaches began to attract visitors and most of the Islands have been developed into popular health resorts.

Though well-charted and plentifully supplied with lighthouses and buoys, the Frisian Islands have been a considerable danger to navigation and many wrecks lie among them. One of the most famous disasters was that of the British man-of-war *La Lutine*, which sank off the Islands in 1799 while carrying a large amount of gold and silver which was insured at Lloyd's. The Dutch government claimed the wreck and granted one third of the salvage to bullion-fishers. Between 1857 and 1859 about £100,000 was recovered by a Dutch company (in the meantime, Holland had ceded to Great Britain half the remainder of the wreck for Lloyd's), but over £1,000,000 worth is still under the ocean off Vlieland. It is the "Lutine Bell" which is rung at Lloyd's to this very day whenever a shipwreck is announced.

The Frisians are divided into three main groups: West, East and North Frisians.

The West Frisian Islands are Dutch, and extend off the Netherlands provinces of North Holland, Friesland and Groningen. They include Texel or Tessel (71 square miles), Vlieland (19 square miles), Terschelling (41 square miles), Ameland (23 square miles) and Schiermonnikoog (19 square miles), with four much smaller islands (among them Boschplaat and Rottum) which are uninhabited. The northern end of Texel is called Eierland, "island of eggs," because of the huge number of sea-birds' eggs found there. In 1629–30 it was joined by a sand dike to Texel and is now an integral part of it. Texel itself was already separated from the mainland in the eighth century, but remained a Frisian province. It was occupied by British troops for a few months in 1799. Terschelling was once an independent domain but was sold to the States of Holland. Ameland belonged to the great Cammingha family from the beginning of the ninth century, held under a direct grant from the Emperor, and in 1369 the Amelanders were declared neutrals during the war between Friesland and Holland; a neutrality which Cromwell reaffirmed in 1654 during the war between England and the United Netherlands.

The East Frisian Islands belong to Germany, extending along the German coast between the estuaries of the Dollart and Elbe rivers. Borkum (12½ square miles) has two lighthouses and is connected with Emden and Leer by steamer; Juist (2¼ square miles) is closest to Norddeich and Greetsiel on the mainland; Baltrum, Langenoog, Spikeroog (4 square miles), Wangeroog (2 square miles) and Norderney (5½ square miles) are all seaside resorts. Early in the eighteenth century Wangeroog was four times as large as today; Borkum and Juist are surviving fragments of the original Borkum Island which measured about 380 square miles – until 1170, when the sea split it in two. There are also four uninhabited islands in the group, including Neuwerk and Scharhörn.

The North Frisian Islands are divided between Denmark and Germany, extending along the coast of Schleswig-Holstein and Danish Jutland. Here are Nordstrand (17¼ square miles), which up to 1634 formed one large island with the neighboring Pohnshallig and Nordstrandisch-Moor; Pellworm (16¼ square miles); Amrum (10½ square miles); Romo (17 square miles), with several villages, of which Kirkeby is the principal; Fano (21 square miles); Mano; Helgoland; Trischen (uninhabited); and several smaller islands which are only a few feet above the level of the sea, and are usually crowned by a single, isolated house standing on an artificial hillock.

The barren coast of the Frisian Islands

Fishing in the Bay of Fundy

Fundy, Bay of

A bay with one of the highest tides in the world. Location *Atlantic Ocean, between northeast Maine, New Brunswick and Nova Scotia.* Dimensions *145 miles long and 48 miles wide.* Map *1, G5.*

Sailors tell of a ship cast ashore in the Bay of Fundy one night, whose crew at daybreak found themselves and their vessel suspended in mid-air, far above the water. Certainly, the Bay possesses one of the highest tides in the world, rising up to 70 feet. The incoming tide foams through the narrow mouth in a bore which at times reaches a man's height, and the tidal range is seldom less than 50 feet.

An elongated inlet of the North Atlantic Ocean, the Bay of Fundy separates New Brunswick from Nova Scotia. It narrows at its head and divides into Chignecto Bay on the north and Minas Channel on the south. Chignecto Bay, in turn, subdivides into Shepody Bay and Cumberland Basin – a body of water the early French settlers named Beaubassin. Minas Channel leads into Minas Basin while Passamaquoddy Bay, a western extension of Fundy, partly separates Maine from New Brunswick.

Though the Bay is very deep, navigation is

extremely dangerous and difficult because of the rapid rise and fall of the tide. At the head of the Bay there are extensive fertile marshes. A submerged forest indicates that the land has sunk at least 40 feet within the last thousand years or so. Fundy's chief harbors are St Andrews on Passamaquoddy Bay, St John in New Brunswick, and Digby and Annapolis on the Nova Scotia coast. The Bay was discovered in 1604 by the French explorer Pierre du Guast, Sieur de Monts, who named it La Baye Française.

Fundy has been a challenge to hydro-electric engineers, who have tried to find some way to harness this tremendous power. It was once proposed that one or more tidal basins should be built, separated from the sea by a dam containing turbines. The rising tide would fill the basins through sluice gates and at high tide they would be closed. After the tide had dropped to half its range, the turbine gates would be opened and the turbines would operate continuously until low tide was reached. Engineers estimate that such a project at Passamaquoddy, which has a 23.2-foot spring tidal rise, would generate huge amounts of useful power. A power project was started by the United States government in the nineteen-thirties, but it was abandoned because of the high cost.

Galápagos Islands

A large archipelago, territory of Ecuador. Location *Pacific Ocean, about 650 miles west of Ecuador.* Area *2,966 square miles.* Map *4, Q7.*

These desolate, fantastic islands, officially known as Archipelago de Colón, home of fantastic creatures, were discovered in 1535 by Fray Tomás de Berlanga, Bishop of Panama. They consist of 13 large and many smaller islands, all of them of volcanic origin. When Bishop Berlanga first saw them, they looked, he thought "as though God had caused it to rain stones," and they were called *Islas de los Galápagos*, Tortoise Islands, from the giant tortoises which crawl over the sharp, sun-heated lava. A later designation for them was *Las Islas Encantadas*, the Enchanted Isles. They were occupied by Ecuador in 1832.

The larger islands of the group include San Cristóbal Island (Chatham Island), Chaves Island (also known as Santa Cruz and Indefatigable Island), Santiago (or San Salvador or James Island), Isabela Island (or Albemarle Island) and Fernandina Island (Narborough). Roughly circular in shape (except for the largest, Isabela), they are unfriendly and almost waterless.

They are famous for an odd reptilian fauna, not only the giant tortoises, familiar in zoos, but giant lizards – the Giant Land Iguanas, which sleep and blink under the prickly-pear bushes (and eat the leaves, thorns and all), and the Giant Marine Iguanas, which feed on seaweed among the surf. Some of the Islands have high craters, rising to about 5,000 feet in their centers. Landscape and reptiles together look like illustrations from some adventure in space travel or like a prehistoric tableau in a museum. But there are more homely animals, too: goats, pigs, donkeys and even cats. They are either survivors of shipwrecks or wild descendants of domestic animals left on the various islands. Sea lions crowd in on the cool Peru or Humboldt Current (which makes the climate temperate).

In 1835 Charles Darwin came to the Galápagos in the *Beagle* and studied the unique fauna. The great Victorian naturalist amused himself by going for Giant Tortoise rides. "I frequently got on their backs," he wrote, "and then giving a few raps on the hinder part of their shells, they would rise up and walk away – but I found it very difficult to keep my balance." Darwin was much amused to see how a Giant Tortoise, whenever he passed, would draw in its head and fall to the ground, "uttering a deep hiss." The tortoises, some of which are believed to be 400 years old, are probably the most long-lived creatures on earth.

Later, in his *Origin of Species*, Darwin declared that his studies on the Galápagos Islands had been the source of his theory of evolution. Since then, many scientists have found the Islands invaluable in the study of evolutionary processes.

The slopes of the volcanic mountains are covered with dense jungle; sugar cane, coffee, yucca, maguey and cattle are raised in modest quantities; exports are lizard skins, salt, sulphur, fish and hides. The waters provide excellent fishing for lobster and tuna.

The population numbers about 1,400, with Charles Island as the main settlement. Many of the Islands are uninhabited. During the Second World War the group served as an important air base, and on Isabela Island, at Villamil, there is an Ecuadorian penal settlement.

Galveston Bay

The center of one of the principal port and industrial regions in the United States. Location *Gulf of Mexico, southern Texas.* Length *About 35 miles.* Maximum width *About 19 miles.* Map *1, A11.*

The entrance to spacious and beautiful Galveston Bay is between the tip of Bolivar Peninsula and the northeastern end of Galveston Island. There are deepwater channels which take ships from the Gulf to the great harbors of Galveston, Texas City and Houston; the Bay is also crossed by the Gulf Intracoastal Waterway. Trinity River is received by its northeastern arm, called Trinity Bay; San Jacinto River flows into the bay of the same name which is the northwestern arm of Galveston Bay. In its eastern part, the Bay is separated from East Bay (about 22 miles long, two to five miles wide) by a series of reefs lying northwest of Bolivar Peninsula; in the southwest, there are links to West Bay (about 20 miles long, three to six miles wide) by various passages which lie between Galveston Island and the mainland.

The city of Galveston is at the eastern end of Galveston Island, at the mouth of the Bay. There are two concrete causeways which connect it with the mainland, both about two miles long. Fronting on the Gulf there is a concrete sea wall, about 7½ miles long, protecting the city from flood.

Through the broad waters of Galveston Bay and along the channels immense quantities of bananas and raw sugar arrive from Latin America; equally large quantities of sulphur, cotton, wheat, flour, metals and sugar are exported. The harbor, fronting on Galveston Channel, stretches for 6½ miles and can accommodate about 100 ocean-going vessels at a time. It is defended by Forts Crockett, San Jacinto and Travis and there is a coast-artillery training center at Camp Wallace, 12 miles from the city. Along the Gulf there is a 32-mile-long bathing beach below the sea wall and a municipal pleasure pier extends into the Gulf.

Galveston Bay and Island were named after Bernardo de Gálvez, the Spanish colonial administrator, about 1782. In 1816 the Island was used by Francisco Javier Mina, a young Spanish soldier fighting on the side of the Mexican revolutionaries, as his headquarters. Later it became a rendezvous of the pirate Jean Lafitte, who remained there with his band until an American warship drove them out about 1821. In 1837 the first settlement from the United States was established. During the Civil War, Galveston was the most important Confederate port on the Gulf. The Federal fleet maintained a blockade in the Gulf throughout the war but the city remained in Confederate hands (except for a few months in 1862–63) until June, 1865. Two naval engagements ended with Confederate victories in Galveston harbor in January, 1861.

In 1900 a West Indian hurricane blew steadily for 18 hours, with a peak velocity of 135 miles an hour, and drove a tidal wave from the Gulf across the city, flooding it to a great depth; more than 5,000 lives were lost and about $17,000,000 worth of property was destroyed. In April, 1947, there was another disaster in the Gulf when a nitrate ship in the harbor of Texas City blew up, destroying most of the city and killing 468 people.

Galway Bay

An inlet on the Atlantic coast of Ireland. Location *Between County Galway and County Clare, Eire.* Dimensions *30 miles long, 23 miles wide (at entrance).* Map *8, B3.*

Great storms come surging often enough into the long inlet on the west coast of Ireland called Galway Bay, an inlet enclosed by Connemara on the north and County Clare on the south. Thirty miles from the sea stands Galway, a sad gray city of many memories; a city which, for all its air of decayed glory, has a strange and haunting beauty. Visitors to the melancholy old sea-port fall quickly under its spell.

In the history of Galway, both the Bay and the city, wind has played a dominant part. Many hundred years ago, sailors discovered that once their ships were clear of Galway Bay, the prevailing west winds would give them a clear run, without any tacking, to southern France or Spain.

There would be nothing like the dreary beating up the Channel which ships bound for London had to go through, and so a flourishing trade grew up with Spain and the Galway merchants prospered.

One of them, James Lynch FitzStephen, Mayor of Galway around 1500, made friends in Cadiz with a wealthy Spanish merchant named Gomez, and when he returned to Galway, he brought with him his new friend's son. Young Gomez seduced the bride of FitzStephen's son, there was a quarrel, and the young Irishman killed his father's guest. The mayor arrested his own son, tried him and condemned him to death; and as there was no hangman who would execute the sentence, he did it himself in a public place, then retired to his house and never left it again.

Even today the old city holds something of the beauty and dignity of Spain. Claddagh, the quarter of Galway where the fisher-folk used to live in their little cabins, was said to be the oldest fishing village in Ireland; a perfectly preserved medieval village. But it has disappeared, having given place to a modern quarter, ugly, but well provided with all the comforts and gadgets which the village lacked before.

Galway city, for all its visible decline, shows signs today of rising again. It has a good golf course, boats can be hired for sailing in the Bay and the salmon fishing in the river is excellent.

The sailing vessel typical of the Bay is the Galway curragh, made of black canvas, 18 feet long by three or four feet wide, usually manned by three or four men who each take a pair of clumsy-looking oars, shaped rather like a spoon that has been cut in half longitudinally; yet these curraghs have been known to brave the great storms roaring into Galway Bay from the west, blotting out the Clare and Connemara mountains with a wall of spray, and often cutting communications between the mainland and Aran for many days at a time. The Galway hooker is a single-masted fishing-smack which is used for shipping horses, cattle, pigs and sheep to and fro. It is also used for bringing turf from Connemara to the offshore islands that have neither turf nor fire-wood; not to mention smuggling poteen to the islands from the illicit stills of Connemara – though officially, these stills no longer exist.

Gibraltar

A British crown colony and naval base. Location *Southwest Europe, at the southern tip of Spain.* Area *2½ square miles.* Map *7, A8.*

The bald limestone head of "The Rock," dominating the western approach to the Mediterranean, must rank among one of the best known sights in the world. From this heavily fortified point, only 8½ miles from the North African coast, British forces have been able to control access to the Mediterranean for over two centuries. The Rock has survived blockade, submarine attack and aerial bombardment during two world wars as resolutely as it survived other famous sieges of the past.

Known to the ancient world as Calpe, Gibraltar has been occupied by Phoenicians, Carthaginians, Romans and Visigoths. Its modern name is derived from the Arabic Jebel-al-Tarik (Tarik's Mount); the Moorish conqueror Tarik captured the Rock in 711 A.D., and was the first to fortify it. The Spanish held it between 1309 and 1333, lost it to the Moors, then regained it in 1462. British and Dutch forces captured it in 1704 during the War of the Spanish Succession, and Sir George Rooke, the British Admiral, took possession of it in the name of Queen Anne. Since that time Gibraltar has remained consistently in British hands, although often besieged and sometimes close to capture – and regularly claimed by Spanish nationalist propaganda.

A well-marked promontory jutting south-by-west into the Mediterranean, its extreme length is only a little over two and a half miles. The Rock rises abruptly from the low, flat ground at its north front in a fine granite wall; its base is partly concealed by a sloping curtain of debris and breccia. The wall culminates at the Rock Gun (1,349 feet); from here the dividing ridge of the promontory extends southward in a sharp, jagged arch with Middle Hill (1,195 feet), Signal Station (1,294 feet), Monkey's Alameda (1,396 feet) and O'Hara's Tower (1,370 feet) as its dominant points. At the last, the ridge is sharply truncated and continues by the well-marked plateau of Windmill Hill and Europa. For most of its length the dividing ridge presents to the east a bold escarpment, mostly inaccessible and

The Rock of Gibraltar

in places almost vertical, with the cliffs having at least a 300- or 400-foot drop and rising to more than 1,000 feet as they approach the sea on the north.

The natural fortress of Gibraltar has been made even more formidable by its many ant-like tunnels and numerous natural caves, with the row upon row of battlements that have been added to its defences from the eighteenth century to the present day.

The town centers around Main Street, a busy thoroughfare which looks like the high street of an English seaside town. The architecture is Victorian. The climate is excellent with fine, dry summers; during the winter the Rock's underground storage tanks, which hold 14,000,000 gallons of water, are replenished by the ample rainfall. A peculiarity of the Rock is the Levanter cloud which gathers over its summit, a damp, gray cloud which occurs when the easterly wind, the Levanter, blows through the Strait.

A free port, where all articles except tobacco and alcohol are sold without duty, Gibraltar has a higher living standard than the surrounding area of southern Spain. Most of the inhabitants are of Genoese or Maltese blood; a rough dialect of Spanish remains the spoken language, and the Spanish atmosphere is heightened by the great many workers who cross the border from La Linea every day to work in the dockyards.

The famous Barbary Apes which live on the Rock were probably introduced by the Moors during the fifteenth century. There is a tradition that as long as they are preserved, Gibraltar will remain secure in British hands. This is a strong enough myth to have inspired a novel by Jules Verne (strongly anti-British) and to have moved Sir Winston Churchill to take immediate steps when, during the Second World War, there was the danger of the apes' extinction. They are all officially enrolled in the army, and have a special N.C.O. in charge of them.

Gilbert Islands

A 400-mile-long chain of 16 atolls. Location *Western central Pacific.* Area *144 square miles.* Map *4, G6–7.*

Sighted by Alvaro Mendana in 1567, the Gilberts were named and explored by Captain Byron in 1764 and declared a British Protectorate in 1892. Since 1915 they have been combined with the Ellice Islands as a Crown Colony.

The Gilbert Islands lie astride the equator, ten of them north of the line – Little Makin, Makin, Marakei, Abaiang, Nikunau, Tarawa, Maiana, Abemama, Kuria and Aranuka – and six, belonging to the Kingsmill Group, lying south of the line – Nonouti, Tabiteuea, Beru, Onotoa, Tamana and Arorae. The capital and port of the colony is Tarawa.

Sir Arthur Grimble, a former Governor, who published his reminiscences in *A Pattern of Islands* in 1955, had nothing but praise for the Islanders.

"The loving-kindness of the. . . Gilbertese towards Europeans," he wrote, "sprang from no feeling of inferiority, but, on the contrary, from a most gracious sense of kinship. Their chief ancestral heroes had been, according to tradition, fair-skinned like ourselves. . . All of these heroic beings. . . were of the red-complexioned, blue-eyed strain called 'The Company of the Tree, the Breed of Matang' . . . When white men were first seen in the Gilbert Islands, nearly 200 years ago. . . the people said, 'Behold, the Breed of Matang is returned to us. Let us receive them as chiefs and brothers among us, lest the Ancestors be shamed.' "

The Gilbertese are Micronesians who grow taro and copra, and have no livestock, but they are expert catchers of octopus and great fishermen.

Good Hope, Cape of

A peninsula at the southern tip of Africa. Location *Southwest Cape Province, South Africa, between Table Bay and False Bay.* Map *10, A10.*

Backed by the looming grandeur of Table Mountain, the Cape of Good Hope juts into the South Atlantic like a giant finger, with a sheer cliff rising to 840 feet at Vasco da Gama Point. To the east of it, past Cape Agulhas, the Indian Ocean begins, and this is the dividing point between two ocean systems, two regions of winds and weather, and two worlds. Westward lies America; eastward India, China and the "Spice Islands."

An Egyptian admiral in the early days of the Egyptian empire is reputed to have rounded the Cape and made his return through the Strait of Gibraltar, but in recorded history the credit for discovering the Cape must certainly be given to the great Portuguese navigators. In 1487 Bartholomew Dias first described to the world the fabulous Table Mountain and its Cape (which he named the "Cape of Storms") where he had erected a pillar – fragments of which remain – to commemorate his passage. In 1497 Vasco da Gama passed south of the Cape on his voyage round the world. From then on the merchant adventurers and sailors of other maritime powers came to know the area, as they voyaged eastward to wrest from the Portuguese their trading monopoly in India.

By the mid-seventeenth century, the Dutch East Indiamen were regularly using Table Bay at the foot of the great mountain as a resting point and repair depot. Out of this grew the Dutch colonial expansion throughout Cape Colony, for the Dutch East India Company was quick to realize that the fertile inland areas would provide a storehouse and victualling point for their fleets. The British conquest of the Cape took place in 1795, when an army was landed with the principal objective of securing it against the French.

Westerly winds prevail over the area and from latitude 35° South an almost continuous passage of low pressure systems give rise to what are known as the "roaring forties." Gales are very common; even in mid-summer, nearly seven days in every month are marked by winds of gale force. In the days of sail, rounding the "Cape of Storms" was no easy business and merchant ships homeward bound from India were often compelled to spend many days tacking back and forth off Good Hope waiting for a favorable wind. It was this, no doubt, that gave rise to the famous legend of "The Flying Dutchman" – the phantom ship reputed to haunt these waters, because her captain had cursed God for failing to send him a fair wind, and was condemned to spend eternity beating back and forth in the stormy water off the Cape.

Heavy and dangerous seas off the Agulhas bank are formidable even for giant modern liners, as they have the undistracted sweep of the whole South Atlantic behind them. But the Cape is not always in an ill mood. On a fine summer day, when the great head of Table Mountain rises in front of the ship's bows and the flying fish are scuttering over the blue sea, only the eternal rhythm of the swell – like a sleeper's deep breathing – exists to remind one that this is the "Cape of Storms" as well as of Good Hope.

Goodwin Sands

A group of dangerous shoals stretching some ten miles. Location *Off the Channel coast of Kent, England.* Map *8, D5.*

The evil reputation of the Goodwins as a destroyer of ships has remained unchallenged for many centuries. It was here that Shakespeare set the shipwreck which destroyed Antonio's fortune in *The Merchant of Venice*, and hardly a year goes by but another broken hulk is added to the thousands which the sands have already claimed.

The Goodwins lie about six miles off the coast of Kent, between the headland of North Foreland and Dover. Their position makes them an inevitable hazard for ships entering the English Channel from the North Sea, or leaving the Thames estuary, bound down-Channel. They resemble a kidney-shaped island hanging off the coast – and this is just what legend holds them to be. They take their name from the eleventh-century Saxon Earl Godwine, among whose land holdings was reputedly an island called Lomea, a few miles off the Kentish coast. It was protected by a sea wall, for the maintenance of which funds were deposited with the abbot of St Augustine, Canterbury. The abbot, so the story goes, diverted these funds, during one of the Earl's absences, into building the massive tower of St Mildred's church, Tenterden. As a result of this, the sea wall broke during a great storm in 1099 and Lomea was overwhelmed. "Tenterden steeple," the saying goes, "was the cause of the Goodwin Sands," and the magnificent church still looks out over the gray broken waters and shoals, a landmark to seafarers.

At low water the shifting muscles of the sands are exposed in several places. They are a desolate sight with the gray North Sea running against them and the water in the channels brownish with stirred-up mud and sand. At high water they are completely covered and only the lightships and bell buoys mark their existence. There are four lightships at the edges of the sands and coastal lights also warn approaching vessels of their proximity. Lifeboat stations on the coast are in constant readiness for rockets or distress signals. In the past several attempts were made to erect a lighthouse in the heart of the sands, but all failed because the shifting bottom makes the erection of piles and foundations impossible.

The Goodwins hold their greatest menace when fog settles over the Channel mouth or when the wild northeaster drives the North Sea before it and the ship running for the English Channel finds the Goodwins under her lee. Once lifted by the wind and high water into the heart of the Goodwins, she will lie there, battered, until the falling tide breaks her back. Modern navigational devices, such as radar and radio beacons, have reduced the number of casualties on the Goodwins. Even so they will always remain a menace to navigation. As a symbol of hopeless endeavor they have given us the old English saying, "to set up shop on Goodwin sands."

Gotland

A large island with many historical monuments. Location *Southeast Sweden, in the Baltic Sea, 50 miles from the Swedish mainland.* Area *1,167 square miles.* Map *8, H3.*

A temperate and mostly fertile island of no great height, with some forests and an equable climate that attracts many visitors in the holiday season, Gotland has a population of about 60,000. Sheep and cattle are reared, and sugar beet and barley are grown for the mainland breweries. It is celebrated as an island of roses, but even more for its numerous medieval churches and especially for its famous walled capital, Visby.

Inhabited since the Stone Age, Gotland was

Part of the city wall of Visby, Gotland

nearly depopulated between 600 and 300 B.C. because of a sudden change in the climate to almost Arctic cold. It became Swedish before 890 A.D. and was converted to Christianity in 1030 by King St Olaf of Norway. In the twelfth century German merchants settled at Visby, and Gotland became the most important northern center of the Hanseatic League; Visby was the principal depot for the products of the eastern Baltic lands and had contacts with Cretan and other ancient Mediterranean civilizations even in remote antiquity. During the Dark Ages it stood at the crossroads of northern and western trade.

Visby is one of the most complete and best preserved of the walled towns of Europe. The towers and their connecting walls surround the city on all but the sea side; the Gothic churches, all disused except the cathedral, most of them roofless but otherwise maintained in repair, preserve its medieval character almost unchanged.

When the Hanseatic merchants raised it to the height of its prosperity, they not only built themselves substantial houses (many of which are still in use), but also devoted part of their profits to the foundation of churches. Then came one of those sudden, unforeseen deflections of trade routes (such as accounted in another part of the world for the eclipse of Petra by Palmyra), which reduced Visby's importance; fires and plagues also reduced its population. In 1362 the island was conquered by Waldemar IV of Denmark; it was returned to the Hanseatic League eight years later, and then became a pirate base. In 1570 the island passed to Denmark but was regained by Sweden in 1645.

Today, Visby is a placid, rose-embowered little cathedral town and summer resort, and Gotland an equally peaceful and attractive island that has not known invasion or war for over three centuries.

Gough Island

A remote volcanic island with large guano deposits.
Location *Tristan da Cunha group, South Atlantic.*
Dimensions *8 miles long, 4 miles wide.* Map 6, *G10.*

Lying 230 miles south-southeast of Tristan da Cunha, on the fringe of the roaring forties, Gough Island is named in error – for the Portuguese had found and charted it as Diego Alvarez island

Atlantic Ocean, the sun over the equat

two centuries before Captain Gough claimed its discovery. From the sea, its outstanding features are its startlingly rugged terrain – it rises to 2,986 feet – and its evergreen vegetation.

Captain Peter Heywood, R. N., who visited it in 1811, found a party of sealers on it "in a most ragged plight, full of grease and filth and clothed chiefly in seal skins." Later visitors included diamond prospectors, Antarctic explorers, whalers and lobster fishermen who all found the beaches notoriously difficult to land on. In 1938 a naval party struggled ashore from a wrecked boat to claim the Island as a dependency of St Helena, and in 1955–56 a British scientific expedition made the first accurate map and set up a weather station which is now maintained by South Africa.

Like all true oceanic islands, Gough has few varieties of animals and plants; but some of Gough's fauna, including a flightless moorhen, are found nowhere else in the world. Sea-birds, including penguins and three species of albatross, breed there in vast numbers, and the beaches are the home of over half the known world-population of one of the rarest southern fur-seals.

Gozo

The second largest of the Maltese Islands. Location *Mediterranean, about two miles off the northwest tip of Malta.* Area *25.89 square miles.* Map *9, D10.*

Although of the same geological construction as Malta, and separated from the larger island only by a narrow strait, Gozo retains a completely individual character. In appearance the two islands are very similar, with prevailing limestone and sandstone characteristics, but while Malta, with its harbor dockyard and light industries, is largely industrial, Gozo is agricultural.

The fields of Gozo are miniature, each bounded by its wall, and the small villages, with their box-shaped, flat-roofed houses, remind one of North Africa. The capital, Victoria or Rabat, is in the center of the island on a steep conical hill. The streets are narrow and the clatter of carts carrying country produce, together with the incessant pealing of church bells, give the town a medieval air. For all the smallness of the island, it is said that some of the villagers in the center have never seen the sea. Their quiet lives are bounded by their homes, their small fields, the local church and the village store. Goats wander through the streets, and vines trained over backyards or café entrances provide most of the shade, for there are few trees.

In the sixteenth century, Gozo was ravaged by the African Arabs, and there are clear traces of African blood in many of the 28,000 inhabitants. The Maltese language is spoken but there are some differences in the dialect. The Gozitans are often mentioned by the Maltese in terms that are generally used by the city dweller to describe the country peasant. Industrious and kindly, the Gozitans are fine fishermen and boat builders. A type of double-ended fishing boat built here is unique in the Mediterranean. It has swift, clean lines and is rigged with twin lateen sails.

Grand Banks

An immense submarine plateau. Location *Off southeast Newfoundland.* Dimensions *420 miles from east to west and 350 miles from north to south.* Maximum depth *About 600 feet.* Map *6, D2.*

A vast area of submerged highlands, the Grand Banks are the crossroads of two great ocean currents – the Gulf Stream, which crosses the eastern edge of the Banks, and the Labrador Current, which envelops the greater part of the plateau. Because of this, the Banks are one of the greatest fishing grounds in the world, particularly for cod. With a depth of 150–600 feet, and a number of shoals where the range is 10–60 feet, the Grand Banks have attracted fishing fleets for almost 300 years, and today American, Canadian, British, French and Scandinavian trawlers and deep-sea fishing vessels meet regularly in these waters.

These meetings have not always been peaceful, for arguments between Britain and France poisoned relations between the two countries for many years. It was not until 1904 that a Franco-British agreement was reached under which Britain paid compensation to some French citizens and made territorial concessions to France in Africa. Similar disputes also occurred between the United States, Britain and Canada; there

aves breaking on the Atlantic coast of Morocco

were times when small and undeclared hostilities were fairly regular over the Banks, with casualties in men and ships. Arbitration, however, settled the controversies before the First World War.

In 1929 a devastating submarine earthquake occurred in the Grand Banks which broke the transatlantic cables. Oceanographers are still arguing about what exactly happened. One theory maintains that after the earthquake huge quantities of slope sediments moved like a wave down the steep undersea precipices and that this movement was of such speed and violence that it changed the configuration of several hundred square miles of the ocean bed. The tidal waves accompanying the earthquake moved in on Burin Peninsula on the south coast of Newfoundland, rising to 15 feet. As Francis P. Shepard pointed out, if such a wave occurred on Long Island or the east coast of Britain, its effect would be almost as bad as that of a hydrogen bomb. The cable breaks that accompanied the Grand Banks earthquake were approximately in line with the great trough emerging from Cabot Strait, and were caused by a combination of spontaneous liquefaction of submarine sediments, landslides or turbidity currents.

Though the Grand Banks have been cleft and shattered by this great earthquake, they still remain valuable fishing grounds. The northeastern section is one of the world's most notorious fog fields. The Labrador Current carries over them hundreds of icebergs each year which are a considerable navigational hazard.

Great Barrier Reef

The largest coral reef in the world. Location *Coral Sea, off the east coast of Australia.* Length *1,250 miles.* Map *4, E8.*

The immense stretch of the Great Barrier Reef extends southeast from the New Guinea coast on the Torres Strait to Swains Reef near the Tropic of Capricorn. Sometimes it runs near to the coast, in other places (as in the south) it is 150 miles from the land. Enclosing a multitude of minor reefs and groups of atolls, it is broken by many passages – some of them shallow, treacherous channels 10–100 miles wide – including the Great Northeast Channel, Trinity Opening and Flinders Passage. There are several islands included within the Reef – the Cumberland, Northumberland and Palm groups, with the individual islands of Hinchinbrook and Whitsunday – and there are many tourist resorts.

When Captain Cook explored the coast of Australia, the existence of the great Reef was not even suspected. He found himself caught in a trap of these partly submerged, scattered specks of dry land, and it took him some time to find, just north of Lizard Island, what is still known as

A coral pool in the Great Barrier Reef

Cook's Passage, before he sailed at last the deep waters lying east of the Coral Sea.

Ever since Cook's day, men have marveled at the beauty and variety of the Great Barrier Reef's almost endless underwater landscape. T. C Roughley, an Australian writer, described it in these glowing terms: "As we gaze into the cool green light of the liquid depths we are transported into a new world and we fairly gasp with wonder at the magnificence of the scene below us. Here are coral gardens that might have been planted and tended by fairies, so strangely different are they from the gardens of our previous experience. Delicate, finely branched coral trees and shrubs, corals like giant mushrooms, corals resembling enormous fans, corals arranged in tiers like a Buddhist temple, coral grottoes, coral caves, corals infinite in their variety, pass by as we slowly and quietly move over the surface. The shape and color are limitless. . ."

The edge of the Reef is a solid platform, hard, unyielding and for the most part elevated and flat. Most of the coral is alive but stunted in its growth, partly because of its elevation and partly because of the swift-running water that passes over it at the ebb and flow of the tide. Along the Reef's edge, the flat surface is broken by many coral pools, some small, others with a diameter of many yards and a depth of 10–12 feet. The bottom is usually composed of sand or sandy-colored coral rock. Fishes of vivid colors and strange patterns, clams and beche-de-mer are plentiful in these pools; so are the Alconarians or "soft" corals – large, irregularly shaped masses with soft leathery or rubbery textures, closely related to the true or "hard" corals but without the faculty of secreting lime.

The western boundary of the Great Barrier Reef is formed by innumerable rocky islands; it is between these and the mainland that the only safe passage for ships lies. They form a chain almost as continuous as the reefs of the outer barrier. Their size and height vary considerably. In the Whitsunday Passage some are several miles long and may rise to a height of nearly 1,500 feet; in the Hinchinbrook Passage they are even larger and grander. The lofty peaks of wild, mysterious Hinchinbrook Island are over 3,000 feet high and the island itself is nearly 30 miles long. Most of these mainland islands are bordered by fringing reefs of varying extent and are favorite tourist resorts.

The origin of this enormous coral reef began with the subsiding of the Queensland coast, which had originally extended farther east than today, especially in the southern part. It was flat or undulating country with a range of hills and lofty peaks a few miles to the east of the present coastline. As this area sank, the sea swept over it and killed all vegetation. It then formed the bottom of a shallow sea and the tops of the highest hills projected above the level of the water as islands. The shallow depth and the warm water favored the growth of reef-building corals, which flourished best in the most favorable conditions on the eastern side of the shallow ledge, where the water was clearer and purer. As the floor of the sea continued to subside, it became almost a race – the coral building upwards and the bottom beneath it sinking. The coral won.

Most of the reefs still remain below the surface but they continue to rise and if present-day weather conditions persist long enough (and the sea floor does not sink any more rapidly) the Great Barrier Reef – or the part that forms the outer barrier – will in ages to come form a long, continuous island.

Greenland

The largest island in the world. Location *Off northeast North America.* Area *840,000 square miles.* Map *5, A11–D9.*

Discovered about 876 A.D. by Gunnbjorn, an Icelander, it was called "Greenland" by Eric the Red, who followed him – a euphemistic name, designed to attract settlers. In 985, 300 people left Iceland and built their houses among the fjords, just west of Cape Farewell (the southern tip), facing Labrador. The chief settlements were Eystribygd, a scattering of farms on low pastureland around Igaliko Fjord (then called Gardar), and Vestribygd, a little farther up the coast.

By the middle of the fourteenth century there were 280 farms and several thousand people. They came under the domination of Norway but had their own parliament or *Althing* which met once a year at Eystribygd where their cathedral

Aerial view of pack ice off the coast of Greenland

(a small but fine red sandstone building dedicated to St Nicholas), a Benedictine nunnery and an Augustinian monastery also stood.

The climate was too cold for growing cereals, though hay and root crops were cultivated. For meat, milk and cheese they raised cattle; for fuel they gathered driftwood or used animal oil. For grain and wood, for building their long boats, they depended on ships from Iceland and Norway. When war and storms interrupted their supplies, they endured lean years. Then the climate began to grow colder; perhaps Eskimos moved south, harrying the settlers. About 1325 Vestribygd was abandoned; about a century and a half later, Eystribygd. For a long while there were few or no supply ships – and when they sailed again, in 1585, they found no one. The farms were abandoned, their inhabitants dead, or fled. Further expeditions searched for survivors or their descendants in 1606, 1636, 1654 and 1670, but without success.

From about 1590 whale fisheries were established on the coast by the English and the Dutch, but resettlement began only in 1721 with the arrival of Hans Egede, a Danish missionary, and his son. They founded Godthaab (Good Hope), the present capital (population about 1,500), six years later. Direct Danish control was established in 1729.

Today, the population of about 25,000 consists largely of Eskimos, with a few hundred Danes. Whaling, sealing, hunting, fishing and cryolite mining (the largest cryolite mine in the world is at Ivigtut) are the chief occupations and sources of income, apart from the presence of several important United States air bases and weather stations.

The interior of the country was first visited by Fridtjof Nansen, who made an east-west crossing in 1888. Commodore Peary's explorations from 1892 onwards probed farther north; T. C. Chamberlin, the geologist who accompanied him, found fossil figs and magnolias in beds under the ice, proving that the land had once enjoyed a subtropical climate. Today, seven eighths of its total area are covered by a vast ice-sheet, pierced round the rim by the summits of the Coastal Mountains. In the center the ice is 8,000–9,000 feet thick; its base, measured by echo-soundings, is sometimes below sea level, so that Greenland may, in fact, be an assembly of separate islands. At the edges the ice-sheet descends to the sea in huge glaciers from which vast numbers of icebergs regularly split off, menaces to North Atlantic shipping. Greenland is continually being probed by glaciological and meteorological expeditions, seeking to unravel the problems of the world's climate and weather – on which the great icecap has an important effect. Although the world's climate is growing warmer, snowfall is so great that the ice is still increasing in thickness.

There is some cultivation in the grassy meadows of the more sheltered southern shores and valleys of Greenland. There, amid stunted birch, alder and pine, potatoes have been raised successfully, turnips reach the size of pigeons' eggs, and cabbages of tennis balls. Around the old Viking farms a few introduced European plants still grow.

Guadeloupe

Twin islands, an overseas department of France. Location *Leeward Islands, West Indies.* Area *687.26 square miles.* Map *2, H3.*

The twin islands of Guadeloupe rise to 4,869 feet in the dormant volcano of Soufrière on Basse-Terre, the western of the twins; Grande-Terre, to the east, is composed of coral limestone and does not exceed 400 feet in height. Basse-Terre is cooler, rugged and well-forested with a higher rainfall than its companion and numerous streams. Bananas, coffee, sugar, cacao and vanilla are the crops on the many small farms concentrated in the coastal areas. Grande-Terre, generally drier, produces sugar and rum. The two are separated by the narrow Rivière Salée channel.

There are various smaller islands which form part of the Guadeloupe group: Marie-Galante, to the southeast, grows sugar; Désirade lies to the south, Les Saintes to the southwest; Saint-Barthélemy and the northern section of Saint Martin to the northwest. The climate is generally healthy and tempered by the trade winds, though hurricanes occur at intervals. Basse-Terre is the most picturesque of the group and the capital is situated on it. There are several thermal springs. The center of Grand-Terre is Pointe-à-Pitre with its sugar mills and rum distilleries. The total population is almost 300,000; on the larger islands it is almost entirely mulatto, while the smaller ones are inhabited by Normans and Bretons.

Guadeloupe was discovered in 1493 by Columbus, who named it after the Holy Virgin of Guadeloupe in Estremadura. The Spanish abandoned it in 1603 without attempting to establish a colony; some 30 years later the French started settlements. Though there have been many British attacks (and several captures), Guadeloupe has been uninterruptedly under French sovereignty since 1816 – with the exception of the southern half of Saint Martin, which has been Dutch since 1648.

The official language is French with a local *patois*; most of the people are Roman Catholic.

Guinea, Gulf of

A wide inlet of the Atlantic. Location *Atlantic Ocean, off West African coast.* Map *6, H6.*

Until fairly recently, the Gulf of Guinea and its coastal area had very flexible geographical limits. Various writers at different periods applied the name both to the large section of the western coast region of Equatorial Africa and to the Gulf formed by the huge bend of the coast swinging first east and then south.

In the widest sense of the name, the Gulf extended from Gambia to Cape Negro with a southern and a northern section. Southern Guinea included the coasts of Gabon and Loango and the Portuguese possessions on the southwest coast; northern Guinea stretched from the Casamance River and included the Niger Delta. In a more restricted use of the name, the Gulf extended from Cape Palmas on the Liberian coast to French Equatorial Africa. There was a time when Guinea was supposed to begin as far north as Cape Nun, opposite the Canary Islands; Gomes Azurara, a Portuguese historian of the fifteenth century, set the boundary as far north as Senegal.

The name itself probably derives from Ghana, or Ghanata, the oldest known state of the western Sudan – a name which has recently been revived for the new Republic of what was once known as the Gold Coast. The name Guinea as applied to the coast and the Gulf appeared on maps of the middle of the fourteenth century, but did not come into general use until about 150 years later.

Flanking the huge Niger Delta near the head of the Gulf are the bights of Benin (on the west) and of Biafra (on the east).

The islands of the Gulf include Fernando Po and Annobón, which are Spanish, and São Tomé and Principe, which are Portuguese possessions. Apart from the immense Niger Delta, the Cameroon, the Ogooué and the Volta rivers discharge their waters into the Gulf.

The coastline of the Gulf is generally low, so that navigators distinguish it only when quite close by its fringe of mangrove trees. The principal exception is in the Bight of Biafra, where the coast is high and bold, with the Cameroon Mountains in the background; there is also some high land at Sierra Leone. In many places the flat, level area continues for 30–50 miles inland.

Vegetation is rich and varied, with the palm-oil tree dominant. The fauna, however reduced by indiscriminate slaughter, is still the typical and beautiful range of African animals. The inhabitants are all of true Negro stock with enclaves of Indian immigrants.

The various sections of the Gulf coast were given different names by the early traders according to their main products. The Grain Coast which stretched from Sierra Leone 500 miles eastwards to Cape Palmas was so called because of the various grains of paradise, Guinea pepper and melegueta, all seeds of different plants of a pepper-like character. Occasionally it was also called Windy or Windward coast, as short but destructive hurricanes were frequent throughout the year. Today, this section of the Gulf coast is shared by the independent republic of Liberia and by Sierra Leone.

The Ivory Coast extended from Cape Palmas westwards and was named after the huge quantities of ivory exported from it. Formerly a French colony, the Ivory Coast is now an autonomous republic within the French Overseas Community.

East of the Ivory Coast were the Gold and Slave Coast, also called after their main products – the slave coast for many centuries exporting thousands of kidnapped Africans until the inhuman traffic was stopped in the nineteenth century. Today the coasts of the Gulf in this section belong to Ghana, Togoland (a former French Trust Territory), the Republic of Dahomey (within the French Commonwealth) and Nigeria. The Niger Delta was for long known as the Oil Rivers.

Only two regions of the coast ever bore officially the name of Guinea – the Portuguese and former French colonies north of Sierra Leone. Of these, Guinea is an independent republic, having left the French community in 1958; Portuguese Guinea remains a troubled colonial area surrounded by the new African states.

The southern section of the Gulf of Guinea is the coastline of the former French Equatorial Africa, with the Spanish enclave of Rio Muni between Cameroun and Gabon.

There has been much argument about the first discovery and exploration of the Gulf of Guinea and its coastline. Two Genoese, Ugolino and Guido de Vivaldo, with Tedisio Doria and others, equipped two galleys and sailed south along the African coast in 1291; but nothing is known of their voyage, except that they passed Cape Nun. In 1346 a Catalan expedition set out for the "river of gold" on the Guinea coast and disappeared. The French sent out several expeditions from Dieppe between 1364 and 1410; but it was the consecutive efforts of the sailors employed by Prince Henry the Navigator of Portugal – Gil Eannes, Diniz Diaz, Nuno Trisam, Alvaro Fernandez, Diego Gomez and others – that made the coast known as far as Gambia. By the end of the fifteenth century the whole region was familiar to Europeans.

The Gulf of Guinea has given its name to a British gold coin, first minted in 1663 from gold imported from the Guinea coast, and to "Guinea-worm," an unpleasant parasitic disease.

Gulf Stream

The largest of the great oceanic warm current systems.
Location *North Atlantic Ocean, from the Gulf of Mexico to the British Isles and the coasts of Europe.*
Map *6, B3–D2.*

First observed by Ponce de León in 1513, the Gulf Stream presented to the early navigators not only a mystery but something of a terror. Once in its waters, the sailor found that the temperature suddenly rose, the sea in places almost seemed to steam, electrical storms were sudden and violent and the golden-yellow gulf-weed gave rise to many legends of ships trapped forever in a region of breathless heat. For centuries the origins of the Stream were obscure.

It was not until the nineteenth century that scientific investigation of the Atlantic and its currents was first undertaken – and even today there still remain many problems.

The Gulf Stream is caused primarily by the Atlantic trade winds, which blow in a more or less steady direction from the Azores and the Cape Verde Islands towards the coastline of America. Between latitudes 20° North and 5° South, year in, year out, there is a vast bulk of water steadily moving westward. When it reaches the American coastline, this water becomes banked up in the Caribbean sea and is then deflected northward by the formation of the land. (It was the age-long effect of the Gulf Stream that shaped the capes on the Atlantic coast of America, notably Cape Canaveral, Cape Fear and Cape Hatteras.)

Initially, the Gulf Stream is narrow and deep with a speed of 3–4 knots, so that it cannot be ignored by the navigators even of modern high-powered vessels. It is easy to see why, in the days of sailing ships, captains and crews became desperate at their slowness when they were trying to beat against the Stream.

Off the Florida coast, where the Stream turns northward along the 100-fathom line towards Cape Hatteras, it is clearly marked. During the day a deepening in the color of the water is visible and there is an appreciable rise in temperature; at night the sea is rich in phosphorescence and the sudden Gulf Stream thunderstorms sparkle like fireworks.

North of Cape Hatteras, however, the Gulf Stream begins to leave the 100-fathom line and gradually turns eastward into the ocean, south of the Georges and Nova Scotia banks. The inner edge, south of Cape Hatteras, gradually becomes the northern edge, north and east of that cape. This edge is relatively sharply defined throughout the year, because along it the cold water of the Labrador Current converges.

East of the forty-sixth meridian the Gulf Stream is no longer a well-defined current. It widens and weakens by fanning out along the east side of the Great Banks. This wide north-easterly and easterly flow is directed across the Atlantic towards the British Isles and the adjacent European coasts, and is known as the North Atlantic Current.

One of the most interesting areas of the Stream is to be found in the Atlantic north of the Bermudas, where the Sargasso Sea with its mysterious weed occurs.

Gulf Stream Counter Current

A counter-current below the level of the Gulf Stream.
Location *North Atlantic Ocean.* Map *6, B3–D2*

It was in 1955 that Henry Stommel announced his theory that a strong southward-moving current must exist under the Gulf Stream. Stommel's theory, developed since the Second World War, was based on the assumption that circulation in the depths of the oceans is *not* caused mainly by the winds but by density differences which, in turn, are caused by differences in temperature and salinity. As for the Gulf Stream, one of the most powerful of the wind-driven currents, it had long been supposed that the influence of the wind was felt all the way to the bottom. Stommel's theory seemed to fly in the face of common sense – yet dramatic confirmation of it came from the ocean itself.

Dr Alan Faller had tested Stommel's idea in the laboratory, using ingenious rotating ocean models which were originally designed by Dr William von Arx. These are essentially large tubs – or segments of them – rotated to simulate the earth's spinning, heated and cooled in the appropriate places to simulate the heat balance of our planet. In one elaborate model, wooden blocks cut in the shape of the major continents can be placed on the tub bottom. In smaller versions, the land barriers are simulated by simple straight walls. By using colored liquids, currents can be traced in these models.

Dr Faller's tests seemed to bear out Stommel's ideas. But it was necessary to trace the currents in the oceans themselves. Dr John B. Swallow, of the National Institute of Oceanography in Great Britain, had long been occupied with the problem of measuring large-scale deep currents directly – for which oceanographers needed something like the wind-tracking balloons of the meteorologists. Dr Swallow developed such an instrument in time to test Stommel's theory on a joint American-British cruise which was made in March and April 1957, in preparation for the International Geophysical Year.

Dr Swallow's undersea "weather balloon" is a neutrally buoyant float, a kind of aluminium tube about ten feet long, which carries weights, batteries and a sound generator that emits a clearly recognisable "ping." By adding the right number of small weights, the buoy can be made to float at any desired depth, where it drifts freely along with the current, sending out "pings" by which a listener on the surface can track it.

Swallow dropped his instrument deep into the waters of the Gulf Stream off the Blake Plateau and followed it on the surface in the British research ship *Discovery II*. At the same time, L. V. Worthington, in the American research ship *Atlantis*, accurately traced the position of the Gulf Stream in the Woods Hole area. In all, seven buoys were released at various times. They all moved south at depths between 6,600 and 9,800 feet. Stommel's counter-current had been established beyond doubt – the Gulf Stream Counter Current, one of the broad diffuse flows that turn into strong currents along the western boundaries of the major oceans.

Hainan

The second largest island off the Chinese mainland, with a population of about 3,000,000. Location *South China Sea, east of the Gulf of Tonkin.* Area *13,000 square miles.* Map *4, B4.*

Hainan, 185 miles long and 100 miles wide, is geologically an extension of the southeast Kwangshi hills, parted only by the shallow Hainan Strait (10–15 miles wide) from the Luichow Peninsula of the mainland. The southern part of the island is mountainous and forested, rising to just under 6,000 feet in the densely forested Li-mu Mountains, named after the Li tribes that inhabit them. The northern part is a low plain where the majority of the Chinese settlements and farms are found.

The tropical monsoon climate permits the cultivation of cocoa, coffee, rubber, sugar cane and tobacco. Along the southern shore, tropical woods and coconuts grow. The interior is rich in minerals including tin, tungsten and gold-copper ores; but above all, large deposits of high-quality iron ore in the southwest. These were originally developed by the Japanese, and are reached by a narrow-gauge railway; the mining centers are at Tientu and Shekluk (Shihlu). Industry is insignificant on the island, whose agriculture supports only about one third as many people as Formosa. A highway circles the island, linking the chief towns along the coast. The principal ports are Hoihow (for Kungshan on the Hainan Strait) and Yulin, which is an important naval base, strategically situated at the southern end of the island and connected with the iron mines.

For many centuries Hainan was used as a sort of Chinese Siberia, to which many political exiles were banished. To the sophisticated mainlander, Hainan was purgatory or hell, peopled by savages, a place of suffering and repentance. Plagued with malaria and leprosy, the exiles watched their flimsy houses moulder in the heavy mists that still shroud the land in January and February, or under the pounding summer rains.

Yet a few found something to admire in the beauty of the ferns and orchids hung profusely in the trees, and in the year-round plentiful fruit – and, indeed, some of Hainan's natural resources were keenly sought after on the mainland. The rare "Chen-Hsiang" tree was said to ward off cholera and malaria when worn as a bracelet, and fragments of it were sent in tribute to the Emperor. The fat of the great 30-foot pythons was exported as a valuable medicine, while their flesh was reserved for gourmets. The "wicked" pangolin (an ant-eater resembling an armadillo), reputed to burrow into graves, was valued highly for its scales, which, cooked in butter or vinegar, cured deafness and drove off ogres from haunted women.

The tattooed Li, the natives of the island, were considered half-animal, and their 20 tribes received such names as "Dog-feet Li," "Head-shaving Li," "Pig-iron Li." These primitive aboriginals today make up a sixth of the population and, in spite of the Communist regime, have retained many of their old customs and dialects. Polynesian in appearance, they worship neither idols nor ancestors but invest every object with a demon, some of which frown on the smallest dishonesty. Debts, recorded on a notched bamboo, are inherited and may be paid centuries after they were incurred.

Hainan has been under Chinese control since 110 B.C. It was fully incorporated into China under the Mongol Yuan dynasty (1280–1368) and became part of Kwantung in the late fourteenth century.

Hatteras, Cape

A famous hazard to shipping. Location *Between the Atlantic and Pamlico Sound, North Carolina.* Map *4, Q3.*

The tallest lighthouse on the Atlantic seaboard, standing 193 feet high, warns the mariner bound for America that he is approaching Cape Hatteras. The light stands on an island at the tip of the cays which frame the inland waterways of Carolina.

Cape Hatteras is important to navigators because at this point the waters of the Gulf Stream begin to leave the 100-fathom line along the American continent and turn eastward into the Atlantic Ocean. During the day the track of the Stream is clearly visible, for the water assumes a different color, the temperature rises and bundles of yellow gulf-weed mark the path of the warm current. Owing to the change of atmosphere and the passage of fronts of cold air over the warm stream, electrical storms are frequent. It is not these, however, which have for centuries given Cape Hatteras its reputation as "the Graveyard of the Atlantic," but the heavy fogs associated with the area. As the Gulf Stream bends eastwards off Cape Hatteras it is met by a cold current flowing down from the north – the Labrador Current. The definition between these two streams is clearly marked, and along the northern edge of the Gulf Stream, where they meet, dense fogs are formed by the juxtaposition of the warm and cold waters.

Hawaiian Islands

A group of 20 islands, the fiftieth state of the United States of America. Location *North Pacific, the largest and most northerly Polynesian group.* Area *6,420 square miles.* Map *4, H4–K5.*

Of the 20 Hawaiian Islands, eight are mountainous, volcanic and inhabited. These are Hawaii (the largest of the group), Oahu, Maui, Kauai, Molokai, Lanai, Niihau and Kahoolawe. The remaining 12 are uninhabited coral atolls – one of which, Laysan, 1¾ square miles, supports the world's largest bird colony: recently 10,000,000 birds were recorded on Laysan in a single season.

Hawaii, 90 by 75 miles, contains two thirds of the entire land area of the group and is dominated by the three volcanoes of Mauna Loa (13,675 feet), Mauna Kea (13,825 feet) and Hualalai (8,275 feet). It has a climate which ranges from tropical at the coast, through subtropical fern and bamboo forests, to the icy chill of the summits and their lava deserts. The world's highest annual rainfall, 489 inches, is on Mount Waialeale (5,080 feet) on the island of Kauai. The capital, Honolulu (population 307,000), is on the central island, Oahu. Nearby is the famous naval base of Pearl Harbor where, on the "day of infamy," December 7, 1941, the Japanese attack on the United States began.

The eighteenth-century followers of Rousseau imagined the little-known islands of Polynesia to be the home of savages both noble and equal. In fact, the society of the Pacific Islands, and in particular of Tahiti and Hawaii, was based on one of the most highly organized systems of aristocracy in history.

Once a chief's primacy had been established – by recalling the seniority of his ancestors for the previous 30 or so generations – he was treated with religious deference and failure to comply with court etiquette led to summary execution. When kings inspected the interior of a visiting ship, their followers immediately dived overboard to avoid standing above his head. So holy was the chief that when lowered from the back of an attendant even the ground he touched thereby became taboo and thenceforth it was barred from cultivation. Hawaiian monarchs, indeed, were so holy that they were not even allowed to feed themselves.

This spiritual power rested on a supernatural force called *mana* which was inherited from both parents and so doubled in each new generation. As the son thus had more *mana* than the sire, he inherited his throne at birth and thereafter his father acted only as regent. An American anthropologist records that, by placing a taboo on his own home, an eight-year-old dispossessed his parents, who were forced to camp out until he relented. Such care was taken to maintain and improve the noble stock that the highest families became a distinct race, physically larger and mentally more alert than their subjects. They were carried everywhere on the backs of attendants, from exercise to meals, from meals to massages (or *lomi-lomi*, a peculiarly luxurious combination of kneading and stretching, joint-cracking and shampooing). Or they reclined on mats, secure in the knowledge that even in their heaven there were sharp class distinctions.

Among the many islands of Hawaii war was almost continuous, played as a chivalrous game rather than fought, and usually for some quite trivial object. Respite was given to an enemy to regroup his forces and food brought to the beleaguered so that they might continue to fight. Not until 1795 were the Islands united under one rule – by a young warrior chief named Kamehameha who became a legendary figure for his courage and generosity. An enemy who tried to kill him with a canoe paddle was pardoned and the law of "the broken paddle" established for the protection of the weak. However, it was said that Kamehameha's conquests were aided by the guns of "foreigners."

During the first decade of the nineteenth century there were about 60 resident whites in Oahu, including half a dozen escaped convicts. While they behaved, they were treated as chiefs and made themselves useful as carpenters, masons and blacksmiths. During the nineteenth century the influx of settlers increased and with them came European ideas of property, particularly when sugar became an important cash crop, controlled from New England. In 1893 Liluokalani, the last Queen, was deposed and a republic proclaimed; and in 1898 the Islands were formally annexed by the United States. In 1960 Hawaii achieved full equality in the Union, becoming the fiftieth state.

Today, only 17 per cent of the total population of 576,000 is of pure or part native Hawaiian descent. The ancient ceremony of placing *leis* around the visitor's neck and the *hula* dancers have been put into the service of tourism and commercialized. Yet anthropologists report that the hereditary chiefs can still recite their vast genealogical rolls, stretching far back into misty medieval times, even to the days before the great ocean-going canoes brought their ancestors to the Islands. And visitors who enjoy the surf and sand of Waikiki Beach, attend native-style feasts or explore the coral atolls do not resent the mixture of old and new.

Hebrides

A group of about 500 islands, divided into the Outer and Inner Hebrides. Location *Off the west coast of Scotland.* Area *About 3,000 square miles.* Map *7, D3.*

It is not easy to explain why Scotsmen – and even strangers – are so strongly moved by the distant thin gray pencil-line of the Outer Hebrides across the Minch, the strait which – with the Little Minch and the Sea of the Hebrides – separates the two groups of the archipelago. There is little enough in the somber landscape of Harrisonian gneiss, the oldest rock in the world, to arouse enthusiasm. Neither the kelp industry nor the architecture of the huddled villages have the true romantic appeal. Both James VI (in the sixteenth century) and Lord Levershulme (the industrial magnate, in the nineteenth) received dusty answers when they tried to raise the standard of living in the islands – by imposing their own ideas. Yet these islands are the homeland to which the Scottish emigrant's thoughts turn persistently. They nourish the memory of Bonnie Prince Charlie, playing a desperate game of tag with the redcoats; not (in spite of legend) always welcomed, yet never betrayed. Their economy was for centuries most precarious – yet strangely satisfying. And their isolation made them, until after the Second World War, an ideal refuge for escapists.

The exact definition of the Hebrides has varied; the term was once used to include all the islands off the west coast. Today, the Inner Hebrides consist of Islay, Skye, Mull, Jura, Coll, Colonsay, Rum, Eigg, Tiree, Lismore and Ulva. The Outer Hebrides run in a long chain from the Butt of Lewis in the north to Barra Head, 130 miles to the south: the group, collectively known as the Long Island, comprises about 100 inhabited islands. The most important is Lewis which, together with its southern extension of Harris, runs for nearly 60 miles north and south. Others in the group are North Uist, Benbecula, South Uist, Barra, the Flannan Isles and St Kilda.

The Outer Hebrides are barren, mostly treeless, and the gray gneiss predominates. On Harris, however, craggy if undistinguished hills rise to more than 2,000 feet, while at places the landscape is unexpectedly transformed by yellow sands and blue sea into almost Mediterranean brilliance. Great cloudscapes arch over it; the steady beat of the Atlantic is everywhere; and the etched line of Scottish mainland hills to the east seems to belong to another world.

Historically, this is a landscape of lost causes and stubborn but often hopeless loyalties. There are still echoes of the summer's day in 1745 when Charles Edward Stuart, the Young Pretender, stepped ashore on Eriskay, the small island off South Uist. The pink convulvulus, first planted (according to legend) following his landing, still grows here; and, also according to legend, still persistently refuses to grow elsewhere.

The Hebrides are rich with relics of the last desperate stages of the adventure that followed; not least with those of Flora Macdonald, who helped Bonnie Prince Charlie, after he was defeated at Culloden, to escape finally "over the sea to Skye."

Long before that time, the Hebrides were ruled by the "Lord of the Isles," a title now held by the heir to the British throne. His dominion followed the retreat of the Norsemen in the thirteenth century after some 500 years of rule over the *Sudreyjar* – the Southern Isles, so called in contrast to the Orkneys and Shetlands. The memory of those days still remains in the title of the Anglican bishop of Sodor and Man, for the Sudreyjar were Latinized in the Dark Ages as the *Sodorenses*.

Herring fishing and the manufacture of Harris tweed are the two main occupations of the Hebrideans. Both are centered on Stornoway on the east coast of Lewis – the largest town in the Hebrides, with a population of nearly 4,000.

Less than 20 miles from Stornoway lies the most important single feature of the Hebrides; the "Stonehenge of Scotland," the great group of standing stones of Callanish – stone circles, avenues, cairns and a multiplicity of archeological relics, many of which still await investigation.

Linked to the mainland by a number of air services – a natural development of wartime activity, which brought the Hebrides into a front-line position in the battle of the Atlantic – the islands have physically lost much of the remoteness which for centuries distinguished them.

Helgoland, *or* Heligoland

A North Sea island, formerly an important naval base. Location *North Frisian group, northwest Germany.* Area *150 acres.* Map *7, E5.*

Set in the middle of the shallow Helgoland Bight, the red sandstone mass of the island with its adjoining strip of white sand dunes is lashed by North Sea gales in winter and for much of the year is shrouded in mist and rain. The island's exposure to the elements may have had something to do with its choice as the site of a temple to Forseti, a Norse god of justice, and later as a shrine to Hertha, a fertility goddess, to which

The rugged coast of Helgoland

pilgrimages were made by the Angles of the mainland. The name of the island is probably derived from *Heiliges Land* (holy land): its inhabitants were converted by St Willibrord in the seventh century.

Throughout most of its later history Helgoland was associated with the dukedom of Schleswig-Holstein. In 1807 it was occupied by the British; a formal cession was made in 1814. In 1890 it was handed over to Germany in exchange for Zanzibar, as a move to limit German colonial expansion in East Africa. This was an unpopular transaction – both among the Germans, who failed to appreciate the strategic importance of Helgoland, and among the British, who were ignorant of the economic wealth of Zanzibar.

Helgoland became an important fortified German base during the First World War, was demilitarized under the Versailles Treaty, re-fortified by the Nazis in 1935, used as a U-boat base in the Second World War and in consequence heavily bombed by the R.A.F. After 1945 the 2,000 inhabitants – mostly Frisian fishermen – were transferred to the mainland and the island was used as a British bombing range. Its fortifications were blown up in the biggest non-atomic blast of history. In 1952 it was returned to Germany and a gradual process of resettlement and reconstruction began.

The main rocky island is triangular in shape and about one mile in length. Except for a narrow beach with a landing stage on the southeast, the coastline is one of steep red cliffs. Above them a green plateau (Oberland) rises to just over 200 feet. The main occupations are lobster and oyster fishing; the plateau provides grazing land and some potatoes. The adjoining sandbank (Düneninsel), separated from the main island by an irruption of the sea in 1720, is a fine bathing beach in late summer for mainland holidaymakers.

Hispaniola

The second largest of the Greater Antilles, shared by the republics of Dominica and Haiti. Location *West Indies, between Cuba and Puerto Rico.* Area *About 30,000 square miles.* Map *2, F3.*

Originally called *Quisqueya* and *Hayti* by its native Arawak Indians, Hispaniola was named La Isla Española when Columbus made his first landing near Cape Saint Nicolas on December 6, 1492. The Indian population soon disappeared under Spanish rule and early in the sixteenth century Negro slaves were introduced in great numbers. During the nineteenth century the island was called both Haiti and Santo Domingo; later the entire island was referred to as Haiti, but in today's usage Hispaniola is generally preferred when referring collectively to the two republics occupying its soil.

The Dominican Republic extends over the eastern two thirds of Hispaniola. Most of the center of the island is covered by the Cordillera Central, stretching from the Haitian border; its highest peak, Monte Tina (10,301 feet), is also the highest in the West Indies. The central mountains are separated by two lowlands from the low coastal range in the northeast. Cibao, the fertile northern plain, and La Vega Real valley, its eastern continuation, are both well-watered. In the southeast there is a dry coastal plain.

About 10 per cent of the Dominicans are of European, mainly Spanish, origin; 20 per cent are Negro and the rest mulatto. The language is Spanish with Roman Catholicism the state religion. The ancient Santo Domingo University was founded in 1538.

The main occupation is agriculture, with sugar still representing more than half of the exports, but the fertile Cibao plain also produces cacao, coffee, corn, tobacco and tropical fruit. Gold has been washed from the rivers since pre-Columbian times; there are deposits of iron, bauxite and gypsum which still remain to be exploited. There are few industries, and most manufactured goods have to be imported.

It was in 1697 that the island was divided when Haiti was ceded to France; in the early nineteenth century the present Dominican Republic's territory changed hands repeatedly: first Haitian, then French and finally Spanish control being established over it. In 1821 the Dominican territory declared its independence but was conquered by a second Haitian invasion. In 1844 it reasserted its independence, and, except for another brief period under Spanish rule (1861–65) has preserved it. From 1904 to 1948 the United States regulated the republic's finances and between 1916 and 1924 American troops occupied the country. The rule of the Trujillo family began in 1930, though the remarkable General Trujillo, a typical Latin American dictator, was assassinated in 1961.

Santo Domingo, the capital, with a population of 273,000, has a modern harbor which handles most of the Republic's trade. Other cities are Santiago, in the center of the rich Cibao region; San Francisco de Macoris, a trading center; Barabao, where most of the sugar of the southwestern area is processed and whence timber and salt are also shipped; La Vega, in the La Vega Real Valley; San Pedro de Macoris; La Romana (the main sugar port); and Puerto Plata (the port for Santiago) and Sánchez, which ship out the agricultural products of the Cibao plain.

The Dominican Republic has about 700 miles of public railroads, as well as many private tracks, mostly on the sugar plantations. There are excellent roads radiating from Santo Domingo and a highway connects the Dominican capital with Port-au-Prince in Haiti.

Haiti, the western third of Hispaniola, is a desperately poor, overpopulated country, whose history is full of bloodshed and cruelty. The French, after getting control of this part of Hispaniola in 1697, brought in African Negroes to toil on the sugar and cotton plantations. In 1798 Toussaint L'Ouverture, a former slave, led a successful rebellion against the French and became a national hero and a symbol of the fight against tyranny. Five years later another former slave, General Jean-Jacques Dessalines, declared the island independent and restored the original Indian name of Hayti (which means mountainous). Bitter, internecine struggles followed between the rival leaders, Henri Christophe (who proclaimed himself Emperor) and Alexandre Pétion. In 1838 France recognized Haiti's independence. After a particularly gory and unsettled period (1908–15), American forces occupied the country, remaining until 1934. American financial control continued until 1947.

Voodoo, a weird mixture of black and white magic, involving blood sacrifice of birds or animals, still has a tight grip on the minds and imaginations of the black Haitians – 95 per cent of the people are Negro, with a small ruling class of mulattoes – in towns as well as in the countryside. Though in the densely populated country (with nearly 300 people to the square mile) the Church and the intelligentsia fight superstition, this makes little difference. Voodoo appeals to a profound feeling for color and rhythm, for pageant and ceremony, and at a deeper level answers an abiding emotional need for mystical experiences – for contact with the greater, transcendental world of the spirit.

Slowly the standard of living is rising, but the native smallholder, replacing the plantation farmer, is still working with primitive methods and productivity is low. The dam at Peligne is to provide irrigation for the fertile but dry Artibonite Valley and the unworked deposits of silver, iron, gold, lead, tin and zinc could be profitably exploited. Bauxite and copper are already mined from the Terre-Neuve district, the richest mineral area.

Apart from the capital (which has a population of 196,000, out of a total population of 3,250,000), the principal towns are Cap-Haitien (market center for the Plaine du Nord, and the second port), Gonaives, an old Indian town, port for the Artiboine plain, and the coastal cities of Port-de-Paix, Saint-Marc, Jérémie, Les Cayes and Jacmel. Communications are poor, with only 150 miles of railroad track and few good roads. There are internal air services linking the main centers.

Hong Kong

A British Crown Colony comprising an island, a peninsula and some leased territories. Location *Southern China, adjoining Kwantung Province, 40 miles east of Macao.* Area *391 square miles.* Map *4, B4.*

Queen Victoria wrote in 1841 that her husband, Prince Albert, was "amused" by the acquisition of the barren island of Hong Kong, which had been bought to create a trade center not under Chinese control yet close enough to Canton and the Chinese mainland. In 1923 Dr Sun Yat Sen, the great Chinese leader, described how, as a student, 30 years earlier, he had wondered at the achievements of the foreigners on the barren rock within a mere 70 or 80 years. Indeed, Hong Kong has proved that its acquisition was well worth while.

The island itself which, with a few minute islets, formed the first Colony, is 11 miles long from east to west, varies from two to five miles in width and rises so steeply to a range of volcanic hills (the highest is Victoria Peak, 1,805 feet), that a very substantial part of the modern city on the north side had to be built upon land reclaimed from the sea. The name Hong Kong was later given to the wider territory which is the British Crown Colony of today – and also, colloquially, to the town officially known as Victoria – a threefold use of the same name which is sometimes confusing.

In 1860 the Convention of Peking added the Kowloon Peninsula and another small island to the Colony. Today the term "Kowloon" always refers to the whole of the town on the northern, mainland, side of the harbor. The administrative area of Kowloon stops at what is called Boundary Street but the built-up area spreads well beyond this into the so-called New Territories, properly, "the Leased Territories" – leased to Great Britain for a term of 99 years under the 1898 Peking Convention. They comprise 198 islands, most of them very small – but one, Lantao, is larger than Hong Kong island itself, and one, Cheung Chau, has a population of 20,000 and a sizeable mainland section north of Kowloon. The total population was estimated at the end of 1959 as 2,919,000, but it has varied considerably during recent years because of the influx of refugees from Communist China. The vast majority live in Kowloon and Victoria and there are places with more than 2,000 people to the acre.

Between Hong Kong island and the mainland at Kowloon is one of the most perfect natural harbors in the world, about 17 square miles in area, varying from one to three miles in depth. During the last century it has been transformed from an almost empty space between bleak, inhospitable shores into the gateway to South China and one of the world's greatest sea ports. On its shores there stand now two teeming cities, depots for almost every conceivable kind of commerce, seats of developing industry and world centers of banking and finance. The importance and prosperity of Hong Kong depend on the harbor and its favorable position at the mouth of the most important river system in South China, within easy reach of Canton, South China's largest city, and midway between the main ports of Haiphong in North Vietnam and Shanghai. Its prosperity and bustling activity were only temporarily interrupted by the Japanese occupation of 1942–45 when, after a brief but stubborn resistance, Hong Kong fell to the invader.

Hong Kong has traditionally always been a free port: this is still the general rule, but with the embargo upon traffic in strategic goods to China, which began with the Korean war in 1950, and the greatly swollen population of recent years, industry has begun to take an increasingly important place. The flood of refugees has created serious problems of unemployment and overcrowding; appalling poverty exists side by side with great prosperity.

Horn, Cape

The southernmost point of South America. Location *Tierra del Fuego, Chile.* Map *6, D11.*

Sir Francis Drake was long credited with the discovery of Cape Horn in 1577; having been driven a long way southwards from the Strait of Magellan by terrific gales, he landed on an island and, stretching his hands over a cliff, claimed that no man had ever been as far south as he. But it is probable that the great black cliffs of the southernmost headland were first seen by two Dutchmen, Willem Schouten and Isaac le Maire, in 1616. They named it Hoorn, after their native town in Holland; it became Horn in English and, less appropriately, Cabo de Hornos (the Cape of Ovens) in Spanish.

One of the worst of many dreadful passages around Cape Horn was that which Admiral George Anson and his squadron experienced in 1741, at the beginning of his famous voyage of circumnavigation of the globe. The ships' sails were split by the wind, the masts and rigging were shattered, and Anson's own vessel was leaking in every seam. Some of the crew were killed by being hurled about below decks or being thrown overboard, and many were seriously injured.

The first woman to round the Horn was a St Malo girl, "an adventurous wench named

Baré," who sailed with the *Etoile*, disguised as a servant to M. de Commercon, a botanist of De Bougainville's expedition. In 1768 she returned safe and sound to France (having confessed her deception in Tahiti) – the first woman to circumnavigate the world.

Many famous navigators and explorers came after: James Cook, William Bligh (who never got round the Cape though he tried for 29 days), Charles Darwin (in the *Beagle*), and hosts of others. Until the building of the Panama Canal and the coming of steam, it was said that no man was a sailor until he had rounded Cape Horn three times. It needed courage, endurance and skill – and even today, when the Cape is practically deserted, the passage round it still demands all three.

Hudson Bay and Strait

An ice-jammed inland sea; the Strait is a main channel of subarctic Canada, navigable with ice-breakers for most of the year. Location *Eastern central Canada, between Northwest Territories and Ungava Peninsula; the Strait extends from northern extremity of Labrador to Hudson Bay.* Area *(Bay) 475,000 square miles.* Dimensions *(Strait) 450 miles long, 40–150 miles wide.* Maximum depth *(Bay) 141 fathoms.* Map *(Bay) 1, C2; (Strait) 1, E1.*

Much of Hudson Bay lies on the same parallels as Scotland, northern England and Denmark. Its climate, however, is arctic and subarctic and its natural inhabitants were born to hunt among pack ice and across tundra. Indians live and hunt in some coastal areas, but except in the James Bay area, where Indians predominate, the small scattered population is mostly Eskimo and there are many Eskimo place names. Caribou, fox and wolf roam the bleak lands that stretch away from the coast; white whales, walrus and seals lounge among the pack ice and polar bears pad across it through the fog that so often hangs over floe and pack.

The Hudson Bay coast, generally low-lying, merges to the east and south beyond the Belcher Islands (where, until comparatively recent years, the Eskimos wore birdskin clothing) into the broken ice of northern Quebec; to the west into the Barren Lands; and to the north into the polar landscapes of Coats and Southampton islands. But the predominant feature of this great inland sea, nearly 1,300 miles long and 600 miles across, is its ice, for it is frozen much of the year and carries great quantities of pack and floe. Masses of this ice reach the North Atlantic by way of Hudson Strait, which is comparatively narrow in places, with its shores forming cliffs 1,000 feet and more high.

It was through this spectacular channel that Sir Martin Frobisher sailed in 1578 in search of the fabled Northwest Passage, and Henry Hudson in 1610 made his way through the Strait, and the masses of ice that grind southwards from the Arctic, into the Bay itself. Bay and Strait were, in fact, one of the approaches along which the early explorers and fur traders reached the heart of Canada. Ships of the Hudson's Bay Company have been navigating into Hudson Bay for nearly 300 years, since 1668, and the trading posts they established there proved some of the foundations from which a Dominion was to grow.

For centuries few people except fur traders and explorers penetrated the Strait into the Bay. But in 1931 a trial shipment of grain was exported to Europe through Fort Churchill (today the chief port of the Bay); and soon after the Second World War, a change almost violent in its suddenness came to this ice-girt shore. Technological developments in aviation and marine navigation brought it within easy reach. Fort Churchill, the fur-trading post, was developed into Port Churchill, the marine terminal through which, with the assistance of ice-breakers, radar and other aids to navigation, millions of bushels of wheat passed towards Hudson Strait and the ports of England and Europe. Very soon, the Eskimos of Belcher Island were watching geologists and mining engineers at work among the iron-ore formations; and on the frozen shores of Rankin Inlet, Eskimos born to hunt were working in newly opened nickel mines. Survey teams began pushing yet deeper into the land surrounding the Bay, seeking ways and means of developing it.

But furs continue to flow through the trading posts of Hudson Bay and its twin Strait, as they always will; and where, no doubt, men will continue to stalk the seal, the walrus and the bear of this subpolar inland sea.

Hyères, Îles d'

A small group of rocky islands on the French Mediterranean coast. Location *Mediterranean, east of Toulon.* Map *9, B7.*

The Îles d'Hyères are vacation islands now, but they have a long history of war and plunder. They were fortified by Vauban under Cardinal Richelieu as outer defences of Toulon; they were captured by the English in the eighteenth century; they were occupied by the Germans in the Second World War and recaptured by American forces. Today the forts, ancient and modern, sink back into the trees and the vegetation.

Porquerolles is the best known and largest of the three chief, inhabited islands. Port Cros is the most compact, the most thickly coated in scrub and pine. The Île du Levant is the most curious – the home of nudists who have a village colony at the western tip of the island.

For the French these are honeymoon islands, tempered with sea winds and basking in the Mediterranean sun.

Iceland

A large subarctic island which is an independent republic. Location *North Atlantic, just south of the Arctic Circle.* Area *39,700 square miles.* Map *7, D1.*

Iceland was colonized from 874 A.D. onwards by migrants from Norway, who brought with them their wives and their thralls – some of them of Celtic origin captured in Viking raids on Scotland. These settlers are reputed to have dislodged a handful of Irish monks – perhaps a party led by St Brendan. During the first century of the settlement, the population increased to about 40,000, but remained almost stationary afterwards for eight or nine centuries. The scarcity of productive land prevented any further increase, and even so the severity of the climate and disastrous volcanic eruptions caused periodic famines. In the eighteenth century there were also depredations by pirates – British, Spanish, Algerian and Turkish.

The early settlers formed a republic, which came to an end in 1262 when they came under the rule of Norway. This was soon replaced by that of Denmark, which lasted for over five centuries, until 1918, when Iceland became a sovereign state but still united with the Danish Crown. In 1944 there was a plebiscite, as a result of which Iceland severed the union with Denmark and became one of the United Nations in 1946.

Iceland lies on the broad submarine ridge that extends from Scotland to Greenland, separating the Norwegian Sea basin from that of the North Atlantic. At various places on this ridge there has been prolonged volcanic activity with extensive outpourings of basaltic lava; this, together with volcanic ash and debris, is the composition of Iceland and some smaller islands. Some of the lava fields are enormous – that of the Odadahraun, north of the Askja volcano, covers over 1,400 square miles. Volcanic activity has continued to the present day: there are over 100 volcanoes, many of them still active. Mount Hekla erupts periodically, sometimes causing much damage to pastures and livestock in the neighboring districts, and the country around it contains numerous hot springs and geysers.

More than two thirds of Iceland consists of utterly barren lava plateaus between 2,000 and 3,500 feet high. From the rugged surface of these, great volcanic peaks rise to heights of 4,000–6,000 feet. The height of these plateaus and the heavy precipitation on them (more than 150 inches annually) combine to maintain the icefields, which cover one seventh of Iceland. The most extensive – and the largest in Europe – is on the Vatnajokull Plateau in the southeast, which contains the island's highest peak, Hvannadalshnjunkur (6,952 feet). The glacier tongues of this icecap and the neighboring ones feed a number of rivers which have cut ravine-like valleys and commonly end in fjords. The lowlands are mostly in the southwest and south and in some of the lower valleys of the rivers; but even in these parts soil suitable for farming is to be found only in patches.

The natural vegetation is semi-tundra, consisting of grasses, bushes and dwarf birch and willow, with sphagnum moss and sedges in the bogs. Whatever woodlands once existed in the sheltered valleys have been cut down for fuel during more than 1,000 years of human occupation. Only one seventh of the island is in any

Crane Beach, Barbac

sense productive and even that is mostly poor meadowland and grazing. Not only is the proportion of land actually cultivated very small, but the crops that can be grown are limited mainly to turnips, potatoes and the cabbage family – though geyser-heated greenhouses now supply such things as tomatoes. Livestock is of chief importance; and though it is difficult to dry the hay crop, as much as possible is saved for the maintenance of the sheep and cattle during the long winters. As cereals do not ripen in the subarctic climate, all supplies of grain have to be imported.

The farming section of the population has been shrinking with the expansion of the fisheries and the establishment of fish-processing plants and some general manufactures. From the northern Arctic waters rich in plankton upon which they feed, cod and herring migrate in shoals to the banks round Iceland for spawning. Among the chief centers of the fishing industry are Reykjavik – a modern town where the hot water supply is pumped from the natural hot springs – Vestmannaeyjar, on one of the islands off the south coast, and Akureyri at the head of a north coast fjord. Fish and fish products such as cod-liver oil account for 90 per cent of exports. Formerly, the bulk of the cod catch was dry-salted for sale to Mediterranean, West Indian and Latin American markets, but since the introduction of the quick-freezing process, more and more are exported as frozen fillets.

Indian Ocean

The third largest ocean in the world. Location *Between Asia, Australia, Antarctica and Africa.* Area *28,350,000 square miles.* Maximum depth *24,440 feet.* Map *10.*

The Indian Ocean is usually associated with tropical weather – with a leisurely ship sailing from Aden to Colombo or from Ceylon to Cape Town – but it is only because many world shipping routes cross it in the tropics that is has this reputation; actually, more than half of it lies outside the tropic zone.

Compared to the Atlantic, few large rivers drain into the Indian Ocean – the Ganges, the Indus, the Brahmaputra and the Irrawaddy are the principal ones. In spite of this, some sections of the Indian Ocean, particularly on the eastern side in tropical regions, have so heavy a rainfall that the surface water at certain times contains very little salt. The same applies to the surface water in the area of equatorial calms.

The deepest parts of the Indian Ocean are off South Australia, where a depression in the sea bed runs down to nearly 3,000 fathoms. Off the south coast of Java, in the Java Trench, a depth of 3,500 fathoms has been recorded.

The monsoons are the most distinctive feature of this ocean, for the winds and weather of the whole of the northern half are dominated by the alternation of the monsoon winds. Caused by the alternate heating and cooling of the immense land mass of Asia (which gives rise to seasonal temperature changes and, therefore, air pressures), the monsoons blow from the southwest between June and September and from the northeast between December and March. The windiest area is a little east of the island of Socotra, where in mid-summer the wind is almost always gale force. It is the southwest and northwest monsoon which brings the subcontinent of India its rainfall. As the wind passes over the warm sea it becomes saturated with moisture which is precipitated as soon as the land mass and mountains of India are encountered. In certain areas, particularly in the north (Arabian Sea and the Bay of Bengal), there are violent tropical storms which can be a danger even to modern steamships. They generally occur at the season when the monsoons are changing.

South of the Seychelles, Chagos and Cocos islands, the prevailing winds throughout the year are the southeast trades. South again, and one enters the area of the roaring forties. Here, the winds blow strongly from the west and roll the long ocean swell before them. These are the winds which, in the days of sail, drove most of the world's trade between South Africa, Australia and China. In this region the Indian Ocean shows its other face: for long periods the sky is overcast and heavy with rain or snow. Although there may be fine intervals, they seldom last for long and in winter 14 days out of every month in the roaring forties are liable to have winds of full gale force – and with them the sweep of giant seas.

ermen's houses on the Bosporus

Indonesia

A large and diverse island group. Location *Malay Archipelago, southeast Asia.* Area *575,893 square miles.* Map *4, A7–C7.*

Among the countries that have gained their independence since the Second World War, the Indonesian Republic, with a population of over 80,000,000, is unique. Its territories are more far-flung, its peoples more varied, its cultures and religions more diverse than those of any state of comparable size in the world. The rice terraces of Java, climbing the hills; the jungle-covered slopes of still smoking volcanoes; the great Buddhist monument of Borobudur; the temples of Mendut, Prambanan, Kalasan and the Dieng Plateau; the tiny coral islands; the dancers of Bali and Surakarta; the huge, still not quite explored mass of Borneo; the "living zoo" of the Moluccas – Indonesia includes them all, and is equally rich in interest to the anthropologist, the archeologist and the natural scientist.

The main islands and island groups are Java, which includes Madura; Sumatra, to which several neighboring islands are linked; Celebes; the Indonesian part of Borneo (Kalimantan); the Lesser Sundas (of which Bali and Lombok are the best known); and the Moluccas.

The interiors of most of the islands are mountainous. In Sumatra, Java and the Lesser Sundas there are several volcanic cones which rise to over 10,000 feet. Kerinchi (12,467 feet) on Sumatra, Maharemu (12,061 feet) on Java and Rinjani (12,224 feet) on Lombok are the highest. Along a line of fairly recent geological mountain building there are more than 70 active volcanoes and many more extinct ones. Yet there are important differences in the relief of the various islands. Sumatra has high mountains rising steeply from its west coast, spreading out to form wide uplands in the Batak area. A flat, alluvial lowland extends throughout the island; huge tracts of it are useless swamps. Borneo is fringed on its southern and western coasts with a similar swamp-belt; the interior non-volcanic ranges seldom rise over 6,000 feet. Celebes, on the contrary, rises to several thousand feet within a few miles of its coast and Mount Rantemario, in the center, is over 11,000 feet. The Moluccas and the eastern Lesser Sundas have a similar configuration, being summits of submerged mountain ranges. Java has many tall volcanic cones but is without a continuous range; its mountains are separated by wide valleys and broad alluvial plains, and there is only a narrow swamp-belt along the coast.

Indonesia's climate, with unimportant local exceptions, is dominated by the equatorial monsoons, with heavy rainfall, high average temperatures and a long dry season in the southeastern part of the archipelago. This climate produces the evergreen rain forests which cover the hill slopes up to about 3,000 feet with valuable timber and thick woody creepers. There is no snowline on the peaks, and shrubs and grasses cover even the summits. Though Java, Madura and Bali have been largely deforested for agricultural purposes, the other islands are still mainly forest-covered.

On the western islands are found many of the larger Asian mammals – elephant, tiger, rhinoceros, orangutan – while Celebes has some individual species, such as the cuscus and the ox-like anoa. Eastern Indonesia has fewer animals but many birds and insects.

The archipelago has been populated by a series of migrations from the mainland of southeast Asia. The last to arrive were the Malays, probably around 2000 B.C. During the early Christian era much of Indonesia came under the influence of Indian civilization. Two early centers of this civilization developed into fair-sized empires – the Sri Vijaya kingdom, which lasted from the seventh to the thirteenth centuries and had its capital at Palembang; and Madjapahit, in eastern central Java, which ruled most of the archipelago during the fourteenth century.

Mohammedanism was introduced by spice traders from western India and brought about the downfall of the Madjapahit empire. Indonesia was split into many lesser states, mostly under Moslem rulers; their constant strife made it easier for the Portuguese and for the Dutch to conquer various parts of the scattered islands. The Portuguese conquered Malacca (in Malaya) in 1551 and set up trading posts in the Moluccas. Their influence was already declining when the Dutch East India Company set up headquarters at Batavia in 1619 and gradually extended its domination over the archipelago. As the spice trade became less important, the Dutch concentrated on Java; but their hold was largely nominal over the outer island until the first third of the nineteenth century. Java was developed as an important source of sugar, coffee, rubber, cinchona and tea. The Dutch brought in many Chinese settlers and the native population also increased rapidly. It took several expensive and bloody wars to consolidate Dutch rule over Sumatra, Borneo, Bangka, Billiton and other outlying islands; the Atjeh War, which lasted from 1873 to 1904, was particularly stubborn.

Indonesia was occupied by the Japanese during the Second World War. After the defeat of Japan, Dr Achmed Sukarno, the nationalist leader, proclaimed the independence of the Indonesian Republic. There was much confused fighting and political negotiation until December, 1949, when the Netherlands finally agreed to transfer sovereignty of the former Dutch East Indies, except Dutch New Guinea.

The majority of the native peoples of Indonesia are of Malay origin with a mixture of Melanesian and Papuan stocks in the interiors of the eastern part of the archipelago. There are over 2,000,000 Chinese, some 70,000 Arabs and until recently – for many have gone to Holland as refugees – at least 150,000 Eurasians. The languages of the Malay groups include some 20 regional dialects – from Atjehnese to Batak, from Javanese to Menangkabau, Sundanese, Balinese, Buginese, Malay and the Dyak languages. The so-called "bazaar" Malay has been for long the *lingua franca;* now it is being developed as the official national language. English is the principal Western language taught, having replaced Dutch. About 66,000,000 are Moslems; the Balinese are Hindu and the peoples of the interiors follow tribal and animistic faiths. Many have been converted to Christianity. There are about 2,000,000 Protestants and half that number of Catholics. About 1,000,000 Chinese are Buddhists.

The chief cities of Indonesia are Jakarta, the capital (formerly Batavia), with a population of 3,500,000, Bandung, Solo and Jogjakarta. Tanjungpriok is the chief port (also the port for Jakarta). Madura's chief town is Pamekesan; Sumatra's Palembang is the main oil port with Medan, Belawan and Padang the other important Sumatran cities. In Borneo, Banjermasin, Balikpapan and Pontianak are important centers; in Celebes, Macassar and Menado; in the Moluccas, Ternate and Amboina; in Bali, Singaraja; and in Western Timor, Kupang.

Inland Sea of Japan

One of the most beautiful seas in the world. Location *An arm of the Philippine Sea.* Area *3,668 square miles.* Map *4, D3.*

Dotted with islands, screened on almost all sides from the storms which scourge the Pacific, and opening into the Sea of Japan only through the narrow Shimonoseki Strait, the Inland Sea – about 240 miles long and 540 miles wide – is an area of great beauty. Its importance in the history and growth of Japan is incalculable, for the early Japanese learned the arts of navigation upon these sheltered waters. It was upon the waters of this large and much indented body of water, with its innumerable fishing ports, that the crafts of the Japanese fishermen were kept alive. It was their only chance for many a year, because after the sixteenth century the Japanese were for over 200 years forbidden to build boats of more than 150 tons – as part of the government's policy of isolation.

There are hundreds of islands – Awaji-shima is the largest – in the Sea. Most of them are several hundred feet high with steep, forest-covered slopes. Some are composed of granite and have softer outlines, with the bare white rock showing through the sparse woodland cover. Formerly called Seto-chi-umi, the islands and main coastlines of the Sea are characterized by low cliffs, shaped by the waves, or rocky platforms. In the little coves there are strips of alluvial land where small agricultural and fishing villages have sprung up; in some places these strips are so narrow that land has had to be reclaimed along the sea edge to provide space for even tiny settlements – many of which have, in fact, spread to the adjacent low hill slopes.

In 1934 the Inland Sea National Park was established, with an area of 706 square miles, covering the area between Shodo-shima and Tomo in the prefecture of Hiroshima.

Intracoastal Waterway

A toll-free route for commercial and pleasure ships. Location *Atlantic and Gulf of Mexico coasts, from Boston to the Rio Grande.* Length *About 3,100 miles.* Map *1, A11–C11.*

The Intracoastal Waterway was an ambitious federal project of the United States which was begun in 1905 and completed in 1949. Following bays, sounds and rivers along the Atlantic Coast of America, many of which have been deepened by dredging (the average depth is 12 feet though some sections are shallower), it occasionally passes through already existing canals, and dips into the Atlantic and the Gulf of Mexico. The various sections include the Cape Cod Canal; the Delaware River (as far upstream as Trenton, N. J.); the Chesapeake and Delaware Canal (which links the Delaware River with Chesapeake Bay); the Dismal Swamp Canal; the Albemarle and Chesapeake (connecting Hampton Roads with Albemarle Sound); and the Okeechobee Waterway, which cuts across the Florida Peninsula, extending as far south as Key West, where, at Fort Myers, the Gulf Intracoastal Waterway begins and continues to the Rio Grande. The Gulf section is 1,066 miles long and 125 feet wide.

The greatest importance of the whole system is commercial – providing cheap and often short routes for carrying manufactured goods and raw materials. When it was first projected, the only big city along its route was New Orleans; by the time it was finished, 21 different ocean parts were connected by it with New Orleans and with one another. The Gulf Intracoastal Waterway, designed and built in 12 years by the United States Army Corps of Engineers, is today acknowledged as one of the world's greatest canals. It carries as much tonnage in petroleum, chemicals, sugar, salt, iron and steel and innumerable other commodities as the Panama Canal, and a good deal more than the St Lawrence Seaway. Some cities have more than doubled their population since its opening; others have become first-class ports, though as much as 30-50 miles inland.

The Intracoastal Waterway crosses the Mississippi delta near New Orleans and is connected by locks with the Mississippi, thereby providing access to the Great Lakes. There are over 30 major ports along it, from Boston and New York to Charleston and Biloxi, from Wilmington to Pensacola, Lake Charles and Port Arthur. Almost half of the Gulf section is in open water; while in Louisiana, in the eastern swamps of the state, high banks had to be built to carry it and guard it against possible mud-slides.

Various plans are already authorized to widen various sections of the great Waterway and carry it across Florida, between the head of the present branch of the Atlantic section to Withlacoochee Bay on the Gulf of Mexico, and to make many more inland cities thriving harbors along its great length.

Iona

A small island famous as an early center of Christianity. Location *Inner Hebrides, Scotland.* Dimensions *3½ miles long, 1½ miles wide.* Map *8, C3.*

From the southwestern tip of Mull – another island in the Inner Hebrides, from which Iona is separated by a mile-wide sound – a ferry service carries a constant stream of visitors, tourists and pilgrims across to the flat strip on which St Columba landed with 12 disciples, intent on spreading the gospel, in 563 A.D.

There is a one-street village and, incongruously, a golf course; from Dunii, 332 feet above the sea at the northern end of the island, there is a fine view to Staffa and the Treshnish Isles. St Mary's Cathedral; St Oran's Cemetery, where 60 kings, Scottish, Norwegian and Irish, are supposed to be buried; the Church of the Priory; the Street of the Dead; and the one cross that remains from the hundreds that stood here before the Reformation – all attract visitors.

St Columba founded his monastery on Iona and carried out from there his missions to the rest of Scotland, the Orkneys, the Shetlands, and even Iceland. During the years following his death, there were frequent pillaging raids by Danes and Norwegians; which may be the reason why St Columba's remains were removed to Ireland at the end of the seventh century.

The plan to restore Iona's ancient buildings was interrupted by the Second World War, but work was resumed in 1947.

Ionian Sea

An arm of the Mediterranean. Location *Between Greece, Sicily and the foot of the Italian peninsula.* Maximum depth *Over 12,000 feet.* Map *7, F9.*

Named after Io, the much-persecuted love of Zeus who was changed into a heifer and driven from land to land until she reached Egypt, the Ionian Sea forms the central basin of the Mediterranean. In its waters, between Sicily and Greece, lies the deepest part of that sea; in places depths of over 12,000 feet can be found, but for the most part it is less than 6,000 feet. In classical times the Ionian was of great importance as the sea link between the states of Greece and their new colonies in Sicily and southern Italy. It was these waters that the Greek sailors sailed when they first consistently navigated out of sight of land, and the Ionian may be called one of the cradles of seamanship. The deep soundings are divided from the western Mediterranean by Sicily and the Cape Bon bank, while on the east there is a similar bank stretching from North Africa to Crete.

The main prevailing winds which give the Sea its character are the sirocco and the gregale. The former, a hot wind which can be either dry or very humid, blows from the south, mainly in spring and autumn. It is most common off the Sicilian coast in the early months of the year. The Ionian sailor, touching the deck of his boat at night, can often detect a damp sirocco on its way by the heavy dewfall. When it blows, the natural indolence of the southern coast of Italy is increased, for the humidity drawn off the sea is intensive.

The gregale is a northerly or northeasterly wind which blows mainly in winter and can raise a very heavy sea in a few hours. When it blows from the northeast, with the full sweep of the Ionian all the way behind it from Albania, the gregale raises dangerous seas off southern Sicily and Malta. Even today the Ionian schooners and coastal traders hesitate to put to sea during the gregale months, and most of the small open fishing boats along the adjacent coasts are laid up during the winter. During most of the spring and summer, however, it is a sea of light winds and long periods of calm. In summer, beyond the reach of land breezes, complete calms may prevail for days on end in the middle of the Ionian. Because it is too deep in most places for fishing, the local boats of Greece and Italy stay in coastal waters. Dolphin, tunny, ray, squid and mullet are all caught in these waters. At night all along the eastern coast of Sicily and the southern coast of Italy the Ionian reflects the myriad stars of the acetelyne and carbide lamps used by the fishermen.

The ruins of many civilizations that litter the Ionian's shores – from fabled Sybaris and Croton in the north to Syracuse and Ithaca on the west and east – make it a sea of enchantment.

Ireland

The second largest of the British Isles, divided between the Republic of Eire and Northern Ireland. Location *Atlantic, separated from Great Britain by the Irish Sea.* Area *32,375 square miles (Eire 27,137 square miles; Northern Ireland 5,238 square miles).* Map *7, C4.*

Eire, extending over roughly five sixths of Ireland, consists of a low central plain almost surrounded by highland areas; some geographers have compared it to a saucer. Along the coasts of Kerry and western Cork the deep inlets of the sea (called *rias*) alternate with steep headlands, assailed constantly by the sea. The highest point of Eire is Carrantuohill (3,414 feet) in Macgillycuddy's Reeks, County Kerry.

Connemara, Mayo, Donegal and Sligo are mostly desolate, peaty uplands, with only occasional bold peaks – such as Mount Errigal (2,466 feet) in Donegal and Croagpatrick (2,510 feet) in Mayo. The rounded granite mountains of Wicklow are split by deep valleys which still show the traces of ancient glaciers.

The lowlands of central Eire are of flat limestone, seldom rising above 300 feet. The limestone has been steadily worn away by the abundant rainfall – the climate is temperate, with not much variation in average temperature, but year-round heavy precipitation which justifies the Emerald Isle's green name – and there are a great many lakes with flat islands. In the depressions there are great peat bogs; the vast Bog of Allen, covering almost 250,000 acres, is the

Sybil Head, Ireland

largest. Moorland predominates, especially in the higher, wetter districts of the west, where there are few trees. Heather and bilberry grow abundantly on the moors; there are large areas where the lack of drainage has turned the bogs into swamps, and aquatic plants – sedge, rushes, sweet gale – grow on thick layers of peat. Most of the forests have disappeared, owing to ruthless exploitation and the depredations of the grazing livestock, so that Eire is one of the least wooded countries in Europe. The fauna is also more restricted even than in Great Britain. Whether St Patrick drove out the snakes or not – as legend says – the only reptile to be found is the lizard; foxes are hunted, but deer and many smaller animals found east of the Irish Sea are unknown.

The glory of Irish history has its roots in the Celtic culture of the Dark Ages; from the eighth to the tenth centuries Ireland, never conquered by the Romans, had a brilliant civilization of its own. St Patrick converted the Irish to Christianity in the sixth century. Politically, the country had been divided into small tribal kingdoms which were united loosely and often transitorily under the Kings of Tara.

In 1171 Henry II, King of England, landed in Ireland, as feudal overlord of Dermot MacMurrough, king of Leinster, who had been banished from his kingdom and had fled to England, becoming Henry's vassal. During the next few years the Anglo-Normans occupied most of the country, expelling the Irish chieftains. Under the Tudors, repeated attempts were made to complete this domination – attempts which were repeatedly foiled by the fact that the Irish had remained staunch Catholics even after the English Reformation under Henry VIII.

The "troubles" of Ireland reached their climax in the seventeenth century, when Cromwell tried to destroy all resistance and succeeded in laying much of the country waste. Nearly all the Irish landowners lost their estates. Large numbers of the ordinary people were driven from their homesteads; at the same time colonists were brought in from Britain. Thus Ulster was settled with Protestants of Scottish stock, which later led to the separatism of the "six counties." The bulk of the population, however, remained Irish and Catholic.

In the eighteenth century Ireland was governed for the benefit of the Protestant minority and of England. In 1800 the Irish Parliament, which had a limited independence, was persuaded to proclaim complete union with Britain. For the next century there was an unremitting struggle to regain independence and to redress the genuine Irish grievances against absentee landlords and the oppression of the Roman Catholic elements. By 1821 Ireland also had the highest population density in Europe. This led to food shortage; millions had to subsist on nothing but potatoes, and the potato famine of 1845-49 caused widespread starvation. Over 1,000,000 Irish emigrated to America, Great Britain and Australia.

Parnell and other Irish politicans continued the struggle for the repeal of the Union. The fight culminated in the Easter Rising of 1916, which was crushed, though guerilla warfare continued. In 1921, at last, Eire was granted independence under the name of the Irish Free State, still within the British Commonwealth, while the six counties of Northern Ireland remained part of the United Kingdom. In 1937 the Free State changed its name to Eire; it remained neutral in the Second World War (though many Irish fought in the Allied forces) and in 1949 it became a republic and withdrew from the British Commonwealth.

The original Irish population consisted of short, dark-haired people who moved to the island during the Stone Age from the Mediterranean. Waves of Celtic invasions changed the culture but not the racial composition, though English and Scots settled in the island in considerable numbers during the sixteenth and seventeenth centuries. In spite of the strong attempts to revive Erse (a form of Gaelic), the majority still speak English, except in the western highlands. About half the Irish are farmers, though most of the crofts (farms) are very small; the main crops are potatoes and oats, used to feed the calves, pigs and poultry raised for sale. There are a few small coal fields; industries, most of them recently developed, include brewing (the famous Guinness stout), distilling (the equally famous peaty Irish whiskey), and sugar refining. Waterford cut glass is a valuable export.

Eire is governed by a President, 147 representatives in the Dáil, and 60 senators who represent the universities, the arts, education and various professions. The capital is "Dublin's fair city" which has been the cradle of so many varied talents – from G. B. Shaw to W. B. Yeats, from Oscar Wilde to James Joyce, from J. M. Synge to Oliver St John Gogarty, not to mention the Abbey Theatre, and a galaxy of Irish actors of stage and screen. Of Eire's 3,000,000 inhabitants, 540,000 live in Dublin, 80,000 in Cork, 51,000 in Limerick. Galway, Waterford, Wexford, Drogheda and Dundalk are the smaller ports; Shannon airport, near Limerick, is an important link in the Atlantic air routes.

Northern Ireland consists of the six counties of Antrim, Armagh, Down, Fermanagh, Londonderry and Tyrone. It has its own parliament, consisting of a House of Commons of 52 elected members and a Senate. The executive power is vested in a Governor. With a population of about 1,407,000, Ulster is a heavily industrialized country compared with Eire. Textiles, engineering, shipbuilding and aircraft industries employ over 100,000 people, and there are important manufactures of tobacco, drink, toys, pottery and furniture. Quarrying and mining are less extensive, but the Northern Ireland fisheries contribute considerable revenue.

The capital of Northern Ireland is Belfast, situated at the mouth of the River Lagan, at the entrance of Belfast Lough, with the great Parliament Buildings at Stormont dominating its heights. Belfast is an important seaport.

Ischia

A rocky island which is a famous health resort. Location *Southern Italy, near the northwest entrance to the Bay of Naples.* Area *18 square miles.* Map *9, D8.*

From the top of Monte Epomeo, the highest point of Ischia (2,589 feet), the land falls away in fertile valleys and tree-lined slopes. On a clear day the whole of the Bay of Naples is visible, Capri rises like a gray whale-back to the south and Vesuvius feathers its smoke cloud over the mainland. Ischia is a gentle island, without the starkness that dominates so many of the others off the west coast of Italy. The climate and the fertile valleys produce fruit profusely; in September, at the season of the Vendemia, or wine-pressing, it approximates more closely than almost any other to the Romantic poets' dream of what a classical island should be.

Ischia is part of the same volcanic system as Vesuvius, and has repeatedly been abandoned because of volcanic eruptions, though Epomeo has not erupted since 1833 and seems now to be quiescent. The hot springs have been known and commercialized since classical times for their efficacy in rheumatic and arthritic complaints. Votive offerings in the churches bear testimony to recovery from these and other complaints, and are matched by votive altars erected to the nymphs of the springs by gouty and dyspeptic Romans.

The principal town, Ischia, on the east coast, stands on a deep, almost land-locked harbor, once the crater of a volcano. Commercial shipping and the island fishing boats lie alongside the bustling quay, for in most places the land shelves steeply to the ancient crater and the water is too deep to anchor. In the early mornings, when the cobbled streets of the town are running with fresh water and the carts creak in from the countryside loaded with olives, grapes and oranges, it is easy to understand why Apollo is said to have favored Ischia.

Ithaca

One of the Ionian group of islands. Location *Off northeast Cephalonia, Greece.* Area *37.2 square miles.* Map *9, F9.*

Ithaca owes its fame almost entirely to its association with the Homeric hero, Odysseus. It has a stark and craggy grandeur; when the rain clouds loom off Anoi, the highest mountain, and the entrance to the port of Vathi is veiled in low-flying scud and spindrift, one feels that Heinrich Schliemann was right in stating that this was undoubtedly the home of the much-traveled hero of the *Odyssey*, though various scholars have held that desolate Leukas, to the north, corresponds more closely to Homeric topography. Numerous attempts have been made to identify the places and localities described in the *Odyssey*, but no one has yet completed the jigsaw puzzle – though the exercise has diverted scholars of every nation.

The port of Vathi, the capital of Ithaca, spreads along the southern shores of the harbor. White-washed and sparkling, it shines like a wedding cake in the sun. After one of the summer thunderstorms the hills rising behind the village glisten as their swaying olive trees lean to the southwest, away from the prevailing wind, the Tramontane.

Like Zante, Leukas and Cephalonia, Ithaca lies on a volcanic fault in the earth's crust and has periodically suffered from earthquakes. Against this background of insecurity and poverty – olive oil and wine are almost the only products – the islanders maintain a cheerful dignity worthy of their ancestry. Many of them are fishermen and on almost any day the Gulf of Molo, on which Vathi stands, is dappled with the lateen sails of their open boats. They wring a hard living from the sea, but no harder than the goatherd on Mount Anoi or the peasant among the gnarled olive trees. At night, the small taverns along the waterfront of Vathi are gay with lights, and the island wine and olives are as good as the roast hare which is one of Ithaca's specialities.

Jamaica

The third largest island of the West Indies. Location *West Indies.* Area *4,411 square miles.* Map *2, E3.*

When Columbus discovered Jamaica in 1494 – he called it St Jago, but the Indian name, Xaymaca, has stuck – he found its coasts peopled by the peaceful, easy-going Arawak Indians, who seem to have lived mostly by fishing. Having nothing but stone-age tools, they had made no attempt to exploit the beautiful wooded interior. Spaniards settled on the island in 1509 and soon began to enslave the Arawaks, import Negroes and clear the lowlands. In 1655, after two unsuccessful attacks in 1596 and 1643, the island fell easily to Cromwell's Admiral Sir William Penn and General Robert Venables and became British. By this time all the Arawaks had long been dead from overwork, disease and suicide.

A center of buccaneering – Sir Henry Morgan, the famous pirate and sailor, had a long association with the island – Jamaica was tolerated in this capacity by the British authorities because it kept the Spaniards away. Port Royal, at the tip of a narrow strip of land enclosing Kingston harbor, became the richest and wickedest town of the West Indies, with over 2,000 houses. It was destroyed by an earthquake in 1692.

Meanwhile, a prosperous rum and sugar industry grew up, sustained by the continuous importation of African slaves but continually disturbed by their revolts. The lowland forests were finally cleared for the cultivation of sugar, and coffee plantations crept up the mountains. With the destruction of woodland on steep hillsides, too many parts of Jamaica acquired their present sadly eroded and ruthlessly exploited character. During the first half of the nineteenth century, however, the island's prosperity declined rapidly; many freed slaves would no longer toil on plantations and Indian coolies were imported to replace them. Later the Chinese and Syrians came, and now form mercantile communities of considerable wealth and consequence.

Within 100 miles of Cuba and 120 miles west of Haiti, Jamaica is about 148 miles long and 52 miles wide. Its eastern half is dominated by the main ridge of the Blue Mountains, rising to 7,400 feet in Blue Mountain Peak, and by the John Crow Mountains, rising to 3,800 feet and receiving an annual rainfall of nearly 300 inches by interception of the prevailing northeasterly winds. In the higher portions of the John Crow Mountains, where little soil covers the rock, the jagged, knife-edged crumbling ledges and boulders are shrouded in a tangled mass of mosses, liverworts, sprawling vines, rotten logs and a dense growth of stunted trees. It is almost impossible to break a trail through such country. One explorer, G. R. Proctor, took four days on one occasion to cover about three miles, though aided by two Jamaican guides with machetes. It is only about 30 miles east of Kingston, the capital, where in the Jones Town area some 50,000 people crowd a square mile.

In striking contrast to the cloud-swathed John Crow Mountains are the Hellshine Hills, with an annual rainfall of barely 30 inches. Here, out of the honeycomb limestone burning to the touch

The coast of Jamaica

and blinding to the eyes in the fierce sunlight, rise tall columnar cacti, thorny acacias and shrubs with small, leathery leaves astonishingly defiant of such cruel conditions. A similar contrast exists in the northwest between the tourist center of Montego Bay, with its fine beach and luxurious hotels, and the difficult, unexplored Cockpit Country southeast of it. Much of Jamaica is, however, covered by grazing land and cultivated areas of greatly varying size, devoted mainly to sugar cane, citrus fruits, bananas, rice, yams, sweet potatoes, beans, pimento, ginger, akee, coconut palms and breadfruit. Upon these crops, the tourist industry, and the bauxite royalties, the prosperity of the island depends.

Jan Mayen

An Arctic island, a Norwegian possession since 1929. Location *Arctic Ocean, east of Greenland, northeast of Iceland.* Area *144 square miles.* Map *5, E11.*

Jan Mayen, the "Devil's Island," or, more often, simply "Jan" to the sinewy Norwegian seal-catchers of the Greenland Sea, is a spot far off the beaten seaways. A craggy, volcanic island, its crumbling lava cliffs are the home of millions of sea-birds. When the winter snows recede, the slopes come alive with flowers, plants and a surprisingly large fauna of insects, spiders and other small invertebrate animals.

Dotted throughout the island are the craters of extinct volcanoes, many so recent in origin that one can break off rope-like bits of lava which look as if they might have cooled decades, instead of centuries, ago. The whole island, in fact, is of Quaternary origin. At Egg Bluff steam still rises from the depths of the earth. Nearby, dominating the entire island, is the mighty Beerenberg, a white cone rising to 8,347 feet almost directly above the surf. Of the several lagoons, South Lagoon is near the narrowest part of the island. Here, also, is the only permanent settlement, a Norwegian meteorological station. There are also scattered trappers' huts, occupied only in winter by men who hunt arctic foxes. Occasionally, in very severe winters, the island becomes connected by pack ice to the Greenland coast.

Jan Mayen is a wild, precipitous place, usually bathed in mist, due to the cold East Greenland Current and the Gulf Stream meeting nearby. It was probably known to the Vikings but was not re-discovered until the seventeenth century. One of the first modern visitors was Henry Hudson, who was there in 1607 and who charted it as Hudson's Tuches. Another early explorer was the Dutchman, Jan Mayen (after whom the island was later named), who landed in 1614. French whalers called it the Île de Richelieu. In the early days of their whale-hunting, the Dutch named it St Maurice or Mauritius, while the English knew it as Trinity or Sir Thomas Smith's Island. Whatever its name, this foggy spot has remained a sort of Arctic no-man's-land with its best beaches littered with barrels and blubber-boiling vats awaiting their nauseous harvest of the sea.

Traces of the handiwork of the past still remain. At Walrus Gat there are sun-baked bricks brought from Holland to build the whaling station; and nearby are half a dozen stranded twentieth-century mines. On the beaches of Mary Muss Bay and North Lagoon there are bleached white skeletons – and, on an adjacent hillside, the burnt-out wreck of a German bomber. On remote hillsides are lonely graves and monuments recalling past tragedies. One is a stone commemorating the deaths of seven Hollanders who remained on the island during the winter of 1633–34 to guard the station against the depredations of Basque pirates. They all perished miserably of scurvy. And in 1961 Jan Mayen still claimed victims – members of a British University expedition who drowned in the icy seas around it when their boat was upset by heavy seas, with only their leader escaping.

Japan

A crescent-shaped archipelago with great density of population. Location *Off the Pacific eastern coast of Asia.* Area *140,680 square miles.* Map *4, D3–E2.*

Japan is a country of infinite variety, whose beauty has been immortalized by the paintings and prints of Hokusai and Hiroshige – a country dominated by sacred Fujiyama, with sprawling forests, peaceful lakes, rushing streams and spectacular waterfalls; with cherry and plum blossom, soaring peaks and volcanic springs. It is also a highly industrialized country with an intricate social morality, with frugal poverty and immense powers of technical expansion, a country of fantastic contrasts and often breathtaking beauty.

The four large islands – Hokkaido, Honshu, Shikoku and Kyushu – together with a string of smaller ones, the Ryukyus – extend off the east coast of the Asian mainland. Rugged and often bleak, they have more than 250 peaks over 6,500 feet, and two large mountain chains run the whole length of Honshu (the largest island), with the western range reappearing in Kyushu and the eastern range becoming the backbone of Shikoku. In Hokkaido, a central knot of mountains sends out the spokes of a series of ranges. There are 192 volcanoes, of which 58 are still active – the most famous of all being the perfect cone of Fujiyama (12,389 feet).

There are few extensive lowlands. The Kwanto or Tokyo Plain is the largest; the Nobi, the Kinai or Settsu, the Ishikari, the Sendai and Echigo plains are the next in area and importance. Earthquakes are so frequent that there are about five recognizable shocks *every* day, though serious upheavals, causing death and destruction, are much less frequent. Japan's rivers are short and swift, easily exploited for hydro-electric power, but of little use as traffic arteries.

Japan's climate is temperate and monsoonal, with the extreme south being subtropical while Hokkaido in the north is almost subarctic. The warm Japan Current (Kuroshio) and the cold Okhotsk Current (Oyashio) modify the temperatures of the eastern shores of Japan; where they meet, they often produce dense and persistent fogs. Rainfall and snowfall are both heavy. Tokyo gets about 35 inches of rain between June and October out of an annual average of 60 inches. Destructive typhoons are frequent in the south in the late summer and autumn. Spring, the season of the cherry blossom, is the most attractive of the year.

More than half of Japan's area is still forest, ranging from subtropical varieties in the south to purely coniferous in the north and on the higher slopes. The Japanese have a deep veneration for trees and the most sacred shrines are usually surrounded by avenues of tall *cryptomeria*. Around eight per cent of the land consists of waste areas with grass too coarse for grazing. The fauna is very varied: bears, apes, stags, antelopes and the Japanese wolf or mountain dog are found together with badgers, foxes, monkeys, otters, moles, rabbits, hares and squirrels. The birds include the nightingale, grouse and raven.

The Japanese or Yamato people originally occupied only the southwest; the rest was the territory of the primitive Ainu tribes, distantly related to European races. From the fourth century A.D. there was close contact for many hundreds of years between the Yamato kingdom and the adjacent parts of Korea. It was through Korea that the Japanese absorbed much of Chinese civilization, culture and religion. Nara, the first true capital, was built early in the eighth century. During the Heian period (784–1192) contacts with the Chinese lapsed and Japan began to develop an independent civilization. The warrior class or *samurai* rose to pre-eminence, mainly because the islands were threatened first by the Mongol forces of Kublai Khan and later by the Spaniards establishing themselves in the Philippines.

Portuguese traders were the first European visitors, in 1543. They were followed by Jesuit missionaries, led by St Francis Xavier, who achieved such success that in 1587 the frightened authorities banned all missionaries from the country. The great national leader, Hideyoshi, though his attack on China through Korea failed, put an end to the constant internal strife between the clans; his work was continued by the first of the Tokugawa *shoguns*, a line of hereditary military dictators who moved the capital to Yedo, present-day Tokyo, in 1603. In 1637 all foreigners were excluded from the country and for more than two centuries Japan remained in complete isolation.

It was Commodore Matthew C. Perry, whose expeditions took place in 1854 and 1868, who reopened Japan to the outside world. The shogunate had fallen, and the Japanese embarked on a dramatic westernization of their country which went hand-in-hand with territorial expansion. Victorious wars against China (1894–95) and Russia (1904–05) were followed in the nineteen-thirties by the extension of Japanese rule over the whole of Manchuria. In 1936 the Sino-Japanese war began, and in 1941 the disastrous aggression against the Western Powers which ended in unconditional surrender on August 15, 1945, and the drastic reduction of Japanese territory coupled with an American occupation.

The Japanese are a mixture of northern and southern Mongoloid stocks with an important element of the aboriginal Ainu – though the pure-blooded Ainus today number only a few thousand in Hokkaido. Before 1868 most of the population were peasant farmers, but today almost half of them live in centers of more than 25,000. This rapid urbanization has created immense problems and tensions which losing the war accelerated and worsened. The democratization of the Japanese constitution and the reduction of the "divine" Emperor to a constitutional monarch have only partly solved these.

Japanese is the main language, which is outside all the major linguistic groups; English is the most widely spoken foreign language.

The staple food and the main crop is rice, with barley, wheat, fruit and tea the other main branches of agriculture. The famous silkworm culture has been badly hit by synthetic fibers. There is little livestock; fish is the chief source of animal protein in the diet. Coal, iron ore and petroleum resources are all inadequate for the national needs. Yet Japanese industry is tremendously varied and productive; textiles, metallurgical products, shipbuilding, chemicals, food processing have all contributed to help balance exports and imports. Japan is the eighth largest trading nation in the world.

Japan's main religion is Shinto, which has proved to be compatible with widespread belief in Buddhism. There are about 500,000 Christians, more than half of them Catholics. Japan has nearly 600 universities, six of them state-owned, with the private universities of Wasedo, Keio and Moji equally important. Japanese culture has found manifold expression in the tea-ceremony, the Noh, Bunraku and Kabuki plays and dramas, in painting and in a rapidly broadening and maturing modern literature.

Tokyo, the capital, has almost one tenth of the 91,250,000 total population and is supposed to be growing at the rate of 1,000,000 people every four years. Kyoto, the ancient imperial capital, is a mixture of ancient crafts and building and modern industries. Osaka is the biggest industrial city, with Nagoya, Yokohama and Kobe following as important centers and ports.

Java

The most important island of Indonesia. Location *Greater Sundas, between Java Sea and Indian Ocean.* Area *48,842 square miles.* Map *4, A8.*

Though in area only the fourth largest island of Indonesia – 650 miles long and 40–130 miles wide – Java, with a population of over 52,000,000, is the heartland of the Indonesian Republic. Jakarta, the capital, is here, and much of the industry is also concentrated in its area. Tibor Mende has called Java "a rhapsody in green; the triumph of human labor over the exuberant indiscipline of nature."

With many active volcanoes, its soil is extremely fertile – and this soil has been fully and carefully exploited for centuries. Groves of palms adjoin forests of rubber trees, followed by rice-fields which look like checker-boards in every shade of green. Others are terraced and flooded, marching up the mountain sides "like an enormous staircase built for a race of giants." Many miles of tangled sugar cane frame cone-shaped volcanoes, with tiny settlements of a few houses scattered over the sloping plains and constantly thickening into villages. Three crops are harvested annually but the "population explosion" is outstripping food production.

The volcanoes run in a long procession the length of the island, some rising steeply to a graceful cone, others with a medley of cones, still others with a vast single cone occupied by a crater lake. The highest volcanoes reach to over 12,000 feet and many – among them the immensely destructive Krakatoa – have erupted in recent times, leading frequently to serious loss of life and property.

If volcanic cones are seldom out of sight in Java, the same is true of planted fields, tangles of trees and flowers and villages. Every inch of available land is cultivated, partly irrigated and partly "dry"; the fields and the roads are edged by masses of richly colored flowers and shrubs. The flower-lover will be entranced by the variety of blooms, especially by the brilliance of so many types of orchids. Java's forests are the home of tigers, leopards, panthers, apes and wild pigs. Within the villages and towns, the native crafts of making colored designs on cloth (batik-work) and the fashioning of tortoise shells still survive.

Buddhism, Hinduism, Islam, Dutch colonialism, nationalism – these are some of the main influences which have helped to mould Javanese life. Islam, though now the almost universal religion, is mixed with various Indian beliefs, and the Indian epics, Mahabharata and Ramayana, are used in Javanese drama. There are many ancient temples, of which Borobudur, built in the eighth century, is the most famous. Dutch influence was predominant from the seventeenth century until the establishment of the Republic of Indonesia in 1949 and in this long period of rule towns were built, roads and railways constructed and the economy of the island improved. Although now politically independent of the Netherlands, the landscape of Java will long retain its imprint of Dutch endeavor. The wave of nationalism which achieved independence for Indonesia had been active for many years before the war. Java remains, as under Dutch rule, the center of government but its position has been seriously threatened since achieving independence by rebellions and local disturbances in the other islands of Indonesia.

Juan Fernández Islands

Two large islands and a small one, belonging to Chile. Location *South Pacific, about 400 miles west of Valparaiso, Chile.* Area *About 74 square miles.* Map *4, Q11.*

The Islands were discovered in 1574 by Juan Fernández (who was also, perhaps, the first European to sight New Zealand and Australia). The two principal islands are Más Afuera, meaning "Farther Out" (33 square miles), and Más a Tierra, meaning "Nearer Land" (36 square miles). The small Santa Clara (about five miles in circumference) and scattered rocks complete the archipelago. The climate is mild and healthy.

Más Afuera consists of volcanic mountains, rising to over 5,000 feet, with springs and waterfalls, goats, sea-birds and, in the surrounding sea, many seals and fish. In Spanish colonial times sealskins were shipped to Lima where they were made into greatly valued hats.

In the seventeenth and eighteenth centuries the more important island, Más a Tierra – which is mountainous, but wooded, and much more fertile than Afuera – was a favorite refuge for British seamen, who harassed the Spanish ports on the Pacific coast of South America. There was a splendid anchorage in Cumberland Bay. On land, the scurvy-ridden crews could obtain fresh water, herbs, vegetables and fruit. Some thoughtful buccaneers introduced goats, which multiplied and became such a valuable source of fresh meat for Spain's enemies that the Lima authorities sent dogs to the island to destroy them; but the goats escaped to the high crags, out of reach.

Sometimes a mutinous seaman would be set ashore on the island, to be rescued months or years later. This was the fate of the Scotsman Alexander Selkirk, who had quarreled with his captain and was therefore marooned on Más a Tierra, where he lived in solitude from 1704 to 1709. He found abundant wood for building a hut and pampas grass to thatch it. He made fire by rubbing two pieces of pimento wood together. Nor was there any lack of food, and goat skins served as clothes. The story of his experiences inspired the writing of *Robinson Crusoe,* though Defoe chose a tropical setting, In 1858, British naval officers placed a commemorative tablet on Selkirk's rocky look-out above Cumberland Bay. In 1741, Lord Anson improved the local amenities by planting lettuces and carrots and plum, apricot and peach trees.

Karpathos

The third largest island of the Dodecanese. Location *Aegean Sea, Greece.* Area *111 square miles.* Map *9, G10.*

Karpathos lies apart from the other islands of the Dodecanese, which stretch like a rocky backbone off the western coast of Turkey. Nearer to Crete than the rest of the group, it commands the narrow straits between Crete and Rhodes. In both ancient and medieval times it was closely allied with Rhodes, but its commanding position

The island of Helsingør in the Kattegat

on the trade routes between Rhodes, Cyprus and Crete gave its name to this part of the Aegean – the Carpathian Sea. At the height of Venetian power in the Mediterranean, Karpathos, like so many other islands, came under Venetian suzerainty. The principal town on the west coast, Arcasse, still has traces of Venetian architecture and fortifications. The finest harbor, however, is a large natural bay on the east coast which is sheltered from the prevailing northerly winds of the Aegean. Another important town, Pegadia or Pigadhia, is on the southeast shore.

Like most of the Dodecanese, Karpathos is comparatively barren, a crested hump of rock from which most of the trees have long since disappeared. Only the craggy olive survives the depredations of the goats which – as elsewhere in this sea – provide most of the milk, cheese and meat for the islanders. The men are peasant farmers or fishermen; they are also fine sailors, and caiques from Karpathos may often be seen crossing the 50 miles or so to Cape Sideron in Crete or to Cape Presso in Rhodes. Sponge fishing was at one time a local activity, but in the past 30 years the trade has declined.

The islanders speak a Greek dialect somewhat similar to that of Rhodes with a number of imported Italian words. In customs and dress they are a mixture of the Cretan and the Rhodian. Some of the coral and silver jewelry of the women is particularly fine.

Kattegat

A strait, part of the waterways linking the North Sea and the Baltic. Location *Between Sweden and Denmark.* Dimensions *137 miles long, 37–100 miles wide.* Maximum depth *410 feet.* Map *7, F5.*

The Kattegat – the name means the "Cat's Throat" – is connected in the north with the Skagerrak, the main entrance to the Baltic; in the south it joins the Baltic proper, through the Sound, the Great Belt and the Little Belt.

Since the salinity of the Baltic is very low, because of the number of rivers flowing into it, and since its actual surface level is a little higher than that of the North Sea, the Kattegat drains away a surface current of fresh water. This can be traced into the North Sea as far as the North Cape in Norway. The level of the Kattegat is about four inches higher than the level of the North Sea.

The Kattegat, with its green-lined shores and warm, almost fresh water, is a popular summer vacation resort. It is a fine sailing area, with the islands of Anholt and Laeso, and the ports of Goteborg and Aalborg to the north. But in winter, when the winds are in the northeast, it can be dangerous: a full northeast gale drives the flood water of the North Sea before it and can pile up terrible breaking seas in the Channel. At its southern end, the Kattegat is almost blocked by the Danish islands, with Helsingor – or Elsinore – at the head of the Sound, and the pleasant port of Aarhus on the mainland at the entrance to the Great Belt.

Kerguelen Islands

An archipelago famous as seal-hunting grounds and whaling bases. Location *Indian Ocean, about 1,400 miles off Antarctica and 2,300 miles off the southeast coast of Africa.* Area *About 2,700 square miles.* Map *10, E11.*

"A wonderful land for crop-growing," reported the French navigator Yves-Joseph de Kerguélen-Trémarec, after his midsummer discovery of the main island in the archipelago (February 1772). A second expedition gave a very different picture, and the unfortunate sailor was thrown into prison, where he died, for misleading the authorities. Now, the island is sometimes called Desolation Island. It is the center of the group, which is 100 miles long and about 20 miles wide, and has some 300 smaller islands dotted around it.

From the 6,210-foot volcanic peak of Mount Ross, down the black basalt and pumice slopes of its numerous snowclad mountains and the crevasses of its glacier, covering a third of the island, to the deep winding fjords and inlets, the scattered rocks and bays of its irregular coastline, this is a rugged, savage land. But, though lashed by tremendous seas, swept by eternal gales and rain, often covered with fog and cloud, its vegetation a weird yellow in contrast with the black rocks, its beaches sometimes littered with huge stranded bergs of fantastic shape, calved from the Antarctic ice, Kerguelen can still spring into sudden beauty in the sunshine of a clear day.

Seams of poor quality coal show that the island once had a far milder climate and a rich vegetation. Now there are no trees and the biggest plant is the Kerguelen cabbage (*Pringlea antiscorbutica*), which reaches three feet in height. Winged insects do not exist – at every flight they would run the risk of being blown out to sea and there drowned – so this plant has abandoned the usual cabbage method of pollen dispersal by insects in favor of broadcasting it in the wind – of which there is a superabundance. The Kerguelen cabbage still retains features of its insect-pollinated ancestry, however, and in sheltered places its flowers sometimes even bear petals.

Apart from this curious vegetable, the only plants are grasses, a few ferns and mosses and a species of Ti-plant (*tracaena*). Yet animal life abounds. On the shores are King Penguins in friendly throngs; on the wastes of boggy land, thousands of teal, so tame that they can be picked up. White rabbits (originally imported to provide food for shipwrecked sailors) and rats scurry everywhere in half-starved multitudes. White, long-haired dogs – descended, it is believed, from an arctic dog which escaped long ago from a German expedition – run like wind through the grass.

Once, sheep rearing was tried, but not a lamb was born and the everlasting moisture soon killed the flock. Today, even the factory built to process the meat and oil of the once-numerous elephant seals (scarce now, except on the inaccessible weather shore) is derelict. In 1950, France sent a mission to the island to survey a site for the establishment of an air base on the route to Australia, and a new settlement was started at Port-des-Français, on the northeastern peninsula. But only a handful of the settlers remain there.

Kermadec Islands

A small volcanic group which gave its name to the Tonga-Kermadec Trench. Location *South Pacific, 500 miles northeast of Auckland.* Area *13 square miles.* Map *4, H10.*

The Kermadecs are in roughly the same latitude as the Lord Howe and Norfolk islands, and lie about halfway between New Zealand and Tonga. Raoul, or Sunday, Island is the largest and most elevated, more than 7,000 acres in extent and reaching over 1,700 feet. Like Curtis, Macaulay, L'Espérance and the smaller Herald Islands in the archipelago, Raoul is of volcanic origin. Thermal activity still occurs. The whole group is perched on the summit of a great submerged crustal upthrust – the outer rim of the western continental margin of the Pacific – overlooking the profound depths of the Tonga-Kermadec Trench to the east. This tremendous deep was discovered in 1895 and has a depth of 30,928 feet, stretching east of the Kermadec Islands and south of Tonga.

The Islands have a pleasantly cool subtropical climate and a vegetation which includes characteristic Pacific trees – the *pohutukawa*, the *nikai*, the *karaka* – with tree-ferns and other species closely related to those of the North Island of New Zealand. Tropical and temperate fruits and many root crops and grasses have been introduced at different times, and parts of Raoul are now covered with thickets of guava and cape gooseberry.

At some time in the past, Polynesian voyagers made a long stay in the Kermadecs and left stone artifacts behind. More recently, the Islands became a rendezvous for whalers. From 1827, sporadic settlements of a few European families sprang up to grow produce and sell it to the whaling crews, but these settlements were short-lived.

Some attempts at settlement were made again between the wars, but none survived long. In 1951 there were only 23 people on Raoul: government employees engaged in operating the radio station and the meteorological station and in maintaining the emergency landing strip built for Allied air craft during the Second World War.

King William Island

An Arctic island, base of several expeditions. Location *Arctic Ocean, in the Northwest Territories of Canada.* Dimensions *110 miles long, 100 miles wide.* Map *5, A7.*

One man failed to realize that King William Land (as it was then called) was an island and not connected to the mainland – and this was the reason why the 129 officers and men of Sir John Franklin's last expedition perished.

The error was made during Sir John Ross's search for the Northwest Passage from 1829 to 1833. (On this expedition the British flag was hoisted at the North Magnetic Pole by Ross's nephew, James Clark Ross.) Their ship, the *Victory*, the first steamship to be used in these waters, was beset by ice in Felix Bay, on the northwest coast of King William Land. From there, James Clark Ross explored the coast in the vicinity; his failure to notice that he was on an island was perhaps excusable, because the narrow strait between King William Island and the Boothia Peninsula was thickly covered with ice and snow. In consequence the cartographers showed a narrow isthmus joining the island to the peninsula.

Sixteen years later, Franklin, in his *Erebus* and *Terror*, set out on another voyage in search of the northwest route to the Pacific. After wintering on Beechey Island, he sailed down Barrow Strait, and down the west coast of North Somerset (Peel Sound or Franklin Channel), until he reached King William Land. Here, because of the error on the map, Franklin sailed to the west – straight into the waiting pack ice, where it piled up on the northwest coast of King William Island, unable to find a way out to the Pacific. There, in September, 1846, 12 miles from land, Franklin's ships were held fast in the ice. Franklin died on June 11, 1847, and the remnants of his party set out to escape by way of the Back River to the mainland. But, weak from exhaustion and lack of food, they died on the way.

After Franklin's failure to return, over 40 expeditions were sent in search of his party, as a result of which the Northwest Passage was discovered. It might well be said that inhospitable King William Island, with its irregular coastline, held the key to the long-sought route to the Pacific.

In 1854, Dr J. Ross established finally that King William Land was an island. In 1906, Roald Amundsen, after spending the winters of 1903 and 1904 on King William Island, took the *Gjoa* through the Northwest Passage. Today, there is a trading post on the island, at the site of Amundsen's winter quarters.

Kodiak Island

A large island, separated from the mainland of Alaska by the Shelikof Strait. Location *Gulf of Alaska.* Dimensions *100 miles long, 10–60 miles wide.* Map *5, B1.*

Kodiak Island is notable as the home of the giant Kodiak bear, exclusively Alaskan and among the largest and fiercest of carnivores. Rugged mountains, rising to over 5,000 feet, wooded on their upper slopes, offer the bears ample cover. They are cunning and fearless and provide dangerous sport for big game hunters.

Kodiak is also one of the main homes of salmon in Alaska; millions of fish pass the Island each year on the annual "run" into Cook Inlet. The Island's main industry is fishing. Its indented coast is studded with canneries and little harbors crammed with small boats. Along the rivers, fishermen have to compete with the bears. Other occupations include agriculture and the raising of cattle and blue foxes.

In the late eighteenth century, Russian fur traders used Kodiak to establish settlements on the Alaskan mainland. The Island passed to the United States in 1867. Its present population, native and white, is around 2,000 – excluding the personnel of the American air base – and is concentrated in the villages of Karluk, Kodiak and Uyak.

The natives have a more or less Eskimo culture with strong Indian influences. Once, they hunted the Kodiak bears with spears, but now prefer the lesser hazards of fishing and farming. This is hardly surprising, for there are records of Kodiak bears weighing upwards of 1,500 lbs, and stories of attacks which, for sheer ferocity, place this link with prehistoric times in the front rank of dangerous big game.

Krakatoa

An active volcanic island. Location *Sunda Strait, between Java and Sumatra, Indonesia.* Dimensions *Roughly circular, about three miles in diameter.* Map *10, H7.*

Krakatoa (which is sometimes called Rakata) is the largest of a small group of islands, the remnants of an ancient, huge volcanic cone. Before 1883 it was a hilly island, about five miles long and three broad, with the remains of other volcanic cones. The highest, Rakata, was about 2,623 feet high. It had been quiescent since 1680, but on May 20, 1883, an active period began which was to last for about 14 weeks. The booming eruptions could be heard at Jakarta, over 100 miles away, and during that summer many visitors came to obtain a closer view of the almost continuous eruptions. Some intrepid investigators even climbed to the very edge of the crater.

Fortunately, there was nobody on the island on August 26, but there were ships in the vicinity going about their normal ways. Eyewitness reports told how a thick black vaporous cloud rose to an estimated height of 17 miles, while heavy explosions were incessant. By 7 a.m. the next morning the black cloud had reached Jakarta, and by 11 a.m. the town was in complete darkness, enveloped by the volcanic dust which heavy rain turned to mud. The darkness was relieved only by flashes of lightning as a tremendous electric storm raged in the Sunda Strait. But by that time, the eruptions at Krakatoa had culminated in four immense explosions. The third and loudest took place at about 10 a.m. and was heard over 2,000 miles away. The sound waves from this series of explosions traveled four times round the earth.

When Krakatoa was next seen, two thirds of it had disappeared; eight square miles, including a large part of Rakata, had simply vanished. In place of the hills there was an abyss over 1,000 feet deep. For miles around the sea was covered with ashes and floating pumice; some fragments were so large that they floated five feet above the sea, forming great banks.

Although there was no loss of life in the immediate vicinity, the explosions caused immense waves, over 50 feet high, which devastated the low shores of Java and Sumatra, causing over 35,000 deaths. A warship was swept inland for three miles and left stranded, mute witness to the force of the waves, which traveled as far as the English Channel.

A strange by-product of the disaster was the series of remarkable sunsets which excited wonder and interest by their extraordinary beauty for two or three years afterwards. These were caused by the volcanic dust, thrown many miles high and swept along by the winds of the world, giving brilliant colors and vivid afterglows.

Kurile Islands

A volcanic island chain extending from the Kamchatka Peninsula to Hokkaido, Japan. Location *Between the North Pacific and the Sea of Okhotsk, Russian SFS R.* Area *5,700 square miles.* Map *4, F2.*

Discovered in 1634 by the Dutch navigator and explorer Martin de Vries, the Kuriles are a group of over 50 volcanic islands, reefs and rocks. They have all the characteristics associated with volcanic areas: boiling springs, sulphurous fissures in the earth, and even a mountain, on Kunashir Island, entirely surrounded by sulphurous springs and a boiling lake not unlike that of Trinidad.

There are 30 large islands in the group, about 20 smaller ones, and a great many rocks; the main islands are Shumshu, Paramushi, Onekotan, Simushir, Urup, Iturup (or Etorofu, the largest and most important) and Kunashir. Most of the islands are of volcanic origin and are mountainous: there are about 16 active volcanoes, the highest (7,657) ft being on Alaid Island.

The Kuriles stand in an area of the sea where currents and eddies maintain a dense growth of seaweed, rather like the Sargasso Sea. The Islands themselves, lying like stepping stones between Japan and Russia, provide a natural breakwater against the North Pacific Ocean. Northwest of them lies the Okhotsk Sea which washes the shores of Kamchatka and Siberia. The limit of drift ice from the Bering Sea and the Sea of Okhotsk passes approximately midway through the Kurile chain.

The three southern islands, Iturup, Kunashir and Shikotan, are reputed to have belonged to Japan since remote antiquity, a theory which is supported by the presence in the islands of the so-called "Hairy" Ainu. The Ainu, who were probably the neolithic inhabitants of Japan, are nowadays few in number and have dwindled fast in the face of modern civilization and contact with diseases against which they have no resistance. One of the oldest and most interesting members of the human race, their culture and way of life was akin to that of stone-age man. Their religion included a special cult of the bear, which is abundant in some of the Kurile Islands. The sacred animals were carefully tamed from their cub days and – like the human sacrifices of some ancient South American civilizations – were treated with special respect and well fed until the day came for them to be ritually sacrificed. Presumably the purpose of this treatment of the totem animal was to ensure success in their bear-hunting expeditions.

The Kuriles were penetrated by the Japanese from the south from 1643 onwards, while the Russians advanced from the north about 70 years later. The boundary between the Japanese and Russian spheres of interest was fixed in 1854 at Friz (Vries) Strait. In 1875 the whole group became Japanese when Russia obtained Sakhalin. In 1945 the Kuriles were occuped by Soviet troops and in 1947 the group was formally annexed as part of Sakhalin oblast.

Kuroshio Current

A large ocean current with several branches. Location *Pacific and Arctic oceans.* Map *4, D4–E3.*

The Kuroshio – also known as the Black or Japan Current – moves northeastward from the South China Sea along the coasts of East Asia. It is a warm current which has a considerable influence on the climate of Japan's southern and southeastern coasts. It has an average minimum winter temperature of 68° F. and warms the coasts of southern Kyushu, Shikoku and Honshu to about the latitude of Tokyo, then it turns east past the Aleutian Islands and south along the North American coast.

A branch of the Kuroshio, the Tsushima Current, creeps northward along the Japan Sea coast, but its influence is less than that of the parent stream. It enters the Sea of Japan through the Korea Strait and then flows north along the western shores of Kyushu and Honshu. Conversely, a cold current, known as the Oyashio, moves southward from the Bering Sea, cooling the northeastern coast of Honshu until it plunges below the waters of the Kuroshio. Lesser cold currents, which tend to drift toward the continental shores of the Sea of Japan, also affect the coast of Hokkaido.

The Kuroshio has a somewhat lower velocity than the Gulf Stream; it is underlain by a rocky bottom at a depth of at least 4,500 feet. This rock bottom occurs on a slope and the rock may have been exposed as the result of landslides. The Kuroshio meets the Okhotsk Current in the Pacific at about 38° North; its western offshoot joins a branch of the Okhotsk Current at about 40° North.

Kvaloy

An island, site of the most northerly city in the world. Location *Norwegian Sea, northern Norway.* Area *127 square miles.* Map *7, G2.*

Of the two Kvaloy islands – both of them Norwegian – the northernmost is the smaller but has the greater population. (The second has an area of 284 square miles and also lies in the Norwegian Sea, six miles west of Tromso.) It also has the distinction of possessing the northernmost city in the world, Hammerfest.

Kvaloy is 17 miles long and 10 miles wide, rising to 2,047 feet. Though it is within 80 miles of the North Cape and its latitude is well within the Arctic Circle – about the same as the extreme northern point of Alaska – the average temperature in January is very little below freezing point. This is entirely due to the North Atlantic Drift of the Gulf Stream; but for this

Hammerfest, the most northerly city in the world, on Kvaloy

beneficial ocean current warming its coasts, Hammerfest and the neighboring coast of Kvaloy would be as ice-bound as the coasts of Arctic Canada, Alaska or Siberia. Otherwise, however, Arctic conditions prevail, and the sun does not set from May 13 to July 29; nor does it rise in the winter between November 18 and January 23.

Around Hammerfest (which has a population of about 3,600) bare, flat-topped hills rise steeply to 400 feet, and reach 2,000 feet inland, providing some protection on the landward side. Conditions are poor on the island for vegetation, and most of it is barren tundra. However, forests of birches have been planted to replace the widespread destruction wrought by the "scorched earth" policy of the Germans towards the end of the Second World War – which included the destruction of the whole of Hammerfest in 1944.

The timber-built houses had been erected after a disastrous fire of 1890. For many years Hammerfest had been a prosperous little shipping and trading town; with its sheltered, ice-free harbor it was in a position of some advantage in trading with Archangel and with Spitsbergen. The chief merchandise was codliver oil, train oil, salted fish, reindeer, fox and seal-skins and eider-down. The town has been largely rebuilt and there is an up-to-date canning factory. In the old days, the town was also an important whaling station; but today much of the shipping trade has moved to Tromso.

Laccadive Islands

A group of 14 coral islands and reefs. Location *Arabian Sea, about 200 miles off the Malabar coast of India.* Area *Variously estimated between 10 and 80 square miles.* Map *10, E5.*

The Laccadives (called in Sanskrit, with considerable exaggeration, *Laksha divi*, One Hundred Thousand Isles) consist of nine inhabited and five uninhabited islands and a good many reefs and shoals. Part of India, their population is about 21,000, mostly Moslem fishermen who speak Malayali. The chief products are coir, copra and fish.

The two main groups of the archipelago are the Amin Divi Islands and the Laccadives proper which include Androth, Kavaraiti and Minicoy islands, separated from the others by the Nine Degree Channel.

The Islands were colonized by Hindus from the Malabar coast in the ninth century A.D. Four hundred years later the inhabitants were converted to Islam by an Arab saint, but to this day their descendants retain a strong Hindu caste feeling. They will not associate with the descendants of castes other than that of their own ancestors – or even live on other islands where such people predominate.

The Portuguese discovered the Laccadives in 1499, and took possession of the island of Ameny, in the center of the group, where they built a fort. In desperation, the Laccadivians sought the help of the Rajah of Cherikul, one of the most powerful princes on the nearby Malabar coast. The Rajah sent over the ablest poisoner he could find, a Hindu named Kadantavanjiraka ("Bored-ear"), who later became converted to Islam and who most efficiently exterminated the Portuguese over a period. The mosque where he prepared the poison still bears his name and is held sacred. The exact date (1549–60) of the bloody retaliation of the Portuguese from their neighboring stronghold of Goa is preserved in an Arabic song in honor of Abu Biker, a man of great sanctity, and still revered, who was massacred with more than 400 others. Although the Portuguese never established themselves again, the Islands lost their independence – to their patron, the Rajah of Cherikul, though he ruled indirectly, through the head of the Mopla sect in Cannanore (a city on the coast).

In 1785 the Amin Divis came under the rule of Tippoo Sahib of Mysore and six years later the East India Company took over the Laccadives. Both groups were assigned to Madras early in the nineteenth century, and in 1956 were transferred to the central government.

Land's End

The extreme southwest point of England. Location *West Cornwall, England.* Map *7, C5.*

A medieval bishop of Exeter once described Land's End in a letter to the Pope as *cauda mundi*, the tail of the world. Here England – or rather,

English Harbour, Antigua, in the Leeward Islands

the once Celtic country of Cornwall – comes to an end. Out to the southwest are the Scilly Isles, sometimes visible from Land's End, with the rocky islet of Carn Bras and the Longships Lighthouse about a mile offshore – then nothing, only endless and mysterious waters.

This tail of the world, as it was before the discovery of America, was known to the Celts of Cornwall as Penwith, which seems to have meant the headland visible from far at sea. The bare moorland peninsula behind the promontory of granite cliffs is still called by this name. Indeed, Land's End was important, prominent and dangerous on the ancient sea routes which here divided between the English Channel and the Irish Sea, the latter a great highway of the prehistoric world to Ireland, Wales and Scotland. Travelers of the Dark Ages usually avoided Land's End, sailing from Wales to the north Cornish coast, going across land, and then taking ship again in the southern Cornish harbors for Brittany.

At Land's End a heathery, rather dull plateau breaks off sharply. A granite mass drops to the water in castle-like sections, in gray and golden towers and crags. Rocks then continue out to sea. There are even finer and more dramatic granite cliffs some way round from the promontory, which is seen at its best when the heavy Atlantic seas batter and dissolve in spray against its prow.

Leeward Islands

A chain of islands including American, French, Dutch and British possessions. Location *Lesser Antilles, West Indies.* Area *About 700 square miles.* Map *2, H3.*

The principal islands of this, the most northerly group of the Lesser Antilles, extend from Puerto Rico to the Windward Islands and include the Virgin Islands (shared by the United States and Britain), Guadeloupe and its dependencies (French), St Eustatius and Saba (Dutch), St

Martin (divided between France and the Netherlands) and the islands of Antigua, Barbuda, Redonda, St Kitts, Nevis, Anguilla, Sombrero and Montserrat, former members of the British West Indies Federation.

Called Leeward because they lie farther away from the main track of the trade winds than the Windward group, the Islands form a curved breakwater against the Atlantic. East of them the long trade wind swell piles up, and west of them the blue Caribbean glitters. The physical appearance of the individual islands is almost entirely determined by this juxtaposition of ocean and sea. The Atlantic side is stern and inhospitable, the Caribbean side sheltered, with long sandy beaches and tranquil harbors. The exception is Antigua with its harbors of St John and English Harbour on the rocky eastern coast.

Most of the Islands were discovered by Columbus or his early successors and for centuries their history reflected the maritime aspirations of the European powers. They have been Spanish, then French, Dutch, then British, and even the Danes – not a very ambitious colonial power – once owned part of the group, which they sold to the United States in 1917. Apart from their stormy history, the Islands have a volcanic geological background; they are peaks of a submerged mountain chain.

Busy St Thomas, in the north, with one of the finest landlocked harbors in the Antilles, bears the mark of American industry and tourism and is a port of call for shipping bound through the Panama Canal. Antigua, on the other hand, has something of the aspect of a Scottish island miraculously set down in tropical sunshine. English Harbour, once the main naval base for the British fleet in the Caribbean, recalls the days of Nelson, and the old slipways and giant capstans stand just as they did in his day. At the other end of the scale comes Guadeloupe, which seems enfolded in the sleep of centuries, with its beautiful Creole women, and with the sails of schooners slipping quietly in and out of its sheltered harbor.

Most of the Islands are extremely fertile, producing sea-island cotton (which took the place of sugar cane and rum as the main product); coconuts, tobacco and vegetables are also grown. There are fruit-processing industries, and the distilling of rum and fishing are other important occupations. The main ports and commercial centers are Saint John's on Antigua, Basseterre on St Kitts and Plymouth on Montserrat.

Lemnos

A large Greek island, important in classical history. Location *Northwest of Lesbos, Aegean Sea.* Area *186 square miles.* Map *9, G9.*

Lemnos was the island of Hephaestus – it was on this spot of land that he fell, according to Greek mythology, when his father Zeus hurled him so unkindly from Olympus. The tale of the lamed god and the name Aethaleia, sometimes applied to the island, both point to its volcanic origin. In ancient times fire was said to have blazed forth occasionally from Mosychlos, one of its mountains, and Pausanias reports that a small island called Chryse, off the Lemnian coast, was swallowed by the sea. There is no volcanic activity now, nor has there been for a long time, but the lava flow, as in all volcanic islands, has created an extremely fertile soil.

Among the Thracians Lemnos was one of the titles of Cybele, and the earliest inhabitants may have been a Thracian tribe called by the Greeks rather unflatteringly *Sinties*, that is, "the robbers." According to a famous legend, the Lemnian women were all deserted by their husbands – whereupon, in revenge, they murdered all the males on the island. This was the origin of the expression "Lemnian deeds" – barbarous, inhuman actions. When the Argonauts landed, they found only women on the island, ruled by Hypsipyle, daughter of the old King Thoas. From the Argonauts and the Lemnian women the race called Minyae was supposed to be descended. The Minyae were expelled by a Pelasgian tribe from Attica. Historically, it is likely that the original Thracian people were considered barbarians by the Greek mariners with whom the development of navigation brought them into gradual contact. Cybele's worship was characteristic of Thrace; the original names of the chief towns Hypsipyle and Myrina are Amazon names, connected with Asiatic Cybele-worship.

Lemnos was conquered by Otanes, one of the

generals of Darius Hystapsis, but regained for Greece by Miltiades, the tyrant of the Thracian Chersonese. The island continued as an Athenian possession until absorbed by the Macedonian empire. The Romans declared its independence in 197 B.C. but handed it back to Athens 31 years later. It came under Roman rule again when Greece became a Roman province, and was subsequently part of the East Roman Empire. During the Middle Ages, Lemnos was ruled by Greeks, Italians and Turks in turn. In 1476 the Venetians stoutly defended it against a Turkish siege; but in 1657 Kastro, one of the two main towns, was captured by the Turks after a siege of 63 days. In 1770 the Russians besieged Lemnos; in 1913, it passed to Greece, was occupied by the Italians and Germans during the Second World War, and is now once again part of the Greek kingdom.

Lemnos has a deeply indented, irregular coastline; at its central isthmus it is only two and a half miles wide. Its highest point is 1,411 feet. The rich volcanic soil produces fruit, grain, grapes, almonds, silk, cotton and tobacco. There are many thousands of sheep. Another product, still used by the inhabitants, is the medicinal earth which was at one time popular all over Europe as *terra sigillata*. The Turks still believed, a few decades ago, that this earth was an antidote to any poison. Galen, the great medieval physician, attended the ceremony of digging up the earth, which took place once a year when a priestess performed the ceremonies and only one waggon load was dug out. In Christian times the same ceremony took place on August 6, the feast of Christ the Saviour. The Lemnian earth has a strong astringent quality.

Lesbos

A Greek island famous for its past civilization, its poets and its sulphur springs. Location *Aegean, off Asia Minor.* Area *632 square miles.* Map *9, G9.*

As one approaches Lesbos – also called Mytilene, or Mitilini, after its chief city – from the southwest, the deep Gulf of Kallone opens like a wound in the long shore. The entrance is narrow, and navigation is difficult; but inside, the Gulf becomes a sheltered land-locked bay. There is a port and fishing village at Sigri, but Kallone is not the most important harbor of the island. There is another on the eastern coast, facing Turkey, a small harbor, but sheltered from the prevailing winds: it is the heart of the island's capital, Mytilene.

Despite the romantic associations of the island with the great lyric poets of the seventh century B.C. – Sappho, Terpander, Alcaeus and Arion – Lesbos is not one of the most beautiful Aegean islands. It has a harsh, rugged quality. The town of Mytilene itself is more commercial than most island capitals – though it was the very fact that Lesbos was an important commercial center in the long-distant past that made it rich enough to cultivate the arts.

Inland, the roughly triangular island is rich and fertile. It has several well-sheltered valleys and on every side trim rows of vines mount the slopes. Wherever the ground is too rough for wheat or vineyards, thick colonies of olive trees lean southerly, their trunks bent by years of the prevailing north wind. Wine, grain and olive oil are the chief crops; marble is quarried and coal is mined. Like all island people, the men who are not working on the land are fishermen and sailors. The seas abound in fish, and sardines form an important catch.

Pentapolis – Five Cities – was once the island's name; but Lesbos, like many Greek islands, is subject to earthquakes, and two of the cities appear to have been destroyed in classical times. Only Mytilene has survived into our day, though the sites of all of them are still visible.

Mount Hagios Elias, or Mount Olympus (3,175 feet), and Mount Lepetymnos (3,176 feet) are the highest points on the island. The former stands west of Mytilene across the narrow Gulf of Gera, which is a fine, protected inlet behind the city, its rocky sides thick with olive trees and its water still and deep.

Ligurian Sea

An arm of the Mediterranean. Location *Northwest coast of Italy.* Maximum depth *More than 9,300 feet.* Map *7, D7–8.*

Stretching from the Italian province of Liguria in the north to Corsica in the south, from Tuscany in the east to the French frontier in the west, the Ligurian Sea has washed the shores upon which so much of Mediterranean civilization, culture and commerce had its birthplace. In the south, it is connected with the Tyrrhenian Sea by the Tuscan Archipelago; in the north, its large, sweeping indentation is called the Gulf of Genoa. This Gulf is enclosed by the Riviera di Levante and Riviera di Ponente, with the mouths of the Centa, Magra, Roya and Taggia rivers and the subsidiary gulfs of Spezia and Rapallo further indenting it.

The mountains at the back of the coastline descend abruptly into the Ligurian Sea so that the coastal strip is extremely narrow in most sections. The division into the two Rivieras is marked by the great city of Genoa itself; the Riviera di Ponente is the section bordering on France and the Riviera di Levante stretches towards the east. Along this coastline the great ports of Genoa, Spezia, and Savona bred untold generations of adventurous seamen who learned their craft on the Ligurian Sea – Columbus and Amerigo Vespucci among them – and here the merchant-republic of Genoa came to the full flowering of its power and then saw its decline. In later days, the Italians had their main naval base at Spezia. For many years past, thousands of visitors have flocked to the famous resorts along the shores in search of sunshine and a gentle sea.

Lion, Gulf of

A wide bay notorious for its storms. Location *Mediterranean, along the southern coast of France.* Map *7, D7.*

Bounded on the east by the Îles d'Hyères and Cape Sicié and on the west by the Narbonne-Perpignan coast of France, the Gulf of Lion (or Lions) has a most varied coastline. At its northern end, the flat Rhône delta land – the Camargue area, where rice is grown and bulls are bred – spills slowly down to the sea. Another stretch of coastline is formed by the easternmost spurs of the Pyrenees; still another by the limestone hills that lie on both sides of Marseilles. Eight rivers flow into the Gulf – from the Tech on the east to the Petit and Grand Rhône on the west – and it has a whole series of capes, including Sicié, Cap Croisette and Cap de l'Aigle. The chief indentations of the Gulf are the Gulf of Fos and Marseilles Bay. The great, bustling and irrepressibly high-spirited Mediterranean city of Marseilles is its main port, with Sète the next in importance.

It is the Rhône and the long valley that lies behind it that determine the weather of the Gulf of Lion. Down the valley from the mountains far to the north run the cold air currents which gather speed as they near the warmer air over the Mediterranean – and so the famous mistral is born, of which the Provençal poets have so often sung, and which can rise with practically no warning. It is a dangerous and destructive wind for small boats, and even bigger vessels feel its buffeting strength.

Lipari Islands

A volcanic group, off northeast Sicily. Location *Tyrrhenian Sea, Mediterranean.* Area *44 square miles.* Map *9, D9.*

The Liparis, comprising Lipari, Panaria, Salina, Vulcano, Stromboli, Filicudi, Alicudi and ten islets (including the uninhabited Basiluzzo), lie on the fault in the earth's crust that stretches from Vesuvius in the Bay of Naples to Etna in Sicily. Between them they display all the characteristics of a volcanic area – from hot sulphur springs and vaporous fissures to the fully active volcanoes of Vulcano and Stromboli. Lipari, the name-giving main island, is also the capital. It lies almost in the center of the group, with Vulcano to the south, Panaria and Stromboli to the north, and Salina, Filicudi and Alicudi to the west.

Ulysses, according to legend, visited the Islands in his wanderings, and Vulcano, of course, takes its name from Vulcan, the blacksmith of the gods, whose workshop was supposed to be under the island's smoking crater. During the Roman Empire, the Islands, on account of their inaccessibility, served as a place of banishment – a practice that was revived under Mussolini, who sent his political opponents there. Today, on the other hand, they are popular Italian tourist resorts. They offer magnificent swimming and unique scenery; they are also one of the best

The Lipari Islands

Mediterranean centers for underwater fishing and exploration. The town of Lipari itself is the seat of a bishop and has all the bustling activity of most Italian island towns; it is the commercial center of the Islands, as well as a market and fishing port.

Many of the houses on the Islands are built of volcanic tufa, for the stone is light and well suited to building. It is a curious sight to see two men with an ordinary saw cutting up the large tufa blocks as if they were wood; one may encounter, too, a man carrying on his back what appears to be a vast block of stone sufficient to crush a man beneath its weight. Pumice mining and cutting is one of the Islands' principal industries. The glassy black obsidian of Lipari has also been exported for many centuries, for sculpture and decorative work.

The Islands produce excellent wine. The best comes from the slopes of Mount Salvatore on Salina, an extinct volcano now green-flanked with the climbing terraces of vines. The fertility of volcanic earth, an admirable soil for vines, is the principal reason why such dangerous areas of the Mediterranean as Vesuvius, Etna and Stromboli continue to be among the most densely populated. (The Liparis have about 18,000 people.) The sulphur springs and mineral vapor baths of the Liparis also continue to be an attraction for the rheumatic and arthritic, as they have been since ancient times.

In places, the Islands present a macabre picture with their steaming sulphurous pools, bubbling mouths of volcanic mud and swirling vapors. But always beyond them there is a glimpse of the blue sea, with the sword-fish boats leaning across it, or the terraced peaks of some mountains, with the neatly planted vines showing where the industry of the Islanders has carved a living out of a treacherous soil.

Lofoten Islands

A group of islands off the northwest coast of Norway, center of an important cod-fishing industry. Location *North Sea, within the Arctic Circle.* Area *About 550 square miles.* Map *7, G2.*

The Vesteralen-Lofoten archipelago (the Vesteralen group is just north of the Lofoten) extends for over 100 miles in a general southwesterly direction from near the Tromso coast north of Narvik. South of that town, they diverge from the mainland, separated from it by the funnel-shaped Vest Fjord. They are the remnants of an outer ridge of ancient rocks, rising from extensive submarine banks. In the Ice Age this ridge had its own independent icecap and suffered intense erosion. As the great ice sheet over Scandinavia melted away, the land rose in these parts so that raised beaches known as *strandflats* occur round the shores, especially on the Vesteralen Islands. Apart from these scattered terraces, the Islands consist of bare, ice-dissected rocky ridges rising in their highest points to 4,000 feet.

Though between 100 and 200 miles north of the Arctic Circle, the Islands have a few farming settlements, depending chiefly on livestock. These and the fishing villages are mainly on the eastern sides of the Islands because these are more sheltered and because most of the *strandflats* are found there. Lying fully in the path of the North Atlantic Drift and the warm southwesterly winds, the Islands are remarkable for an exceptionally high winter temperature for their latitude – 45° F. above normal. It is, in fact, possible to grow barley and root crops on them, but owing to the scarcity of suitable land, there is very little cultivation. The farmers are driven to collect seaweed to supplement the supplies of winter fodder for their cattle.

The Lofoten Islands are noted for their fisheries. From February to April great shoals of cod migrate southwards from the Barents Sea to the various banks for spawning. Upon their arrival in the Lofoten waters, an intensely active but short fishing season begins, operated by more than 25,000 fishermen. Many of these come from the south for only a few months. Owing to the treacherous currents of the tidal races among the Islands, fishing round the Lofotens is often dangerous, though motor-powered vessels have now been in general use for some time, and have substantially reduced the loss of life.

The chief centers of the fishing industry are Svolvaer and Henningsvaer in the Lofotens and Harstad in the Vesteralens. They have large sheds for preparing the fish, stands for drying the catch, and plants for extracting cod-liver oil as well as for making fish meal from the waste material. Freezing plants have also been added to turn an increasing proportion of the catch into frozen fillets; and the mainland railway from Trondheim has been extended towards Narvik to get the products speedily to the southern ports.

If it were not for the harvest of the sea, the Lofoten-Vesteralen Islands would be almost uninhabited; because of it, the population of the Lofotens alone is about 30,000. Rain-drenched and remote from the center of Norwegian life, their importance lies essentially in serving as bases for this valuable seasonal industry.

Lombok

A large, roughly circular island close to Bali. Location *Lesser Sundas, Indonesia, between the Java Sea and the Indian Ocean.* Area *1,826 square miles.* Map *4, B8.*

Separated from Bali by the Lombok Strait and from Sumbawa by the Alas Strait, Lombok rises with bold, sheer coasts from the ocean. Two mountain chains cross its length; the northern is volcanic, rising to 12,224 feet in Mount Rinjani, one of the highest volcanoes in the archipelago. It is surrounded by a plateau with lower summits and a magnificent lake, 8,200 feet high. The southern chain rises just above 3,000 feet. Between the two, there is a broad valley or terrace with a range of low volcanic hills. The rich alluvial plains alternate with forest-clad mountains and stretches of thorny jungle. The plains are under intensive cultivation under an ancient and elaborate system of irrigation which makes the island extremely beautiful. The small rivers are used only for irrigation and for the growing of rice, which is of excellent quality. Coffee, corn, sugar, cotton, tobacco, indigo and *katyang* (native beans) are also grown in the plains.

For the naturalist, Lombok has always been of special interest, as it is in the border district of the Australian region with its cockatoos and curious megapods, or mound-builders, its peculiar bee-eaters and flightless thrushes.

The natives are predominantly Sassaks (or Sasaks), who are Moslems and of Malayan stock, closely related to the Javanese, quite different from the Balinese Hindus, who conquered but could not convert them. Formerly divided into four states (Karang-Asam Lombok in the west, Mataram in the northwest, Pagarawan in the southwest and Pakutan in the east), Lombok was invaded and subjected to Balinese rule by Agong Dahuran in the early nineteenth century; the union under a single rajah tributary to Bali was established in 1839. The Dutch, who had visited the island first in 1674 and had started trading the following year, landed an expedition at Ampanam in 1894 and advanced towards Mataram, the capital of the Balinese sultan, who had defied Dutch authority and cruelly oppressed his Sassak subjects. The first expedition was repulsed, but another, stronger, stormed the sultan's stronghold and took another citadel, Tjakra Negara – both after desperate resistance. The old sultan of Mataram was captured; he and other Balinese chiefs were exiled and the sultan's heir was killed by his own bodyguard. Lombok was placed under direct Dutch-Indian control which lasted until the Second World War, when the Japanese occupied the island with the rest of the archipelago. Today, Lombok is part of the Indonesian Republic.

Long Island

A large island, part of which forms two boroughs of New York City. Location *Parallel with the New York and Connecticut shore, extending east-northeast from the mouth of the Hudson.* Area *1,401 square miles.* Map *1, F7.*

There are 11 Long Islands in the world – one in Alaska, one in the Bahamas, two in Newfoundland, one in Nova Scotia, one in New Guinea, one in New Zealand, one in Scotland and three in the United States – but the largest and most important, with a population of well over 5,000,000, is the one which Long Island Sound, the Narrows of New York Bay and the East River separate from the east coast of the United States.

White men first settled on the low-lying island, hummocky with its terminal moraines, sandy with the outwash of the last great ice-age glaciations, in 1636. Both Dutch and English colonies sprang up before the English took exclusive possession in 1664. Here the Battle of Long Island – a British victory – was fought on August 27, 1776.

For a long time the Island was a largely rural area, with fishermen, whalers and farmers going about their peaceful pursuits. But as the great metropolis on Manhattan Island began to burst its bonds and spread outwards, more and more of Long Island was absorbed by it. The large boroughs of Brooklyn and Queens are coexistent with Kings and Queens counties of the Island. But even today the eastern part, far more thinly settled than the rest, has many old villages which have not been spoilt by the urban explosion, where one can still find solitude among the dunes, the briar and the blackberry, within sound of the sea. Connected to the mainland by a system of bridges, highways and ferries, Long Island is the home of millions, the goal of vacationers who do not want to go far afield, and the biggest recreation area in the world.

Except for two ridges which run the length of the Island – one near the north shore and the other along its center – and for the bluffs on the north, Long Island is low; even the bluffs and the ridges do not rise higher than 400 feet at their maximum.

Along the northern coast, there are many bays and harbors, mainly in its western section. These are barred from each other by moderately high, forested peninsulas, whose local name is "necks." This is the area of residential communities, the homes of commuters and several resorts; here, too, are the headquarters of many yacht clubs.

The southern shore is framed along 75 miles of its length by a barrier beach. Here are large, sheltered bays – Jamaica, Great South, Moriches and Shinnecock – well-protected from the pounding of the Atlantic. This is the area of the long, sandy public beaches. Coney Island, the westernmost of the series of sand bars, has a year-round population of about 50,000 people, but is visited every summer by over 30,000,000. Its boasts a three-mile-long boardwalk, roller coasters, ferris wheels, carousels, freak shows, waxworks, shooting galleries, dance halls, Turkish baths, swimming pools and numerous restaurants. During the average summer, Coney Island sells over 100,000,000 hot dogs; during the mid-September Mardi Gras, which lasts a week, there are beauty and baby competitions and a final, climactic display of fireworks. Long Beach and Jones Beach, if less well known to the rest of the world, are equally well-patronized, and so is the Rockaway Peninsula. Fire Island or Great South Beach extends for about 40 miles, 5–7 miles off the mainland, with a great many summer communities along its shore.

In the eastern half of the Island there are a good many large country estates. Long Island has also some importance as an agricultural area. Its potato and truck farms supply New York City; it raises millions of ducks, and the oyster banks of Great South Bay send their succulent bivalves all over the country. It is also the site of two great airports – La Guardia and International Airport (Idlewild). Its highways and landscaped parkways give quick access to its various sections.

Loyalty Islands

A coral group of three large islands and many small islets. Location *Southwest Pacific, 60 miles east of New Caledonia.* Area *800 square miles.* Map *4, F9.*

The Loyalty Islands were not discovered until the beginning of the nineteenth century, when Dumont d'Urville charted several of them. When France occupied New Caledonia – just one step ahead of Britain – the group was added to the French possessions in the southwest Pacific.

Uea, or Uvea, is the northernmost of the group, with a population of about 2,300; 23 miles long and about three and a half miles wide, it has a large lagoon formed by its western coast and two parallel rows of islets. It is also the most fertile of the Loyalty Islands, with a large copra production. Its chief town is Fayahoué. Lifu, roughly semicircular, is about 40 miles long and 10 miles wide. The chief town is Chépénéhé. Finally, Maré, the southernmost of the group, with a population of 3,300, is about 22 miles long and 18 miles wide, rising to 300 feet – the highest elevation in the group – and produces oranges in addition to copra.

The Islands are of comparatively recent elevation, but there is a thin coating of soil covering the rocky surface, so that yams, taro and bananas can be grown. Lifu has large caverns which contain fresh water, rising and falling with the tide from some deep underground source.

The Islanders are Melanesians but there is a strange mixture of tribal cultures and languages. In Uea one tribe uses a Samoan and another a New Hebridean form of speech. For many years the natives had a rather dangerous reputation as cannibals but are now among the most civilized Melanesians.

Lundy Island

A small rocky island, a famous bird sanctuary. Location *Off the North Devon coast, at the entrance to the Bristol Channel, England.* Area *1,047 acres.* Map *8, C4.*

Famous as "Puffin Island," whose owner once issued his own stamps and coins, Lundy is only 3½ miles long and ½-1 mile wide: a solitary granite outcrop with rocky tiers rising in places to 800 feet, and providing only one opening for the small boats that bring a constant flow of tourists during the summer.

Strategically placed athwart the shipping lanes from Bristol, the Island was for many centuries a favorite base of pirates – Turkish, Spanish and French. Earlier still, it was the home of the lawless Marisco family, whose forays against all comers grew steadily more ambitious, until both the Island and Marisco Castle, the remains of which still exist, were granted by Henry III to the Knights Templar.

All that Lundy can boast in the way of architecture are two lighthouses, which have replaced the single light formerly in the center of the island, a few houses and a small church. Its population is less than 30. Visitors are drawn by the many thousands of sea-birds which nest on its cliffs and by the fine coast scenery. Natural tunnels are numerous and there is a naval signal station.

Macao

A Portuguese colony on the doorstep of Communist China. Location *At the mouth of the Canton River, South China Sea, 40 miles west of Hong Kong.* Area *Six square miles.* Map *4, B4.*

Macao sits on the Kwantung coast "upon a little hanging island fixed to a greater island . . . sticking to the land by a little slip," as a seventeenth-century description reads. It is a monument to the enterprise of the Portuguese *descobridores*, or merchant-adventurers, of the sixteenth century, who established the first direct communication between Europe and the Far East. Only a classical gateway, the Porto de Cerco, and that "little slip" separate this Portuguese town – the whole coony has a population of over 380,000 – from Red China. The neighboring two islands of Taipa and the single one of Coloane are included in the colony and shelter the harbor. On the seaward side of the peninsula the Praia Grande esplanade skirts the shore for a mile and a half. Spacious old houses and stately churches cover a hillside overlooking the bay.

In 1517, six years after Alfonso de Albuquerque had occupied Malacca, a Portuguese ship was allowed to shelter at Macao. Previously the Portuguese had used other harbors in this region. Forty years later, in recognition of help in destroying pirates, they were granted the lease of Macao at a rent of a few hundred dollars per annum. The port became the chief stopping-place for Portuguese ships trading from the Indies (Goa) to Malacca and Japan. There, merchants and Jesuit missionaries had their headquarters, with the right of visiting the Canton markets twice a year. A bishopric was inaugurated in 1580. The foundries imported copper from Japan; here "cannon. . . are to be had at a reasonable rate," as a visitor recorded in 1665. Two Dutch attacks in 1622 and 1627 were successfully repelled. But by 1662 the Dutch held Malacca, and Macao entered its slow, picturesque decline.

To a certain extent, Macao has always subsisted by the sufferance of the Chinese. From the start, the Viceroy of Canton controlled the food supply to the peninsula. In return the Macao authorities despatched 400 soldiers to aid the last Ming emperor in his unsuccessful struggle against the Manchu invaders. The force returned without seeing action. In 1849 the rent to the Chinese emperor was discontinued, an action ratified by China 40 years later when foreigners were clamoring at many gates. The growth of Hong Kong in the last century, and the gradual silting up of its harbor, were the greatest blows to Macao's trade.

A fire in 1825 destroyed Macao's finest building, the cathedral of São Paolo, but left a façade above the wide steps to attest to the beauty of the greatest of the churches built in the Far East. The college and church of São José, on a height in the middle of the town, and other churches and houses of the seventeenth century, give the city a unified architectural beauty. A grotto commemorates the involuntary stay of the romantic and unhappy Luis de Camoens, whose poetry and travels epitomize the century of Portugal's glory. Ordered from Goa to Macao in 1556 for his satires on the great, he floated ashore from his wrecked ship clutching a spar with one hand and the manuscript of his *Lusiad* with the other. It was not until 1569 that he was able to get back to Lisbon.

Today, Macao lives from exporting fresh and salted fish, from the tourist trade, from smuggling and from gambling. It has a healthful though humid climate and though its trade with Communist China is intermittent, it has managed to survive in somnolence and elegant decay on its "little hanging island."

Macassar Strait

A broad channel connecting the Celebes Sea with the Java and Flores seas. Location *Between Borneo and Celebes.* Dimensions *600 miles long, 80–230 miles wide.* Map *4, B6–7.*

Stretching from the northern tip of Celebes on the east to the much indented coast of Borneo on the west, the wide Macassar Strait is studded with islands. The largest are Laut and Sebuku, off the southeast coast of Borneo. Macassar itself, the largest town of Celebes, is at the southeastern end of the Strait.

In 1625 the Portuguese settled in Macassar; 35 years later they were driven out by the Dutch. Through the wide Strait the people of the adjoining coasts have been in contact with Europeans for three centuries even though Celebes has remained under virtual control of native sultans. The town of Macassar gave its name to macassar oil – derived from the seeds of *Schleichera trijuga*, and used as a basis for cosmetics – which is still exported in considerable quantities, together with copra and rattan. Our Victorian ancestors used macassar oil as hair oil, hence the need to protect upholstered chairs by antimacassars.

In January, 1942, American and Dutch air and naval forces attacked a big Japanese convoy in the Macassar Strait. The battle raged for five days, but the Allies could not prevent the Japanese from landing at Balikpapan and occupying Borneo.

Today, the Strait and its coastline are part of the Indonesian Republic.

McMurdo Sound

An ice-locked channel which has played an important part in Antarctic exploration. Location *Between Ross Island and Victoria Land, Antarctica.* Dimensions *About 92 miles long, 25–45 miles wide.* Map *3, D9.*

Discovered by Sir James Clark Ross in 1841, McMurdo Sound is deeply indented by great bays beyond which huge glaciers tumble down over the lower slopes of the towering mountains. Here is Cape Evans, one of the many spurs of Erebus, closest to the great volcano, and the grand snowy peak with its smoking summit is always visible from the long Sound. Far above the Sound stand the beautiful Western Mountains, with numerous lofty peaks, deep glacial valleys and clear-cut scarps – "a vision of mountain scenery that can have few rivals," as Captain Scott wrote in his diary.

Ross did not push far enough to the south to discover the extent of McMurdo Sound – he thought it was only a bay. But in 1908 Captain Scott found not only deep water but a suitable wintering place at its southern end. Both his expeditions wintered here and his memorial cross still overlooks the bay. Ernest Shackleton built a hut in McMurdo Sound, sending back his *Nimrod* to New Zealand for the winter and making a daring, though unsuccessful, attempt to reach the South Pole from this base. Scott's second, tragic journey also had McMurdo for its starting point. He and his party reached the South Pole, only to find that Amundsen had forestalled them, and perished on the way back.

McMurdo Sound was the site of the airfield which established the South Pole station in "Operation Deepfreeze" (1955). Seven American ships assembled in New Zealand, and the icebreaker *Glacier* landed a small party at Scott's old base of Hut Point in the Sound, after which the rest of the personnel and over 10,000 tons of equipment were landed. The Americans found an iceberg, about the size of *seven* Manhattan Islands, wedged in the strait: it had pushed back the fast-ice from Hut Point more than 20 miles north of where it had been before. This made landing operations easier, for it sheltered McMurdo Sound from the open Ross Sea swell. Within two weeks an air-strip on sea ice four miles from Hut Point had been laid out, which served throughout the Antarctic operations. By early March, 1956, a small settlement was built half a mile from Scott's shelter, with 35 major buildings – of which the washrooms were bigger than Scott's entire hut.

In 1958 Admiral George Dufek had a permanent runway built on the Sound, which could be extended for intercontinental flight. It was called Marble Point, after its dominant rock, and it is exactly halfway between South America and Australia. In the same year, Sir Vivian Fuchs and his team arrived at McMurdo at the end of their Antarctic crossing, to add the latest chapter in its long history of human associations and exploration.

Macquarie Island

An uninhabited volcanic island. Location *South Pacific, 850 miles southeast of Tasmania.* Dimensions *21 miles long, 3 miles wide.* Map *3, B10.*

Fred Hasselborough, sealing in the *Perseverance* in 1810, came one day to this misty island and discovered a very profitable fauna, for his coming initiated a bonanza period of seal hunting (for furs and oil) and penguin boiling (for oil) which was not checked until this century, when Macquarie Island came under the benevolent occupation of scientists. Macquarie is now a dependency of Tasmania and an important base for the Australian National Antarctic Research Expeditions. The hunter is no longer welcome.

Because of its intermediate position between Australia and the territories of the Antarctic, Macquarie is ideally placed for meteorological, aurora, magnetic and cosmic ray observations. In addition, the Island offers a huge study-sanctuary for all kinds of penguins – such as the King, the Royal, the Gentoo, and the seemingly suicidal Rockhopper Penguins who, when they sense danger, leap in alarm into stone crevasses, without apparent harm. Also protected are various kinds of seal.

In the autumn, the din caused by bad-tempered, breeding sea elephants fills the Island. At other times, it is impossible to walk on the beaches because they are thick with penguins; these are sometimes liable to take a tetchy peck at human intruders, but generally their attitude is one of mild curiosity. The rich vegetation of the Island includes the footprint-recording green cushions of *Amorella selago*.

Madagascar

A large island constituting the Malagasy Republic. Location *Indian Ocean, about 240 miles from the east coast of Africa.* Area *227,602 square miles.* Map *10, C8.*

For a number of reasons, Madagascar can claim to be among the most unusual islands in the world. Geologists and zoologists generally agree that it is a fragment of a lost continent, to which the name Lemuria has been given – from the lemurs of Madagascar, gentle, large-eyed primates which are neither monkeys nor apes. This continent stretched as far as India and is believed to have been destroyed in a series of vast volcanic eruptions. When it sank into the Indian Ocean, only the fragment of Madagascar was left behind. On its eastern coast, Madagascar plunges sheer into the ocean, the mountains falling steeply, straight into sea depths of 15,000 feet – a clear indication of a sharp severance from the ancient land mass.

The island's rocks and volcanic structure also bear witness to its origin; the subsoil is formed of granites, gneiss and crystalline schists. Warm water springs are frequent and earthquakes are not uncommon. Rich in iron, Madagascar also has gold, although it is not one of the world's major gold areas. Precious stones are found and so are graphite, mica and rock crystal. There are believed to be some uranium deposits.

The eastern coast presents an almost unbroken appearance, running practically straight with few bays or indentations. The main port on this side of the island, Tamatave, is protected from the Indian Ocean only by a line of coral reefs. On the northwest coast, on the other hand, the land is deeply cut; Marinda Bay, Mahajunga Bay and the port of Majunga are all in this area. Southwest and south, where the land shelves gently towards the Mozambique Channel, the coast is almost unbroken except for the estuary of the Onilahy River.

The temperature is tropical with two clearly defined seasons – the rainy, humid season from November to April and the dry, cool season from April to November. The high central plain of the island is temperate and suitable for European settlement; the modern capital, Tananarive (or Antananarivo), is situated here in the Imerina Highlands.

Madagascar can lend some weight to the legend that it was the home of the fabulous giant roc, for the remains of many large prehistoric birds have been found here and the bones of many vast reptiles and lizards. Even the present-day fauna has a strange and special individuality which sets the island apart from anywhere else in the world. Twenty-five species of bats, many varieties of chameleons, tree-frogs, poisonous spiders, giant tortoises and brilliantly colored birds (unknown elsewhere) are found. The flora, too, is exotic and strange – innumerable types of orchids, tree-mosses, ferns and fragrant flower-bearing trees, and the only genus of cactus truly native outside America. The finds of the naturalists and botanists confirm the geological theory that Madagascar is an island which has long been isolated from other regions.

Its native inhabitants – the population is

5,312,000 – raise almost as many problems as its fauna and flora. The original Malagasys seem to be of Malayo-Polynesian and Melanesian stock. In their rituals, their customs and their physical appearance, they have a good deal in common with the inhabitants of the Indian and Polynesian archipelagos. The island has been known to the Arabs for many centuries and there is a large mixture of Arab as well as Negroid blood. (The slave trade from the east coast of Africa continued well into the mid-nineteenth century.) The Malagasy language is liquid, soft and attractive. The animistic religion of many of the people is, like the island itself, a compound of cruelty and gentleness. The Supreme Being is called by the Malagasys *Andriamanitra* – the Fragrant One.

Portuguese explorers discovered Madagascar as early as 1500, but their attempts – and those of the French – to establish trading posts were foiled repeatedly. Later the pirates of the Indian Ocean started to haunt the island's shores, and innumerable European adventurers – among them the picturesque and well-meaning Count Maurice Benyovszky, who actually became king of the island for a brief period – tried to establish themselves. In the nineteenth century there was a long-drawn-out struggle between Britain and France to gain the predominant influence at the Malagasy court. The Malagasy kings and queens – Radama I (1810–28), Radama II (1861–63), Queen Ranavalona I (1828–61), Queen Rasoaherina (1863–68) and Ranavalona II (1868–83) – alternately encouraged and resisted the opening up of the country. In 1885 Queen Ranavalona III recognized a general French protectorate. Ten years later the French occupied Tananarive and formally abolished royal power. It was ten years before resistance was crushed and French rule firmly established.

During the Second World War, British troops occupied strategic points to prevent the Vichy Government from providing bases for the Axis Powers, and later handed them over to the Free French forces. In 1946 Madagascar became a French overseas territory under the new constitution. Constitutional reforms were introduced in 1957, giving the island internal autonomy; in October, 1958, Madagascar adopted republican status while remaining within the French community. Complete independence was proclaimed in June, 1960, and immediately afterwards the first President of the Malagasy Republic, Philibert Tsiranana, signed agreements with France confirming continued membership of the French community. The former dependencies of Madagascar, Juan de Nova, Europe Island and Bassas-de-India, remained integral parts of France; Saint-Marie, off the east coast, is recognized as a dependency of the Malagasy Republic, but its inhabitants have a dual Franco-Malagasy nationality.

Madeira

An island famous for its wine. Location *North Atlantic, about 600 miles southwest of Lisbon, 400 miles west of Morocco.* Area *About 286 square miles.* Map *6, F3.*

Madeira rises from the Atlantic in shining, rugged precipices, scarred here and there by dark ravines. From the sea, the island has a striking beauty. The eye is always led back to the central peak, Pico Ruivo, rising to 6,106 feet and often snow-covered. Like the neighboring islands – Porto Santo, and an uninhabited group of islets, the Desertas – Madeira is volcanic in origin, the summit of an immense mountain rising sheer from the depths of the Atlantic Ocean. There are no evidences of volcanic activity in any of the Madeira group today, and it is clear that the islands must have been formed over a very considerable period of time.

The Phoenicians are reputed to have been the first discoverers of Madeira, but there is little evidence to support this theory. In the fourteenth century, according to a romantic tale, an Englishman, Robert Machin, eloping with Anne d'Arfet from England to France, was driven here by a gale, so that the two lovers became the first settlers. Madeiran guides still show the place on the coast, Machico, where they landed. The first historical record of the Madeira group is from 1418, when João Zarco first sighted Porto Santo. Two years later, Madeira itself was discovered by the Portuguese, and Prince Henry the Navigator soon began colonizing the uninhabited archipelago.

The cultivation of the vine which has made Madeira so famous began within a few years of

Santa Cruz harbor, Canary Islan

the Portuguese occupation, but for a long time sugar cane remained the staple product of the island. It was the English proclamation in 1663 that wine from Madeira might be carried in English ships to any English possessions or colonies that made the fortune of the island's wine trade. The sugar cane was uprooted and intensive cultivation of the grape began. Today, in an island only 30 miles long, with a population of about 270,000, there is hardly a square foot of workable earth that is not planted with vines. Nearly all the interior is uninhabited, being largely given over to viticulture. The villages are usually built on rocky outcrops or at the heads of ravines where no profitable earth can be worked. The cultivation on terraces reaches right up to 2,000 feet.

Maelstrom

A strait which has become the epitome of dangerous whirlpools. Location *Lofoten Islands, North Sea.* Dimensions *About three miles across.* Map *7, G2.*

Known also as the Moskenstraum or Moskenstrom, the Maelstrom is a strait running between Moskenesoy on the north and Mosken islet on the south. The word is probably of Dutch origin, from *malen*, to grind or whirl, and *stroom*, current. The Maelstrom appears on Mercator's atlas of 1595, and the first detailed notice about it is in the writings of the Bishop of Arebo in the seventeenth century, which were later elaborated by Peter Dass.

The current runs with the tides, alternately six hours from north to south and six hours from south to north, and, in certain conditions of wind and tide, produces large and dangerous whirls.

In medieval times the strait was thought to be unfathomable, but in fact its depth does not exceed 20 fathoms (it has a bottom of rock and white sand), and its danger has been much exaggerated. The tales of ships being swallowed in it are mere fables. Only when the wind is in the northwest and opposed to the reflux of the current from the south, does the Maelstrom attain its greatest fury: at other times small boats can cross it in perfect safety. But the ancient tales caught the imagination of Edgar Allan Poe and in his *A Descent into the Maelstrom* (1841) he gave a highly imaginative, terrifying description of the "smooth, shining and jet-black wall of water, inclined to the horizon at an angle of some forty-five degrees, speeding dizzily round and round with a swaying and sweltering motion, and sending forth to the winds an appalling voice, half shriek, half roar, such as not even the mighty cataract of Niagara ever lifts up in its agony to Heaven."

Magellan, Strait of

A winding, storm-swept series of channels. Location *Between the Atlantic and the Pacific, separating the mainland of South America from Tierra del Fuego.* Dimensions *350 miles long, 2–20 miles wide.* Map *6, C11.*

The Strait of Magellan is a winding passage, separating Tierra del Fuego and the adjoining islands to the west from the mainland of South America. Its Atlantic entrance is at Cape Virgins, its Pacific entrance at Cape Pilar on Desolation Island. Except at the Atlantic end, where it just touches the shore of Argentine Patagonia, it is bordered throughout by Chilean territory; but although it is within Chilean territorial waters, it is a free international waterway.

After the First and Second Narrows, not far from the Atlantic entrance, there is a broad stretch running due south, from which a confined passage leads northwest past Brunswick Peninsula and Desolation Island to the Pacific. In this western section, the Strait traverses a wild and desolate highland region intersected by a maze of fjords; it is itself of the fjord type, bordered by mountains that carry icefields from which here and there glaciers descend to the water's edge.

The Strait was discovered in 1520 by Ferdinand Magellan, whose name it has borne ever since. Magellan, who was convinced that Asia could be reached by sailing west, was given a commission by the King of Spain to discover a route to the Moluccas, or Spice Islands, which would be an alternative to the route around Africa controlled by the Portuguese. Magellan's small fleet skirted south along the Patagonian coast to Cape Virgins, where the great discovery was made. "We found by miracle, a strait...

hing boats on Lavinia Beach, Ceylon

which is a hundred and ten leagues long . . . and it issues in another sea which is called the peaceful sea."

As Magellan found, the passage of the Strait is not easy for sailing ships. The tide range is up to 60 feet and tide-rips up to 13 knots occur in the narrowest channels. Besides these hazards, frequent mists and fogs and unpredictable winds add to the terrors of shipwreck in the desolate western section, so that the Strait was generally avoided by sailing ships, for which the Cape Horn route, although stormy, was preferable. Contrary to its name, the Pacific Ocean in these regions is tempestuous, making the entry into the Strait dangerous for such vessels. Magellan Strait, indeed, came into general use only in the age of the steamship, and then only for little more than half a century until the Panama Canal became available in 1914.

The bulk of the steamer traffic through Magellan Strait was long-distance trans-oceanic, either between the west coast of South America and North Atlantic ports or eastwards (only) from New Zealand to Britain. It has never been of much use to South American countries for trade, as it lies over 1,000 miles beyond the limits of the populous regions on either side. Even for Chile it serves only to link the remote and thinly populated sheep-farming country of Magellanes, east of the wild mountain zone, with the rest of the country. There is only one town of importance on the Strait: Punta Arenas, which has developed as a port of call for passing ships and as a center from which wool and frozen mutton are exported. Magellan would see little difference if he navigated his Strait today.

Malacca, Strait of

One of the most important shipping lanes in the world, between Europe and the Far East. Location *Between the Malay Peninsula and Sumatra.* Dimensions *500 miles long, 30–200 miles wide.* Map *10, H6.*

It was in about 1400 that the port of Malacca was established on the Strait to which it gave its name, rising rapidly to become a great center of the spice trade. After its rulers accepted the Mohammedan faith in 1414, the religion spread throughout the archipelago, and during the century that followed the whole Malay Peninsula as well as neighboring parts of Sumatra came under the rule of Malacca.

But in September, 1509, the Portuguese fleet of López de Sequiera anchored off Malacca. Looking along the quay of the great harbor, they saw gigantic Chinese junks with tremendous sails made of matting, their hulls built high out of the water; Malayan *praus* and the deep south-sea outriggers; Arab dhows whose lateen sails rose in sweeping and elegant grandeur against the turquoise-colored sky. Constant activity, an ant-hill of life and movement, incessant bartering and bargaining, a babel of the languages of the eastern world – for Malacca, the "Queen of the Straits," was a real international harbor. True, it was only in late autumn and winter that, because of wind conditions, sea traffic passed through the Strait of Malacca; the normal sea route to and from China was then through the Sunda Strait and past the Philippines. But spice-traders were bound to make use of Malacca, and since the trade was mostly barter, every type of merchandise passed through this great seaway: African slaves, gigantic stacks of cinnamon, cloves and pepper, tremendous vessels of Japanese saké, carefully packed crates of the finest Chinese porcelain, sandalwood from Timor, precious stones from Ceylon, cashmere from Bengal, finely chiseled swords from Damascus, carved ivory from Siam and lovely Circassian concubines.

Sequeira and many of his crew were lured ashore and murdered by the Malays, but Ferdinand Magellan, serving under Sequeira, managed to fight his way through the Malay mob and rescue the last survivor of the landing party, his friend Francisco Serrão. Two years later Magellan returned to redeem Portugal's tarnished honor. After several weeks of hard battles with shifting fortunes, the greatest harbor of the Far East became Portuguese.

Malacca and the Strait remained under Portuguese rule until 1641, when the Dutch took over; though in both cases domination was restricted to Malacca and the country immediately behind it. But as Penang's importance rose in the eighteenth century, Malacca's declined, and Singapore, at the southern end of the Strait, overshadowed both of them.

Today, the Strait is again one of the great waterways of the world. George Town, on Penang island, is one of the chief ports of the Malay Federation, sending tin, rubber and copra through the Strait. It is linked by ferry to the mainland at Prai and to the Singapore-Bangkok railway. It is the nearest port of call to the Thai capital for vessels routed south through the Strait. It also serves the developing northeast coast of Sumatra. Malacca itself has only offshore anchorage today and has been superseded by Port Swettenham, the port of Kuala Lumpur. But the junks, praus, dhows and outriggers still share the waters of the Strait with the modern liners and cargo-boats.

Maldive Islands

A chain of low-lying coral islets under British protection. Location *Indian Ocean, south of the Laccadive Islands, southwest of Ceylon.* Area *About 115 square miles.* Map *10, E5–6.*

From southernmost Addu Atoll and Fua-Mulaku to Ihavandiffulu Atoll in the north, the Maldive Islands stretch their coral chain across the Indian Ocean.

Most of the 16 principal atolls, which consist of many hundreds of islets, have grown up on the eastern side of submerged banks, for on the west they are exposed to the southwest monsoon, the seasonal wind which sweeps across the Indian Ocean to unload its moisture on the subcontinent of India. A typical atoll like Addu is a horseshoe-shaped reef of coral enclosing a still lagoon. The shifting pattern in such lagoons, from the milky white of shallow water near the coral-sand beach to the greens, purples and blues of the deeper parts, is a fantasy of color. The palm trees lean eastward before the prevailing wind and there is no sound except the boom of the surf on the coral reefs.

The inhabitants – the population of the group is about 90,000 – are of mixed Indian, Arab and Sinhalese blood; they are Mohammedans almost without exception. They are remarkable seamen, building their own boats and trading between the Islands, India and Ceylon. Coconuts and copra form the basis of their trade while tortoise-shell as well as the beautiful cowrie shell are still exported for use by the Indian and Sinhalese jewellers.

What is possibly the last square-rigged sailing vessel in the world still in active commission works out of the Islands. Like the inhabitants of similar coral atolls in the Pacific, the natives of the Maldives are sailors and fishermen almost as soon as they can walk.

During the first quarter of the sixteenth century the Portuguese tried to establish settlements on the Islands, as they had already done in the Laccadives. They were unsuccessful and the Maldivians turned for protection to Ceylon. Until recent years the hereditary sultan of the Islands was a tributary to the British Government of Ceylon. During the Second World War many of the Islanders were evacuated to India and Ceylon. At the same time the vast lagoon of Addu Atoll was turned into a flying boat base for submarine and coastal reconnaissance.

Malta

A historic Mediterranean island. Location *About halfway between Gibraltar and Suez, 60 miles south of Sicily.* Area *94.87 square miles.* Map *9, D10.*

Though it is a small island, Malta contains within its battlemented walls, its narrow fields and crowded villages, one of the richest histories of any island in the Mediterranean. Its dominating position across the main lines of trade and shipping have made it a highly desirable base of sea power from the days of the Phoenicians to our own times. Formed largely of sandstone and Tertiary limestone, its prevailing color of a tawny ocher is relieved from monotony by the brilliance of the well-cultivated fields. In spring the island is a crazy quilt of wild flowers, and the flowering clover which is widely grown seems like a reflection of the sea beyond the Grand Harbour – one of the best in the Mediterranean.

A fragment of the land-bridge which once united Africa with Italy, Malta has many traces of a rich neolithic history. A number of megalithic temples or sanctuaries still exist. Most notable are those at Hal Tarzien and Mnaidra, which are built of large limestone blocks and contain remarkable bas-reliefs of animals as well as human figurines of clay and stone. At Hal Salfieni is the Hypogeum, a rare form of primitive ossuary cut out of solid rock – a foreshadowing of the later tunnels and caves of Malta. Among the most interesting primitive antiquities of the island are the so-called "cart-ruts" – parallel grooves worn in the rock whose origin is still in dispute. At Birzebuggia some of these cart-ruts run out under the sea; modern free diving techniques will probably enable archeologists to cast some new light on their history and purpose.

Phoenicians, Greeks, Carthaginians and Romans were the successive masters of Malta in the pre-Christian era. Here St Paul was shipwrecked, as the Acts of the Apostles relate: "And falling into a place where two seas met, they ran the ship aground... and when they were escaped, then they knew that the island was called Melita." St Paul's Bay commemorates the legendary landing site on the east coast of the island. It was as a result of this accident that the Maltese became one of the earliest converts to Christianity, destined later to be one of the main bastions against Mohammedan expansion in Europe. After the division of the Roman Empire, Malta was apportioned to Byzantium. The Arabs conquered it in 870 but the Normans of Sicily regained it for Christendom in 1090.

The most impressive monuments of the island's past are to be seen in the palaces and fortresses of the Knights of Malta. After the Great Siege of 1565, when the knights under La Valette successfully drove off the Moorish fleets, the present system of fortifications was completed. (The island had been given by Charles V to the Knights Hospitalers, who were also called the Knights of St John of Jerusalem, and later, the Knights of Malta.) They make Valetta one of the finest examples of a fortified city in the world, and the entrance to the Grand Harbour is unrivalled in dignity. On one side, the great shoulders of Fort St Angelo bulk against the sky, and on the other loom the high walls, the deep embrasures and the frowning bastions of La Valette's masterpiece. For over two centuries, from this almost impregnable island the galleys of the Knights harassed Turkish shipping. (In a boat pound behind St Angelo one can see where their galleys were moored during the winter months, and in tunneled caves the quarters of the captured Moorish galley slaves.)

In 1798 Malta surrendered to Napoleon but two years later the people rose and blockaded the French garrison in the citadel until the British fleet arrived. In 1814 Great Britain formally annexed the island by the Treaty of Paris and Malta became one of the most important links in the defense system of the Empire. In the Second World War Malta defied air and sea attacks which lasted almost continuously for three years and earned the George Cross, awarded collectively for outstanding civilian heroism. It remained a most essential base for the Allied operations in Africa and the Middle East. In the devastating raids 1,540 civilians were killed and about 35,000 homes destroyed or damaged. A postwar grant of £30,000,000 was made by Britain for general reconstruction. Since 1958 the island's constitution has been the subject of repeated negotiations but self-government was suspended and a new interim Constitution was introduced in April 1959; Malta's future form of government and exact position in the British Commonwealth still await final settlement.

Although the island's soil is shallow, it is extremely rich. Vines, oranges, figs, apricots and nectarines flourish as well as maize, wheat and barley. One of the most densely populated areas in the world – with 324,000 people – Malta cannot afford to waste a square yard of cultivable land. Water remains a constant problem and large underground cisterns, dependent on rainfall, are becoming inadequate to cope with modern demands. The seas around the island contain almost every variety of Mediterranean fish, from the dolphin to the flying gurnard and the rainbow-colored wrasse. The local boats are of a distinctive shape, unlike any others in the Mediterranean, and the harbor boats or *dghaissas* are a unique feature of the Maltese scene. At night the waters of Grand Harbour and of the other creeks and bays are criss-crossed by the wavering glow-worm lights of the *dghaissas*. In the distance the crackle of squibs, the flash and boom of thunder-crackers and the winging tracery of rockets show that one of the island villages is holding a fiesta.

Instinct with life, the narrow streets of Valetta, the capital, present a vivid spectacle on a summer day. Weaving among the modern cars amble the horse-drawn *carossas* and all about sounds the curious Maltese language, as unique as the history of the island, combining Arabic with Italian and having many root forms of Phoenician. Eighteenth-century baroque churches stand cheek-by-jowl with Edwardian and Victorian "seaside styles," while the ramparts are a monument to the greatest age of fortification in Europe.

Man, Isle of

A large resort island off the coast of Britain. Location *Irish Sea, between Lancashire and Northern Ireland.* Area *220.7 square miles.* Map *7, D4.*

The Isle of Man is criss-crossed with narrow gauge railways – little trains which wander off through fields of meadowsweet, with the large brass domes of the engines a proud fantasy. Rich in scenic beauty, it attracts many thousands of visitors – some of whom come to visit the capital, Douglas, while others attend the famous motorcycle races. From its mountain top, Snaefell (2,034 feet), Ireland, England, Scotland and Wales may all be seen, on a fine day; and indeed, the varied features of Manx landscape could be called a concentration of all these lands. In country districts the visitor may easily find the loneliness to meditate on the quaint lore of a race which once, on the day after Christmas, used to bury a wren to sing dirges in the Manx tongue – yet had the shrewd wit to compose a proverb saying: "Don't marry an heiress unless her father has been hanged."

Douglas, on its splendid bay, has more to offer than may be apparent at first glance. Many late Georgian castellated mansions still reward the visitor. Designed by John Welch, they belong to a time when aristocratic debtors from England and Ireland found asylum in the Manx realm. Castletown, the former capital, boasts a Norman castle, seat of Manx kings, and a dial with 13 faces which was reputed to tell the time by the moon as well as the sun. Peel, one-time center of the important kipper industry, is a port endowed with ruined St Patrick's Castle on an islet; while Ramsey, second to Douglas, is a town of character. Today 55,213 people live on the island, but there are ten times as many annual visitors.

The island was dominated, so legend tells us, by the Manx magician Mannanan, who kept strangers away by conjuring up mists; and later by Irish missionaries, and still later by the kings of Norway. The Vikings occupied it around 600 A.D. In 1286, the English Crown took over its protection and presented the Lordship of Man to the Stanleys, who became Earls of Derby. The seventh Earl gave his name to the famous Derby Race, which was first run on the dunes near Castletown. In the late eighteenth century, the privileges of taxation were bought back by England; yet the Isle of Man still has its own Parliament (the second oldest in the world, with its lower chamber called the House of Keys) and its own flag (an emblem of three legs). The Deemster (High Court Judge) swears to be as impartial as "the herring bone does lie in the middle of the fish."

At the southern extremity of the island is the Calf, an isle where falcons were bred by the Stanleys to be presented to the sovereigns of England; but no one can account for the presence on the main island of the famous cats that have no tails.

Manhattan

An island comprising the central part of New York City. Location *Between the Hudson, Harlem and East rivers and New York Bay.* Dimensions *12½ miles long, 2½ miles wide.* Map *1, F7.*

When Peter Minuit bought an island from the Manhattan Indians in 1626, paying for it with trinkets worth $24, he had, of course, no idea that this wooded tract of land at the head of one of the world's finest natural harbors would grow into the greatest city of the western hemisphere. Until 1664 it was called New Amsterdam; then, the English having supplanted the Dutch, it became New York. Today it is officially one of the five boroughs of Greater New York, with an area of 22 square miles; Randalls, Wards and Welfare islands are all part of the borough, and Manhattan and New York are practically synonyms. Within this comparatively narrow area, bordered by the two rivers, by Spuyten Devil Creek and by New York Bay, the greatest concentration of wealth and art and the most astonishing variety of humanity have grown up. Until 1874 New York

An aerial view of Manhattan

City was virtually restricted to Manhattan; only in the last 90 years has the great city burst its boundaries and sent its floodtide of people and buildings over the mainland and the neighboring islands, swallowing several Westchester communities.

The growth of Manhattan coincides with the floodtide of European emigration which lasted from the eighteen-seventies to the First World War. Between 1865 and 1900 no fewer than 13,260,000 immigrants entered the United States, most of them through New York. Of these, hundreds of thousands did not move beyond the eastern seaboard. By 1890 there were as many Germans here as in Hamburg, twice as many Irishmen as in Dublin and two and a half times as many Jews as in Warsaw. That is one of the reasons why Manhattan is among the most cosmopolitan cities in the world – though it is also the most changeable, the most rapidly developing, the most inconstant metropolis, and whatever is true about it today might be overtaken and refuted by the events of tomorrow.

Yet, with new skyscrapers going up every week and all but the most venerable historical memorials falling to the wrecker's bulldozer and steel-ball, Manhattan still preserves a microcosm of American history. Old Castle Clinton at the small Battery Park was originally built as a fort in 1807; it has been an amusement center, an immigration station and a famous aquarium, and has now been partially reconstructed and will become a national museum. Fraunces Tavern, built in 1719, where George Washington said goodbye to his officers in 1783; Trinity Church, which occupies the seat of a parish created in 1697; the Subtreasury Building, standing on the site once occupied by Federal Hall, the first seat of the national government, where Washington took the Presidential oath in 1789; St Paul's Chapel (1764), the oldest church building in Manhattan; Cooper Union (founded 1859), one of the leading colleges of art and engineering, where Abraham Lincoln soared to national prominence when he spoke there before his election in 1860 – these are all landmarks in the history of the Union.

Built roughly on the grid system, with its main avenues running south to north from the Battery and its cross-streets roughly east to west, Manhattan is a city with an orderly and generally symmetrical ground plan. Except in the Wall Street area, the Lower East Side and Greenwich Village, it would be difficult for the stranger to lose his way on Manhattan, knowing that 42nd Street is inexorably followed by 43rd. Broadway is the only major artery that cuts diagonally across the grid – and can boast of being one of the longest streets in the world, running 150 miles north to Albany.

Yet symmetry does not mean monotony. Not only does the immensely varied and ever-renewed architecture – ranging from the Empire State Building to the huge glass monolith of the United Nations building, from the daringly *avant garde* Guggenheim Museum to the towers of Rockefeller Center – guarantee this, but the often blurred yet still discernible national enclaves. There are Jewish, Italian, Russian, Spanish, Greek, German, Chinese, Polish and Hungarian Manhattans, some fairly large, some restricted to a street or two. There is Harlem with its large Negro population and, more recently, there are the areas which the huge Puerto Rican influx has stamped with its characteristics. There are the towering apartment houses overlooking Central Park (the largest park on Manhattan); the serene precincts of the Cloisters to which John D. Rockefeller moved a Spanish monastery, a medieval adjunct to the great Metropolitan Museum, on the glittering rocks above the Hudson; the glare, vital bustle and noise of Times Square and Broadway.

Manhattan has had its share of writers, composers, painters and chroniclers who have tried to capture its magic. There have been books, films and musicals devoted to almost every important street or square within its limits, from Washington Square to 42nd Street, from Fifth Avenue to Riverside Drive, from Greenwich Village to Fulton Fish Market. Because of this, it has stamped its many-faceted image upon the minds of untold millions throughout the world. Grant's Tomb or Carnegie Hall, Madison Square Garden or Union Square, Hell's Kitchen or Harlem, Skid Row or St Patrick's Cathedral, have become as familiar to people in five continents as their own main streets and square. This image is constantly renewed by television, by books and magazines, of which Manhattan is a primary producer and distributor. Its image is projected by the hucksters of Madison Avenue, by the studios of the television networks, by the newspapers and department stores, just as much as by Tiffany's or the luxury shops of Fifth Avenue, by the great hotels and the innumerable cosmopolitan restaurants – or the automat. Tammany Hall and Boss Tweed, Murder Inc. and Mr Costello, the Bowery bums and the racketeers, have been just as integral a part of this multi-colored image as the Metropolitan Opera House, the noble public library or the Empire State Building.

The Irish cop, the Chinese laundryman, the talkative taxi-driver, the father-confessor barman, the "men in gray suits" – to choose only five Manhattan types at random – have also acquired world-wide fame or notoriety. So have the open-air chessplayers of Washington Square, the skaters of the Rockefeller Plaza, or the majestic doormen of the hotels, nightclubs and apartment houses.

Manhattan, or rather New York City, is also one of the world's greatest ports, with its wharves and piers able to handle the largest passenger liners or tankers. New York Bay, enclosed by the shores of northern New Jersey, Staten Island, Manhattan and Brooklyn, with its carefully maintained channels and anchorages, receives more cargo and passengers than any other harbor in the western hemisphere. While 2,000,000 people live on the island, more than twice as many flood in every day from its suburbs and hinterland. Manhattan is connected by an intricate network of bridges, rail, vehicular and subway tunnels and ferries with the other boroughs of New York and with New Jersey. The South Ferry Plaza on the Battery is the terminus of the ferry lines, with the Brooklyn-Battery tunnel's entrance nearby; express highways run along the western and eastern sides of the island, also from the Battery. The Brooklyn, Williamsburg and Manhattan bridges stretch across the East River; the Holland Tunnel leads to New Jersey; the Lincoln Tunnel starts on the West Side; the George Washington Bridge crosses the Hudson River. The Grand Central Terminus, on 42nd Street, is one of the world's largest rail passenger terminals. Triborough Bridge links Manhattan to Queens and the Bronx.

But power, wealth, poverty and violence represent only certain facets of the crowded island. Its great universities and libraries, its fine museums and concert halls, its surprising nooks and crannies, make it not only one of the most fascinating, but one of the most rewarding places in the world – still justifying Walt Whitman's sonorous lines:

. . .nested in nests of water-bays, superb,
Rich, hemm'd thick all around with sailships and steamships,
An island sixteen miles long, solid-founded,
Numberless crowded streets, high growth of iron, slender, strong, light,
Splendidly uprising toward clear skies. . .

Marajó

A large alluvial island dividing the Amazon and the Pará rivers. Location *Amazon Delta, eastern Pará, Brazil.* Area *18,519 square miles.* Map *6, D6.*

The southwestern half of Marajó, opposite the mouth of the Tocantine River, is covered with dense tropical forests, and the northern central area with uninhabitable swamps, while the rest of the island – which nowhere rises more than 25 feet above sea level – consists of immense level plains or savannas, varied here and there by clumps of trees or artificial mounds. Some of these mounds are as much as 200 yards long, 80 yards wide and 40 feet high; they are the burial places or village substructures of vanished ancient Indian tribes. The Indians have left abundant pottery remains, in the form of bowls, burial urns, curious figurines and *tangas* – triangular, curved pottery fig-leaves worn by the women and shaped to the body. In some places pottery covers the ground in a vast mosaic, proof of the large population in days gone by.

Among the most important inhabitants today are the *vaqueros*, or cowboys, who look after herds of cattle – for the whole savanna region is divided into ranches, some with over 50,000 head of cattle, which supply meat to the neighboring mainland. Living as they do under semi-aquatic conditions – in the driest weather the general height of the land is little more than three feet above river level – the *vaqueros* spend their lives as much in canoes or on ox-back as on horses. The cattle they tend are subject to a multitude of peculiar hazards: hunger and thirst in the dry season, when all but the largest rivers are dry, and the vegetation is parched and withered; drowning in the wet season, from January to June, when much of the land is flooded to a depth of six feet or more; and at all times, to the depredations of the swarms of crocodiles or caymans that live here. Marajó is still in the Age of Reptiles; these great saurians, in their overwhelming numbers, are the dominant form of animal life on the island. When the water retreats after the rains and most of the land surface is deep, sticky mud, they are at their most rapacious, for the unfortunate cattle cannot escape them if stuck in the mud or marooned on the small patches of higher ground. Each year at this season thousands of full-grown beasts are killed or eaten alive.

Killing caymans is not merely an exciting form of sport for the Marajian *vaquero*, but one of his most important duties. They mostly work in threes; approaching the swampy ground, where the crocodiles live, on oxen (more sure-footed than horses in mud) or in canoes, one *vaquero* jumps into the water and picks out a crocodile which he chases towards the shore – they are rather cowardly and inclined to flee when pursued. Meanwhile, another *vaquero* stands ready on dry ground with his lasso. First one, then the other, fling their ropes, securing the beast firmly round the neck and snout from behind and in front, so that it is held tightly, unable to move. Then a third cowboy severs its spinal column with a sharp knife. As many as 300 of the huge reptiles are killed in a single day and night by a trio of men. Jaguars are also a danger – but despite these vicissitudes, the life of a Marajian *vaquero* is in general as easy-going, as free-roaming, as that of any other cowboy in the world.

The main settlements of Marajó are Soure, a popular health resort, on the east coast and Arariúna. The island has a population of about 130,000.

Marianas Islands

A group of volcanic islands which played an important part in the Second World War. Location *Western Pacific, 1,500 miles east of the Philippines.* Area *370 square miles.* Map *4, E5.*

When the sailors of Magellan first visited these small volcanic islands, scattered over 500 miles from north to south, they found that the inhabitants would carry off everything that was not nailed fast to the decks of the ships. So they called the whole group *Los Ladrones*, the Islands of the Thieves. However, Spanish cartographers did not approve of such a pejorative name; a century and a half later the Islands were rebaptized the Marianas, in honor of Queen Maria Anna of Austria, widow of King Philip IV of Spain. In 1899, the Spaniards, being in considerable financial embarrassment after their defeat in the Spanish-American war, sold them to Germany. In 1914 they were occupied by the Japanese, and in 1918 they were made a Japanese mandate. They remained in this state from 1922 to 1935 when they became Japan's possessions and were built up as important naval and air bases. Guam, however, the largest of the group (210 square miles, with an estimated population of 66,910), remained in American possession, the United States forces having occupied it at the beginning of the Spanish-American war. In December, 1941, the Japanese captured Guam after stubborn American resistance; but it was recaptured by the United States forces by August, 1944.

The Guamanians are of Chamorro stock mingled with Filipino and Spanish blood, and have a language of their own which belongs to the Malayo-Polynesian family but has a considerable admixture of Spanish. In 1950, Guam was given statutory powers of self-government and Guamanians are now United States citizens. A governor is appointed for a four-year term and a 21-member single-chamber legislature is elected every other year. There is a District Court with original jurisdiction in cases under Federal law. Guam is not only an important naval and air base but also an essential link in transpacific air travel. Its fertile valleys are framed by mountains in the south which rise to 1,334 feet; it produces rice, coconuts, coffee, cocoa, tobacco, pineapples and indigo, though its principal export is copra.

Agrihan, in the northern section of the group, is uninhabited, and has the highest elevation of the Marianas (3,166 feet). Its area is 18 square miles and it has some unworked phosphate deposits. Pajaros is the northernmost of the Marianas. Rota is larger than most of the other islands of the group, extending to 33 square miles; it has a population of about 700. Its volcanic base is covered with coral limestone, and some curious ancient stone columns have been discovered close to its airfield, amid its extensive sugar plantations. Saipan is the second largest in the group, after Guam, and was the most important Japanese base. Its extinct volcano, Mount Tapotchau, rises to 1,554 feet; it has a population of over 5,000 and is, like the rest of the Marianas (except Guam), held by the United States under a United Nations Trusteeship.

In the Second World War Saipan was the scene of bitter and bloody battles, until the Japanese were overcome. Today, there are three airfields on the Islands, of which Isely Field is the largest, and an American naval base at Tanapeg Harbor. Tinian, about three miles southwest of Saipan, saw equally stubborn fighting in 1944, when it was captured from the Japanese, who had an important airfield on the 39-square-mile island. Here, too, some ancient stone monuments have been found. The port of Sunharon Roads on the west coast is important, and in 1948 a leper colony was established on Tinian.

The inhabitants of the Marianas – apart from the original Chamorros – are Micronesians and Japanese, the latter the most numerous. Under the Trusteeship, all the Islands are being developed and their manganese ore, sulphur and phosphate deposits are being increasingly exploited.

Marianas Trench

A great submarine depression, the deepest known. Location *North Pacific Ocean, east of southern Marianas Islands.* Depth *36,960 feet.* Map *4, E5.*

The deepest point known on the earth's surface was discovered on January 23, 1960, in the Marianas Trench, a curving abyss in the floor of the Pacific Ocean, over 300 miles long and up to 30 miles wide, with a narrow, steep inner gorge.

The Trench was first discovered in 1899, when the Nero Deep (31,614 feet) was measured southeast of Guam. For over 30 years, this was considered the deepest in the world, until in the nineteen-thirties a depth of 32,197 feet was found nearby. Then, in 1960, the United States Navy's bathyscaphe *Trieste*, carrying the Swiss scientist Jacques Piccard – son of the inventor of the bathyscaphe – and Lieutenant Don Walsh, made a descent of more than seven miles to the bottom of the Marianas Trench. The depth reached was considerably greater than the record of 24,000 feet which the same craft had established two weeks earlier; it was 2,800 feet greater than the depth indicated for the Marianas Trench in soundings by a Soviet oceanographic ship in 1957.

The bathyscaphe consisted of a 58-foot-long tank, resembling a small submarine, with a ball-shaped gondola six feet in diameter underneath. It carried equipment to measure currents, temperature and the salinity of the water, together with depth indicators, a tape-recorder and still and movie cameras. The gondola was packed with absorbent silica gel to keep the instruments dry. Through eight-inch windows, made of a special glass which becomes plastic under pressure, the scientists were able to make their observations. To give the bathyscaphe surface buoyancy, its compartments were loaded with 30,000 gallons of high octane fuel. During the descent the buoyancy was lessened gradually by admitting sea water into two of the compartments, which equalized the pressure at great depths inside and outside the float. The craft carried 13 tons of iron pellets, and the gradual return to the surface was made by discharging these pellets at a rate of about a ton for every 3,000 feet.

On the way down, twilight came at 600 feet when it was impossible to tell colors apart and at 1,000 feet the light had completely vanished. Formless plankton streamed past, giving a sensation of great speed. At 15,000 feet, the explorers lost voice contact with the underwater telephone above them, but recovered it at the bottom of the descent. At 27,000 feet, the rate of descent was checked to two feet per second by dumping ballast. At the bottom, a white fish a foot long, shaped like a sole, with a protruberant eye on each side, came into view. The descent was made in four hours and 42 minutes. The bathyscaphe remained at the bottom under a pressure of nine tons per square inch for half an hour. The journey back to the surface was made in three hours and 27 minutes. "One of the greatest moments of the dive," wrote Jacques Piccard, "came at about 1,200 feet. We started to see daylight again . . ."

Marmara, Sea of

A body of water between the Black Sea and the Aegean. Location *Between European and Asiatic Turkey.* Area *About 4,300 square miles.* Maximum depth *About 4,500 feet.* Map *7, G9.*

Marmara (also spelled Marmora) is the Propontis of the ancient world, and owes its modern name to the Island of Marmara with its famous marble quarries. Passing through the long strait of the Dardanelles, with its many ghosts, from Xerxes to Hero and Leander, from Byron to the ill-fated Gallipoli expedition in the First World War, the Sea of Marmara opens to the view, with Marmara Island lying across the mouth of the channel and Aphisia and other smaller islands to the east of it. The current runs strongly in the Sea, though not so noticeably as in the strait, or at the far end in the Bosporus. It is a surface current, draining away the fresh surface water from the Black Sea while underneath it a deep salt water current flows in from the Aegean.

The Sea of Marmara is comparatively shallow. Enclosed by rocky coasts, it can be extremely treacherous despite its small size – especially when a northerly gale blows from the Black Sea. Small boats and coasters take shelter at such times under the lee of one of the islands, for the sea is short, steep and breaking. On a fine day the passage along its coast is enchanting, for the remains of castles and Turkish tombs shine on the heights and although the shores are mostly steep and harborless, in many places the rich green of pine trees runs right to the water's edge.

Marquesas Islands

A group of 11 islands, a French possession. Location *Oceania, South Pacific Ocean.* Area *492 square miles.* Map *4, L8.*

The Marquesas consist of two widely separated archipelagoes. The southern includes Hiva Oa, Fatua Huku, Fatu Hiva, Motane and Tahuata and is sometimes called the Mendaña Islands; the northern consists of Nuku Hiva, Hatutu, Eiao, Motu Iti, Ua Huka and Ua Pou. So scattered and isolated are the two groups that almost two centuries elapsed between their discovery.

The Spaniards came upon Fatu Hiva in 1595. Four Spanish galleons dropped anchor under the towering cliffs; their commander, Alvaro Mendaña, on his way to Samoa with 400 settlers and soldiers, named his new find Magdalena. From a small, serene bay a fertile, well-cultivated valley led back between sharp, craggy, 2,000-foot-high ridges. Some outrigged canoes put out from the shore, packed with natives: tall, magnificent, bronzed men and a few equally statuesque women. They paddled fast and in silence towards the galleons. The Spaniards called twice to them, but perhaps the calls were not heard, or were misunderstood. Finally, losing their nerve, the soldiers fired. The firing continued, with musket and cannon, until nearly all the natives within range had been killed. By the time the fleet sailed on again, two days later, after securing some provisions from the natives' gardens, over 200 Fatu Hivans had been killed.

At Tahuata, another heavily populated (but today uninhabited) island a little farther north, the Spaniards paused again to take on fruit and water. At first all was amity and Mendaña exchanged presents with the chiefs. The Spaniards planted maize; but then came the inevitable dispute, followed by another massacre. As he sailed away, Mendaña named the islands Islas Marquesas de Mendoza, after the wife of the Viceroy of Peru.

The next visitor to Fatu Hiva, Captain Cook in 1774, nearly two centuries later, found the Islanders suspicious – but there were still several thousand of them. Today, Fatu Hiva has only 200–300 people left, living witnesses to man's inhumanity to man

The northern group was discovered in 1791 by the American navigator Duncan Nathaniel Ingraham, who named it Washington Islands. In 1813 Commodore David Porter took formal possession of the Marquesas, but Congress failed to take appropriate action and in 1842 the entire group was acquired by France.

It was somewhere around 200 A.D. that the ancestors of the Marquesan race reached the Islands by way of Samoa. They brought dogs, pigs, chickens and probably seeds of yam and taro in their long canoes. (There are no indigenous mammals, only some ten kinds of land birds, a lizard and a few insects in the isolated group.) The colonizers found a sublime landscape of towering mountains – the highest, on Hiva Oa, reaches 4,130 feet – deep, fertile valleys, sheltered coves and inlets, all clad in luxurious vegetation with over 400 plant species. Here they flourished until there were between 80,000 and 160,000 of them. Under their powerful chiefs they led long voyages of conquest even to distant islands in other groups or warred with neighboring valleys. They were cannibals, yet friendly and hospitable to strangers. . . until the Spaniards came. Highly artistic, they covered even their beak-headed war clubs with delicate arabesques; fearless – yet terrified of death, peopling deserted villages with cannibal specters. Robert Louis Stevenson called them "annoying and attractive, wild, shy and refined. . ." By 1888 the terrible tragedy of the Marquesas was entering its last act. "The tribe of Hapaa," Stevenson wrote, "is said to have numbered some 400 when the smallpox came and reduced them by one fourth. Six months later a woman developed tubercular consumption. The disease spread like a fire about the valley and in less than a year two survivors, a man and a woman, fled from this newly created solitude . . ."

Whalers, traders and missionaries brought or helped to spread syphilis, smallpox, tuberculosis, alcoholism. Between 1842 and 1870 the French fought a long and bloody war of conquest and then introduced Negroes from Martinique, Chinese and Annamese to work on the plantations – and with them, the use of opium. Gauguin, who died here in 1903, cursed the authorities in vain. Perhaps leprosy was the last major disease introduced – it is now widespread in this former earthly paradise, where today there are less than 3,000 people. Yet everywhere the ruined overgrown house terraces testify to the wealth and abundance of the past.

Marshall Islands

A group of 32 atolls and 867 reefs, important in the Second World War and as the site of postwar atomic tests. Location *Western central Pacific.* Area *70 square miles.* Map *4, F6–G6.*

With a population of over 10,000, the Marshalls form two parallel chains, each 500 miles long, running northwest to southeast, about 100 miles apart. The eastern chain is called Ratak ("Sunrise"), the western Ralik ("Sunset"). Some of their 32 atolls are among the world's largest: Kwajalein, 78 miles long and about 20 wide, with 18 islets; Jaluit, 38 miles by 21, with some 50 islets; Eniwetok, an almost circular ring 23 miles in diameter, with 40 islets; Bikini, 22 miles by 11, with 36 islets; and Alinglapalap, Rongelap, Mili, Wotje and Maloelap, only slightly smaller. These are true atolls, rings of living coral, growing outwards to the open sea and leaving behind their massive dead skeletons to be piled up by the pounding waves into islets (the highest point in the Marshalls, on Likiep, is only 33 feet above sea level) or scoured and dissolved away into openings, passages and lagoons. The sandy lagoon floors are only 150–250 feet down within their great coral frames.

These floors are built up, as the coral grows outwards and dies away behind, by deposition of detritus from the dead edge in already shallow water – for reef building only goes on in shallow water, less than 300 feet deep, because reef corals and algae need sunlight and cannot grow below that depth. Various theories account for the existence of so much land at just the right depth. Darwin's is the most important – that the land was slowly subsiding and the corals built up and up on their own skeletons, keeping always just below the surface.

The surface of the reef islets, a rubble of coral limestone, has only a sparse topsoil produced by the decay of plants. Coconut palms, breadfruit trees, bananas, papaws, yams, taro, pandanus, arrowroot, imported pigs and poultry (there are no native mammals, except perhaps rats and bats and a few native land birds), provide a little to eat, but most food comes from the lagoon and reef, which swim with fish, molluscs and crustaceans. Food and lack of raw materials for tools, building and pottery have always been a problem on these low islands, and few of the original invaders from Indo-Malaysia (ancestors of the present Micronesian inhabitants) remained, most of them pressing on to the south and east. Later, when mass-emigration ceased to be a solution to over-population, because the known lands farther on were already occupied, infanticide became common. Wars provided some balance, but distances even between adjacent islands were too great for them to be more than sporadic. The last big raid was in the eighteen-seventies, when a flotilla of canoes, packed with warriors, set out for the Caroline Islands, 500 miles to the west, conquered Pingelap and returned. They used remarkable navigation charts of wooden strips, which showed the islands, winds and currents of the region.

The Marshalls, discovered by Spaniards in 1526, became German protectorates in 1885. In 1914 the Japanese occupied them and from 1922 to 1935 they were Japanese mandated territories; then Japan claimed sovereignty over the group. In the Second World War the Marshalls were captured after bitter fighting by United States forces in 1944. Here, at Bikini and Eniwetok, the postwar atomic and hydrogen bomb tests took place; the people of these islands were transferred to other atolls where suitable homes were provided for them. In 1947 the Marshalls became United States territory under United Nations trusteeship.

Martha's Vineyard

An Atlantic island, formerly a famous center of whaling and fishing. Location *15 miles off southeast Maine, 5 miles south of Cape Cod.* Dimensions *20 miles long, 15 miles wide.* Map *1, G7.*

Martha's Vineyard was discovered and named by Bartholomew Gosnold in 1602, though the meaning of the name is obscure. On seventeenth-century maps it sometimes appears as "Martin's Vineyard." The island was settled in 1642, by which time Nantucket, across Muskegat Channel to the southeast, was well established as a whaling center. Martha's Vineyard soon followed, as harbors were developed at Edgartown, Oak Bluffs and Vineyard Haven. From then onwards, until the coming of the larger iron ships and steam, of the harpoon gun and the gradual extermination of whales in warmer waters, whales were the islanders' constant thought and preoccupation.

Now they catch lobsters and smaller prey on hook and line and the craft they tend are pleasure yachts and launches. For this is a great summer resort with an airport, hotels and numerous cottages, and the interior has been set apart as a state forest. A chill reminder of more ancient things is the long whistling of the buoys on the sand bars, the mournful wail of sirens and hoot of blowers when sea fogs trap the vacationing visitors, sometimes for days on end, among the sand dunes and long drifted beaches of the little island.

Martinique

A volcanic island which has suffered much from earthquakes, eruptions, tidal waves and hurricanes. Location *Windward Islands, West Indies, between Dominica and St Lucia.* Area *427 square miles.* Map *2, J3.*

Martinique is tropical and exotic. Volcanic peaks, clothed in forest, soar up behind the capital, Fort-de-France, and trade wind clouds heavy with moisture droop over the dense green of the interior where the *fer-de-lance*, one of the world's deadliest snakes, moves like a whiplash. Lafcadio Hearn, who visited the island on his way to Japan, described its brilliant hibiscus flowers and the beauty of its Creole women. Paul Gauguin, some years before he went to Tahiti, came to Martinique, and it was here that he first painted the colors and the people of the tropics.

In 1900, the capital was the busy, booming town of St Pierre on the northwest coast. With a population of 40,000 and a fine anchorage sheltered from the prevailing trade winds, it was one of the most thriving cities in the Caribbean. But the town was overshadowed by the somber volcano, Mont Pelée, and on May 8, 1902, the mountain exploded, causing one of the worst disasters in history. A rain of ashes and fire swept over the city; within a few hours more than 40,000 people were killed. With the exception of one merchant vessel, all the shipping in the harbor was destroyed. There was only one survivor in St Pierre – a colored convict in an underground jail house. For the remaining 15 years of his life he toured the world with Barnum's Circus as one of the oddities.

Martinique is a two-faced island. One face is sunlit with tropical flowers and blue, sheltered coves; the other is represented by the violence of nature. In the last 300 years it has undergone 33 hurricanes, 7 earthquakes, 3 volcanic eruptions and 11 tidal waves.

Sugar, rum, coffee and cocoa are the principal exports; Martinique rum is famous throughout the West Indies. Although sugar cane plantations occupy large tracts of territory, much of the island is dense jungle and impossible to cultivate. The *fer-de-lance*, which makes the undergrowth so dangerous, was reputedly imported by French planters from the mainland of South America to prevent their Negro slaves from running away.

At the turn of the century Martinique was very prosperous. Its sugar and fruit fetched high prices in France – prices which were reflected in the comfort and luxury of the plantation owners and shippers. But the disaster of St Pierre and the availability of cheaper sugar from other parts of the world all contributed to the island's economic decline.

The island had a stormy history from the moment when it was first discovered by Columbus until it was restored to the French by Admiral Lord Rodney in 1763, having been captured by the British the year before. It changed hands twice more before it was finally handed back to the French in 1814. In the Second World

War the governor of Martinique adhered to Vichy after the fall of France, but under Allied pressure it was brought under Anglo-American and later Free French control. In 1946, Martinique became one of France's overseas departments. Its population is 255,600, with Trinité and Marin the principal towns after Fort-de-France.

Climatically, Martinique is similar to most of the Windward Islands with a mean annual temperature of 80° F. The rainfall, however, is heavy and the humidity high, with the result that the low coastal plains are unsuitable for Europeans during the hot months. The bulk of the population is of mixed blood; the Creoles are of light coffee complexion and justifiably proud of their distinctive features and beauty.

Massachusetts Bay

An inlet of the Atlantic, divided into several bays. Location *Between Cape Ann and Cape Cod.* Length *About 65 miles.* Map *1, G7.*

Massachusetts Bay's main divisions bear names that are intimately linked with early American history. Boston Bay, Cape Cod Bay, Plymouth Bay, Glouchester and Salem are the cradles of the settlements that spread and grew into the founder-states of the Union.

"They had no friends to wellcome them," wrote William Bradford in his *History of Plymouth Plantation*, "nor inns to entertaine or refresh their weather-beaten bodys, no houses or much less townes to repaire to . . . Besides, what could they see but a hidious and desolate wilderness, full of wild beasts and wild men?"

Yet the Pilgrims' courage built a beachhead in the wilderness; expanding slowly, it became the Old Plymouth Colony, stretching from Cape Cod's tip to Narragansett Bay, from Scituate to Nantucket Sound. Today modern Plymouth is a bustling, busy market and manufacturing community of about 14,000 people; a noted resort from whose yacht club hundreds of white sails go scudding across the Bay. From the top of the granite monument to Miles Standish in Duxbury, north of Plymouth, there is a breath-taking view on clear days over Plymouth, Kingston and Duxbury bays, the green and white of Gurnet Point, Saquish Head, Clark's Island and the tall, pine-clad headland of Manomet – with Cape Cod's upraised arm in its whole 65-mile sweep clearly outlined in the distance. All these and many more are landmarks in early American history and much-visited, much-loved places in America's present.

On the Boston Bay arm of Massachusetts Bay, the capital of the Bay State grew to a metropolis of almost 5,000,000 people: Salem, home of the great whaling captains with its "widows walks" and an inexhaustible treasure trove of seafaring memories; Cape Cod's long, curved sandy spit with its famous vacation centers and theatrical and artists' colonies; Gloucester Bay with its resort villages and its excellent harbor – all these are part of the Massachusetts Bay area. If a visitor saw nothing else of the United States, he would see enough to form a comprehensive picture of America's history and manifold traditions.

Mauritius

A British Crown Colony in the Indian Ocean. Location *Mascarene group, Chagos Archipelago.* Area *720 square miles.* Map *10, D8.*

Mauritius, with its population of over 632,000, is a mountainous but highly fertile and thickly populated island, 39 miles by 27, about 450 miles east of Madagascar. Isolated by great oceanic depth, the whole group is believed never to have had human inhabitants before it was discovered by the Portuguese in the early sixteenth century. It was the home of huge flightless pigeons, the Dodos and the Solitaires.

The island's one mammal was a fruit-eating bat, so the blue-gray Dodo (*Raphus cucullatus*), large, plump, heavy and flightless, lived a quiet life without enemies in the tropical woodland which then covered the plains, the ravines and the small jagged mountains of Mauritius. However, in 1507 a second mammal arrived in the shape of man, when the Portuguese came ashore but did not settle. In 1512 they landed again, and left several pigs in the island paradise. In 1638 the island was colonized by the Dutch; by 1692 the Dodo, thanks to the depredations of pigs and men, was extinct. Men destroyed the birds more perhaps to entertain than to feed themselves: occasionally ships' stores were eked out by a

Sugar cane fields on Mauritius

slaughter of Dodos, but cooked Dodo was abysmally tough. Sir Thomas Herbert, who visited Mauritius in 1629, wrote that to civilized stomachs they were "offensive and of no nourishment." However, for wonder, shape and rareness, he thought that the Dodo vied with the Phoenix of Arabia. Ridiculous to look at, unable to fly or defend itself (though it could bite), the Dodo has survived only in speech as an affectionate symbol of stupidity. The name may be from the Portuguese *doudo* ("fool") or the Dutch *dodaers* ("round behind"). Today there are only a few odd bones and a dozen skeletons in museums – and many drawings and paintings of the seventeenth century – to remind the world of this innocent victim. Rodriguez, in the same group, also had an allied Solitaire of its own and Réunion a White Dodo. Both are now extinct.

The Dutch, who had named Mauritius after the Stadtholder, Prince Maurice of Nassau, abandoned the island in 1710. Five years later the French took possession of it and changed the name to Île de France, but did not settle it until 1721. Under them it became a great center of trade. In 1789 the seat of French government in the East was moved from Mauritius to Pondicherry, and in 1810 a British force took the island. French language and law have been preserved under British rule, though the earlier name, Mauritius, has been restored.

The population is made up of Indians, Europeans (mainly French) and persons of mixed descent. Mauritius grows sugar, maize, tea, tobacco and foodcrops. Its climate is more subtropical than tropical, except at low altitudes; the summers are extremely humid. Tropical cyclones are frequent, and those of 1892, 1931, 1945 and 1960 did much damage to crops and buildings. Port Louis, the capital, is a very lively place, with local groups of poets, painters and composers and a charmingly indolent way of life. Port Louis has an excellent harbor, and the island is linked by air to Africa, Australia and Europe.

Mediterranean

A great inland sea, cradle of European civilization. Location *An arm of the Atlantic Ocean, between Europe and Africa.* Area *1,145,000 square miles.* Maximum depth *14,449 feet (off Cape Matapan).* Map *7 and 9.*

Stretching from the Strait of Gibraltar to the coasts of southwest Asia, the Mediterranean can claim to have given birth not to one civilization but to a whole galaxy of cultures. On these almost tideless waters and in the gentle, temperate climate surrounding them, the whole pattern of Western culture and civilization as we know it has been erected. The Mediterranean carried the trading vessels of the Phoenicians, its shores were fought over by Carthaginians, Greeks and Romans. The Romans triumphed and for long centuries it was the *Mare Nostrum*, Our Sea – a claim which Mussolini revived, though with scant success, in our own century. During the Middle Ages it nurtured the rise of the great maritime city states, Genoa and Venice. Later, when the route to India around the Cape of Good Hope was discovered, its importance declined as a main shipping route; but when the Suez Canal was opened in 1869 it quickly regained its place as one of the world's most frequented seas, linking Europe and Asia.

Today, along the shores of the Mediterranean, we find the awakened nationalism of the new African states, the conflicting interests of Israel and the Arab countries, Communist ideologies and Western democracies, in uneasy neighborhood. The stormy Atlantic, the vast Pacific and the other oceans of the world have largely been explored or discovered by the descendants of men who first learned to sail upon the Mediterranean. Most of the philosophies, technologies, religions and ideologies which have changed the face of the Western world grew to maturity in the lands and islands of this most human of all seas. No wonder the French have set up both a Society of the Friends of the Mediterranean and a Mediterranean University.

Geologically, the Mediterranean is a remnant of a vast ocean which at one time encircled nearly half the globe. When the waters finally retreated from Asia Minor and eastern Europe, it was left behind, together with the Sea of Marmara and the Black Sea, to which it is still connected through the Dardanelles. It falls into four clearly defined regions, separated by submarine ridges.

The most important is the western basin, between Gibraltar, Sicily and the Cape Bon banks. Here are the small Italian islands of Elba, the Ponsa group, the Liparis and the islands in the Bay of Naples, together with the major islands of Corsica, Sardinia and the Spanish Balearics. The Gulf of Lions in the northwestern corner, notorious for its winter storms, can be one of the most dangerous areas in the world. Over this stretch the northerly mistral prevails, a gale-force wind that hurls itself down the valley of the Rhône, raising a wild sea in a few hours.

The second and central section of the Mediterranean is formed by the Adriatic and the Ionian seas. The former is the shallowest and the latter the deepest part of the whole area. The central basin is governed largely by the sirocco, a hot southerly wind that blows from Africa, and the bora, a northerly wind occurring in the Adriatic. The bora can be even more violent than the mistral.

The third and fourth sections of the Mediterranean are the Aegean Sea, which divides Greece from Asia Minor, and the easterly Levant Basin. The climate in this area is determined largely by the etesian or northerly winds, which blow throughout the summer and give the Aegean especially a coolness and a clarity of atmosphere lacking in most other parts of the Mediterranean.

Although for months on end the Mediterranean can be an idyllic sea with long periods of calm or light airs, it was not for nothing that the Greeks called their sea-god Poseidon, the earthshaker. The trident with which he is usually depicted was more than the symbol of fishermen. It was with his trident that Poseidon split the rocks, lashed the sea into fury and called forth the wild, white-maned sea horses. The American small boat sailor Carl Petersen, who completed a single-handed circumnavigation of the globe in 1953, stated that the weather he encountered between Crete and Malta was worse than anything he had experienced in the Atlantic, Pacific and Indian oceans. On the other hand, in spring and summer, when gentle breezes blow off the islands, bringing with them the scent of pines and sun-dried herbs, when the waters are stirred only by the delicate catspaws the ancients called the footsteps of Thetis, one understands why Poseidon is also represented by the friendly dolphin, the symbol of a calm sea.

Almost tideless, with a maximum rise and fall in most places of little more than a foot, the Mediterranean has few currents. Because of the losses from surface evaporation, it is subject, however, to two surface currents; one flowing in from the Atlantic at the Strait of Gibraltar and the other from the Black Sea by way of the Dardanelles. As this fresh surface water flows in, so a reciprocal movement of denser, more saline water moves slowly out at a greater depth. In a few exceptional places, such as the Strait of

Mykines (left) and Tindholm, most westerly of the Faeroe Islan

Messina, a regular tidal stream occurs. The rarity of such tides can be gauged by the fact that to classical writers like Homer the straits were exceptional, terrifying and haunted.

The absence of tides makes the Sea comparatively easy for the navigator and it is this lack of tidal movement which gives the Mediterranean something of its special, timeless quality. The shrubs and bushes on the Ionian Islands that grow right to the water's edge, the sun-warmed bricks of the old fortress guarding the entrance to Syracuse, the ancient mole at Delos and the frowning walls of Malta's Castel St Angelo seem to have been preserved in some amber moment of time. The passage of hours, days or centuries has never been marked here by the inexorable advance and retreat of the tides.

The many cultures and civilizations that have arisen on the shores of this Sea owed their origin not only to the easiness of navigation but to the mild climate, with its short winter and benevolent long summer. Throughout the summer, in most regions, the barometer remains high and the light winds that drive the small fishing boats and private yachts of today were ideal for the primitive sailing craft of the Phoenicians, Greeks and Romans.

Coastal fishing still plays an important part in the economy of most Mediterranean countries and the design of many of the boats is traditional. Off the southwestern coast of Sicily, for instance, open boats with lateen sails and oars cross every summer to North Africa to fish the Kerkennah banks. With eyes painted on their bows and branches at their mastheads to ward off evil spirits, they have changed little – if at all – in 2,000 years.

Mergui Archipelago

About 900 islands, famous as pearl-fishery grounds. Location *Off the Tenasserim coast of Lower Burma, Andaman Sea.* Map *10, G4–5.*

The Merguis, close to the coast of Lower Burma, represent summits of submerged mountain ridges. There are over 900 of them, ranging in size from tiny rocks to fair-sized islands, such as King Island, which shelters the town of Mergui on the mainland, at the mouth of the Tenasserim River. The more important are Bentinck, Domel, Elphinstone, Kisseraing, Ross, St Matthew's, Sellore and Sullivan islands.

Forming part of the Republic of Burma, the islands' outer fringe provides shelter for the coasts. The rainfall is as heavy as in Arakan but they are closer to the equator, which makes the dry season shorter, and some islands have rubber plantations. But generally there are mountains and jungles covering most of their area, with rhinoceroses, tigers and snakes making the interiors far from inviting. The coastlines are rugged and much indented, and often fringed with mangrove swamps. There are only scattered settlements with fishing villages of bamboo huts built out over the water. The population is Salon, closely related to the Malays; primitive people who are often called the sea-gypsies because of their roaming, restless way of life.

The Archipelago produces birds' nests and has tin and tungsten mines. But for a few decades the islands were best-known for their pearl fisheries. These were established only in the eighteen-nineties, when they were mostly worked by adventurous Australians; later, they were leased to a Chinese syndicate which sub-leased them to individual adventurers, charging so much per pump for the pearling year. The chief harvest was then, as it is today, mother-of-pearl, which is enough to pay working expenses; and there was (and still is) the chance of finding a pearl of price – some worth several thousand dollars have been discovered. Recently, however, the pearl-fisheries have declined both in activity and in the value of the pearls netted.

Messina, Strait of

A strait famous since antiquity, with many whirlpools and strong currents. Location *Joining the Ionian and Tyrrhenian seas, between Italy and Sicily.* Dimensions *20 miles long, 2–10 miles wide.* Maximum depth *About 300 feet.* Map *9, D9.*

The narrow Strait of Messina is not so menacing to the modern navigator as it was to the ancients in their small open boats. It must have been terrifying to Odysseus and his shipmates, for, as *The Odyssey* depicted it: "Verily whenever she belched it forth, like a cauldron on a great fire she would seethe and bubble in utter turmoil, and high overhead the spray would fall on the tops of both the cliffs. . ." Even so, the Strait is not without its hazards, for the current runs fiercely through it; and at its narrowest point, the Strait is no more than two miles wide. A project has been mooted to span this gap by what would be one of the largest bridges in the world; it would also have to be a very high one to allow the largest ships to pass underneath.

The main current in the Strait runs from south to north for a period of six hours; then there is a "stand" of the tide until the current starts again in the opposite direction. This tide or current is lunar and solar in origin although it is greatly affected by the prevailing winds. The Strait is at its most dangerous when the southerly or sirocco wind is blowing hard, augmenting the northerly rate of the current. On a fair day the small boat sailor can still appreciate how fearsome the Strait must have appeared to the ancients – remembering that the early Mediterranean sailors were unfamiliar with tides, and there seemed something especially evil about the Strait because of this.

When the current is running from the north the waves boom on the sea-wet rock of Scylla, while beyond it, amber in the sunshine, lies the old town that takes its name from the goddess. The current in the Strait rises nearly a foot during the flood tide when numerous small whirlpools form near the Sicilian coast where Charybdis is marked on the chart. A confused sea is set up and overfalls, dangerous to small boats, spread out from the Italian mainland. Sometimes, if the tide is accentuated by the wind, fish of the angler type (which normally live at the bottom of the sea) are hurled to the surface. On average days when the current is not unusually severe, the Strait is thronged with local fishing boats, for the area is rich in many types of fish passing through as they migrate from one part of the Mediterranean to another.

During the seasonal migration of swordfish, special boats designed for their capture operate on the Sicilian side of the Strait. These have a crow's nest built into the mast where the lookout can see down into the water and detect the fish when they are still invisible to the harpoonist in the bows. The modern and the ancient world are still neighbors in the Strait of Messina. On the one hand, fast, modern ferries run back and forth between Messina and Reggio on the Italian coast; on the other, the open boats with their lateen sails, gaily painted and with eyes on their bows so that they can "see" their way, differ little from the craft of the Homeric heroes.

Mexico, Gulf of

A huge arm of the Atlantic Ocean. Location *Southeast coast of North America, bordered by the United States and Mexico.* Area *700,000 square miles.* Maximum depth *12,480 feet.* Map *6, A3.*

The Gulf of Mexico stretches for about 1,000 miles from east to west and 800 miles from north to south. Its shoreline extends along Florida, Alabama, Mississippi, Louisiana and Texas; the Straits of Florida, between Florida and Cuba, connect it with the Atlantic, and the Yucatan Channel, between Cuba and Yucatan, with the Caribbean. It has wide continental shelves declining from its coast to an average depth of 4,700 feet, and the Sigsbee Deep, off the Mexican coast, reaches almost three times this depth.

Though its size approaches that of the Caribbean, the Gulf does not contain any islands of any size. Its northern shores were long undeveloped, with few ports. However, it receives several important rivers, including the Mississippi and the Rio Grande, both of which have large and complex deltas. Good harbors are at a premium, because the generally low shores are fringed with flat, sandy islands and a good many lagoons so that channels need constant dredging. The principal ports are Veracruz and Tampico in Mexico; Galveston, Houston, Port Arthur, Beaumont, New Orleans, Mobile and Tampa in the United States; and Havana in Cuba.

The most colorful period in the history of the Gulf was the age of pirates in the late eighteenth and early nineteenth centuries, when Jean Lafitte set up his headquarters on the doorstep of New Orleans and helped to frustrate the British siege of the city – in a battle which was actually fought after peace had been concluded between the two countries. Both France and Spain left traditions of their cultures and civilizations on the shores of the Gulf, giving them a special flavor and color. And today, with the tension between the United States and Cuba, the age of buccaneers, pirates and adventurers seems to have become reincarnated, at least in some respects – though the waters of the great Gulf remain neutral as ever to ideologies and international conflicts.

The Gulf has an important current – a branch of the Equatorial Current – which has its entrance through the Yucatan Channel, flows out by the Straits of Florida and joins the Antilles Current. The two unite in the Florida Current, which is actually the beginning of the great Gulf Stream system.

Mid-Atlantic Ridge

An immensely long submarine stretch of land almost midway between Africa and America. Location *From South to North Atlantic.* Map *6, E3–10.*

The Mid-Atlantic Ridge forms the most striking feature of the floor of the Atlantic. This great longitudinal "rise" is known as the Dolphin Rise in the north and the Challenger Rise in the south. It slopes gently towards the deep-sea plain on either side and is S-shaped, following the general trend of the coastlines with remarkable fidelity. It is covered by an average depth of about 8,000 feet of water. In the North Atlantic the ridge widens to form the broad Telegraph Plateau, which extends across the Ocean from Ireland to Labrador.

There are also several transverse ridges connected with it. The Walvis Ridge runs in a northeasterly direction from the neighborhood of Tristan da Cunha to the African coast, and the Rio Grande Ridge trends, with less continuity, from the same area towards the South American coast. In the north a broad ridge rises from the Telegraph Plateau and runs northwestwards from northern Scotland to southeastern Greenland; the water over this ridge averages about 3,500 feet in depth and the Faroes and Iceland represent its projecting higher parts. The Wyville-Thomson Ridge lies between northern Scotland and Iceland.

The Romanche Deep cuts across the Mid-Atlantic Ridge, to a depth of 24,000 feet.

Most true oceanic islands project from the Mid-Atlantic Ridge, notably the Azores in the north and lonely Ascension and Tristan da Cunha in the south. St Helena lies just east of the Ridge and appears to rise quite steeply from the deep-sea plain, as does the tiny Brazilian island of Trinidad to the west of the Ridge. The Challenger Ridge begins off the Guinea Coast and extends in a course midway between South America and Africa, to the same parallel as the Colorado River in Argentina.

Mobile Bay

A large arm of the Gulf of Mexico. Location *Southwest Alabama, Gulf of Mexico.* Dimensions *35 miles long, 8–18 miles wide.* Map *1, C11.*

It was in 1702 that Pierre Lemoyne, Sieur d'Iberville, and his brother Jean Baptiste Lemoyne, Sieur de Bienville, came to the low, sandy coast of the Gulf of Mexico and founded the city of Mobile, naming it after the Mobile or Maubile Indians, a Muskhogean tribe. The Indians have long since disappeared – though they were easily converted to Christianity by the French – but their name has been preserved in the Bay, the river and the city.

Mobile remained the capital of Louisiana for 18 years. The original settlement, standing on Twenty-Seven Mile Bluff, about 20 miles from the present city, had to be moved in 1710 because of the disastrous floods of the previous year. Under the Treaty of Paris (1763) Mobile was ceded to Britain as part of Louisiana east of the Mississippi. Seventeen years later, the Spaniards, under Don Bernardo de Galvez, the governor of New Orleans, captured it. It remained Spanish until 1813, when President Madison ordered General James Wilkinson to seize Mobile for the United States. The action was based on the claim that Mobile was part of Louisiana sold by France to the Union ten years previously; the Anglo-Spanish alliance in the war of 1812 made the move strategically essential. Here, in August, 1814, General Andrew Jackson set up his headquarters, repairing Fort Bowyer, at the mouth of the Bay, just in time to resist the British attack which came a few weeks later. Fort Bowyer was actually captured by the British forces more than six weeks after peace had been declared, but no move was made against Mobile. Soon, the city and the Bay area were flooded by a tide of immigrants from up country, and the Americanization of the whole coast region proceeded rapidly.

As Mobile was the only seaport of Alabama, it was essential that communication with the Bay and the Gulf of Mexico should be improved. In 1826 the channel to the Gulf had a minimum depth of only 5½ feet through Choctaw Pass and 8 feet through the Dog River bar; but dredging work went on incessantly and during the Civil War Mobile was already an important seaport of the Confederacy. The Federal blockade began in May, 1861, but the swift Southern ships regularly slipped past the blockading squadron and continued the important trade with West Indian and European ports. At last, on August 8, 1864, Admiral David Farragut took a Federal fleet of four iron monitors, seven wooden sloops of war and several gunboats into the channel by passing the Confederate defences – Fort Gaines on Dauphin Island and Fort Morgan (on the site of the old Fort Bowyer) at Mobile Point – captured the formidable Confederate ironclad ram *Tennessee*, destroyed one gunboat and drove another aground. Fort Gaines and Fort Morgan both surrendered within a month and the blockade became effective. Mobile itself fell to the Federal forces under General E.R.S. Canby after 25 days of stubborn resistance.

Today, the Bay is crossed in its southern part (which is called Bon Secours Bay) by the great Intracoastal Waterway, which passes into it from Mississippi Sound. The channel has been deepened to 32 feet and broadened to 300–500 feet, entering the Gulf of Mexico between Dauphin Island and Mobile Point, so that Mobile has become one of the most important shipping centers of the South, with long miles of docks, warehouses and forests of cranes. The Mobile River enters the Bay at Mobile after flowing 45 miles through the delta region, draining an area of 42,300 square miles with its tributaries.

Moluccas

A large island group of eastern Indonesia, the traditional "Spice Islands" of the East. Location *Between Celebes and New Guinea, in the Arafura, Banda, Ceram and Molucca seas.* Area *33,315 square miles.* Map *4, C7.*

The Moluccas, with a population of well over half a million, form a northern and southern group. In the northern are Morotai, Halmahera (the largest of the whole archipelago), Ternate, Tidore, Makian, Bachan, the Obi and Sula islands; the southern group, spread in a rough semicircle, comprises Amboina, the Banda Islands, Buru, Ceram, the Abu Islands, the Kai Islands, the Tanimbar Islands, the Babar Islands, Kisar and Wetar.

The name Moluccas, formerly the Spice Islands, conjures up the very spirit of the tropical East Indies, and the names of many of the islands have an exotic sound in keeping with the romantic, varied history of the archipelago. Their wealth in spices was recognized by the Spaniards and Portuguese early in the sixteenth century and later by the Dutch and English. The Portuguese were forced out by the Dutch in the early years of the seventeenth century and the English merchants who had settled in Amboina were decimated in 1623 by their Dutch rivals in the so-called "Massacre of Amboina." The struggle against Spain lasted another 40 years, but after that the only rivals to Dutch power were the local sultans of Ternate and Tidore, who were soon persuaded to accept, at least passively, Dutch suzerainty. Amboina, with Macassar in Celebes, became the chief trading center of the eastern half of the archipelago, but politically the Moluccas have never been important compared with the larger islands farther west.

A sea trip through the group is a compelling experience. In the north the twin volcanic islands of Ternate and Tidore shelter close beside the long western coast of the large island of Halmahera, which apes the outline of Celebes, its near-western neighbor. A shelf of fairly shallow water borders these islands, but west of them depths increase in the Molucca Passage. Ternate's volcano (5,416 feet high) is still active and the little port, the seat of the old sultanate, nestles at its foot. Within its harbor there is a medley of sailing boats and outrigged fishing craft. As one sails southwards, groups of other islands close to Halmahera are passed; the next port of call is bustling Amboina on the small island of the same name, near to Ceram. Here earthquakes are common but there are no active volcanoes. They appear again, however, in the Banda group south of Ceram, where Gunong Api fumes and smokes almost continuously. The southernmost groups of islands are arranged in a great arc round the deep Banda Sea; some, like the Aru Islands, are low and swampy; others, like Babar and Wetar, are hilly with steep coasts; but all are little known and thinly peopled.

For the naturalist, the Moluccas are a fascinating and absorbing region to visit. The fauna and flora of Amboina were described as long ago as the late seventeenth century by the Dutch naturalist Rumpius, and in the middle of the last century A. R. Wallace, who spent a long time in the islands, was struck by the singular character of the few mammals living there, by the beauty of the many insects, especially butterflies, and by the brilliant coloring of the birds. Among the mammals there are three kinds of opossum, with long tails and thick woolly fur, civet-cats, wild pigs and the babirusa, a pig-like animal, also found in Celebes. The birds include some of the most spectacular in the world: crimson parakeets, multicolored kingfishers and the wonderful birds of paradise.

Culturally, the Moluccans exhibit an immense variety. There is a broad division between the coastal peoples (often referred to by the general term "Malays") and those of the interior, who are usually described by the comprehensive term "Alfoer." But within these two general categories there are important differences: thus some of the "Malays" are Christians and others profess Islam; some of the "Alfoer" have been converted to Christianity but most of them worship local spirits and in the southern island of Tanimbar totemism is practised. Christianity was first brought to the Moluccas by St Francis Xavier, who spent several months on Amboina and Ternate in 1546 and also visited Halmahera and Morotai. Among the coastal peoples intermixture with Europeans took place; some of the native customs and rites are permeated with western features. Agriculture is generally primitive and the chief native occupation is the cultivation of coconuts, from which copra is prepared. The sago palm grows wild and sago provides the main article of diet. Cloves and nutmeg are still grown, but they are of much less importance than in the days when the Moluccas first attracted Europeans to their shores.

Monhegan Island

A small, rocky island, a noted summer resort. Location *Lincoln county, southern Maine, in the Atlantic.* Area *2.5 square miles.* Map *1, G6.*

The people of Monhegan Island – there are less than 100 of them – are sturdy fisher-folk who make half their living in the winter, when in the waters around their homes they catch the delicious lobsters for which Maine, and their island in particular, is famous. By self-discipline they have made themselves rich and the envy of their neighboring competitive lobster-fisheries; they have voluntarily imposed on themselves a size limit to the lobsters they catch – putting back into the sea all that are too small – and they have declared a close season, to give the lobsters time to grow.

The other half of their living they make out of the summer visitors. Monhegan is a noted artists' colony where many well-known painters come to use the settings of the fisher-folk's cottages, the gaudily painted lobster floats, the wickerwork pots, the drying nets and upturned boats, the daisy-spangled meadows, the sun-hot rocks and wave-beaten cliffs.

The island, which is ten miles off the coast, has a lighthouse station. Off its shores, the battle between the *Enterprise* and the *Boxer* was fought in the Anglo-American war of 1812.

Monte Cristo

A small, rocky island, made famous by Alexandre Dumas père. Location *Between Corsica and the Italian coast, 25 miles south of Elba, Tyrrhenian Sea.* Area *3.5 square miles.* Map *9, C8.*

Monte Cristo has exercised a special fascination ever since the 12-volume novel of Dumas the Elder first appeared in 1844. Dumas could have imagined few settings more remote from the fashionable Paris he loved than this lonely islet in the Tuscan Archipelago. Monte Cristo's nearest neighbors are the other two small islands of

Pianosa to the north and Giglio to the east. It is possible that at one time they were all joined to the Italian mainland, and the remains of prehistoric animals found in Pianosa seem to confirm this.

From seaward, Monte Cristo is a crested lump like a whale's back which resolves itself as one nears the coast into stark sides with the green of trees and undergrowth thick on its slopes. There is no port and, until the Second World War, the island was the private property of the kings of Italy. A shooting lodge was maintained for royal guests. At certain seasons – like most of the islands on the west coast of Italy – Monte Cristo becomes a staging point for migratory birds, bound north for Europe in the spring and south for Africa in the autumn.

For the lover of solitude the small coves and deserted beaches have a true Robinson Crusoe flavor. It is not surprising, perhaps, that the Camaldulians, a tenth-century religious order whose members were dedicated to solitary lives of prayer and meditation, once established a monastery on Monte Cristo; its remains are still standing.

Monterey Bay

An inlet of the Pacific around which some of the earliest settlements in California were established. Location *Western California, 65 miles south of San Francisco.* Length *26 miles.* Map *4, N3.*

Juan Rodriguez Cabrillo, the discoverer of Alta California, sighted Monterey Bay first in 1542 – but he did not enter it and bad weather forced him back within a few miles of San Francisco Bay to San Miguel Island. It was another 60 years before Sebastian Vizcaino sailed into the Bay and gave it the name of Monterey.

Here the Coast Ranges of California are broken to give an outlet to the seashore. Monterey Peninsula, rugged and almost perfectly square, thrusts four miles northwest into the ocean, with Monterey Bay and Carmel Bay washing its sides. At the back of Monterey Bay the Santa Cruz Mountains rise abruptly to the Santa Lucia Range, which is the towering backdrop of Monterey city, on the Peninsula. From the east the Pajaro River flows into the Bay; to the southeast the wide, fertile valley of the Salinas River stretches inland.

It was on Monterey Bay that the Spanish colonization of California really began. A mission and presidio were established at Monterey town in 1770 and though a year later the mission was moved to Carmel, Monterey remained the capital throughout the years of Spanish supremacy and alternated with Los Angeles as capital of the Mexican province. On July 7, 1847, Commodore John Drake Sloat raised the American flag over Monterey and in September, 1849, the first constitutional convention in California met at Colton Hall – a building which was erected from the proceeds of fines levied on gamblers and drunkards and from the sale of town lots, and which still stands on its original site.

Today the entire Peninsula is a popular, all-year playground with excellent fishing, hunting and bathing. Scenic drives along Monterey and Carmel bays include such points of interest as Seal Rock, Cypress Point and the "golfers' Mecca," Pebble Beach Golf Course.

Mont-Saint-Michel

A small islet containing one of the great monuments of Gothic architecture. Location *Bay of Saint-Michel, English Channel, near the northwest coast of France.* Area *Three acres.* Map *8, C5.*

Many have found this small, rocky island, with its towering abbey and medieval fortifications, a symbol of spiritual unity. For Mont-Saint-Michel is more than a tiny village and a great monument – it is a frame of mind, a terse summary of centuries of thought and creative art.

The village rises in three levels from the base of the rock, connected by steeply winding lanes and passages, towards the crowning splendor of the Abbey buildings, of which the chief group – six of them, facing the sea – is known as *La Merveille.* They fully deserve to be called "The Marvel." They were constructed in three stories – cellars, refectories and dormitories – in the thirteenth century by architects who transformed an earlier Romanesque abbey to create the unique and exquisite cloister of the Abbey church. The religious tradition of Mont-Saint-Michel goes back to 718 A.D. but the Benedictine foundation was not established until 966 by Richard I, Duke of Normandy. Up to 1623, when they were replaced by priors, a line of abbots strengthened and embellished the whole; and though its military history has been turbulent – it was attacked by the English many times during the Hundred Years War – the buildings and fortifications survived to be well preserved after being classified as a historical monument in 1874. Even the Second World War, in which near neighbors like Avranches and St Malo suffered badly, spared Mont-Saint-Michel. Connected by a mile-long causeway to Pontorson, with a population of about 150, the great Abbey and the village remain one of France's leading tourist attractions.

Mont-Saint-Michel

Montserrat

One of the smaller of the Leeward Islands, with many volcanic features. Location *West Indies, 33 miles northwest of Guadeloupe.* Area *37.5 square miles.* Map *2, H3.*

Discovered in 1493 by Columbus, who named it after the great Spanish monastery near Barcelona, Montserrat was first colonized in 1632 by Irish settlers under Sir Thomas Warner. It has been one of the islands involved in the Caribbean tug-of-war between France and Britain. Twice the French captured it – in 1664 and 1782 – but finally it was restored to Britain.

Montserrat is a typical volcanic island; its highest mountain is the sulphur-bearing Soufrière – one of several mountains bearing the same name – which rises to 2,999 feet. There are three smaller active Soufrières, sulphurous vents and innumerable hot springs; earth tremors are frequent, and the island lies in the path of the seasonal hurricanes. The sulphur and gypsum deposits are near Plymouth, the capital. As in many other Caribbean islands, sea-island cotton has replaced sugar cane as the chief crop; tomatoes, carrots, onions, limes and lime products are also exported. The compact island has charming scenery and a healthy climate.

The inhabitants of Montserrat – the population is around 15,000 – are mostly Negroes who are notable for speaking with a strong Irish brogue, the legacy of the original Irish settlers.

Mount Desert Island

A large, mountainous island, famous as a vacation and sailing center. Location *Frenchman Bay, southern Maine, Atlantic Ocean.* Area *About 100 square miles.* Map *1, G6.*

Connected to the mainland by a bridge, Mount Desert Island no longer deserves the name Champlain gave it in 1604 when he visited this large, wooded piece of land off the Maine coast. A narrow fjord, Somes Sound, bites deeply into the southern half of the Island, dividing it along its six-mile length into eastern and western areas, each about ten miles long and five miles wide. There are many lakes and along the eastern coast Cadillac Mountain rises to 1,532 feet.

Eleven years after Champlain's visit, the Jesuits established a mission on Mount Desert, but the first permanent settlement was not made until 1762. Mainland visitors began to discover and develop its facilities about 100 years ago. In 1919 the Acadia National Park was established, covering about 44 square miles of the "stern and rockbound coast" of Maine and a large part of Mount Desert Island, including a wild-life sanctuary for animals and birds and a marine biological laboratory.

The most important settlement and the best port on Mount Desert is Bar Harbor at the gateway to Acadia National Park, on Frenchman Bay. Settled in 1763, it was originally called Eden and did not receive its present name until 1918. There are many yachting clubs in the little town, which was the center of a disastrous fire in 1947 which razed most of its buildings and also did considerable damage to the Island's timber stand. Northeast Harbor and several other resort villages share the influx of summer visitors from the eastern states.

Mozambique Channel

An important shipping lane for East African navigation. Location *Between Madagascar and the mainland of southeast Africa, Indian Ocean.* Dimensions *Over 1,000 miles long, 250–600 miles wide.* Map *10, B7–9.*

Along the western side of Madagascar, as on the opposite mainland shore, there are marine Jurassic deposits which indicate that the ancient Mozambique Channel was much wider than its present, still considerable, width. The western edge of the Madagascar plateau, at 3,000–4,000 feet, forming the uppermost of a series of well-developed terraces, descends in easy gradients to the Channel. The shore here is generally low and shelves gradually; but the Mozambique Channel's greatest depth is nearly 10,000 feet, and this depth occurs about halfway between the great island and the African mainland. All the great rivers of Madagascar flow into the Channel and the best Madagascar ports, Majunga and Tuléar, are also on this western coast.

The Channel narrows between Mozambique in Portuguese East Africa and Cape St André. The Comoro Islands are at its northern entrance; the southern part is marked by the small islets of Bassas-de-India and Europe. On the mainland the most important estuary is that of the Zambezi River. The chief ports, apart from the two on Madagascar, are Beira, Lourenço Marques and Mozambique. The Mozambique Current flows through the Channel, then along the coast of southeast and southern Africa, where it is also called the Agulhas Current. A warm ocean stream, it has an important influence on the climate of both Madagascar and the African coastline which it follows.

Mulatas Islands

Over 300 coral islands, inhabited by Cuna Indians. Location *Off the northeast coast of Panama.* Map *2, E5.*

The Mulatas or San Blas Islands stretch for about 80 miles along the Caribbean coast of Panama, just off Darien. They are part of San Blas Territory and are under a Governor who lives on Porvenir, the most westerly of the group.

In 1925 Panama, bent on asserting its sovereignty, sent troops to the Mulatas. All were killed – and so were the Indians who had in any way collaborated. Racial purity and independence had to be preserved – and ever since there has been no attempt to interfere with the sturdy, self-governing people.

Only a few coconut palms grow on the Islands and the Cunas have to rely upon the mainland for water, fuel and most of their food. Their maize, banana and vegetable patches are often 2–3 miles inland and they have to cross a mile or more of sea to cultivate them. But the Islands are unusually healthy, free of malaria, dysentery and hookworm, the curses of mainland Panama. Their inbreeding does not seem to have weakened them – except that it has produced a very large number of albinos, white-skinned, yellow-haired, pink-eyed "moon-children," who are regarded as holy.

Tradition is preserved by means of songs – some of which take three days or more to sing yet are performed each year on feast days. The *Kantules* or chief singers are as important as the village headmen and spend much of their time in training their successors.

The chiefs are elected in each village by representatives of every household; they, in turn, form a council and elect the supreme chief. Matriarchy, however, rules the villages: daughters are more welcome than sons because their husbands live with their in-laws, work for the family and add to its wealth.

The male Cunas usually wear blue cotton trousers and white cotton shirts, but the women are as bright as china dolls. Their hair is glossy and smooth, they have long black lines down their noses, their cheeks are painted bright red, their wrists, ankles, necks, noses and ears jingle with gold rings and ornaments. The gold is extracted by the Indians themselves from secret mines.

In the seething, uneasy world of the Caribbean, the Mulatas represent perhaps the last oasis of independence and peace.

Mull

The largest of the Inner Hebrides, famous for its history and a sunken treasure ship. Location *Argyll, Scotland.* Area *351.2 square miles (including adjoining small islands).* Map *8, C3.*

Mull's coasts are lace-edged with the sea-lochs of Mingary, Cuan, Tua, Loch-na-Keal, Scridain, Buy, Spelve and Don – inlets of the sea, some of which rise to towering, picturesque cliffs. There are several freshwater lakes of which Loch Frisa, Loch Ba and Loch Uisg are the most important. For the mountaineer who loves sheer towers and precipices, there are Ben More (3,185 feet), Ben Buy (2,354 feet) and Ben Creach (2,289 feet). The basalt cliffs near Carsaig are honeycombed with caverns and spanned by natural arches. The valleys are filled up with lava flows and volcanic ashes of the Miocene Age; granite and basalt are the main rock formations. Mull has even more rain than the average Hebridean island, so that there is little agriculture but plenty of sheep and cattle; the quarries yield granite and freestone. There is excellent hunting in the Ben More deer forest and even better fishing in the lochs and streams.

The castles of Mull, Duart and Aros are still show-places. Close to Duart is a lighthouse, erected in memory of William Black, the novelist, whose many books are set in the region. About midway between Mull and Lismore is the Lady Rock, visible at low water, on which, in 1523, the cruel Lachlan Maclean of Duart marooned his wife – a daughter of the second earl of Argyll – expecting that she would be drowned by the tide. But the lady was rescued in the nick of time by her clansmen and Lachlan Maclean was later killed by her brother.

Apart from the villages of Lochbuie and Salan the only place of importance on Mull is the town of Tobermory, standing on a pretty bay, with the granite houses spread on tree-clad heights. It was founded in 1788 as a station for fishing boats and has regular steamer connection with Stornoway, Oban and Glasgow. But Tobermory's main claim to fame is the great Spanish galleon *Florencia* which, after the defeat of the Armada, anchored in the Bay. Her commander, Don Pereira, demanded provisions from the local chieftain, MacLean. After some formal exchanges, a bargain was struck: the MacLeans, being in the middle of a feud with the MacDonalds, demanded Pereira's aid to crush his enemies, for which he would victual the *Florencia* – in exchange for part of the gold she carried. But the bargain went sour. Though the Spaniards killed quite a few MacDonalds and MacLean did deliver the provisions, no gold was paid over. MacLean thereupon locked up three Spanish officers as hostages; the Spaniards took a clansman prisoner and held him on board. This man (who may have been either MacLean's son or someone called John Smollett), when he heard sails being hoisted on the galleon, broke into the gunpowder store, struck flint and blew the ship in half.

That is how the *Florencia* came to rest in the mud within a stone's throw of Mull's coast. Ever since the sixteenth century there have been repeated attempts to salvage her gold – for it was firmly believed that the *Florencia* was the bullion ship of the Armada and carried over "thirty millions of cash hidden under ye Sell of ye Gun Roome." With many interruptions and setbacks some silver and gold have been recovered from the "Tobermory Galleon" – but the main store of gold, if it exists, still rests in the mud and silt of Tobermory Bay.

Mull, like most of the Hebrides, has been steadily losing its population. There were over 4,000 at the beginning of the century; the latest census records only 2,420. Life is hard in the Hebrides, and young people tend to drift to the mainland and better-paid jobs. Yet the beauty of Mull still attracts visitors, from eminent politicians to amateur fishermen and vacationists.

Mykonos

A mountainous, rocky island. Location *Cyclades, Greece, Aegean Sea.* Area *32.5 square miles.* Map *9, G9.*

The attractions of Mykonos are nearly all man-made. The landscape is gaunt and rocky, ribbed by abrupt ravines: an arid place where only thistles and thin, dry grasses manage to find a roothold. At one spot, near the monastery of

The island of Mykonos

Tourliani, there are a few fields of barley, and on the light soil beyond they grow tomatoes and eggplant. The narrow, terraced slopes produce some sparse vines; but by and large it is an infertile, bleak setting for an enchanting little town.

The man-made attractions are concentrated in the port. Here are houses, chapels, dovecotes and windmills in the purest Cycladic style, a wonderful geometric harmony. Of all the isles of Greece, Mykonos is the most perfect and exquisite in its simplicity. The houses are white cubes, disposed along the contours around the bay and reached by narrow, twisting lanes from the harbor front. They are not old, but follow the tradition of centuries. The windmills above the town, helmeted with thatch, grind the barley on windy days – and most days are windy on Mykonos. From the inhabitants of the dovecotes scattered around the outskirts the islanders obtain an alternative diet to fish and an excellent manure for the stony fields. There are some 360 chapels – more, it is claimed, than in Rome – which are the epitome of latter-day Byzantine architecture. They alone provide notes of color in an otherwise dazzlingly white environment; for the domes of the churches and the semidomes over the altars are colored dark rose or blue. The effect is charming.

Every landowner has his chapel, his dovecote and his house; of the three, the house is the least luxurious, usually only two rooms, one on the ground floor and one, reached by an outside stair whitewashed like the rest, above. The roof is nearly flat, shaped to receive the rain at the center where the cistern is stored, for there is a great scarcity of water on Mykonos. The chimneys alone are turned into architectural features, decorated with shells and pottery. The windows are simply shuttered openings, cut in the direction of the best view.

Mykonos has little history; for centuries it has been self-sufficient, dependent for a livelihood upon the fruits of the sea rather than of the land. Recently it has become important as a tourist center; the boats with tourists come here to make the rough crossing to ancient Delos, only two miles away. For them there is a new hotel in the north of the town. But the town of Mykonos is still lovely and unspoiled as it must have been for centuries past.

Nantucket Island

A former whaling center, now a popular summer resort and artists' colony. Location *Off southern New England coast.* Area *46 square miles (including Muskeget and Tuckernuck islands).* Map *1, G7.*

"A mere hillock, and elbow of sand; all beach without a background," Hermann Melville described Nantucket – the island which, shortly after the beginning of the nineteenth century, counted as the third most important commercial center of Massachusetts, ranking immediately after Boston and Salem.

Nantucket, separated from Martha's Vineyard by the Muskeget Channel, owes its formation to glacier movement which also threw up Martha's Vineyard and Long Island as part of the same moraine ridge. Crescent-shaped, Nantucket Island is 14 miles long and has a population of nearly 4,000. There are a few small hills, all less than 200 feet. Little vegetation thrives on the sandy soil but a few trees vary the low-lying landscape.

Nantucket was discovered in 1602 by Bartholomew Gosnold, an English sailor whose name is associated with the early colonization of Virginia, when he traveled down the coast of New England; but it is probable that the Island was known to exploring Norsemen from Iceland centuries before. Originally settled by Indians from New England, it was purchased in 1641 and colonized around 1659. The town of Sherburne was built in 1673 but later the main settlement moved to Nantucket Harbor on the northern coast. Nantucket town was incorporated in 1687 and the county formed eight years later. After the first sperm whale was taken in 1712, the Island rapidly began to achieve fame as a base for whaling expeditions.

But in the eighteen-thirties, New Bedford, a mainland port favored by easier access to the developing industries and population centers of the northeastern states, began to monopolize the whaling industry. The Nantucket catch decreased – though in 1842 the fleet based on the Harbor still comprised 90 major vessels. Sankaty Head Lighthouse was built in 1850, standing on a bluff on the east coast, and the first American lightship station was established six years later about 50 miles offshore, beyond the Nantucket Shoals, which stretch for about 27 miles off the southeastern tip of the Island.

The original Nantucketers were all Quakers and the two elements of Quakerism and whaling formed the character of the island. Today, there are thousands of visitors, attracted by the good beaches and the picturesque fine old houses; Nantucket's landscapes have been preserved on hundreds of canvases.

Naples, Bay of

A semicircular inlet of the Tyrrhenian Sea, of spectacular beauty. Location *Between Gulf of Gaeta and Gulf of Salerno, Italy.* Dimensions *About 20 miles long, 10 miles wide.* Map *7, E8.*

No amount of postcards and popular songs can cheapen the enduring and exciting beauty of the Bay of Naples. It has become the very symbol of Mediterranean skies and sun, of the gaiety and tragedy that go together in such close company in southern Italy. Along its shores Pozzuoli and Portici, Torre del Greco and Torre Annunziata, Castellamare di Stabia and Vico Equense, Sorrento and the great seaport and teeming city of Naples itself, are stretched out in a glittering array – though unavoidably more attractive from the distance than on close acquaintance. In the east, Vesuvius rises, and even when the sky is overcast and the volcano is wrapped in mist, with the air muggy and a drizzle rippling the smooth surface of the Bay, this counts only as an intermission in the dramatic brilliance and the ever-changing panoramic display. Pompeii and Herculaneum, the biggest museums in the world, offer their ruins for inspection. Ischia and Procida, wooded and mountainous islands, stand sentinel at the Bay's entrance, and Monte Sant' Angelo, rising to over 4,000 feet, completes the backdrop in the southeast. Capri stands by itself, as a paramount attraction, with legends of Tiberian cruelty and with Axel Munthe's San Michele, a monument to gentle, humanitarian tolerance.

Approached across the Bay, blue as a glossy postcard, the city of Naples offers an incomparable view, the long white line of the distant city glittering in the sun. In the teeming city itself, life is a never-ending show, sad, tragic and tragic-comic, often squalid, blending laughter and tears – all within the sound, the smell and the glitter of the Bay.

Narragansett Bay

A bay with many inlets and islands. Location *Rhode Island, Atlantic Ocean.* Dimensions *30 miles long, 3–12 miles wide.* Map *1, F7.*

Narragansett Bay, long and narrow, almost cuts the smallest state of the Union into two. At its entrance is Rhode Island, with the popular and once highly exclusive summer and sailing resorts of Newport and Portsmouth; at its head, where the Providence River enters it, Providence has been an important shipping center. Prudence and Conanicut islands are also in the Bay.

Just west of Fall River in Massachusetts, Narragansett sends the six-mile-long and three-mile-wide Mount Hope Bay to meet the Sakonnet River in the south, while the main bay is southwest from it at the northern end of Rhode Island. Here this arm or inlet is crossed by the Mount Hope Bridge, built in 1929, which is one of the largest in New England. The Sakonnet River arm of Narragansett Bay extends about 14 miles from the Atlantic to Mount Hope Bay; Sakonnet Point juts out as a peninsula into the Atlantic east of the mouth of the river.

The town of Narragansett is on the western shore of the Bay. Town and Bay were named after the Narragansett Indians, once a powerful Algonquin tribe which occupied much of the shoreline. Under their chief Canonicus they were friendly to the early Rhode Island settlers, and his successor, Miantonomo, entered into a tripartite treaty with the Connecticut colonists and the Mohegans. But after Miantonomo was executed, his son, Canonchet or Nanuntenoo, turned against the white people; at least, the tribe's loyalty was suspected, and in 1675, at the Great or Cedar Swamp (where South Kingstown stands today), they were decisively defeated by the men of Plymouth Colony, led by Governor Josiah Winslow; a monument commemorates the engagement.

Today, Narragansett Bay has forgotten the Indian wars; but it still remembers the great hurricane of 1938 which devastated so much of its coastal villages and towns.

Nauru

A coral atoll with large phosphate deposits. Location *Southwest Pacific, 1,300 miles northeast of Australia.* Area *Eight square miles.* Map *4, F7.*

Each year Nauru exports over 1,000,000 tons of the dusty-gray or light brown material from the huge phosphate deposits of its central plateau; the phosphates are treated with sulphuric acid to be converted into superphosphates, and the annual export is sufficient to top-dress more than 100,000,000 acres of half-barren Australian farmland for the growing of wheat. The total phosphate resources of Nauru are estimated at over 42,000,000 tons and there are another 14,000,000 on Ocean Island, 160 miles away to the east.

Discovered by the British in 1798, annexed by the Germans in 1888, Nauru was occupied by Australian forces in 1919 and is now a United Nations Trusteeship held jointly by Britain, Australia and New Zealand and administered by Australia. The population has almost doubled in the last ten years – there are now over 4,000 people living there, mostly Nauruans or other Pacific islanders with a few Chinese and Europeans. Curiously, the methodical and scientifically-minded Germans never discovered during their occupation what wealth lay under their noses. It was Albert F. Ellis, a young New Zealander working temporarily in the Sydney office of a mining and trading firm, who made the discovery in 1900. The large piece of rock used as a doorstopper kept catching his eye. It came from Nauru, said the manager, and was petrified wood; but Ellis was not completely satisfied. He surreptitiously knocked off a fragment and tested it with acid. The Pacific Phosphate Company came into being and the three governments of Britain, Australia and New Zealand paid more than 10,000,000 dollars for its assets when they took it over, 19 years after Ellis's discovery, and vested the exploitation rights in the British Phosphate Commissioners. Ellis rose to be head of this commission.

Nauru, formerly Pleasant Island, is an oval of solid coral limestone, without harbors or even large breaks in the fringing reefs that surround it. Everywhere the limestone has been weathered into jagged pinnacles and on top of it, impregnating it, is the great layer of guano, produced by centuries of bird-droppings. Rain sinks at once through the porous rock; before the white man came and installed catchment tanks and distilling apparatus, the island suffered periodically from drought. Nauru had wells, but on Ocean Island fresh water was obtained solely from the *banga-bangas*, deep underground caverns with which the limestone is riddled. Emigration was sometimes the only hope of survival when these ran dry – though life might be sustained for a while by catching flying-fish and sucking the water from their eyes, or by coconut-water.

Coconuts, pandanus, pawpaws, mangoes, soursops, guavas, limes, bananas, jackfruit – a wide variety of useful trees now grow here, and the natives, still in their old villages, prosper by supplying the phosphate company with vegetables and fish, though most of the mine labor comes from other islands. For fun they tame the superb man-o'-war or frigate bird (an ocean soarer with six-foot wings and legs so atrophied that it cannot rise off the ground but must be provided with a framework of sticks to rest on). Away they fly all day, winning their food by attacking other birds and forcing them to drop the fish they have caught – then catching it in mid-air. Then at night they come back to their owners, who often use them as decoys, casting a weighted line over the wings of the stranger bird as it flies near and so ensnaring it.

Both Nauru and Ocean Island were occupied by the Japanese from 1942 to September, 1945. Today, Nauru is administered under a United Nations Trusteeship; Ocean Island, discovered in 1804, is part of the Gilbert and Ellice group.

Naxos

The largest island of the Cyclades group. Location *Aegean Sea, Greece, east of Paros.* Area *169 square miles.* Map *9, G10.*

Once a center for the worship of Dionysus, according to Greek mythology it was here that Theseus abandoned Ariadne; certainly a most beautiful place to be abandoned in. Nàxos is still an island rich in vines, in olives, wheat and fruit trees. The lemon is cultivated with special care and from it the islanders make one of the best Aegean drinks, a liqueur called Citron.

Colonized by the Ionians and reaching its golden age in the late sixth century B.C. as the ruling center of the Cyclades, Naxos was sacked by the Persians in 490 B.C., joined the Delian League and became subject to Athens after the revolt of 450 B.C. From 1207 to 1566 it was the seat of the Aegean Duchy of Venice. In 1579 it became Turkish territory and in 1832 part of Greece. It was of Naxos above all that Lord Byron used to dream when he was in England, and he told his friends that it was there he intended to retire one day.

Mountains run up behind the fertile valleys and dominate the small town and harbor which looks eastward across the narrow straits to Paros. Mount Dryos rises to 3,284 feet; the granite and marble quarries have been worked for untold centuries and the sculptors of Naxos were famous in classical days. The Venetian rule left its mark upon Naxia, the capital, which climbs from the harbor in a series of terraces, steep alleys and square, box-like houses. The population – over 20,000 – finds its living in growing almonds, figs, and barley, breeding sheep and goats, producing a famous white wine and exporting granite, marble and emery.

New Britain

The principal island of the Bismarck Archipelago. Location *Southwest Pacific, 55 miles northeast of New Guinea.* Area *14,600 square miles.* Map *4, E7.*

The Germans called it New Pomerania; when the Australians took it over in 1914, it was renamed New Britain and today it forms part of the Australian Trust Territory of northeastern New Guinea. It is a huge volcanic island about 300 miles long and 50 miles wide, extremely mountainous (the highest peak, Ulawan, rising to 7,546 feet), with several active volcanoes and many hot springs. Its shape is almost a perfect crescent except where the Willaumez Peninsula projects northward. The broad, irregular Gazelle Peninsula in the northeast is joined to the main body of the island by a narrow neck. Here is Rabaul (the former Herbertshöhe), which was a main Japanese naval base from 1942 to 1944, with Cape Gloucester and Gasmata as subsidiary naval and air bases.

Much of the coast is extremely steep, but at some points the mountains recede and the shores are flat, bordered by coral reefs. The vegetation is tropical and rich; coffee is the main agricultural product and there are copper, gold, iron and coal mines. Until fairly recently, New Britain was largely unexplored, and much of its interior is still unmapped. The natives are Melanesians, a powerful, well-formed race, closely resembling their Papuan kinsfolk of eastern New Guinea, with a complex system of tribal traditions, taboos and animistic religious ceremonies. They have several dialects which resemble Fijian – except for the numerals, which are Polynesian. The population numbers over 80,000 and still lives under very primitive conditions.

New Caledonia

A volcanic island. Location *Southwest Pacific.* Area *8,548 square miles.* Map *4, F9.*

New Caledonia was discovered by Captain Cook in 1774, when he touched the island near its northwestern extremity, at the haven of Balade. The coast and the surrounding seas were first closely explored by Joseph de Bruni d'Entrecasteaux in 1793. Sealers and traders in sandalwood came next, but the fierce inhabitants made any settlement impossible. In 1843 French missionaries landed and claimed the island for France; this claim was withdrawn when Britain protested. In 1851 a French landing party was attacked by the natives at Balade and massacred. France and Britain annexed the group almost simultaneously, but finally the British claim was abandoned. In 1854 Nouméa (originally called Port de France) was founded; in 1860 New Caledonia became a colony distinct from the French Pacific possessions.

Four years later a penal settlement was set up on Nou Island, off Nouméa. There were two native insurrections, the first in 1878 and the second in 1881, both of which were put down only after much bloodshed. The penal colony was abolished in 1894.

During the Second World War the island and its dependencies chose the Free French cause; in 1942 an American air base was established at Nouméa to prevent Japanese invasion. In 1946 the group became an overseas territory of the French Union; its population numbers nearly 70,000.

About 248 miles long and 31 miles wide, New Caledonia has a mountainous interior, with plains in the coastal regions. The highest peak is Mount Panié (5,412 feet). There are no extremes in temperature, and though the rainfall is heavy, there is no malaria; but the island lies in the path of tropical hurricanes. A large livestock economy has been developed and there are important coffee plantations. In addition the mineral resources, not yet completely developed, are extremely rich. There are large nickel mines and nickel smelters at Yaté and Doniambo; other minerals that are found in important quantities include chrome, antimony, cinnabar, cobalt, copper, gold, manganese, mercury, iron lead and silver.

New Caledonia has a great variety of fine timber trees: the scattered growth of niaulis on the lower hills provides timber, bark and cajeput oil. Breadfruit, sago, banana, vanilla, ginger, arrowroot and curcuma grow wild; orange, indigo, lucerne and European vegetables are also grown. There are very few mammals, among them the rat and several varieties of bat, including the *Pteropus*. The kagu (*Rhinochetus jubatus*), a strange, wingless ground bird, is found nowhere else. There is an abundance of turtles on the coast and plenty of fish – of which the tetrodons (globe-fish) are highly poisonous, especially at certain seasons.

The natives are a mixture of Melanesians and Polynesians, whom the French called *Kanakas* (from *canaques*, a word meaning "man" which they applied indiscriminately to many Pacific peoples). Javanese and Tonkinese indentured laborers have added to the mixture.

The dependencies of New Caledonia include the Loyalty Islands, the Isle of Pines, the Huon Islands, the Chesterfield Islands, Walpole Island and the Belep Islands. The Wallis and Futuna Islands are a separate protectorate, but are also under the administrative authority of New Caledonia.

Newfoundland

A huge island, famous for its fishing grounds. Location *Easternmost province of Canada, Atlantic Ocean.* Area *156,185 square miles (land and water).* Map *1, H4–J4.*

The shores of Newfoundland look inhospitable at first sight. A rough triangle in shape, its deeply indented coasts rise in dark, frowning cliffs, miles upon miles of rocky walls, 200–300 feet high, with little green to relieve their bleakness. The large bays – these include Fortune, Hermitage, Placentia, d'Espoir, St George, Port au Port, Bonne, St John, Hare, White, Notre Dame, Bonavita, Conception, St Mary's and the Bay of Islands – alternate with bold promontories and headlands, small fjord-like inlets and peninsulas like the Great Northern, Burin and Avalon which have been carved into massive and majestic forms by the battering of the Atlantic gales. The steep, barren, rocky shores present no pebbly beaches; it seems as if Newfoundland would be defended by dark, lofty and rocky ramparts to repel the constant attack of the sea.

Inland, however, one finds an undulating plateau, with many low hills. As one sails up the fjords that cut into the rocky walls, the shores open up with dark green forests that sweep down to the water's edge. The estuaries are studded with islands of all shapes and sizes – Fogo and Random are the largest, with Belle Isle off the northern tip. The waters are criss-crossed by busy boats; the shores lined with fishing hamlets with rough stages and fish flakes for landing and drying the cod.

The highest mountains of Newfoundland are the Long Range Mountains in the northwest, rising to 2,666 feet in Gros Morne. Around the heads of the bays there are large tracts of excellent timberland. But the most outstanding physical feature of the island is its immense number of lakes and ponds; more than one third of its area is actually water. These lakes range from the huge Grand Lake (120 square miles), Red Indian (70 square miles), Sandy (49 square miles) and Gander (46.5 square miles) to small ponds and tarns. They are found in every position: in mountain gorges, in depressions between hills, in valleys and frequently in hollows

A fishing and farming settlement on Newfoundland

near the tops of the highest hills. From the tops of some of the highest mountains 60–150 ponds and lakes have been counted. They are all relics of the glacial age, having been scooped out by glaciers when the whole of Newfoundland was under a 2,000–3,000-foot-thick ice-mantle, and down its mountain gorges huge glaciers threw off millions of icebergs. The lakes, together with rivers like the Humber, the Victoria, the Gander and the Terra Nova, form valuable sources of hydro-electric power for the great news-print factories at Grand Falls and Corner Brook, the copper, gold, lead, silver and zinc mills at Buchans, the fluorspar mines at Great St Lawrence and the many lumber mills.

The climate of Newfoundland is most strongly influenced by the cold Labrador Current; while the annual rainfall is moderate, the central area receives up to 120 inches of snow yearly. Arctic and subarctic animals, caribou, wolves, bears, foxes, otters and lynxes are plentiful; there are hundreds of mink and fox farms. The main occupations are still fishing and fish processing; cod, salmon, herring and lobster provide large catches. The Codroy and Humber River valleys are the main centers of dairy farming and cattle raising, while industry is mostly concentrated on the Avalon Peninsula. The 459,000 Newfoundlanders live in the capital, St John, in the other principal centers, such as Grand Bank, Harbour Grace, Corner Brook, Wesleyville and Channel-Port aux Basques (where the steamers from Nova Scotia have their terminus), or in scattered farms and villages. During the Second World War, American air bases were built at Placentia, Gander and Stephenville. Of these Gander grew into an international transatlantic airport of great importance. At Heart's Content (Trinity Bay) the transatlantic cable terminates; the first such cable was laid in 1858 between Valentia, in Ireland, and Newfoundland.

John Cabot discovered the island in 1497 and claimed it for Britain. A formal claim was established by Sir Humphrey Gilbert in 1583. English, French, Spanish and Portuguese fishermen competed for the rich catches and gradually the English gained the upper hand. The first capital was established at Ferryland in 1616 and in 1637 the island was given to Sir David Kirke as a county-palatinate. The French settled in the south of the island; the Treaty of Utrecht (1713) assigned Newfoundland to Britain while safeguarding the French fishing monopoly on the western and northeastern so-called French Shore. These rights were finally bought by Britain in 1904; another fishing dispute, with the United States, was settled by the International Court of The Hague in 1910. In 1927 most of Labrador was put under Newfoundland jurisdiction; by a plebiscite in 1949 Newfoundland became a province of Canada with a Lieutenant-Governor, an Executive Council and a Legislative Assembly of its own.

New Guinea

One of the largest islands in the world, divided between Dutch New Guinea (claimed by Indonesia as West Irian) and the Australian-administered New Guinea Territory. Location *Southwest Pacific, separated from northern Australia by the Torres Strait and the Arafura Sea.* Area *About 304,200 square miles.* Map *4, C7–E8.*

One place only in the western Pacific escaped the traders, the slave-dealers and kidnappers and the missionaries, escaping also the toll of death and disease – the great green island of New Guinea. This was chiefly because its savage inhabitants proved utterly intractable; they soon acquired a bad name among white travelers and so most of New Guinea remained *terra incognita* until after the First World War.

New Guinea is a bird-shaped island (the western end is called *Vogelkop*, Bird's Head) about 1,500 miles long. A series of high ranges runs along its entire length: in the west, the Nassau Range (containing Mount Carstensz, 16,400 feet, the highest island peak in the world) and the Orange Range; in the east, the Bismarck Mountains and the Owen Stanley Range, which became famous in the Second World War as the first point at which the Japanese advance in the Pacific was stopped. The peaks rise above the matted lowland jungles and mountain moss-forests. Although it is a hot, equatorial land, the New Guinea Alps have permanent snowfields and alpine lakes. Much of the Dutch (western) half still remains unknown and it is only during the last 30 years that the Central Highlands of Australian territory have become more gradually and systematically explored.

Until after the Second World War, Australian New Guinea was itself divided into two parts: Papua, which has always been Australian, and the Territory of New Guinea, the coasts of which were once meagerly settled but sternly ruled by Germany. Within a few months of the beginning of the First World War, an Australian force landed and defeated the weak German opposition. Between the wars Australia administered New Guinea under mandate; both Papua and the Territory of New Guinea became models of colonial administration in which the interests of the inhabitants were kept paramount. This was

Native fishing boats, Papua, New Guinea

largely due to Sir Hubert Murray, who went to Papua first in 1904 and became a legend in his lifetime. He gradually eliminated head-hunting, though the great houses with wall-niches adorned with dozens of bleached skulls remained as village exhibits long after fresh ones ceased to be gathered. Cannibalism still exists in many remote areas of the island, but it was in Murray's territory, patrolled by a band of handpicked district officials, that it was first brought under almost complete control.

The fauna of New Guinea consists largely of marsupials and monotremes (the lowest order of mammals); reptiles are represented by many different kinds of venomous snakes and crocodiles. Butterflies exist in great variety and the tropical birds include the cassowary and, above all, the birds of paradise. The male birds of paradise, some of them of almost unearthly beauty, live in the rain forests and, though seen only with difficulty, are expertly caught by the Papuans, who use them extensively for decoration in their ceremonial feasts and dances. The first described species was named by Linnaeus *Paradisea apoda*, the footless bird of paradise. The specific name *apoda* was related to the sailors' legend that these weirdly beautiful birds possessed no legs – that they lived in heaven where they needed none. The reason for the legend is that although native taxidermists carefully preserved the skins and the attached plumes, they could see no use for the unadorned feet and simply cut them off. Today all species of birds of paradise are rigidly protected. Other notable Papuan birds are the mound-builders and bower-birds. The former are often called incubator-birds, because they scrape together a mound of decaying debris and in this lay their eggs which are then incubated by the generated heat. The chicks of some species probably never meet their parents.

Most of the native Papuan mammals are marsupial, carrying their newborn young in a special belly pouch. They include the climbing tree-kangaroos, a specialized offshoot from ground kangaroo stock which, in the dense forests of New Guinea, have taken to the timber. The most notable of the few non-marsupials is the spiny ant-eater, an egg-laying mammal related to the platypus. Although it is beaked, it clearly shares many internal features with reptiles. The third group of mammals includes the bats, among them the big fruit-eating flying-foxes with a wing-span of about five feet, a delicacy to the natives. Wild dogs and wild pigs were originally introduced by the Melanesians when they settled in New Guinea many thousands of years ago. The other natives are Negritos and Papuans. The total number of Europeans on the island is still less than 20,000.

Netherlands New Guinea occupies an area of 159,375 square miles and has an estimated population of 730,000; it comprises the western half of the island together with the offshore islands, Schouten, Japen, Raja, Ampat and Salawati. A conference between the Netherlands and Indonesia agreed that the future status of New Guinea would be decided by negotiation between the two parties within a year of the transfer of sovereignty to Indonesia (December 27, 1949). A joint Dutch-Indonesian Commission was formed to investigate the facts and to report back to the two governments. But the two sides of the Commission failed to agree and though Indonesia persistently claims "West Irian," this part of New Guinea remains under Dutch sovereignty.

In 1949 Papua and the Territory of New Guinea (including the islands of New Ireland, New Britain, Bougainville and Buka in the Solomons) were combined for administrative purposes under the same headquarters at Port Moresby (in Papua). The Territory of Papua includes the southeastern portion of New Guinea together with the Trobriand, Woodlark, D'Entrecasteaux and Louisiade groups of islands; of its area, 87,540 square miles belong to New Guinea; the official estimate of the native population is 470,890. The Trust Territory of New Guinea includes Northeastern New Guinea, with a total area of 69,700 square miles, and the adjacent islands of Manam, Karkar, Long, Bagabag, Schouten and D'Urville (or Kairiku), and its main centers are Lae, Bulolo, Finschhafen, Wau, Medang, Wewak, Goroka and Mount Hagen; the Bismarck Archipelago, the Admiralty Islands and the two northernmost Solomon Islands also belong to it. The total population of the Trust Territory is estimated at about 1,360,700. New road systems have been built since the Second World War and a thriving coffee industry has been established in the highlands; there are regular air services from Australia to Lae and Rabaul and to Port Moresby and equally regular sailings between the main ports of New Guinea and Australia.

New Hebrides

A 400-mile-long chain of islands; an Anglo-French condominium. Location *Southwest Pacific, 1,100 miles east of Australia.* Area *About 5,700 square miles.* Map *4, F8–G8.*

The volcanic and coralline islands of the New Hebrides extend between Fiji and the Solomons. The largest is Espiritu Santo, followed by Epate (with Vila, the capital of the condominium), Mewo, Epi, Malo, Malecula, Pentecost, Tanna, Aoba, Ambrym, Erromanga and Aneytum in the main group and the Banks and Torres islands completing the chain, which has many remarkable features. The natives, mostly Melanesians with a few Polynesians and occasional remnants of a pygmy Australoid type (doubtless the original inhabitants), are among the most intelligent in the Pacific. They evolved for navigation a sextant made from a coconut shell and have sailing charts, made from coconut palm ribs, with shells to represent islands, showing data such as wave swells – all based on the keenest observation of extremely subtle phenomena. In their arts, alongside weird ritual masks, highly intellectualized "continuous line" drawings are found.

The sadder, therefore, that their relationship with the white man has been one long series of disasters. The traders who came to the islands to cut sandalwood massacred them and destroyed their villages and crops; then, until late in the last century, being near enough to Queensland, Australia, they became a favorite resort of "blackbirders," who kidnapped them, often killing many in the process, to sell them to the sugar plantations. Here, though not actually slaves – many were even returned to the islands after a spell of years – their labor was forced and many died. No wonder they became the toughest natives in the South Seas and sought revenge, killing missionaries, repulsing the landing crews of traders and slavedealers – which, in turn, led to punitive expeditions and the shelling of their villages.

Even now, despite the enormous decline in population following the introduction of the diseases of civilization (there are some 66,000 people in the group, compared to about 1,000,000 when the white man first came), large areas are still unsafe for strangers and cannibalism is still practised, though with less fervor than formerly.

Many strange customs survive: on Pentecost Island, for example, there exists one of the most hair-raising tests of valor and manhood known, which takes place every year. A rickety-looking tower, up to 80 feet high, of tree trunks lashed together with bush-vines, is constructed in the middle of a clearing. At various heights diving boards project from it. Round each ankle of the man to be tested a length of vine is tied of exactly the right length and breaking strength. Then the diver plunges head first towards the ground below – 20 feet, if he is a young boy, 80 feet or even more, if a man of prestige. As he nears the end of the drop the vines stretch, arresting his fall, and snap, dropping him gently to earth into a forked up and slightly softened bed. The slightest miscalculation and he would be killed, his neck or back broken, or at least his legs pulled out of joint. Yet, the natives say, no one has ever been hurt.

The islands produce pandanus, coconut palms, orchids and some sandalwood together with copra, coffee, cocoa, and mother-of-pearl. The natives are ruled by chiefs who are divided into five degrees. To climb socially, a man must give a series of dances (dancing is the most important means of self-expression) at which an ever-increasing number of pigs are sacrificed and eaten. Pigs are money and to get them – for they are not bred – a man must either be popular enough to borrow them in quantity or feared sufficiently as a sorcerer to be given them. The value of a boar is in direct ratio to the length of its tusks, which are trained to grow into sweeping circles; in some places, hermaphrodite pigs are held the most costly.

Discovered in 1606 by Pedro Fernandez de Quiros, the group was placed in 1887 under an Anglo-French naval commission and the condominium was established in 1906. In the Second World War, the New Hebrides supported the Free French cause and became a military and naval base.

New Ireland

The second largest island of the Bismarck Archipelago. Location *Bismarck Archipelago, Territory of New Guinea, southwest Pacific.* Area *3,340 square miles.* Map *4, E7.*

New Ireland, about 230 miles long and extremely narrow – except at its southeastern end – is a mountainous, heavily forested island. The Schleinitz Mountains cover its center; Mount Lambel, its highest point, rises to 7,054 feet. The chief town and port is Kavieng, in the north; the population is about 19,000. Copra, from a few plantations, is the chief product.

The most interesting aspect of New Ireland – as of the Bismarck Archipelago in general – is to be found in the customs and traditions of its primitive Melanesian inhabitants. Agriculture, ancestor worship and cannibalism, conceptions of fertility, life and death, are all interwoven. In the northern part of New Ireland, the ancestor cult is practised by a secret society which on certain occasions performs public dances, wearing fantastic masks. These, when not in use, are kept in special shrines. In the Laur district, the southern part of the island, ancestral figures are carved in limestone and set up in a building to which no women are admitted – though they occasionally gather in front of them to voice their complaints.

New Ireland, like New Britain, forms part of the Territory of New Guinea and is administered by Australia under United Nations trusteeship.

New Zealand

A British Dominion, consisting of two large and several small islands. Location *Pacific Ocean 1,200 miles southeast of Australia.* Area *103,416 square miles.* Map *4, G10–11.*

The two main islands of New Zealand are North Island, 510 miles long and up to 200 miles wide, and South Island, 480 by 210 miles. These two, with the Cook Islands and Niue and the Ross Dependency, form the Dominion, in which a total population of over 2,500,000 people live.

New Zealand's position in the South Pacific is roughly the same in the southern hemisphere as that of Great Britain in the northern. The climate is temperate; North Island has been likened to Portugal and South Island to Switzerland, though the omnipresent influence of the sea offsets the differences due to the changes in latitude.

North Island has several mountain ranges, rising to the active volcano Ruapehu (9,175 feet) and the quiescent Mount Egmont (8,260 feet). Their windward, wetter flanks are rugged and richly vegetated, with plants like giant tree-ferns evoking the evolutionary past and thriving in the warm moisture. North of Ruapehu is a curious, pumice-covered plateau with Lake Taupo in its middle. In this volcanic area are the geysers, hot pools and springs, solfateras, fumaroles and mud-volcanoes, some of them renowned for healing properties.

South Island's most impressive feature is the range of the Southern Alps, snow-topped, with many glaciers, rising to 12,349 feet in Mount Cook. The southwest coast is cut into deep fjords. Of the glaciers, the Tasman (18 miles long), the Franz Josef and the Fox are the best known. The New Zealand rivers are, for the most part, too short and rapid for navigation; the Waikato, the Wanganui and Clutha are the most important, none of them longer than 300 miles. The climate has a very small annual range of temperature, which permits some growth of vegetation all the year round. Even in South Island very little snow falls on low levels.

New Zealand has been the home of the Maoris – Polynesian immigrants with a stone-age culture – only since the fourteenth or fifteenth century. The first European to see it was Abel Tasman in 1642. Cook visited and charted both islands in 1769 and he returned to them in 1773, 1774 and 1777. Though he annexed the islands in the name of Britain, his government rejected his action and they did not become a British colony till 1841, to be given Dominion status in 1907. But after Cook's journeys, sealers and whalers settled along the coasts and trade in timber and flax followed. The first missionaries arrived in 1814 and in 1832 a British Resident was appointed. Though the 1840 Treaty of Waitangi guaranteed the Maoris possession of their lands, they became belligerent in 1854 and attempts to subdue them in the next decade led to much bloodshed. Today the 158,000 Maoris live peaceably, mainly in North Island, and more and more of them live and work in the towns. The capital is Wellington, in North Island, with a population of 144,000; other large centers are Auckland, Christchurch, Dunedin, Hutt, Palmerston North, Hamilton, Invercargill, New Plymouth, Napier, Timaru and Nelson.

Few countries can have undergone such changes in so short a time as New Zealand. In 1840, more than half of North Island was covered with thick evergreen jungle; twenty years ago, practically none of the original forest was left – though man-planted trees, particularly the Monterey pine, which grows extremely fast here, are now redeeming vast eroded areas from the consequences of thoughtless tree-felling and the agricultural methods of New Zealand's early settler days. Elsewhere, many of the original grasslands have been burned or grazed out of existence. The islands are developing rapidly both agriculturally and industrially; vast dams have been built and the geothermal steam resources of the Volcanic Plateau are being tapped, and may be capable of supplying 1,000,000 kilowatts. Road development in the last decades has been extremely rapid and in 1959 there was one vehicle to every three people.

New Zealand has special biological interest. Three-quarters of its flowering plants are endemic and the majority do not much resemble those of Australia or the nearer parts of Polynesia. It has no native mammals except bats, nor marsupials, nor snakes. Dogs and rats were imported by the earliest Maoris – though the latter unintentionally. There being originally no predators, many birds have lost their powers of flight – like the quaint kiwi and the very rare *takahe* (*Notornis*). Wingless cranes are not long extinct. The various kinds of moa have also vanished; they were rather like the kiwi, with the same kind of hairless feathers, but completely wingless, and the largest stood 12 feet high. They were possibly part of the Maoris' diet.

The final zoological quirk is the tuatara, a lizard-like creature often sharing its burrow with a kind of petrel; it is one of the world's "living fossils" for it is the only surviving member of an order of reptiles, the *Rhyncocephalia*, dating from the end of the Primary era, before the first dinosaur appeared. Over two feet long and olive green in color, the tuatara has a vestigial third eye – the pineal – on the top of its skull.

Nicobar Islands

A group of 19 small islands, part of the Indian State of Nicobar and Andaman. Location *Indian Ocean, between Little Andaman Island and Sumatra.* Area *635 square miles.* Map *10, G5.*

Divided roughly into three sections, with Car Nicobar in the north, Katchall, Comorta, Nancowry and Chowra in the center and Great and Little Nicobar in the south, the Nicobar Islands are largely sandstone and clay; the lower ones are often coralline. The biggest, Great Nicobar, rises to 2,105 feet and is the only one to have a good freshwater supply from numerous streams, although rainfall is fairly heavy throughout the year. Wild life is varied though there are few mammals; some of them, like buffaloes, have been introduced to Comorta by the Danes, who once laid claim to the group. Coconut, betel and a species of breadfruit grow extensively but there is little good timber. The main occupations are woodworking, canoe building, palm-mat and basket weaving, and there are potters on Chowra. The trading centers are at Nancowry Harbour and Chowra.

In the early fourteenth century, Odoric of Pordenone published the first account of Nicobar (which he called Nicuveran) and astounded his readers by a hair-raising description of an island 2,000 miles in circumference peopled by naked cannibals who worshipped oxen and had dog-heads. Strangely enough, the Nicobarese – of Mongoloid stock – claim to be descended from a man who mated with a bitch. The traditional dress of the men (if they wear anything at all) is a loincloth with a kind of tail behind. There is, however, no evidence that they have ever been cannibals and their religion is animistic – despite strenuous efforts of Christian missionaries. The people have Burmese and Malayan affinities while the languages of all but one tribe belong to the Mon-Khmer group of Indochina. The Nicobarese are short-headed and fairly small in stature though sturdily built. Social organization is based on the village; land is owned by the community. Inter-island trade is considerable and governed by a strange system of taboos. For instance, canoes may not be made in the island of Chowra, while pottery may be manufactured only there, though all the pot-clay must be brought from another island.

The Islands were occupied for short periods in the eighteenth and nineteenth centuries by Austrians, Danes, British and French, until 1869, when they finally passed into British possession. The Japanese held them during the Second World War, from 1942 to 1945. Today they form part of the Republic of India.

Nootka Sound

A small sound with several inlets, important in the history of British settlement of the North Pacific coast of America. Location *Off Vancouver Island, Pacific Ocean.* Map *4, M2.*

Nootka Sound stretches along the southern and eastern coasts of Nootka Island, a large body of land in southwest British Columbia with an area of 206 square miles. Nootka Island is largely uninhabited, with a little fishing and lumbering centered around Nootka village on the southeastern coast. The Sound has a number of long, narrow arms of which Muchalat and Tahsis inlets are the most important. In spite of its smallness and relative unimportance geographically, Nootka Sound has played an important part in the history of exploration and settlement in the West.

The mouth of the Sound was first visited in 1774 by the Spanish explorer Juan Perez, but he made no detailed examination. This was carried out in 1778 by Captain James Cook, on his third voyage of discovery. He encountered the Indian inhabitants, decked in beautiful feathers, who came out to the ships in their canoes, and trade by barter was quickly under way. Cook's party soon realized that the Indians were acquainted with iron and that, like the Polynesians, they were cannibals. "The most extraordinary of all the articles which they brought to the ship for sale," Cook wrote, "were human skulls and hands not yet quite stripped of flesh which they made our people plainly understand they had eaten ..." The Indians were willing to barter everything, including their holy idols and totem-poles – though these only in exchange for brass and copper, while the others could be had for iron. Brass and copper were so much in demand that, as Cook reported, in the end the sailors got rid of all fittings, containers, candlesticks and even the buttons of their clothes.

Cook first proposed the name of King George's Sound for the inlet, one of whose innermost arms was later called Tahsis Canal. His task had been to make a detailed examination of the northwest coast to find a navigable northeast passage from the Pacific into the Atlantic Ocean, possibly by way of Hudson or Baffin Bay.

The strait of Juan de Fuca, south of Vancouver Island, had been considered a likely opening of such a passage by the Spaniards and also by John Meares, another English navigator. In 1788 Meares established a fortified port at Nootka as a base of operations, but the Spaniards seized this next year – an action which almost led to an Anglo-Spanish war. Having set up a colony at Nootka, the Spaniards remained in possession until 1795. The controversy between England and Spain was actually settled in 1790 by the Nootka Convention, which opened the way to British settlement along the northwest Pacific coast.

The modern Nootka village has in more recent years been an important center for fishermen and lumbermen; not far away, to the north of Nootka Island, is the important Zeballos mining camp.

Norfolk Island

A small volcanic island, a dependency of Australia. Location *South Pacific, 930 miles northeast of Sydney.* Area *13 square miles.* Map *4, G10.*

In appearance Norfolk Island is a small segment of paradise: melons and passion fruit, pineapples, bananas and oranges riot wild in the mellow climate, free for the picking. There are bright birds amidst the dark foliage of stately conifers (some of them 200 feet high, 30 feet in girth, for this is the home of the famous Norfolk Island pine, *Araucaria excelsa*, for whose timber the Island was originally seized by the British Navy). There are brilliant flowers and butterflies; white beaches, and sea breezes softening the heat of the endless sun. With an airfield built in 1943, there are fortnightly air services to Australia and New Zealand with a constant influx of wealthy visitors.

Yet Norfolk has one of the most sinister histories in the Pacific. When Captain Cook discovered it in 1774, it was uninhabited. The first settlers who came in 1788 were convicts. A great fort was built (its ruins still stand) and for about 65 years, with only one break, the place was a penal colony, scene of some of the worst horrors in British history. "Whatever their age, the average time of death for the prisoners was in the eleventh year after their arrival – from dysentery," wrote one of the warders. The cruelty and bestiality of both guards and prisoners became legendary; there are savage tales told about the two unsuccessful mutinies that occurred.

In 1853 the convict settlement was closed and three years later an even stranger colony arrived from Pitcairn Island – the descendants of the mutineers of H.M.S. *Bounty*. Many of them soon returned to Pitcairn, but those who remained on Norfolk flourished and now number about 1,000. Though nearly all bear fine old mutineer names, they are almost puritanically law-abiding.

In 1955 a modern whaling station was established on the Island. Local government was granted in 1960 by the creation of the Norfolk Island Council with power to control roads, electricity and other municipal services.

North Atlantic Current

A great current, or drift, terminal section of the Gulf Stream system. Location *North Atlantic Ocean.* Map *6, E2–A1.*

It is near the Grand Banks, southeast of Newfoundland, that the Gulf Stream proper meets the Labrador Current and the two unite to form the North Atlantic Current, a warm drift which influences the climate of Britain and northern Europe. The mainstream of this drift has a velocity of about six miles per day. After the union of the two parent currents, the North Atlantic Current loses its characteristics of a clearly-defined warm current; its surface temperature is about 60° F. north of the Azores. Frequently it is also masked by the shallow wind-drift surface movements of the water, which are caused by the prevailing westerlies.

The North Atlantic Current is split into several terminal branches. The Irminger Current flows north and west past the south coast of Iceland, joining the East Greenland Current, which emerges from Denmark Strait. It has a daily velocity of about 17 miles. The Canaries Current cools the northwest coast of Africa; it branches off south from the North Atlantic Current in the latitude of the Azores, travels southwest along the Saharan coast of southwest Morocco and Spanish West Africa, then turns west in the latitude of Senegal towards the Cape Verde Islands. Its velocity is the same as that of the Irminger Current, so is that of the Norwegian Current, another terminal branch of the North Atlantic Current, which flows north along the coast of Norway before branching into the Barents Sea and moving past Spitsbergen. This is perhaps the most decisive current in moderating climate.

Northeast Passage

A sea passage between the Atlantic and Pacific oceans, long sought by navigators. Location *North of Russia.*

The search for a passage to the Pacific by way of the northeast was a long one. This route through the cold seas north of Europe to the riches of Cathay was a favorite dream of merchants and sailors from the sixteenth century onwards. Sir Hugh Willoughby set out in 1553 but perished with 62 companions on the coast of Russian Lapland. The Dutch tried several times before the end of the sixteenth century and discovered Bear Island and Spitsbergen. Henry Hudson failed to get farther than Novaya Zemlya in 1608. Other Englishmen tried and failed, as did Danes, Norwegians, Russians and Swedes, all defeated by the weather conditions and the ice. Some returned, some were killed by hostile Samoyeds, some died of cold when their ships were wrecked in the treacherous seas, but no amount of failure could deter men from the search. In the early eighteenth century Vitus Bering sailed through the Strait that was later named after him and eventually made his way to Alaska.

The attempts continued through the eighteenth and nineteenth centuries – but it was not until 1879 that the passage, round East Cape, was accomplished by Nils Adolf Erik Nordenskjold, later created a baron for his achievement. Nordenskjold was born in Finland but commanded a cosmopolitan expedition in his *Vega*, a ship of 300 tons, and three cargo boats, which left the party at various stages of the voyage. The four ships sailed from Tromso in July, 1878, were a mere 120 miles from their goal by the end of September, but were then frozen in for ten months, until July, 1879. "... The forenoon of the 18th passed," Nordenskjold wrote. "We sat down to dinner at the usual time, without any suspicion that the time of our release was now at hand. During dinner it was suddenly observed that the vessel was moving slightly. Palander (captain of the *Vega*) rushed on deck, saw that the ice was in motion, ordered the boiler fires to be lighted, the engine long ago having been put in order in expectation of this moment, and in two hours, by 3.30 p.m. on July 18th, the *Vega*, decked with flags, was under steam and sail again on the way to her destination ..."

The destination was the Pacific and though they met with dense fog, on July 20 they sighted the easternmost promontory of Asia, the East Cape. Soon they were in the middle of the sound uniting the North Polar Sea with the Pacific, "and from this point the *Vega* greeted the old and new worlds by a display of flags and the firing of a Swedish salute ..."

In 1918–20 Roald Amundsen repeated the exploit and several explorers followed in Nordenskjold's tracks. More recently the Northeast Passage has become a regular shipping lane for the Siberian ports; Soviet icebreakers, some of them atom-powered, aided by aerial reconnaissance and weather stations, keep it navigable from June to September.

North Sea

A shallow arm of the Atlantic, providing one of the finest fishing grounds in the world. Location *Between Great Britain and the European continent.* Area *222,000 square miles.* Maximum depth *2,165 feet.* Map *7, E4.*

A dour sea, cold and rarely friendly, the North Sea keeps even in summer its gray tones and inhospitable appearance. In winter, when the wind is from the east, it is one of the coldest and most broken seas the sailor is likely to encounter. It is out of this gray tumble of shallow water that most of the fish consumed in England is caught and for hundreds of years generation after generation of British seamen have fished these waters. It is a breeding ground of fine sailors and of heroic qualities. The Vikings came across it in their long boats to conquer the British Isles; and on it, British, Dutch and Germans have more than once contended for mastery. It was once known as the German Ocean.

In the glacial period, the North Sea most probably extended between France and England, ending in a small inlet near the present Strait of Dover. Over thousands of years soil, stone and vegetation were pressed into it from the massive ice formations of Scandinavia and Scotland, gradually raising the sea bed. Subsequent changes in the earth's structure and climate lifted the sea bed some 500 feet above the surface, forming a land bridge between the British Isles and Northern Europe. An immense plain was formed where a giant river (of which the present Rhine is only the beginning) carved its way. Into this river flowed all the tributary systems of Britain, Scandinavia and Germany. The sea level rose and the present bed of the North Sea contains the hidden world of that great plain. The Sea is still shallow, little more than 180 feet on average, and it shelves from north to south as it approaches the British Isles. Approximately in the center, it is crossed from east to west by the famous Dogger Bank.

The Dogger provides much of the fish that are eaten in all the countries surrounding the North Sea; it has long been the favored trawling ground during the winter months. Herrings are the principal catch of the North Sea and a great percentage of them are taken with the trawl in this area; so are mackerel, haddock, cod, whiting and plaice. In summer, on the other hand, the best fishing grounds tend to be off the coast of the Continent. It is for this reason, among others, that the extension of territorial waters from the limit of three to six or even twelve miles has been opposed, especially by the British, as such an extension would severely limit the operations and the catch of British trawlermen.

The character of a sea is usually determined to some extent by the nature of the coastlines fronting upon it and the North Sea is no exception. Its coasts are mostly low sand dunes and long stretches of marshes and mud flats. Even on the eastern coast of England, where the shore is slightly higher than on the Continent, the cliffs are comparatively low. For long sections, only fenland, mud and marsh run down to a sea that deepens almost imperceptibly. It is on the Dutch coast that the most amazing land reclamation in the world has taken place; thousands of acres have been literally seized back from the sea and the most elaborate system of dykes, sea-wall defences and pumping machinery has lifted fertile acres into the sunlight. On the British side, coastal erosion is a great problem, which is being studied more and more intensively. A general rise in the sea level of about four inches in the present century, combined with a gradual subsidence of the land mass, has in recent years led to disastrous tidal surges, such as those of 1953 and 1961.

Since the seventeenth century, when the Dutch Admiral de Ruyter broke the boom at Gillingham, destroyed the fort at Sheerness and burned the stores at Chatham, it has been clear that whoever controls the North Sea controls the Thames and its approaches. It would, in fact, be safe to say that this has been realized as a cardinal point of British policy ever since King Alfred the Great turned his attention to building an efficient navy as a bulwark in the North Sea against marauding Danes. During the two world wars this cold and stormy sea was the scene of numerous actions between the British Navy and the German High Seas Fleet, the most notable of which was the Battle of Jutland. It was of this battle and of Admiral Jellicoe that Winston Churchill, then First Lord of the Admiralty, remarked: "He was the only man who could have lost the war in an afternoon." During the Second World War the North Sea was again the scene of many actions – destroyer battles, encounters between torpedo boats, submarine attacks on convoys and the deadly upheaval of magnetic and acoustic mines under the keels of thousands of tons of merchant shipping.

The tidal system of the North Sea is divided into three main movements – a southward-going tide flowing down the northeast coast of Britain, another major tide entering the Sea through the Strait of Dover and flowing up the Dutch coast, and a third, moving to the southeast down the coast of Norway. The highest tides are experienced in the Wash, in England, where the range is about 18 feet, and the weakest on the Norwegian coast. Navigation today in the North Sea is no longer the hazard it was, for the area is well-buoyed and covered by radio beacons and wireless-telegraphy direction-finding systems. Radar and echo-sounding devices (which even small trawlers carry) have taken some of the danger out of the area. Even so, when a northeast gale blows in winter, and the shallow Sea is so disturbed that mud is stirred up from its bottom, it remains, as always, treacherous and cold – the Vikings' sea.

Northwest Passage

A sea passage between the Atlantic and Pacific, subject of a long search. Location *Arctic Archipelago of Canada.*

When Roald Amundsen, in his little ship the *Gjoa*, sighted the whaler *Charles Hanson*, less than 20 miles south of Nelson Head in the Beaufort Sea, on August 26, 1905, he had sailed through the Northwest Passage – he and his crew being the first to sail from the North Atlantic to the North Pacific.

The dream of this passage had obsessed men and nations for over three centuries and the dream was to cost the lives of many men and the loss of many ships, crushed in the ice, lost without trace or shamefully abandoned. Even for Amundsen, the journey was not yet over – he still had to get through into the Bering Sea and, as it was too late in the season, submit to being frozen in for another year.

The list of seamen who attempted to find the Passage since Robert Thorne first proposed, in 1527, a route to Cathay via the North Pole, reads like a roll of honor and the place names along the route bear witness to the zeal of the voyagers in pursuing their ideal. Until the nineteenth century the quest was mainly prompted by the search for riches. Cathay was known to be the source of great wealth; the Spanish and

Lancaster Sound, part of the Northwest Passage

the Portuguese barred the way to the south; therefore, the way for Englishmen and Dutchmen lay to the northwest or northeast.

The Treaty of Tordesillas in 1494 gave to Spain all lands west of a line running 370 leagues west of Cape Verde, and to Portugal, control of the east. This line, after Magellan's voyage, was extended round the earth by the Treaty of Saragossa in 1529, but the arbitrary division of the world in this fashion only spurred the British and Dutch in their endeavours to find the Northwest Passage, particularly after Drake's famous voyage with its return of 10,000 per cent of the backers' investment. Companies such as the Cathay Company, in which the first Elizabeth held shares, the Northwest Company, the Merchant Adventurers and the Hudson's Bay Company were all formed to exploit the riches of the north or what lay beyond the north; and Martin Frobisher, John Davis, Henry Hudson, William Baffin, Thomas Button, Luke Foxe and others all tried on their behalf, but all were turned back by ice. Even Captain Cook, who had hoped to return from his third circumnavigation of the world via the Northwest or Northeast Passage, failed to find a way through from one ocean to the other.

By the early nineteenth century, men had begun to search for the Northwest Passage because they still thought it was there, for its own sake, as men tried to climb Everest, although later a prize of $100,000 awaited the successful navigator. From the end of the Napoleonic Wars the names of the explorers, many of whom were sent out officially by the British Admiralty or the government of the day, have an even more familiar ring. Under Sir John Ross and his nephew James Clark Ross, Sir Edward Parry and Sir John Franklin, numerous attempts were made; but each time, although more was added to the knowledge of the area and maps were corrected or extended, the explorers were always turned back.

When Sir John Franklin failed to return from his last voyage, begun in 1845, over 40 expeditions were sent in search of him, and on one of these Captain Robert McClure and his party walked over the Northwest Passage; on their return to England, McClure was knighted and he and his party were awarded $50,000 – half the prize intended for the discoverer of a navigable passage. On a later voyage Sir Leopold McClintock found, but did not traverse, the only feasible passage through to the Pacific.

But although other attempts were made in the ensuing decades, it was not until Amundsen tried that success was achieved. In 1899 young Amundsen had found in a collection of books he had bought one of McClintock's books predicting that if a passage were found it would be farther south than previous expeditions had tried. This was the route he took in the *Gjoa*, a tiny sailing vessel with a small auxiliary engine. The ship had originally been a herring boat and it was a mere 72 feet long with a 20-foot beam, and a displacement of 47 tons. With a crew of six he set out at midnight (to avoid creditors) on June 16, 1903, and reached San Francisco, on the other side of the world, in the late summer of 1906.

The route lay south of Greenland, through Davis Strait and Baffin Bay to Beechey Island. After surviving a grounding and a fire on board, the *Gjoa* reached Beechey Island, where Amundsen halted to locate the North Magnetic Pole, which had shifted since James Clark Ross had made his observations in 1831. Then he sailed south to King William Island, where he spent the next two winters ice-bound in a sheltered, land-locked bay, making magnetic observations and getting to know the Eskimos of Boothia. It was the knowledge of living at sub-zero temperatures which he gained here that was to stand him in good stead a few years later when he made his dash to the South Pole. During this period, too, one of his crew came upon traces of the last Franklin expedition.

It was not until August 13, 1905, that the *Gjoa* was able to free herself and continue her voyage to the Pacific. From now on the route was practically unexplored and uncharted, but bearing in mind McClintock's prediction, Amundsen went as far south as he could before turning west – going east and south of King William Island instead of north and west as Franklin had done. Then the route lay through Simpson Strait where at one point there was a mere inch of water under the keel, through narrow Dease Strait which separates Victoria Island from the Canadian mainland, through Coronation Gulf, Dolphin and Union Strait, south of Banks Island, into the Beaufort Sea, where they met with the *Charles Hanson*, a whaling ship out of San Francisco.

Thus ended an epic voyage which brought to an end a dream that had started nearly 400 years before. Today the southernmost route of the Northwest Passage runs from the Atlantic through Davis Strait, Hudson Strait, Foxe Channel, Foxe Basin, Fury and Hecla Strait, the Gulf of Boothia, Prince Regent Inlet, Bellot Strait, Franklin Strait, Victoria Strait, Queen Maud Gulf, Dease Strait, Coronation Gulf, Dolphin and Union Strait and Amundsen Gulf, to the Beaufort Sea of the Arctic Ocean and into the Pacific. Almost every name commemorates one of the brave men who made Amundsen's achievement possible. There is also a central route and a northernmost one; the three routes are all interconnected by a number of north-to-south passages for alternative routing.

Novaya Zemlya

A large archipelago, with scanty population and important mineral resources. Location *Arctic Ocean, between Barents and Kara seas, USSR.* Area *35,000 square miles.* Map *5, H9.*

Separated by a narrow channel (Matochkin Shar), the two principal islands of Novaya Zemlya lie across the polar seas like a scimitar, with the pack ice of the Barents Sea on their western edge and that of the Kara Sea on their eastern. Their island neighbors, Spitsbergen and the Franz Josef archipelago, are polar. So are their natural inhabitants, polar bear, lemming and foxes; the surrounding seas are inhabited by walrus, seals and whales and the seas are heavy with ice. Formidable mountains rise to 4,000 feet in the south island and around 3,500 feet in the north island. The only vegetation in the valleys and open country is that of the tundra. Winter cold can be severe, especially on the islands' east coast, with strong winds; in summer, when the ice breaks up, fog hangs over the water. Nevertheless, Novaya Zemlya, with an estimated population of under 1,000, is strategically important.

The Norse were probably the first to reach these islands, in the tenth century. Later, Scandinavian explorers, British, Dutch and Russian travelers touched them. Russian trappers had reached their northernmost extremities by the sixteenth century and the Russian Savva Loshnik was the first to circumnavigate them, in 1760–62. In 1877 Russia settled Samoyeds there.

Since the nineteen-thirties, the Soviet Union has thought of Novaya Zemlya in terms of defense, and more so since the early nineteen-forties when German submarines passed through the Kara Strait, between the islands and Russia's Arctic coast, to attack shipping serving Russia's industrial settlements along the coast and deltas of Siberia. Thus, the polar scimitar that formerly attracted only explorers has become a shield in a new defense system.

Oceania

A collective name applied to Melanesia, Micronesia and Polynesia; sometimes including Australia and New Zealand. Location *Pacific Ocean.* Map *4.*

The three main divisions of Oceania, the general name attached to islands and archipelagoes in the Pacific, are fairly arbitrary though commonly accepted. Frequently a whole continent – Australia – is included, not to mention New Guinea and the Bismarck Archipelago, though strictly speaking only the three widely scattered island worlds should belong under this heading.

Melanesia, "black islands," is the westernmost of the three divisions. It includes the islands north and east of Australia – New Guinea, the Bismarck Archipelago, the Admiralty and Solomon islands, the Louisiade Archipelago, the Santa Cruz and Loyalty islands, the New Hebrides, New Caledonia, the D'Entrecasteaux Islands and the Fiji Islands. The Melanesians are short, dark-skinned, with frizzy black hair and negroid features.

Polynesia – whose name means "many islands" – is the easterly part of Oceania, extending over an immense triangular area from Hawaii in the north to Tonga in the southwest and Easter Island in the southeast. It includes those islands originally inhabited by Polynesian people – tall, with light brown skin and straight or wavy hair – and its main groups are Hawaii, Samoa, the Ellice, Line and Phoenix islands, the Tokelau group, the Wallis and Futuna (or Hoorn) Islands, Tonga, the Cook Islands and Niue, French Polynesia (including the Society Islands, the Marquesas, the Tuamotu Islands, the Austral Islands, the Mangareva Islands and Rapa Island), Pitcairn Island and, finally, isolated Easter Island. Polynesia is divided politically: the administering powers are the United States, Great Britain, France, New Zealand and Chile.

Micronesia consists of four archipelagoes – the Carolines, Marianas, Marshalls and Gilberts – and such isolated islands as Nauru and Ocean Island. Guam, the largest of the Marianas, is administered by the United States as an "unincorporated territory." The remainder of the Marianas, the Carolines and the Marshalls constitute the United Nations Trust Territory of the Pacific Islands, which is also administered by the United States. Nauru, in the same category, is administered by Australia. The Gilberts and Ocean Island (with the Ellice Islands which are part of Polynesia) are a British colony with a certain measure of autonomy. The Micronesian people are not a distinct racial group, but a mixture of Melanesian, Polynesian and Malay stock.

There is, both geographically and anthropologically, some overlapping between the three regions, and their borderlines are not always clearly defined. But here, within the limits of Oceania, the essence of the Pacific is contained, and whatever changes the white man has brought, much of the ancient culture, religion and art of the native peoples still survives.

Okhotsk, Sea of

A large arm of the North Pacific along the coast of Siberia. Location *West of Kamchatka Peninsula and Kurile Islands.* Area *590,000 square miles.* Maximum depth *11,060 feet.* Map *4, F1.*

The Sea of Okhotsk has played an important part in the gradual expansion of the Muscovite Empire towards the east. It has been the main outlet for Siberia, across the formidable coastal ranges, and it was the boundary agreed between the Russians and the Chinese in the Treaty of Nerchinsk (1689), the first ever concluded between China and a Western power. It was a boundary that was to last for a century and a half. Russia agreed to withdraw north of the Amur, to remain west of the Shilka River, and to share the wild Stanovoi Range with China; though the eastern part of the frontier, near the Sea of Okhotsk, was left undelimited, the treaty ensured the peace Russia then needed. In 1941

Russia began to build a railway line from Komsomolsk in the south, running along the coast of the Sea of Okhotsk, to reach Kamchatka and the Bering Sea.

Connected to the Sea of Japan by the Tatar and La Pérouse straits, and to the Pacific by the passages between the Kurile Islands, the Sea is the main summer outlet for Siberian ports. It is icebound from November to June with many floating icefields in the extreme south; heavy fogs are frequent throughout the year – yet its harbors, Nagayevo, Okhotsk, Ayan, Abashiri and Gizhiga, are essential doors into the Pacific. Okhotsk played a considerable part in bringing the precious tea of China to the Russian Empire; the fishing and crabbing centers along the west coast of the Kamchatka Peninsula have made a substantial contribution to providing food for the maritime areas. The fauna of the Sea has always interested naturalists because of its local species and the general composition of its animals (70 species of molluscs and 21 of gastropods were found in its waters).

The Okhotsk Current, called by the Japanese *Oyashio*, the Father Stream, carries cold meltwater south from the Bering Sea along the eastern coasts of the Kurile Islands, Hokkaido and northern Honshu. A branch passes into the Sea of Japan through the Sea of Okhotsk and Tatar Strait, continuing south along the shores of Korea, meeting the Tsushima Current (a branch of the Japan Current) at about 40° North. It has a general chilling effect on the coastline of Japan.

Orkney Islands

An island group, 50 miles long and 35 miles wide, consisting of 90 islands and islets, two thirds of them uninhabited. Location *North of Scotland, separated from the mainland by Pentland Firth.* Area *376.4 square miles.* Map *7, D3.*

Stretching out as if to close, with the Shetlands, the northwestern exit from the North Sea, the Orkneys were of crucial value to Britain in the First World War and of even greater importance in the Second, when Germany controlled the Norwegian coast at places only 300 miles from the Orcadian capital of Kirkwall. Underlining this war-time importance of geography was the great anchorage of Scapa Flow, 55 square miles of island-bound water, an important base for British fleets in both wars until the Germans penetrated its defenses with disastrous success.

Of the long chain of islands, holms and skerries, Mainland – once known as Pomona – slightly more than 200 square miles in area, and Hoy, 50 square miles, are the two largest islands and among the few which rise more than 500 feet above the sea. Hoy, 1,500 feet high in places, has fine sea-cliffs. Although stretching so far to the north – on the longest day of the year there is 18 hours between sunrise and sunset – the Orkneys have a mild climate. The North Atlantic Drift section of the Gulf Stream not only encircles them but winds like an arterial system of tepid waters through every sound and inlet.

The Orkneys were conquered more than 1,000 years ago by Harold Haarfagr, the first king of united Norway. The ties with Scandinavia lasted until 1468, when sovereignty of the Islands was mortgaged by Christian of Denmark and Norway to James III of Scotland for his wife's dowry – a pledge which was not redeemed.

Kirkwall, capital of the Orkneys, standing on a narrow neck of land only two miles across, is notable for its harbor, its red and white freestone cathedral of St Magnus, built in the twelfth century and enlarged during the next 400 years, and the ruined Bishop's Palace, a massive building in which King Haakon died broken-hearted after losing the battle of Largs in 1263. Stromness, where Gow, Sir Walter Scott's "Pirate," was born, is the only other town in the Orkneys; here, the whalers of the Hudson's Bay Company once made their most northern call and here – or more accurately from the cemetery outside the town – some discern in the profile of the cliffs of Hoy, across Hoy Sound, a likeness of Sir Walter himself.

Gaining their livelihood by a mixture of crofting and fishing, many of the 26,000 Orcadians still hold their land on *udal* tenure. In contrast to feudal tenure, this acknowledges no superior and on one occasion a southern judge, trying a disputed case, asked of whom the land was, in fact, held. "Of God Almighty," replied the advocate.

Thrown by geography into the storm of

modern wars, aided by the "Churchill Barriers" which now fortuitously link Mainland to its southern neighbors as well as barring one approach to Scapa, Orcadians still retain links with their past more immediate and more real than those of most people. One reason may well be the constant sight of the rich archeological impedimenta of the islands – the stone circles of Stenness, the numerous tumuli which dot the landscape, Maes Howe, a huge chambered cairn, one of the finest in Britain, and the prehistoric settlement of Skara Brae, superb in its detail showing how men and women lived in the archipelago more than 2,000 years ago.

Together with wind, rock and water, these archeological remains exemplify the elemental character of both the Orkney tradition and the Orkney landscape.

Pacific Ocean

The largest ocean in the world, extending from the Arctic to the Antarctic. Location *Between the Americas, Asia and Australia.* Area *64,000,000 (with adjoining seas 70,000,000) square miles.* Maximum depth *36,960 feet.* Map *4.*

About 11,000 miles wide at the equator and over 9,000 miles long from north to south, the Pacific contains more islands than all the other oceans put together, and with its bordering seas its area represents about one third of the surface of the earth, one half of all the oceans and more than the entire land mass of the globe. In the Marianas Trench it contains the maximum ocean depth recorded, and several other deeps or troughs reach a depth of over 30,000 feet. These deeps generally run parallel with the Ocean's continental borders or along lines of islands. They originate many earthquakes and accompanying tidal waves. The Pacific is an active volcanic area and the Kingdom of Tonga includes the remarkable Falcon Island (Fonuafo'ou), a volcanic mound which alternately appears and disappears. Typhoons are also frequent; indeed, the Ocean often belies the name "Pacific" which Magellan gave it during his abnormally calm voyage to the Philippines in 1520–21.

The International Date Line cuts the Pacific into two parts. With certain exceptions, the line follows the 180th degree of longitude; between the two sides of it there is a difference of 24 hours in time. For political and administrative reasons there are two deviations from this: in the north the Aleutian Islands are all included on the American side of the Line; while south of the equator there is a long bulge to the east between latitudes 5° and 51° South in order to keep the Fiji Islands and Tonga together from the point of view of time and also to keep the Chatham and Kermadec islands on the same side as New Zealand.

Although the Portuguese navigator Antonio d'Abreu is believed to have sighted New Guinea as early as 1511, the first white man to survey the wide expanse of the great Pacific Ocean was the Spanish soldier of fortune Vasco Nuñez de Balboa who in 1513 beheld it from the legendary "peak in Darien" and claimed its lands and coasts for the Crown of Spain. The first Englishman to set eyes on the Pacific and to sail across it was Sir Francis Drake who, in 1572, when he was privateering in the Spanish Main, followed Balboa's example of two generations earlier. He climbed a ridge in Panama from which he could survey the Atlantic and Pacific and, having gazed longingly on the Pacific, prayed on his knees that "the Almighty of His goodness would give him life and leave to sail once in an English ship in that sea." His prayer was granted when he made his famous circumnavigation of the globe in the *Golden Hind* between 1577 and 1580. The first European to enter the Pacific was one of the greatest of the navigators, a Portuguese in Spanish service – Fernão de Magalhães, whom we generally know as Magellan. He sailed into it in 1520 from the strait which now bears his name and it was he who named it Pacific because it was so kind and gentle to him during his voyage to the Philippines.

The achievements of Magellan, Drake and the other European navigators of the Renaissance, braving the unknown in small and overcrowded ships with the minimum of equipment and with aids to navigation which to the modern mariner would be primitive indeed, were truly magnificent. Yet earlier peoples had anticipated by many centuries their crossings and re-crossings of the great Ocean. These peoples, the Melanesians, Micronesians and Polynesians, are entitled by their fantastic voyages in frail canoes up and down the Pacific to be regarded as the greatest ocean pathfinders in history. Thor Heyerdahl's theory claims that the Polynesians entered the Pacific from South America; but according to the generally accepted view, Polynesians, Micronesians and Melanesians all came from southeast Asia.

It cannot be established with any certainty when these migrations began, but the earliest probably took place about 2,000 years ago. Of the three races now considered indigenous to the Pacific, the Polynesians were the latest arrivals. Though they were outstanding navigators in the areas they knew, traveling by the stars, by such natural indications as the green reflection of an atoll, as yet invisible, on the underside of a cloud, the almost imperceptible indications of currents or absence of certain birds, the evidence is all against their taking any deliberate voyages into the unknown. Eventually they settled as far north as Hawaii, as far south as New Zealand's South Island and as far east as Easter Island; but the journeys there were almost certainly made by craft blown off their course. One authority has estimated that nearly a quarter of a million people lost their lives in the course of 20 or possibly 30 centuries to achieve the settlements which now exist.

The course of the negroid Melanesians – the "black islanders" – is the easiest to follow. These dark people entered the Pacific by way of New Guinea, then continued southward through the Solomon Islands, New Hebrides and New Caledonia until they reached the most easterly of their homes in Fiji.

The Micronesians, "the people of the small islands," are the least traveled of the three. They entered the Pacific through Indonesia and the Philippines and are confined to the atoll groups of the Marianas, Caroline, Marshall and Gilbert islands (but not the Ellice Islands, which are peopled by Polynesians) and Nauru. Roughly speaking, the boundary between Micronesia and Melanesia is the equator, while Polynesia lies east of the 180th degree of longitude, except for the Maoris of New Zealand and the Ellice Islanders, who live to the west of it.

The islands of the Pacific fall into two main physical categories, the volcanic and the coral atolls. By far the largest in the first group are the islands of New Zealand, where volcanic activity is still present, although this is by no means the case in all the Pacific islands of volcanic origin. Those in tropical latitudes are distinguished by their mountainous character, dense forest and jungle vegetation, depth of rich soil and great fertility aided by heavy rainfall. They are hot, humid and sometimes malarial; the interiors are rugged and often hard of access. Such islands are the characteristic home of the Melanesians and in the larger ones the difficulty of the terrain hampers communications and human contacts; this is the main cause of the multiplication of languages, characteristic of all Melanesia except Fiji.

The coral atolls are created by the coral polyp which, given the warm temperature it needs and water of normal marine salinity, will build upon the lip of a submerged volcano's crater or other submarine projection on the ocean bed until it reaches the surface. When this happens, its labors appear as elliptical or sometimes circular crowns of coral rock, generally 200–400 yards in width and encircling intermittently (or, more rarely, completely) an inner piece of water known as the lagoon. The normal atoll is seldom more than a wave throw of 15 feet above sea level, since the polyp dies when it reaches the surface; and on the thin dusting of soil which it collects only the coconut and the pandanus palms will normally grow.

Besides these visible islands, the Pacific conceals numerous "sea-mounts" or *guyots*, isolated flat-topped cones, presumably of submarine volcanoes, which sometimes rise to within a few hundred feet of the surface. These have recently acquired a strategic significance – for those which rise high enough are being plotted as possible berths in which submarines may rest on a solid surface when firing ballistic missiles.

In the sixteenth century the Pacific was dominated by the Spaniards and the Portuguese. In the seventeenth the English and the Dutch gained a foothold. France and Russia followed in the eighteenth; Germany, Japan and the United States in the last century. The first half of the nineteenth century saw the end of the era of European discovery and re-discovery and the beginning of territorial colonization by the white powers (other than Spain, who had combined exploration with annexation from the start). By the twentieth century the United States had extended its Pacific interests by the purchase of Alaska, by a series of agreements with Japan and by the acquistion of the Hawaiian Islands, the Philippines and Guam. In the second half of the nineteenth century the Polynesian kingdom of Tahiti was annexed by France; the chiefs of the Fijian Confederation applied to be admitted under the sovereignty of Queen Victoria. The Japanese drive for Pacific supremacy, at least partly motivated by the immense growth of population within the narrow confines of her islands, came to a climax in 1941. The short-lived Japanese conquests reached their extreme limits in New Guinea and the Aleutians respectively and came to an end in 1945, when the dominating role in the Pacific passed to the United States – though the challenge of Russia and Communist China is rapidly developing. With the wide and swift development of air travel – there have been scheduled crossings of the Pacific since 1935 – the largest ocean in the world seems to be shrinking; but its beauty, its opportunities and dangers remain as varied and as numerous as ever.

Palau

A group of volcanic and coral islands, a major Japanese naval base in the Second World War. Location *Western Caroline Islands, western Pacific, about 550 miles east of the Philippines.* Area *188 square miles.* Map *4, D6.*

The Palaus or Pelews were first sighted by Ruy Lopez de Villalobos in 1543; they remained in Spanish possession until 1899, when Germany bought them; and, like most of the German-owned islands, they were handed over to Japan after the First World War. The Japanese fortified them and built one of their major naval bases here – the only one to be taken by the United States forces before the end of the Second World War.

There are 26 islands in the group, the southern archipelago being coral, the northern volcanic. All of them lie within a coral barrier reef. They are well wooded with extensive savannas in the interior, the climate is healthy and the water-supply adequate. There are only a few indigenous rats and bats but the sea around the islands is rich in fish and molluscs and there are no less than 56 species of birds, about a dozen peculiar to the group.

Babelthuap, the largest of the group, has an area of 143 square miles and is one of the volcanic islands. It has long, wooded hills with chalk cliffs; it also possesses valuable bauxite deposits. Ngardok Lake, about 1,000 yards long, is in the northeastern part. Arakabesan is another wooded, volcanic island, about two miles long and three-quarters of a mile wide; it served as a Japanese army camp in the Second World War. Koror, near Babelthuap, is about three square miles, and rises to 459 feet. Malakal, the fourth of the volcanic islands, is about three-quarters of a mile in diameter and rises to 393 feet; it has the chief harbor of the group.

Of the coral Palaus, Angaur is about three square miles in area; it is the southernmost of the group and has valuable phosphate deposits. Aurapushekaru is three miles long and rises to 613 feet. Kayangel, 15 miles north of Babelthuap, consists of four wooded islets. Peleliu, six miles north of Angaur, is six miles long and two miles wide; its important Japanese airfield was taken by the American Marines in 1944 after bitter fighting. Urukthapel, six miles southwest of Babelthuap, is about ten miles long and rises to 587 feet.

The main products of the Palaus are copra, dried bonito, tapioca and bauxite. The population – about 6,000 – is Micronesian, shorter and darker than their kinsmen in the other Caroline Islands. They usually have the frizzy hair of the Melanesians and used to paint their bodies in brilliant colors, especially yellow. Two curious customs are gradually dying out – one is the institution of an honorable order bestowed by the king, called *klilt*, and the other a society for mutual aid, sometimes restricted to women, which had considerable political influence. Before the Japanese took over, there were five different kinds of currency in the islands, consisting of beads of glass and enamel to which a supernatural origin was ascribed. The Palaus, like the rest of the Carolines, are under United States administration.

Palm Beach

A famous resort area, situated on a long, narrow barrier beach and connected by bridges across Lake Worth lagoon to West Palm Beach. Location *Southeast Florida, between the Atlantic and Lake Worth.* Map *2, D1.*

In October, 1870, Harper's Magazine warmed the imagination of its readers with a description of a new Eden on the east coast of Florida. Responding to the lure of a year-long summer, an adventurous few went south to check up on the glowing reports which said that fish were so plentiful that boats could hardly move, that Seminole Indians daily brought haunches of fresh venison and 500-lb turtles to sell for pennies and that land cost five cents an acre. Though much of this proved pure fantasy, settlement started in 1871 and Palm Beach was named in 1887 – because of the numerous palm trees which had grown from the cargo of coconuts carried by a Spanish ship wrecked off the coast in 1879.

In 1893 the American financier Henry M. Flagler, an associate of John D. Rockefeller in Standard Oil, visited the area and was impressed by the swaying palms. He built a 1,600-room wooden hotel which catered only for carefully selected guests. Some came as anglers, others for the sunshine, still others to dabble in land speculation. Some came in private pullmans, others anchored offshore in luxury yachts and everybody prospered.

Noting Flagler's success, a horticulturalist named Collins turned to hotel building when his crop of avocados failed. By 1909 Palm Beach county was formed. In 1913 Carl Fisher, a multi-millionaire, built a bridge to start the development of Miami Beach, 70 miles farther south. Thousands of acres of swampland were reclaimed, hotels, parks, golf courses and roads laid out. In 1918 the colorful and highly unorthodox Addison Mizner, who had tried a number of careers until he settled on the one of fashionable architect and interior decorator, came upon the scene. The Florida land boom which got under way in the nineteen-twenties was to a considerable extent his work. Fantastic fortunes were made almost overnight. Mizner designed the most exclusive of all Florida settlements, Boca Raton, with a 219-foot-wide approach road which had twenty lanes and a canal for electrically-driven gondolas down the center – not only the world's widest highway but, being only half a mile in length, its shortest.

The boom burst in 1926. The fantastic fortunes dissolved in thin air – in spite of numerous "Have-Faith-in-Florida" clubs. Yet today boom and crash are equally forgotten. Palm Beach and Miami have their fortunes solidly established – even if they are built largely on sand, with giant suction hoses sweeping up loose materials from the ocean floor and depositing them to add to the land. Skyscraper hotels line the ocean-front, the 4,000 people who live the year round in Palm Beach play host to millions and there are many beautiful estates scattered over the district.

Panama Canal

A waterway built by the United States, linking the Caribbean and the Pacific. Location *Panama, Central America.* Length *50.5 miles.* Width *300 feet.* Depth *45 feet.* Map *2, E5.*

It was in 1523 that Charles V of Spain ordered an investigation into the possibility of cutting a canal across the isthmus of Panama. From then on for almost four centuries the principal maritime nations of the world gave much serious consideration to the project. In 1876, Colombia – to which the isthmus then belonged – gave a concession for the construction of a canal to a French promotion corporation, which conducted surveys during a period of two years. A report was made to an international congress held at Paris in May, 1879, over which Ferdinand de Lesseps, the builder of the Suez Canal, presided. The congress advised the construction of a canal at sea level and in 1881 the work was undertaken by the Universal Interoceanic Panama Canal Company of which De Lesseps was named as head. But the amount of work to be accomplished proved to be much greater than estimated. Various machinations, shady deals and interminable wrangles led to a major political crisis in France and "Panama" became a synonym for scandalous, crooked deals. De Lesseps, formerly a national hero, was execrated, as thousands of investors lost their

Gatun Locks, Panama Canal

money and an ugly mess of bribery and corruption was uncovered. The company went into receivership in 1889. A new company was formed to carry on the work, and excavation was resumed in 1894. This continued until 1904, when the United States government acquired the effects of the French company in Panama.

Congress had authorized the President two years earlier to purchase the rights and property of the French company for $40,000,000. This led to the abandonment of a similar project under which Britain and the United States were to build a canal together in Nicaragua and on which agreement had been embodied in the Clayton-Bulwer Treaty. Negotiations started with the Government of Colombia for the cession, upon payment of $10,000,000, of the territory through which the canal was to be constructed. At the last moment the Senate of Colombia refused to ratify this treaty. This led to the secession of Panama on November 3, 1903. The new Government was immediately recognized by the United States – which had naturally encouraged its formation – and a treaty was ratified on February 26, 1904, in which rights of sovereignty over a strip of land ten miles wide, extending across the isthmus, were ceded to the United States. The United States guaranteed the Republic of Panama's independence and agreed to pay it $10,000,000 and an annuity which was to begin nine years after the ratification of the treaty.

Though the French had done considerable work, at least as much remained to be done. When the Americans set to work in 1904 the greatest problem was the stamping out of yellow fever, which was taking a terrible toll of the construction workers. W. C. Gorgas, who had succeeded in freeing Havana from yellow fever during the Spanish-American war, did notable work again as chief sanitary officer and made it possible for Colonel G. W. Goethals, whom President Theodore Roosevelt had appointed chief engineer in 1907, to complete the great work in seven years. The Panama Canal was opened for traffic in August, 1914, and though landslides have several times blocked the passage of Gaillard Cut, and the Canal's limited capacity has definite drawbacks, it remains one of the great engineering feats of the modern world.

The Canal contains 12 locks in twin flights; three steps at Gatun on the Atlantic side, one at Pedro Miguel and two at Miraflores on the Pacific side. Each lock chamber is 1,000 feet long and 110 feet wide. Transit from sea to sea usually takes eight hours. The least width is in Gaillard Cut and the greatest in Gatun Lake, where the channel can be made much broader at any time by cutting down trees and by a small amount of dredging. (In August, 1939, Congress approved the building of a new set of locks, but this was shelved because of the Second World War and post-war opinion has favored a sea-level route.) The Panama Canal Company is engaged in a $26,000,000 Canal improvement program. Gatun Lake is 85 feet above sea level; the Canal's channel through all parts of the Lake, including Gaillard (Cuilebra) Cut, is 42 feet.

In January, 1955, a new treaty was signed between Panama and the United States, increasing the annuity to Panama from $430,000 to $1,930,000 and agreeing to hand over to the Republic land and railroad yards valued at $25,000,000, to construct a high-level bridge over the Pacific entrance to the Canal at a cost of about $25,000,000 and to extend commercial and other privileges to the Republic. The Canal Zone, administered by a nominee of the United States government, has an area of 533 square miles and a population of over 41,000.

Pantelleria

A small Italian island, heavily bombed in the Second World War. Location *Off Sicily, Mediterranean Sea.* Area *32 square miles.* Map *9, C10.*

Nine miles long and five miles wide, with a population of 10,306, Pantelleria is the peak of an extinct volcano rising out of the straits between southwestern Sicily and the Maouin Peninsula of North Africa. It lies a little east of the Cape Bon banks; the highest point, the extinct crater of Magna Grande, is 2,743 feet high, and forms a landmark for navigators. During the Second World War the island was subjected to a heavy "saturation" raid by American and British bombers, to destroy its value as a military base and prepare the way for the invasion of Sicily. Today, the island has reverted to the peaceful and somewhat timeless life which it had enjoyed for centuries until Mussolini's regime momentarily brought it into the limelight.

Pantelleria is fertile, though it lacks fresh water, and when the rain catchments fail, water has to be imported from Sicily. Like so many volcanic areas, the soil is highly suitable for the grape, and the wine of the island is excellent, somewhat similar to Marsala.

Those who are not engaged on the land work as fishermen. In their lateen-rigged boats, with oars or sometimes small diesel engines to assist them, they go as far afield as the Cape Bon and Kerkennah banks off Africa. Their long open boats with crews of six or eight can often be seen in mid-Mediterranean many miles from land.

Like the Aegadian Islands to the north of it, Pantelleria may once have been joined to the land bridge that united Sicily with North Africa. At any rate, there is much evidence of neolithic man on the island, including a neolithic village on the east coast which is protected on the seaward side by a rampart of obsidian blocks.

Parry Islands

An archipelago west of Baffin Bay. Location *Western central Franklin District, Northwest Territories, Arctic Ocean.* Map *5, C7.*

Captain William Edward Parry, R.N., was one of the great Arctic explorers. His first taste of the Arctic came in 1818, when he was second in command to Captain John Ross on the journey to search for the Northwest Passage. They sailed down Lancaster Sound but turned back because Ross was convinced that it was landlocked. Parry disagreed, and the following year he commanded another expedition. It was on this voyage that Parry discovered and named a number of islands lying on either side of Lancaster Sound, Barrow Strait and Viscount Melville Sound – a group which has since been named the Parry Islands.

Uninhabited and covered with tundra, the Islands were visited again and explored by the expeditions sent out to search for Sir John Franklin's ill-fated expedition, 30 years later.

Parry wintered in 1819–20 in a small bay, Hecla and Griper Bay, on Melville Island, which is 16,503 square miles in area. Devon Island, 21,606 square miles, bounded by Baffin Bay and separated from Baffin and Somerset islands by Lancaster Sound, is 320 miles long and about 80–100 miles wide. In its eastern part an ice-covered plateau rises to about 3,000 feet with an altitude of about 2,000 feet in the western section. Grinnell Peninsula, which extends northwest, was only recently proved to be part of Devon; formerly it was believed to be a separate island. A former post at Dundas Harbour on Lancaster Sound has been abandoned. Bathurst Island, 7,272 square miles, is between Devon and Cornwallis islands and Melville Island, separated from the latter by Byam Martin Channel; it is 160 miles long and 50–100 miles wide. Its irregular coastline is mostly hilly and deeply cut by the Erskine and May inlets. Cornwallis Island, 2,592 square miles, is between Bathurst and Devon islands, 70 miles long, 30–60 miles wide; at Resolute Bay, on the southeast coast, there is a weather station maintained jointly by the United States and Canada. Prince Patrick Island, 6,696 square miles, is northwest of Melville Island; it is 150 miles long and 20–50 miles wide. Its coastline is irregular and its center rises to a plateau of over 1,000 feet. Here, too, there is a United States-Canadian weather station, at Mould Bay.

The Parry Islands form part of the group known since 1954 as the Queen Elizabeth Islands, named in honor of Queen Elizabeth II.

Perim

A small, barren island, once a notorious haunt of pirates. Location *Aden Colony, in Bab el Mandeb strait.* Area *Five square miles.* Map *10, B5.*

A flat, bare islet of unfriendly volcanic rock, Perim occupies a position as commanding in the Red Sea as Gibraltar in the Mediterranean. Crescent-shaped, it is about three miles long by two miles wide with a population of about 360. The crescent encloses on the southwest a natural harbor with some 30 feet of water. The tip of Cape Bab el Mandeb on the mainland, the southernmost point of the kingdom of Yemen, lies to the northeast beyond 1½ miles of shallow strait. Perim has no natural supply of fresh water and the annual rainfall is 2½ inches, while the average temperature is nearly 90° F. in the summer months.

The first European navigators who sighted Perim seem to have been wary of establishing themselves on the island. The Portuguese admiral Afonso de Albuquerque explored it in 1513, but no permanent occupation was made until 1799, when Perim was garrisoned by Britain as a counter to Napoleon's designs on India. But this period of occupation was short-lived; by 1801, the lack of fresh water had driven the soldiers elsewhere.

Throughout the eighteenth century, however, Perim had been the haunt of pirates, both European and Arab, "committing frequent Robberies and Barbarities," as a contemporary account described. "Captain Evory was the first that led the Way in anno 1695, and the Pirates finding great Booties, purchased with small Danger, from the traders into the Red Sea, had a Project to be Masters of the Key of that Door, so they found the Island Prim, which was within Gunshot of Babelmandeb, to have a good commodius Bay for the security of their shipping." It was from the shelter of Perim that Captain Evory achieved his greatest coup, the capture of the great ship of the Grand Mogul bound for India from the pilgrim port of Jidda, laden with treasure and hundreds of passengers, including the daughter of the Mogul himself.

The need for a coaling station on the Red Sea after the opening of the Suez Canal in 1869 renewed interest in Perim, which had been annexed by Britain in 1857. In 1883 the Perim Coal Company opened a depot on the southwestern side, and by 1916 there were 1,300 people living on the island. With the increasing use of oil-fired ships during the twentieth century, the fortunes of Perim declined again. In 1936 the harbor was closed to shipping and only a lighthouse and a meteorological station remained of what still is, geographically, the "Key of the Door" to the Red Sea.

Persian Gulf

A shallow arm of the Arabian Sea, a major oil-shipping lane with famous pearl fisheries. Location *Between Iran and Arabia.* Area *90,000 square miles.* Maximum depth *300 feet.* Map *10, C3.*

The Persian Gulf probably played a part in the history of man as soon as he made his earliest attempts to navigate the open sea. But in the twentieth century the Gulf's importance is due to a local industry little more than 50 years old – oil. In various places bitumen (a heavy, gluey kind of petroleum) seeps from underground oil deposits and lies on the surface of the earth. The builders of some of the first boats to sail on the Persian Gulf, many centuries before Christ, knew it as an excellent caulking material; it was also used as mortar in the palaces of their rulers. But oil became important economically only with the invention of the internal combustion engine. After a major discovery of oil in Persia in 1908, exploration extended to the coasts of the Gulf. Bahrein, off the nearby Arabian coast, and Kuwait revealed rich deposits and several refineries were built. The first undersea oil field was discovered in 1951, off the coast of Saudi Arabia, 100 miles south of Kuwait. Today, oil in the Gulf provides phenomenal local wealth and considerable unrest in international politics.

Despite its great area, the Persian Gulf is almost everywhere less than 300 feet deep. Near its head, where the Shatt al Arab contributes the silt-laden waters of the Tigris, Euphrates, Kuraun and Kharkeh rivers, the 20-fathom line is 70 miles, and off Trucial Oman 100 miles, from the shore. Ships of more than 5,000 tons can rarely approach within five miles of land. Yet where the Gulf emerges into the Indian Ocean, the sea floor drops abruptly to 500 feet in the Strait of Ormuz and 10,000 feet in the middle of the Gulf of Oman. Shoals and reefs make the coastal waters perilous, especially close to the Arabian shore. Here are the pearl banks famed in antiquity and still fished today. Off this western shore, the many small islands are low-lying patches of sand or coral; those of the Persian littoral are rocky and scarped. High temperatures, little rainfall and great humidity are characteristic of the whole region.

With the mountains of Persia close to its eastern coast, and the arid, unfriendly sands of Arabia on the west, the Gulf was destined to become an important channel of communication for the inhabitants of Mesopotamia as soon as they began to build boats. Nebuchadnezzar II founded a port at Teredon, at the head of the Gulf, and in 326 B.C. Nearchus, the lieutenant of Alexander the Great, returned by sea along the Persian coast of the Gulf from the eastward limit of Alexander's conquests on the Indus River. The Gulf's ports are described in the writings of classical geographers and Pliny discusses the effect of heavy silting from the Tigris and Euphrates. In Pliny's day, the Gulf extended some 25 miles farther north than it does today; in early classical times, Basra, now about 40 miles inland, was a flourishing seaport. Most of the mariners came from the northern ports, particularly from Kuwait, where the dhow-building industry is very ancient.

The establishment of the Cape route from Europe to the East during the sixteenth century deprived Middle Eastern traders of great revenue from trans-shipment trading, for much of the merchandise passing northwards through the Gulf in the Middle Ages made its way to Europe. This may have been why many of the seafarers of the Persian Gulf turned to piracy. The main center of their operation was the present-day Trucial Oman – for many years best known as the Pirate Coast. During the Second World War the Gulf played a vital part as a route for lease-lend supplies to the Soviet Union.

Peru Current

A cold ocean current which has an important climatic influence. Location *South Pacific, along the coasts of northern Chile, Peru and southern Ecuador.* Map *4, Q11–R10.*

The Peru or Humboldt Current – named after Alexander von Humboldt, the great German naturalist – is a broad, languid flow, moving up along the west coast of the South American continent until, a few degrees south of the equator, it swings to the west to join the South Equatorial Current. On the shoreward side there are flows and eddies which, combined with the prevailing coastal winds, produce a process known as upwelling. A predominantly southeast wind blows surface water away from the coast and this is replaced by water welling or moving up from moderate depths, carrying phosphates and other fertilizing minerals that feed one of the richest populations of marine life in the world.

As Robert C. Cowen pointed out, life in the Peru Current is incredibly fertile, supporting untold millions of sea-birds whose guano deposits give Peru an endless supply of high-grade fertilizer. In a single year 330,000 tons of guano have been harvested. This means that the guano birds themselves caught over 4,000,000 tons of a small sardine-like fish, the anchoveta. At the same time, fishermen caught 120,000 tons of the fish directly, plus a substantial haul of larger species that feed on the anchoveta. The abundance of the anchoveta is phenomenal – and this is just one species, showing how immense the plant and animal plankton, the base of the food pyramid in the sea, must be to support such a population.

But now and then disaster strikes. The life-giving flow of the Peru Current slackens or moves out to sea. Close to shore upwelling ceases, surface temperatures of the inshore water rise to abnormal heights and often a current of warm, less saline water moves in from the north – locally called *El Niño*. The normal fish population dies or moves out, to be replaced by tropical forms. Fishermen must set their nets deeper to catch the accustomed species. And the guano birds, deprived of their food, abandon their fledglings and strike out blindly to the north or south. Others fly excitedly in circles, only to die of starvation on the beaches. The bird population may be reduced to one fifth or one sixth of its original size. All along the coast, rotting bodies of fish and birds foul the air. Sometimes there are so many that the hydrogen sulphide gas they release blackens the paint on ships, a phenomenon known as "Callao painter," from the name of the Peruvian port.

Originally, *El Niño* was the name given to the southward invasion of warm water. But the phenomenon is more complicated, a complex of meteorological and oceanographic conditions that has several characteristic features, some of which may be more intense in one year than another. Some of these may even be normal aspects of Peru's coastal climate in the first half of the year, reaching destructive proportions only in *El Niño* years. Such conspicuous outbreaks have been reported for 1891, 1925, 1941 and 1957–58. As Dr Warren Wooster of Scripps Institution of Oceanography discovered, there is a general weakening of atmospheric circulation in the *El Niño* years. This is reflected in a weakening of the southerly prevailing winds that produce upwelling along the Peruvian coast. As it dies down, no longer bringing cool waters from the depths, the surface waters are heated by the sun. Meanwhile, the northern boundary of the Peru Current moves farther south than usual and tropical waters from the north can move down the coast.

These conditions are sometimes accompanied by an invasion of "Red Tide," a bloom of tiny organisms that poison the waters and kill multitudes of fish. At other times, the normal fish population may simply move out or go deeper down to stay with the water environment to which it is accustomed, while tropical species come in as their accustomed environment moves south. In either case, the sea-birds lose their food supply.

Philippine Islands

An archipelago of some 7,000 islands, an independent republic since 1946. Location *Souhwest Pacific, off southeast Asia, in the Malay Archipelago.* Area *115,600 square miles (of which 114,830 are land).* Map *4, C4–6.*

After surviving mutiny, tempest and all the other perils of the first voyage around Cape Horn, Magellan no doubt felt that his troubles were over as he made landfall in the Philippines in 1521. He was well received, first on Samar, a large island on the east of the group, then on nearby Malhou. Encouraged, he set sail for Cebu where he became blood brother of the ruler and made a spectacular number of conversions to Christianity among the natives. As agent of the sultan of Cebu and for the greater glory of the King of Spain, his master, Magellan then led a ridiculously undermanned military expedition against the ruler of Mactan Island. Defeated ignominiously, he died of his wounds.

When he discovered them, Magellan called the Philippines the Isles of St Lazarus, but they were later renamed after the child who was to become Philip II. An occupation force was sent out in 1564. The peoples who inhabited this new outpost of the Spanish empire were a curious mixture of tribes of Malay stock, aboriginal Negritos, Chinese, Arabs and other Asiatic races. Arabs had first come trading to the Islands in the tenth century, when they were still under the influence of the Sumatran kingdom of Sri Vijaya. These early traders brought Mohammedanism which survives (in a rather unorthodox form) among the fierce Moros of the southern islands. Under Spanish rule, most of the Filipinos became Christian, but the more primitive races (about ten per cent of the population of 24,000,000) have remained pagan; today, the Islanders speak some 85 different dialects. After English and Spanish, the most important is Tagalog, in which a considerable literature has developed.

The Islands remained a Spanish possession until they passed to the United States after the Spanish-American war in 1898 – though there was a brief British occupation between 1762 and 1764 – and the Moro pirates were not subdued until the late nineteenth century. A movement for independence had started before American rule. José Rizal, the great national leader, was succeeded by Aguinaldo, and the Filipinos were just as firmly determined not to submit permanently to American rule as they had fought against Spanish colonial subjection; so that after Admiral Dewey had defeated the Spanish fleet in Manila Bay, the United States found herself up against a long guerilla war. In 1935 the Commonwealth of the Philippines was established with Manuel Quezon as first president, and a ten-year transition period of "controlled autonomy" began. This was interrupted by the Second World War, the heroic but unsuccessful defense of Bataan and Corregidor and the Japanese occupation of the Islands, which ended with the return of General MacArthur and the swift liberation of the Philippines. On July 4, 1946, the Republic of the Philippines came into being and under its dynamic president Ramon Magsaysay, a period of reconstruction and economic development began, which is being continued under Magsaysay's successors after his tragic death in an airplane accident. The United States still has important bases on the Islands and economically and culturally the ties of the two countries remain very close.

The Philippines are part of a line of "stepping stones" extending from Japan to Indonesia. In the north of the archipelago is Luzon, the largest; south of it the line forks on either side of the deep enclosed basin of the Sulu Sea. In the west the principal islands are Mindoro and Palawan; in the east are the Visayan Islands (Samar, Masbate, Leyte, Cebu, Bohol, Negros and Panay); in the south is Mindanao. Scattered about these 11 principal islands, which have about nine tenths of the land area and the population between them, are some 7,000 rocky islands and islets of which only about 400 are permanently inhabited, while most of them have not even a name.

To the northeast of Mindanao is the ocean trench known as the Mindanao or Philippine Trench, the second deepest hole in the earth's surface, reaching, according to the latest measurements, 35,948 feet. (The Marianas Trench is 36,960 feet deep.)

Many of the Islands are mountainous; Mount Apo on Mindanao is 9,690 feet, and Mount Pulog, in eastern Luzon, 9,606 feet. There are many active volcanoes and earthquakes are a constant menace. The soil is partly volcanic and partly coralline in origin and is most fertile in the river valleys of the large islands. More than half the area of the Philippines is covered by forest. The chief crops are rice and a type of banana called *abaca* from which the Filipinos obtain the fiber known as Manila hemp. Coconuts, sugar cane, maize and tobacco are also grown. Among the natural resources are iron ore, chromite, sulphur, copper and coal, but the principal mineral exploited is still the gold of Luzon and Masbate which attracted the Spaniards to the Islands 400 years ago.

The capital and the principal port is Manila, on Luzon, a sprawling city rebuilt after its almost complete destruction by the Japanese in 1945. Its atmosphere is an attractive and lively mixture of Spanish, American and Filipino elements, with many modern buildings, including hotels, churches and, above all, universities, some of which have over 20,000 students.

Phoenix Islands

Eight small atolls, site of a transpacific airbase. Location *South Pacific.* Area *11 square miles.* Map *4, H7.*

Discovered in 1859, the Phoenix Islands consist of Canton, Enderbury, McKean, Birnie, Phoenix, Gardner, Hull and Sydney islands. Although previously inhabited only intermittently, they were formally incorporated in the Gilbert and Ellice Islands colony in 1937 and were chosen to receive some of the overflow population of the Gilbert Islands, which had become so seriously overcrowded that there was not enough food for all. Under the Phoenix Island Settlement Scheme, some 800 Gilbertans had been settled on Gardner, Hull and Sydney atolls before the outbreak of war in 1939.

Canton Island was chosen as headquarters of the Phoenix Island District. Its situation in the center of the Pacific, with a lagoon of convenient size, made it a useful intermediary stop for transpacific air traffic. In March, 1938, the United States, having found the air base at Pago-Pago in American Samoa unsatisfactory, decided to exercise a claim to Canton and the adjacent Enderbury, the two largest atolls. Much negotiation followed; in April, 1939, the United States and Britain signed an agreement setting up joint control over the two atolls for 50 years – without prejudice to their respective claims.

The Islands were formerly worked for phosphates; now they produce copra. The total population is just over 1,000.

Pitcairn Island

A small island, famous as the home of the descendants of the Bounty mutineers. Location *Southeast of the Tuamotu archipelago, South Pacific.* Area *Two square miles.* Map *4, M9.*

Unlike the majority of the islands in this part of the Pacific, Pitcairn, though volcanic, is without coral reefs, rising abruptly, with rugged, precipitous cliffs of dark basaltic lava, to a height of over 2,000 feet. In the valleys the soil is volcanic and fertile, but there are no streams and the gradual deforestation has led to drought. However, the climate is variable and rainy. It produces breadfruit, pandanus, coconuts and bananas; the animal population consists mostly of goats. When Philip Carteret discovered Pitcairn in 1767, the Island was uninhabited; but stone axes, remains of carved stone pillars (resembling those of Easter Island) and skeletons with a pearl-mussel beneath the head pointed to earlier occupation. Pitcairn was the name of the midshipman who first sighted the Island.

It was in 1790 that some of the mutineers of the *Bounty* left Tahiti with Fletcher Christian as their leader. The party consisted of eight Englishmen, six Polynesian men and twelve Polynesian women. They sailed to Pitcairn, where they burned the *Bounty* and settled down to communal life. The first years were unhappy, with strife and debauchery, and by 1800 all the men were dead except Alexander Smith, later known as John Adams, who became a responsible leader and successfully educated the youthful generation left in his charge. In 1808 an American ship, the *Topaze*, discovered the strange colony by accident; in 1817 two British ships visited it and in 1825 the exploring ship *Blossom* put in at Pitcairn. When John Adams died in 1829, he was succeeded by George Hunn Nobbs, who had settled at Pitcairn the year before. The fear of drought made the Islanders move to Tahiti in 1830 but they were shocked by the morals and disappointed by the climate and returned to Pitcairn. A little later an adventurer named Joshua Hill turned up on the Island; claiming government authority, he terrorized the Islanders until a British man-of-war removed him in 1838.

In 1856 the whole of the population – 60 married people and 134 young men, women and children – were transferred to Norfolk Island because of overpopulation. By then they had become models of propriety, loyalty to the Crown, sobriety and even industry. After two years two families returned to Pitcairn and their example was followed by several others. Pitcairn was visited by ships in 1873 and 1878 and the colony was found in excellent order; but by the end of the nineteenth century reports spoke of intermarriage bringing about a "deterioration of intellect, morals and energy"; there was the danger of the Islanders drifting into imbecility. However, this proved to be a great exaggeration.

A colony of fur seals on the Pribilof Islands

Today Pitcairn has a population of about 150 and forms, with the nearby uninhabited islands of Henderson, Ducie and Oeno, a British colony under the High Commissioner of the western Pacific at Suva, Fiji.

Pribilof Islands

A group of four islands, major breeding grounds of fur seals. Location *Bering Sea, off southwest Alaska, north of the Aleutian Islands.* Area *About 64 square miles.* Map *5, D1.*

It was Gerasim Pribilof, a mate in the service of a Russian sealing and wild-fowling company based on Unalaska, who discovered St George, the southernmost of the group, in 1786, and named it after his ship. The larger island of St Paul, 27 miles to the northwest, was not seen from St George until the following year, because of the extremely foggy climate. These two islands and the satellites of St Paul, Otter and Walrus islands, lie about 180 miles north of the Aleutian chain.

The Russians found here the main breeding-ground of the valuable Alaska fur-seal, and they established communities of Aleuts on St Paul and St George to gather the annual fur-harvest. In 1872 and 1873, Henry W. Elliott, a clerk in the United States Treasury, was commissioned to investigate the Pribilofs, their resources, inhabitants, seals and other native animals. He turned in a report that became a book which went into several editions and inspired Rudyard Kipling's famous story *The White Seal.*

The United States acquired the Islands with Alaska in 1867. By the end of the century the seal population was seriously reduced. In 1911,

England, Japan, Russia and the United States signed the North Pacific Sealing Convention to regularize the killings. Today the Islands are entirely administered by the American Fish and Wildlife Service. By judicious husbandry the seal population was gradually restored until in 1941 the fur-harvest equalled the figure taken in the great years of the eighteen-eighties – over 1,500,000 skins, excluding the two- and three-year-old seals which stay at sea. Yearly crops fluctuate normally between 80,000 and 100,000 skins, while the total seal population stays fairly stable; possibly it is as much as the carrying capacity of the Bering Sea will allow, though recent work on reducing mortality among pups may increase numbers still more.

To live for a while on the Pribilofs and meet the seals is a strange experience. The Islands are windswept, treeless, hilly expanses of basalt and lava-sand, for most of the year misty and foggy. But in summer, when the sun breaks through, it illuminates swards of the beautiful flowers for which the Islands are famous. As far as the eye can see there are carpets of deep blue lupins, bordered by the yellow Aleutian poppy. Among these live local races of birds, including a rare sandpiper and a rose-finch. Many wind-drifted migrants also visit the Islands, which are the only place in the United States where several Siberian birds have been seen. Upon the cliffs of basalt and tuff breeds a remarkable community of sea-birds. The North Pacific is the evolutionary home of the auk family, and eight species nest on the Islands, ranging from the tiny least auklet to the big tufted puffin. The red-legged kittiwake, which nests commonly on both St Paul and St George, breeds only in two other known places in the world, and the Islands are headquarters for a species peculiar to the Bering Sea – the red-faced cormorant – and for the Pacific fulmar. Arctic foxes are common in the interior of both islands and Steller's sea lion breeds on some of the beaches; though the walrus now visits the Pribilofs only rarely.

Today St Paul has an air-strip and a regular weekly commercial service, and both St Paul and St George are supplied by vessels of the Fish and Wildlife Service. There are modern houses and comforts in the settlements and the Aleut natives preserve their religion and social habits. A team of biologists is engaged in a program of research into the ecology of the fur-seals. These belong by concession to the St Louis Company, but killings are strictly supervised by the resident staff of the Fish and Wildlife Service.

Prince Edward Island

One of the Maritime Provinces of Canada, a large, fertile, intensively cultivated island. Location *Gulf of St Lawrence, between New Brunswick and Nova Scotia.* Area *2,184 square miles.* Map *1, H5.*

In June, 1534, Jacques Cartier sighted Prince Edward Island but mistook it for part of the mainland – though the Northumberland Strait which separates it from continental Canada is up to 30 miles wide. The mistake was soon discovered, and by the end of the sixteenth century it had been baptized Isle of St Jean; then, in 1798, it was renamed in honor of Edward, Duke of Kent, who was then commanding the British forces in North America. In 1603, Champlain annexed it for France; in 1663, it was given in grant by the Company of New France to Captain Doublet. He failed to make permanent settlements and lost the grant. It was not until after the Peace of Utrecht that the French tried to colonize the Island seriously; in 1719 the Comte de St Pierre began to establish fisheries and a trading company. He spent large sums but he failed and his grant, too, was revoked.

In 1758, after the capture of Louisbourg, the Island was occupied by a British force and in 1763 it was finally ceded to Britain. It was placed under the administration of Nova Scotia but later was given separate government. Its first parliament met in 1773. A survey was made in 1764–65; in 1767 the Island was divided into townships of about 20,000 acres each and grants were made to individuals – most of them mere speculators who were absentee landlords. In the early nineteenth century many Scottish immigrants settled in the Island and an agitation began for the compulsory purchase of lands and the sale of smaller holdings to genuine settlers. In 1873 Prince Edward Island joined the federation of Canada and the land difficulty was solved by satisfying the settlers' demands. Today, with a population of about 103,000, the Island is governed by a Lieutenant-Governor, an executive council and a Legislative Assembly of 30 members popularly elected.

Prince Edward Island is about 145 miles long and up to 35 miles wide, with a low and undulating surface that does not rise above 450 feet. Its rivers are short and non-navigable; the coastline is also low and much indented by bays of which Bedeque, Cardigan, Cascumpeque, Egmont, Hillsborough, Malperque and Tracadie are the largest, while the rivers include the Eliot, the Hillsborough, the Orwell and the Yorke. The climate is moderate and maritime. There are large dairy farms, much cattle raising and growing of seed-potatoes; the main crops are barley, wheat, oats and fruit. The St Lawrence yields lobster, cod, mackerel, smelt and herring, with extensive oyster beds. Charlottetown, the capital, has an important airport; the other towns include Alberton, Georgetown, Kensington, Montague, Port Borden, Souris and Summertown. The whole Island is crossed by a railroad, and a train ferry links Port Borden to Cape Tormentine in New Brunswick.

Prince of Wales Island

A large Arctic island. Location *Southern central Franklin district, Northwest Territories, Canada.* Area *13,736 square miles.* Map *4, L1.*

Prince of Wales Island has several namesakes. There is one in the North Pacific, off southeast Alaska, the largest island in the Alexander Archipelago with an area of 2,231 square miles; another in the Torres Strait, north of Cape York Peninsula, North Queensland, Australia, the largest in the Strait with an area of 75 square miles; Penang, in the Strait of Malacca, the oldest British settlement of the Malay Peninsula, also bore this name and so did Ahe, an atoll in the northern Tuamotu Islands in the South Pacific. But the largest and most important Prince of Wales Island is the Canadian Prince of Wales, lying between Victoria Island, Boothia Peninsula, Somerset Island, Bathurst Island and Melville Island, separated from its neighbors by McClintock Channel, Franklin Strait, Peel Sound and Viscount Melville Sound.

The Island was discovered by one of the expeditions sent out to search for Franklin's lost men and ships. Later, in the spring of 1859, a sledging party under Captain (later Sir) Allen Young explored most of the huge territory; subsequent expeditions followed the irregular, hilly and steep coastline, which is much indented, especially by Ommanney Bay in the west and Browne Bay in the east. Uninhabited and bleak, Prince of Wales Island was found to be the site of the magnetic pole in 1948.

Principe Island

A volcanic island, an overseas territory of Portugal. Location *Gulf of Guinea, about 140 miles west of Spanish Guinea.* Area *54 square miles.* Map *6, J6.*

Discovered by Portuguese navigators, together with São Tomé, 90 miles to the south-southwest, in the late fifteenth century, Principe has always been linked politically and economically to its sister island. Geologically, both are part of a chain (which includes the Spanish islands of Fernando Po and Annobon) of ancient volcanic peaks extending from the Cameroon Highlands of Africa southwestwards into the Atlantic Ocean.

Principe Island is very roughly rectangular in shape, about ten miles long and six miles across at its widest part. Towards its northeastern end, it rises to 3,110 feet. Geologically, Principe is mostly basalt, and its rich volcanic soils and humid climate provide suitable conditions for growing cacao and – on the mountain slopes – coffee. Copra and palm oil are also produced today, while at one time the Island had a very successful sugar industry which, however, declined. There are also insignificant traces of lignite, petroleum and natural gas.

The inhabitants (about 7,000 in number) are of very mixed origin. When the Island was first settled there was a small native population, but as soon as agriculture began large numbers of slaves were imported from the African mainland. Each Portuguese soldier stationed on the Island was permitted by royal decree to take one of the female slaves as a concubine, and so there was a rapid growth in the mixed population. Bantus are still brought to the Island to work the plantations as contract laborers.

Puerto Rico

Smallest and easternmost of the Greater Antilles, United States territory. Location *West Indies.* Area *3,435 square miles.* Map *2, G2–3.*

The site of the first permanent European settlement in the New World – it was discovered by Columbus in 1493 – Puerto Rico, and especially its capital, San Juan, built on a tiny island guarding the entrance to a magnificent, almost land-locked harbor on the north coast, has for centuries been contested as one of the most important strategic bases in the Americas.

From the time the Spanish organized their conquests, each year two great treasure fleets would enter the Caribbean a little to the east of the island. There, one fleet would make for Cartagena and Puerto Bello to load up with pearls and Peruvian gold; the other for Vera Cruz, to take on the silver of Mexico and the treasure of the Philippines and the Indies. A year later, the two fleets would join again in Havana and sail northwards to Spain along the Gulf Stream. Because Puerto Rico was midway between the points of entry and departure, from 1539 onwards great efforts were made to improve the defenses lest the island should fall into the hands of freebooters or hostile powers. The early strongholds of La Casa Blanca (home of the Ponce de Leon family; it was from here that the discoverer of Florida set out on his quest for the "Fountain of Youth") and La Fortaleza were implemented by the formidable cliff-top Morro Castle at the western end of the island, designed by the great military engineer Antonelli. As it was being built, Drake, with 23 ships and an army of 3,000 men, dropped anchor offshore. But a cannonball carried away his stool while he sat at dinner, and killed three of his officers; next day, though he succeeded in burning some ships in the harbor, he was driven off.

Three years later George Clifford, Earl of Cumberland, arrived in his flagship, the *Scourge of Malice*, and two weeks later his standard rose above the battered ramparts. But after five months, dysentery among his troops forced Cumberland to abandon the island. In 1625 came another ferocious attack, this time by the Dutch, which was very nearly successful. So narrow an escape alarmed the Spaniards, for England, France and Holland had already seized most of the smaller West Indian islands, and her position was becoming more and more insecure. Work on strengthening the fortifications began in 1630 and continued for over 150 years, creating one of the world's greatest fortresses. By 1678 the castle of San Cristobal had been built on the other side of San Juan, on a promontory half a mile to the east of El Morro, to which it was joined by a great wall, often over 50 feet high, enclosing the city. In 1765, alarmed by the British capture of Havana, the Spaniards brought out the engineer, Tomás O'Daly, to complete the work. By the end of the eighteenth century, at a cost of some 6,000,000 pesos, a vast series of walls and ramparts rising 140 feet and more above the sea, covering over 200 acres of land and mounting over 400 guns, had been constructed on the tiny island. The capital city itself, which they defended and enclosed, covered only 62 acres.

But by the eighteen-twenties a strong movement for independence had started. Slavery continued until 1873 and it was only the Spanish-American war that ended Spanish rule. On October 18, 1898, the United States took formal possession, and the treaty of cession was ratified in 1899. A constitution which was approved by Congress came into force in July, 1952, establishing the Commonwealth of Puerto Rico with full powers of local government; there is a Legislative Assembly of two elected houses and a Governor popularly elected for a term of four years. Puerto Rico is represented in Congress by a Resident Commissioner, elected for a term of four years, who has a seat in the House of Representatives but no vote. Puerto Ricans are citizens of the United States.

During American rule great improvements have been made in the industrialization and welfare of the island. Yet Puerto Rico is one of the most densely populated territories in the world – 666 people to the square mile, with a total population of 2,264,000 – and unemployment has driven large numbers to emigration, mostly to the United States, where their traditions and way of life have created serious problems in New York and other cities. The majority of the Puerto Ricans are of Spanish descent; Spanish and English are the official languages, yet even the English-speaking people have their roots in Spanish habits and customs. Sugar, tobacco, coffee, grapefruit and pineapples are the chief exports, and plantations of them cover the fertile coastlands. The interior is covered with jumbled mountains, rising to 4,400 feet in the Cerro de Punta. The only good harbors are at San Juan and Ponce. In 1961 Puerto Rico became the headquarters of the Caribbean Organization for Economic and Social Co-operation.

Puerto Rico faces a great many difficult problems, apart from over-population, and its imports are still considerably more than its exports. But with an increasing network of roads, and with public schools having an enrolment of over 700,000, there is reasonable hope that Puerto Rico will achieve a more prosperous future.

Queen Charlotte Islands

An archipelago of about 150 islands, belonging to Canada. Location *Western British Columbia, northwest Pacific.* Map *4, L1.*

A compact group, the Queen Charlotte Islands are geologically composed mainly of Triassic, Cretaceous and Tertiary strata, penetrated by intrusive rocks. Separated from Alaska by Dixon Entrance, from the British Columbia mainland by Hecate Strait and from Vancouver Island, farther south, by Queen Charlotte Sound, the Islands were first visited by Juan Pérez in 1774, then by Captain Cook in 1778. They were surveyed and named in 1787 by Captain George Dixon, whose ship was called the *Queen Charlotte.* They have excellent harbors, valuable seams of bituminous coal and anthracite, abundant timber and prolific fisheries – yet their total population is still under 2,000. Long before the First World War, the halibut fisheries of Hecate Strait attracted the attention of fishing companies, and great quantities are still taken regularly and shipped to the mainland in cold storage.

The heavily wooded Queen Charlotte Mountains run southwest from the western part of Graham Island, forming the backbone of Moresby Island and terminating on Kunghit Island; they are highest on Graham Island, where they rise to 4,100 feet.

Of the main islands, Graham (2,485 square miles) is the largest. Only 60 miles west-southwest from Prince Rupert, it is separated from Moresby Island, its southern neighbor, by Skidegate Inlet and Channel. Its length is 70 miles, its width 20–55 miles. Among its inlets is Massett Sound, which broadens into Massett Inlet in the center of the island. Lumbering, fishing, fish canning and stock raising are the main occupations; the chief villages are Massett, Queen Charlotte and Skidegate. Large anthracite deposits are still unexploited.

Moresby Island is 1,060 square miles, 85 miles long and 4–34 miles wide; the Queen Charlotte Mountains rise to 3,810 feet on it. Its chief villages are Sandspit (with a radio station) and Aliford Bay, both on the northeast coast. Kunghit Island, the smallest, is 83 square miles in area, separated from Moresby Island by the Houston Stewart Channel. At Rose Harbour, in the north, there is a small Canadian whaling station.

The native inhabitants of the archipelago are the Haida Indians, who have been called "the finest race and the most advanced in the arts of the entire west coast of North America." Certainly, the Haidas developed to its highest degree the peculiar conventional art of the northwest coast Indians, which was found in decreasing importance among the Tsimshians on the west, the Tlingit on the north and the Kwakiutl and other tribes farther south on the Pacific coast. The carved totem posts of the Haidas, standing outside their heavily framed houses or at a little distance from them, represented the coats of arms of the various families of the tribes, and generally were designed in a bold, original manner, highly stylized but always recognizable in portraying the tribal animal. But the Haida Indians, if not actually decreasing in numbers, are not increasing, and much of their old skill and artistic invention is being lost.

Queen Elizabeth Islands

A large archipelago, mostly uninhabited. Location *The Canadian Arctic.* Area *About 200,000 square miles.* Map *5, C7.*

Along a great hydrographic furrow, stretching west from Lancaster Sound to McClure Strait, the islands of the Canadian Arctic Archipelago form a group which in 1953 was named Queen Elizabeth Islands, after Queen Elizabeth the Second. They form part of Franklin district in the Northwest Territories. Some of the larger islands within the group are Amund Ringnes (1,764 square miles), Axel Heiberg (13,583 square miles), Bathurst (7,272 square miles), Cornwallis (2,592 square miles), Devon (2,606 square miles), Ellef Ringnes (4,266 square miles), Ellesmere (including Grant Land, Grinnel Land, Sverdrup Land and Lincoln Land, 77,392 square miles), Melville (16,503 square miles) and Prince Patrick (6,696 square miles). The elevation of these huge, scattered islands varies from 8,400 feet on Axel Heiberg to 400 feet on the smaller island of Lougheed (504 square miles).

The apex or "Ultima Thule" of the Queen Elizabeth Islands is Cape Columbia, on the northern tip of Ellesmere, which was Robert Edwin Peary's jumping-off point for the Pole. This cape is 625 miles from Lancaster Sound and 760 miles from McClure Strait. The triangle therefore includes more than 200,000 square miles, of which 150,000 square miles are land.

It was William Baffin, sailing in 1616 along the coast of Baffin Bay, who first explored the archipelago, and his map used to appear on charts for the next two centuries with the note "according to William Baffin but not now believed." In 1818 Alexander Ross confirmed Baffin's discoveries and in 1819 Sir William Edward Parry extended them west along Barrow Furrow to Melville Island, discovering the Parry Islands. The exploration of the Parrys was largely completed during the search for Franklin's lost expedition by various expeditions between 1850 and 1855. Others, like Elisha Kent Kane, Isaac Israel Hayes, Charles Hall, George S. Nares, Adolphus Washington Greeley and Robert Peary, pushed farther north and outlined the east coast of Ellesmere along Smith Sound, Kane Basin and Kennedy and Robeson channels in the period 1855–1909. The Nares expedition (1875–76) discovered the northern coast of Grant Land as far west as Point Alert, and later Peary extended this survey west to connect it with Axel Heiberg Island. Between 1898 and 1902 Otto Neumann Sverdrup, the Norwegian mariner and explorer, made a great single contribution to mapping the Islands by his work in Jones Sound, Norwegian Bay and Eureka Sound, surveying the northern coast of Devon, the southwestern coasts of Ellesmere, Axel Heiberg, King Christian and the Ringnes islands. In 1916–17 Vilhjalmur Stefansson continued the discoveries, finding Brock (414 square miles), Borden (4,000 square miles) and Meighen (360 square miles) islands.

Another stage in the exploration of the Arctic regions north of the Canadian mainland was reached in 1953, when the Royal Canadian Air Force completed the air-photographing of the Queen Elizabeth Islands, and Sverdrup's name was commemorated as that of a group within the archipelago.

There is still a good deal to be discovered about these immense, largely ice-covered territories. Off Flagler Fjord, for instance, Sverdrup and his companions came upon a dead Eskimo settlement. The age of this and other relics of human habitation found by the expedition has never been established. It is thought probable that they were of the Thule culture, in which case the sites must have been occupied at some time between the eleventh and nineteenth centuries, but probably not later than the sixteenth century. The time at which the last of these early inhabitants abandoned the Queen Elizabeth Islands is not yet known. In recent times Eskimos commonly crossed from Greenland to the north of Ellesmere Island, but only on hunting trips. Some scholars believe that the first European visitors to the archipelago were Norsemen from the medieval settlements on the west coast of Greenland, which lost contact with Europe and eventually disappeared. Sverdrup and others found small stone structures, recalling the ancient Norse custom of building similar shelters to attract the eider ducks to the same locality each year so that their valuable down could be collected.

The definitive charts of the archipelago were commissioned by the Canadian government and published in 1955; but many of the Islands are still awaiting detailed exploration, especially of mineral resources. It is possible that within the next decade or so the Queen Elizabeth Islands will become valuable both as a strategic outpost and as a commercial and mining area.

Rapa Iti

A volcanic island, scene of recent important archeological discoveries. Location *French Oceania, South Pacific.* Area *16 square miles.* Map *4, L9.*

Rapa Iti lies thousands of miles west of mysterious Easter Island, but contains similar traces of a lost race of master builders. It was discovered by Captain Vancouver in 1791 – the first European to see the castellated ridges and the fortifications, reminiscent of medieval Europe. Annexed by France in 1887, the island is mountainous, rising to 2,077 feet, and has some good harbors. It has a small population of about 300 and exports copra.

But Rapa Iti is famous for its archeological remains, investigated by Thor Heyerdahl, the eminent Norwegian explorer, during his Pacific journeys. He found that the overgrown fortifications of Morongo Uta consist of 12 fortified villages, which must have been inhabited by a much larger population than the island has today. Before his visit it was believed that the island had neither dressed stone blocks in the style of Easter Island, nor human figures carved in stone: but Heyerdahl found both in the hills, being taken by the natives to a bluff high above the valley east of Morongo Uta. Here he was shown a remarkable rock chamber where, according to legend, the bodies of kings in ancient times had lain in state before being buried.

No theories have yet become generally accepted as to who these master builders were – but, as Heyerdahl pointed out, they seem to have had an unlimited amount of time and patience to produce monuments that looked like "the golden castle of the fairy tale."

Ré, Ile de

A small, fertile coastal island, off La Rochelle. Location *Bay of Biscay, western France.* Area *33 square miles.* Map *7, C6.*

The Île de Ré was separated from the French mainland in relatively recent times, though the exact date is unknown; erosion has changed the coastline considerably, even within the last few centuries. About 15 miles long, the island is in general low and sandy. The main part is attached to the western extremity (Ars de Ré) by a narrow sandbank, and Loix, on the north, is cut off at high tide. The natural vegetation is limited: evergreens of various kinds, tamarisk and juniper grow in small clumps.

Most of the western part of Ré is salt marsh, fed by sea water from the Fier d'Ars, an inlet dividing Ars from Loix. The marshes are cut up into open pans (*aires*) where the sea water is allowed to evaporate. The water deposits crystalline salt, which is carefully removed with wooden rakes. Flies and mosquitoes breed vastly in these unhealthy marshes and the people provide their donkeys with hats and leggings as a protection.

Norman pirates in the ninth century were the first invaders to discover Ré as a base from which to dominate the coast of Poitou. Many people were driven away by the raiders, and in order to encourage resettlement some fiscal privileges were granted, which led to Ré becoming an important commercial center. It was often under attack from English fleets during the Middle Ages and was a Protestant stronghold which changed hands several times in the French religious wars of the sixteenth and seventeenth centuries. An English expedition under the Duke of Buckingham besieged the garrison unsuccessfully for four months in 1627. The fortifications erected by Sébastien le Prestre de Vauban, notably at St Martin, the capital, made the island impregnable in later wars.

After the French Revolution, Ré lost the privileges that had made it virtually a free port; its trade, apart from the export of salt, declined, and it became known chiefly as the site of a transit prison for convicts sentenced to deportation overseas, a practice discontinued in 1938.

Red Sea

A long, comparatively narrow sea between Asia and Africa, an important trade route in antiquity. Location *Between the Arabian Peninsula and northeast Africa, in the Great Rift Valley.* Area *170,000 square miles.* Maximum depth *Over 7,000 feet.* Map *10, B3–4.*

The history of the Red Sea begins at a remote point in geological time when the Great Rift Valley was formed, separating the Middle East into two parts along the line marked by the Jordan Valley, the Wadi el Araba and the Gulf of Aqaba. The Red Sea is a southern extension of this line. A number of islands in the south are composed of volcanic materials connected with the formation of the Rift Valley.

The Sea is 1,400 miles long and over 200 miles across in parts, but the entrance to the Indian Ocean in the south at Bab el Mandeb is only 15 miles wide. In the north two hornlike extensions (the gulfs of Aqaba and Suez) embrace the Sinai Peninsula. The Red Sea itself is enclosed on both sides by high country fronted by a strip of low, sandy coast. On the Arabian side there is a continuous mountain mass of sandstone and granite behind the low coastal plain formed from sand and coral and the steeply rising Tihama plateau. There are few good harbors. Jidda is the traditional port of entry for pilgrims to Mecca, while in the Yemen there is a sheltered but shallow harbor at Hodeida beside the ancient coffee port of Mocha.

The Red Sea's main importance has always been as a trade route. It served the Egyptians as long ago as the second millenium B.C., and later King Solomon and the eastern traders of the Roman Empire. However, it lacked a direct natural communication with the Mediterranean. A man-made canal joined the Gulf of Suez and the Nile in classical times but this dried up and was not replaced until 1869 when the Suez Canal was opened.

A deep channel extends down the center of the Sea, never more than 110 miles across and becoming much narrower at the northern and southern ends. Outside the main channel numerous reefs and shoals make navigation impossible except for those familiar with the locality; the coastal waters are used only by Arab dhows. There are also vicious cross-currents, terrifying sandstorms and violent winds to add to the hazards, coupled with extremely hot, humid conditions. The high rate of evaporation and very low rainfall produce a very high salinity and an average summer temperature of 85° F. in the water.

The winds of the Red Sea have exercised a decisive effect upon its use by travelers throughout the ages. In the north the prevailing winds are northwesterly the whole year round; a sailing vessel from the east cannot use a following wind on the last 800 miles of her journey from the middle of the Red Sea to the port of Suez. Sailing vessels are also hampered by the fact that for most of the year the prevailing winds in the southern part of the Sea are southeasterly, although from June to September they blow from the north. In these unfavorable sailing conditions most Red Sea traffic until comparatively recent times consisted of galleys rowed by slave oarsmen. But Arab merchants realized that slaves and their oars took up valuable cargo space, and built sailing ships of a special kind. The lateen rig of the Arab dhow with one or two great triangular sails hung on yards suspended from the mast is specially adapted to beating almost into the eye of the wind. The square-rigged European ships of the Middle Ages and later, designed for Atlantic conditions and for running before the wind under the largest possible spread of canvas, met an invisible barrier halfway up the Red Sea.

But the greater danger from pirates and the more unfriendly land journey via the Persian Gulf made the Red Sea the preferred short sea route to the east. In consequence Suakin and Quseir on its western shores at the limits of the southeasterly breezes were developed as porterage ports for the "overland" route between Europe and the east. Vessels would unload their cargo at one of these two ports and it would be carried by camel or donkey to the Nile to be transported by river boat to the Mediterranean. The overland system was adopted with modifications for the passenger traffic which arose from the establishment of European communities in India – but with the opening of the Suez Canal and the coming of the big steamship the Red Sea became a more or less uneventful corridor in the main traditional route between east and west.

Réunion

A large island of volcanic origin. Location *Indian Ocean, about 400 miles east of Madagascar.* Area *970 square miles.* Map *10, C8.*

The largest island of the Mascarene group – which includes Mauritius and Rodriguez – Réunion is 50 miles long and 45 miles wide. Its volcanic origin is still clearly evident, with two definite centers of eruption. The older, extinct, central massif culminates in the Piton des Neiges (10,069 feet), which owes its name to the fact that snow often falls, though it rarely lies for as much as a week at a time. The flanks of the mountain are seamed by deep radial gorges, carrying many streams to the sea. In the southeast is the more recent Piton de la Fournaise (rising to 8,612 feet), which was very active during the eighteenth century but is now more or less quiescent; the last important eruption was in 1860. The spurs of the central massif are divided by narrow valleys, often flooded by torrential streams.

The main watershed runs from the northwest to the southeast and on each side of it there are distinct geographic and administrative regions. The Windward district, owing to the heavy rainfall brought by the southeast trade winds, is humid, and vegetation is luxuriant, with a considerable area of forest. The Leeward district is drier.

Réunion lies in the path of cyclones and hurricanes; it was battered by disastrous storms in 1829, 1868, 1944 and 1945. The average summer temperature is 79° in the lowlands of the tropical coast, but more moderate in the uplands of the interior, where the health resorts of Hell-Bourg and Cilaos are situated.

In the early days coffee was the chief crop of the island, though coffee plantations have been largely replaced by sugar (from which industrial alcohol and rum are distilled); vanilla, tapioca, manioc and essential oils (such as geranium and citronella) are also produced. The island has some industries; chocolate, cigarettes, canned goods, fiber sacks, flour and vegetable oil are the most important.

An artificial harbor built in the eighteen-eighties at Pointe-des-Galets, on the coastal railroad which connects Saint-Benoit and Saint-Pierre (the capital of the Leeward district), has greatly improved Réunion's links with the outside world. The population of 301,000 is largely French Creole, with Indians, Chinese, Malagasy and Negroes representing less than three per cent of the total.

Discovered in the early sixteenth century by the Portuguese, Réunion was not settled until 1642, when a colony was established by the French, who named the island Bourbon seven years later. It passed from the French East India Company to the French Crown in 1764–67; in the next 70 years it changed its name four times, being called Réunion in 1703, Bonaparte in 1806, Bourbon a third time in 1815 and finally Réunion once more in 1848. It was under British occupation from 1810 to 1815; slavery was not abolished until 1848. During the Second World War, Free French forces captured it in 1942, and in 1946 it became an overseas department of France.

The capital, St Denis, is also the administrative center of the distant islands of St Paul, New Amsterdam and Kerguelen. The Crozet Islands and Adélie Land in the Antarctic are also dependencies of Réunion.

Rhode Island

The largest island of the state to which it gave its name. Location *Narragansett Bay, Atlantic Ocean.* Dimensions *About 15 miles long, 1–5 miles wide.* Map *1, F7.*

When the great ice-sheet of the last Ice Age retreated, a series of low, rounded hills was uncovered near the limit of its farthest extension in North America. The sea, replenished by the melt-water, rose about 300 feet all over the world, drowning part of the new landscapes, creating Narragansett Bay – a shallow, lake-like, island-filled bay, scene of immemorial Indian clambakes.

Probably the first European to see Rhode Island, the largest island in the Bay, was the Dutchman, Adriaen Block, in 1614. Anne Hutchinson and others bought Rhode Island from the Indians for a few dollars in 1638, two years after Roger Williams, a refugee from religious persecution in Massachusetts, had founded Providence, now the state capital, on the mainland. Known to the Indians as Aquidneck, Rhode Island was renamed in 1644. Peace with the Indians was maintained until the outbreak of King Philip's War (1675–76).

Constant religious bickering with surrounding settlements soured the Rhode Islanders, who were excluded from the New England Confederation, and made them jealous of their tiny territory's boundaries – at last given legal definition as "Rhode Island and Providence Plantation" in a charter of Charles II in 1663. Although the first state to declare its independence of Britain (and the last to ratify the Federal Constitution of the United States), Rhode Island clung to its beloved charter until the Dorr Rebellion of 1842, which achieved general male suffrage.

Rum, smuggling, slavery, molasses, whaling, fishing, trading with the enemy – Rhode Island's ports had the same sort of story as any others in New England well into the nineteenth century. Then came increasing numbers of settlers – English, Irish, French Canadians, Poles, Italians – industrialization (chiefly textiles) and the rich. Newport, in the south of the Island, though some of its glory has faded, became a most fashionable resort.

Rhodes

Largest island of the Dodecanese, with a long and dramatic history. Location *Dodecanese, Greece, in the Aegean Sea.* Area *542 square miles.* Map *9, H10.*

Rhodes is the capital of the Dodecanese group and the most easterly island in the Aegean Sea, only 12 miles from the Turkish coast. It is blessed with a fine climate, natural beauty, fertile land and a harbor surmounted by one of the most picturesque cities in the Mediterranean.

Part of the ancient fortifications on Rhodes

The island is some 44 miles long and 20 miles wide. A mountain ridge runs from north to south, forming its backbone, reaching its highest point at the center in Mount Attairo (3,986 feet). From its peak there is a fine view over the eastern Aegean and southwestwards over the Sea of Crete to Mount Ida, visible on a fine day. Northwards is the mountainous coast of Asia Minor, while to the northwest the other islands of the Dodecanese lift their rocky crests from the clear sea. Visibility is mostly good, for Rhodes is cooled by the west and north winds; their regularity gives the island the clarity that is peculiar to the whole of the Aegean. These two winds determine the equable climate of Rhodes. During the summer it is cooled by the north wind, and the temperature rises uncomfortably only during July and August, when a hot wind off Asia Minor brings an oven-like heat not unlike the North African khamseen.

The climate and the fertile soil combine to make Rhodes one of the most fruitful islands in the eastern Mediterranean. Every kind of grain grows in the sheltered plains; oranges, figs, pomegranates and vines are intensively cultivated. Carobs and almond trees as well as olives grow on the mountainsides. The thick pine forests which in ancient times were one of the island's chief assets were largely destroyed during the Turkish occupation; but enough of them remain to give some of the hills a richness usually lacking in Aegean islands.

The city of Rhodes lies at the northeastern end of the island and climbs up from the sea around a natural amphitheater. It is an important trading and industrial center, producing brandy, soap, rugs and cigarettes and engaged in shipbuilding, flour milling and fruit drying. It is a walled, medieval city and much of its architecture is the work of the Knights Hospitalers of St John, who held it from 1309 to 1523.

The history of the island of Rhodes goes back to about 1000 B.C., when it was colonized by the Dorians, who formed the city states of Camirus, Ialysus and Lindus, part of the Dorian Hexapolis. Rhodes remained independent (and colonized Gela in Sicily) until the Persian conquest, late in the sixth century B.C., and participated in the Ionian revolt which led to the Persian Wars. It was part of the Delian League for about 50 years, but withdrew during the Peloponnesian War in 411 B.C. The original three city states united in 407 B.C. to found the federal capital city of Rhodes. It was after the death of Alexander the Great (323 B.C.) that Rhodes entered its golden age of power and prosperity. The famous Colossus, one of the Seven Wonders of the World, was erected in 285 B.C. A statue of the sun god Helios, it was 100 feet high and stood at the entrance to the harbor until it was destroyed by an earthquake in 224 B.C. In the second century B.C., as Roman power expanded in the Mediterranean, Rhodes declined in importance. Cassius captured and sacked it in 43 B.C. Later it became the seat of a famous school of rhetoric of which Julius Caesar was a notable pupil.

Rhodes remained part of the Byzantine Empire until the hosts of the Fourth Crusade captured Byzantium (Constantinople) in 1204; it was held by the Genoese for a brief period and was conquered in about 1282 by the Seljuk Turks. The Knights Hospitalers re-took the island in 1309 and it was only by sacrificing 100,000 men that Suleiman I was able to conquer it in 1523.

The Italians took Rhodes in 1912; it was occupied by the Germans during the Second World War and ceded to Greece in 1947.

Roanoke Island

Site of the famous "lost colony." Location *Dare county, eastern North Carolina, between Croatan and Roanoke sounds.* Dimensions *12 miles long, 3 miles wide.* Map *1, F9.*

Roanoke Island lies in the mysterious coastal waters between the long arm of sand that reaches out through Kitty Hawk to Cape Hatteras and the North Carolina swamps. It is chiefly notable as the site of Sir Walter Raleigh's "lost colony" and the presumptive burial place of Virginia Dare, the first English child to be born in America. It is still isolated and undeveloped; its principal industries are fishing and, in summer, the tourists who come to Paul Green's open-air theater. It combines the bleached dignity of wooden houses and wharfs with all that is atmospheric in wide skies and mists from the sea and remains of places where the American past can be felt as something both innocent and remote.

It was in 1584 that the navigators Philip Amadas and Arthur Barlowe, exploring for Sir Walter Raleigh, were so impressed with the Island that their reports led to the despatch of a band of colonists under Sir Richard Grenville. These colonists landed in August, 1585, and built a fort, but they were forced to return home the following year. In 1587 Raleigh tried again with another group under the leadership of John White and some progress towards the establishment of a permanent colony seems to have been made. However, White himself had to return immediately for supplies, leaving his settlers behind him, and he was long delayed in England by the Armada crisis. When in 1591 he was able to sail again, he found that the colony had disappeared. Disease, attacks from hostile Indians or migration into the interior have all been suggested as possible explanations, together with the possibility that the whites may have been absorbed by some friendly tribe. Some remains have been discovered in what is now the Fort Raleigh National Historic Site (established in 1941).

It was some time before the English tried "western planting" again; in the spring of 1607, the newly formed joint-stock London Company sent three small ships into Chesapeake Bay and up the James River to Jamestown, an adjacent area which Raleigh himself had actually selected before his agents preferred Roanoke.

Since 1937, *The Lost Colony*, Paul Green's historical drama, has been performed every year and draws many visitors. And if it commemorates a mystery and a failure, it must be remembered that at Kitty Hawk – also in Dare county, which is named after the long-dead child – the Wright Brothers flew their first airplane and began a greater revolution than those first colonists ever dreamed about.

Ross Sea

A large inlet of the Pacific. Location *Antarctica, between Cape Adare and Cape Colbeck.* Map *3, D9.*

The Ross Sea is a huge bight on the Pacific side of the Antarctic continent, corresponding to the Weddell Sea on the Atlantic side. Into both a westerly current sweeps, running in a clockwise direction and flowing out towards the northeast, carrying pack ice and icebergs far out into the open ocean. Unlike the Weddell Sea, the Ross Sea has no ice-trap piling up the pack ice, for the mountainous coast of Victoria Land does not project far northward upon its western border. The pack ice that forms in the Ross Sea is far less formidable than that of the Weddell Sea. It moves slowly with the current to the northeast and out as a long stream across the entrance to the bight, but south of it there is, throughout most of the summer, a great stretch of open water, an enclosed sea, hemmed in by pack ice to the north and to the south bounded by the great Ross Barrier. In late summer this enclosing band of pack ice disappears and the Ross Sea lies open right up to the Barrier face.

This great Barrier is a floating shelf of ice, 400 miles long from one side to the other and, throughout its length, about 100 feet high. Flat or gently undulating on top, beneath it is more than 1,800 feet of water. Breaking strains continually set free great slabs of it which float away as immense tabular, flat-topped icebergs, drifting northwards until they reach warmer waters. Here they begin to melt, changing their center of gravity in the process, and, rolling over, assume bizarre and fantastic shapes. They float away into the Ross Sea, ice-castles 150 feet high, streaked with shadow and girdled with foam.

Captain Thaddeus Bellingshausen reached the wide mouth of the Ross Sea during the important Russian expedition in December, 1820, and was stopped by the continuous pack ice, which was too heavy for his two small ships. The Sea and the Shelf Ice were both discovered by Sir James Clark Ross in 1841. In the eighteen-seventies Svend Foyn financed a reconnaissance expedition to the Ross Sea to look for whales – which did not find any, but confirmed the existence of plenty of open water. This was the first expedition that actually landed on the mainland of the Antarctic continent, at Cape Adare.

Carstens Borchgrevink, a Norwegian who took part in the expedition, spent the winter of 1898–99 at the Cape, at the western entrance of the Ross Sea. Borchgrevink's expedition steamed down the Ross Sea, following the route of the *Erebus* and *Terror* in which Ross himself had made his original discoveries nearly 60 years earlier, landing briefly on some of the islands and repeating the Ross Survey along the face of the great Barrier, finding it had receded a good many miles in the six decades. A short march even took them inland on the Barrier before they turned homewards.

Amundsen sailed his *Fram* all the way to the Ross Sea on his dash to the South Pole, landing at the eastern end of the Ross Barrier and then meeting Scott's party at the Bay of Whales, where Little America, the permanent Antarctic base of the United States, stands today.

In 1914 Shackleton made an attempt to cross the Antarctic continent from the Weddell to the Ross Sea and part of his party laid depots along the proposed route to the foot of the Beardmore Glacier. The attempt failed – three men were lost – but after the First World War Captain Carl A. Larsen pioneered further explorations, especially of Discovery Inlet, a curious long rift in the Ross Shelf Ice which Scott had discovered in 1902 – an inlet over 1,500 feet deep which needed over half a mile of steel hawser to anchor Larsen's *Sir James Clark Ross*, a single screw steamship. Larsen had negotiated a five-year lease of the Ross Sea area from the British government and established large-scale whaling in the high southern latitudes. In six years Larsen's Ross Sea Company caught whales worth in an approximately $10,000,000.

It was again on the Ross Shelf Ice that Admiral Byrd established his headquarters, Little America I, in 1929, a few miles from Amundsen's base in 1911. Among other things, Byrd was anxious to prove whether or not there was a channel between the Ross and Weddell seas, and in two flights he established that there was at least a high icecap blocking the way; though it is possible that such a channel exists which the icecap, many thousands of feet in thickness, has filled up. It was the gap between Graham Land and the Ross Sea that Byrd's expedition narrowed, but it proved the most difficult sector to penetrate. Subsequent Little Americas were established on and around the Ross Sea with Number V for "Operation Deepfreeze" being built in an inlet of the ice shelf about 30 miles east of the Bay of Whales. Since then the area of the Ross Sea has become the scene of both American and Russian exploration, Antarctic meteorological and strategic stations have been established and practically the entire shoreline of the vast, iceberg-packed expanse of water charted and explored.

Rügen

The largest German Baltic island, with many popular seaside resorts. Location *Northeast of Stralsund, Mecklenburg, East Germany.* Area *357.7 square miles.* Map *8, G4.*

A bird's eye view of Rügen reveals a grotesquely shaped island separated only by the Bodden and the Greifswalder Bodden, two narrow arms of the Baltic, from the mainland. The island's curious outline looks as if it has been caused by marine erosion, but in reality it is due to the fact that Rügen is a small archipelago; the individual islands have been joined in the course of time by sand spits.

Properly speaking, Rügen is the largest of these ancient islands, nearest to the mainland and the city of Stralsund. The principal additions were Willow to the north, Jasmund to the northeast and Mönchgut to the east of Rügen proper. The main land masses consist of glacial deposits with chalk cliffs projecting above them, especially in Jasmund, where the Hertaburg rises to 505 feet.

Rügen has been continuously inhabited since very early times. The island is rich in late stoneage remains and over 200 megalithic monuments were still standing in the early nineteenth century, though only a few of them have survived to the present day. Later, the island was occupied by Slavonic tribes who settled along the adjoining coasts. The island and the neighboring mainland formed a principality under its own pagan rulers who during the twelfth century were converted to Christianity by the forceful King Waldemar of Denmark. In 1325 the Slavonic dynasty died out and Rügen became part of Pomerania. Sweden acquired the island in 1648 after the Thirty Years War and in 1815 it became part of the Kingdom of Prussia and so eventually of the German Empire. It was taken by Soviet troops in May, 1945, and is now part of East Germany.

Today, nearly 100,000 people live in Rügen

though its economic activities are few. The island is chiefly known for its herrings and geese, but the chalk country provides grazing for cattle and some sheep, and in the lower parts cereals, sugar beet and potatoes are grown. The island's communications with the mainland were much improved by the construction, in 1936, of the *Rügendamm* to carry the railroad 1½ miles across to Stralsund, but its separateness has been emphasized by the survival of antique customs and dress. The most popular seaside resorts are Binz, Putbus and Sellin; the chief town is Bergin and the largest port Sassnitz.

Ryukyu Islands

An archipelago divided into three groups, scene of final battles in the Second World War. Location *Between Formosa and Kyushu, separating the East China Sea from the Atlantic.* Area *1,803 square miles.* Map *4, C4–D3.*

The Ryukyus have also been called the Liukiu, Liu-chiu, Luchu, Loo-choo or Riukiu Islands, according to the various Western transliterations of Japanese characters. The three groups into which the 750-mile-long chain of volcanic and coralline islands is divided are the Amami-gunto in the north (consisting of Amami-o-shima, Tokuno-shima, Okinoerabu-shima, Kikai-shima, Yoron-jima, Tikara-gunto and many scattered islets); the Okinawa Islands in the center (which, apart from Okinawa itself, include Kerama-retto, Ie-jima, Kume-shima, Daito-shima, Iheya-shoto and many coral islets); and in the south the Sakishima Islands (Ishigaki-shima, Miyako-jima, Iriomote-jima, Irabu-shima, Yonaguni-shima, Tarami-jima, Sebkaku-gunto and, again, a sprinkling of coral islets).

The Ryukyus are not particularly attractive. Their climate is semi-tropical with abundant rainfall and there are frequent typhoons. The fauna consists principally of poisonous snakes, wild boars, black rabbits and deer. The forests include camphor, banyan and banana trees (mostly in the southern group) with Japanese cedars and pines in the north. The principal produce is sugar cane and sweet potatoes; the Islanders also manufacture Panama hats and some textiles. Small ponies are bred with some cattle, pigs and goats; a famous durable vermilion-colored lacquer is still much in demand for table utensils in the main islands.

The mythical founder of the independent Ryukyu monarchy was Tinsunshi, the "Grandson of Heaven." His descendants were driven from the throne by a revolt near the end of the twelfth century; but Shunten, son of Tamemoto, a member of the famous Minamoto family, who had been exiled from Japan and had married in the Islands, became the victorious leader of the old national party. He introduced reading and writing. Chinese invasion began around 605 A.D. but there was no annexation; it was only in 1372 that China first obtained from the Ryukyuans the recognition of her supremacy. At the end of the sixteenth century the king of the Islands refused Japan assistance against Korea and in 1600 the Prince of Satsuma invaded the Ryukyus with 3,000 men, took the capital by storm, captured the king and carried him off to Kagoshima. A few years later he was restored to his throne on condition of acknowledging Japanese suzerainty and paying tribute. The canny Ryukyuans, however, continued to pay tribute to China, too; and China never attempted to bring them under military rule. In 1879 Japan put an end to this divided loyalty, dethroning the ruling prince, pensioning him off and converting the Ryukyus into a prefecture under the name of Okinawa – a word which means "extended rope," referring to the straggling, spread-out chain of the Islands. China protested, and at a conference in Peking an agreement was signed to divide the archipelago equally. The Chinese government refused to ratify this agreement and the dispute was finally settled in 1895 when Japan acquired Formosa and her title to the Ryukyus was also acknowledged.

Though Captain Broughton of the British warship *Providence* was wrecked on the Islands towards the end of the eighteenth century, it was not until 1816–17 that Captain Basil Hall and Captain Murray Maxwell obtained detailed information about the Islands. The people, so the expedition recorded, showed a curious mixture of "courtesy and shyness." From 1844, Catholic and Protestant missionaries attempted to convert them to Christianity, but their efforts had little success. Commodore Matthew Perry, in 1853, added largely to the knowledge of the Islands and concluded a treaty with the Ryukyuan government.

In the Second World War Okinawa was the scene of a decisive and bitter battle. After the Japanese surrender, Amami-gunto, Okinawa and the Sakishima Islands were placed under an American military governor. In 1951 a native civil administration was formed.

Saba

A small, almost inaccessible island, part of the Dutch Antilles. Location *Northwest Leeward Islands, West Indies.* Area *Five square miles.* Map *2, H3.*

Saba is an extinct volcano, rising to 2,851 feet, with vertical sides soaring straight from the sea, and only two possible landing points; its principal settlement, Bottom, lies in the depths of the crater. The Dutch took possession of Saba in 1632.

Nobody knows when the ancestors of the people of this great natural fortress – which was one of the last strongholds of the buccaneers – arrived, or where they came from. There are now about 1,600 of the islanders; blue-eyed, rosy-cheeked, fair-haired. Many of them bear Scottish names; and although they are taught Dutch in their schools, in everyday life they speak English. It is startling, in the largely Negro West Indies, to find an island of white people, to see them working quietly at their gardens and potato patches, making boats or shoes (or, in the case of the women, delicate lace), a thousand feet or more above the sea in the hollow shell of an extinct volcano.

The sea plunges to great depths all around Saba and landing is a perilous affair, even in fair weather, by small boat to a tiny rocky platform amid the wave-lashed cliffs. Until recently, the only way up the precipices to the inhabited regions above was by means of a nightmarish staircase cut in the rock, called "the ladder." Now the islanders own a jeep, and a steep winding road, almost as frightening as "the ladder," climbs 900 feet and through a chasm of rock to the interior of the crater. There, in an idyllic, almost European, landscape of green fields, trees and wild flowers, gardens and grazing cattle, stands a small, trim town of white houses and red roofs. High up on the rim, amid giant tree-ferns, are two more villages: Windward Side (1,200 feet) and St John's (1,900–2,000 feet); clinging to the outer slopes is Hell's Gate, its houses chained to the rocks to prevent the wind from blowing them into the sea.

The men of Saba are famous throughout the islands as sailors and boat-builders. Cedar, locust and various other trees are used, felled high up on the mountainside; the boats, complete in every detail (for there is no shore where they might lie while being fitted), are carried or warped on rollers down to the tortuous paths to the sea. In spite of the dangerous landing, Saba has many times in the past been attacked by pirates and hostile nations – but never with success, for the islanders had a simple and effective defense at their disposal: directly the invaders were ashore, they would hurl down upon them avalanches of boulders, of which piles were always kept in readiness.

Sable Island

A shrinking sandy island, scene of many shipwrecks. Location *Off southeast Nova Scotia, Atlantic Ocean.* Dimensions *About 20 miles long, one mile wide.* Map *1, J6.*

Sable Island, shaped like the crescent moon, stretches from east to west, 180 miles east of Halifax, Nova Scotia. Formed of sand, it is merely the visible portion of a huge sandbank or shoal, 75 miles long and 10 miles wide, on the outer edge of the continental shelf. It was named for the French *sable*, meaning sand.

The Island was probably discovered by some of the first navigators to North America; it appears on Reinal's map of 1556 as Santa Cruz and also on Cabot's map of 1544. The Marquis de la Roche landed on it in 1598 and found some wild cattle, probably left by earlier, shipwrecked visitors. The Marquis was forced to leave 50 of his colonists on the Island for five years – of whom only 11 survived. Since then its grim history has included so many shipwrecks that it has long been known as the "graveyard of the Atlantic."

In 1801, Nova Scotia established the first relief

Erosion on the coast of Sable Island

station on the Island. In 1873, the Canadian Federal Government built two powerful lighthouses and introduced coastguard service. Sable Island is without trees, but vegetables are grown by the few resident families, and about 300 wild ponies manage to subsist on it. The Island is gradually shrinking: a couple of centuries ago it was twice as long and wide as today. It does not form part of any county of Nova Scotia, but its inhabitants have access to the Halifax courts and vote in Federal elections in Halifax county.

St Helena

A small British island, famous as Napoleon's last prison and place of death. Location *South Atlantic, about 1,200 miles west of Africa.* Area *47 square miles.* Map *6, H8.*

St Helena, "a meer wart in the ocean," as an early mariner described it, is probably the best known of all the solitary islands in the world. Situated 955 miles south of the equator, 760 miles southeast of Ascension and 1,800 miles from the coast of South America, it is 10½ miles long and 6½ miles broad. Yet to explore its dramatic peaks and tropically lush valleys would take many days, even allowing for the exciting motor rides the few mountainous roads provide. Volcanic in origin, considered by some to be "the oldest land in the world," it rises perpendicularly out of the deep ocean bed with superb, almost forbidding, cliff scenery; while inland, deep ravines lead to rock summits which retain traces of prehistoric vegetation. The climate is mild and equitable because the southeast trade winds keep the temperatures down. Many of the breathtaking views owe something to the fields of New Zealand flax, once a flourishing export. Among many beautiful birds, the wire bird, which prefers walking to flying, is the sole surviving member of the indigenous fauna.

Discovered by the Portuguese navigator João de Nova in 1502 (probably on St Helena's day), it remained unknown to other European nations until 1588. It was then uninhabited and thickly covered with forests – which have mainly disappeared through the ravages of imported goats. St Helena was used as a port of call for vessels of all nations trading to the East, until annexed by the Dutch in 1633. There was, however, no occupation, and the English East India Company seized the island in 1659. It was ceded to the British Crown in 1834. Its local history is rich in incident, with dark chapters relating to slaves, cruel governors and mutinies – and happier times of peace and prosperity, before the opening of the Suez Canal ended the island's usefulness for shipping.

St Helena is chiefly famous as the place of the Emperor Napoleon's final exile from 1815 to 1821 – a purpose for which the island was lent to the British Government by the East India Company. Napoleon's home at Longwood, now beautifully restored and protected against termites, and his empty grave – his body was taken back to France in 1840 – are show places which, owing to a gift of Queen Victoria, have the curious distinction of being on French soil though on a British island. St Helena even has a French acting vice-consul. Apart from Napoleon, several other troublesome people have been confined here, including a Sultan of Zanzibar, a Zulu chieftain and several Boer generals.

The capital and only town is Jamestown, with

a pleasant eighteenth-century atmosphere. The population is less than 5,000. The colonial-style planters' mansions in the countryside are mostly in ruins; for the economic situation of the island is very difficult, though phormium (flax fiber) and lace-making have recently been established as basic industries. There are many forts; other outstanding features include a cliff-face stairway of 699 steps, a castle, the Government House and a tortoise which was the contemporary of Napoleon. St Helena is also the capital of a British Dependency to which, since 1938, the islands of Tristan da Cunha, Gough, Nightingale and Inaccessible in the South Atlantic have belonged.

St Kilda

The largest of a group of rocky islets, a famous bird sanctuary. Location *Outer Hebrides, Inverness, Scotland.* Dimensions *3 miles long, 2 miles wide.* Map *8, C2.*

Apart from St Kilda itself, this small cluster of islands and rocks in the Atlantic Ocean consists of Soay and Boreray, each about a mile long, and numerous stacks and rocks, of which Stac an Armin, 627 feet high, and Stac Lee, 544 feet high, are the largest. The immense vertical cliffs, rising to 1,397 feet on St Kilda and 1,245 feet on Boreray, are the highest in Britain.

It was in July, 1840, that two men from St Kilda, hunting sea-birds on Stac an Armin, saw a great black bird, with a white belly, sitting bolt upright and staring at them. It was like nothing else they had ever seen – in place of wings it had two short stumps, a mere six inches long, and under each eye it had a white spot. Unknown to them, it was the last Great Auk (*Alca impennis*), a strange, flightless sea-bird, penguin-like in its mode of life and once abundant in the Hebrides. Filled with horror, thinking it was a witch, they beat it to death. Today, some 70 skins, as many eggs, and a few hundred bones in museums, are all that remains of the species.

But if the Great Auk is extinct, other sea-fowl flourish and increase on St Kilda: the rare Leach's Petrel, for example, has recently formed new colonies. It is the St Kildans themselves who have gone. Excavations show that Viking settlements here were among the first in the Western Isles and the islands have been continuously in-

Soay, St Kilda

Lighthouse on the Magdalen Islands, in the Gulf of St Lawrence

habited, until recently, ever since. They became Scottish, with the rest of the Hebrides, in 1312, by gift of the King of Norway to King Bruce. Their indigenous mouflon-like sheep, the Soay sheep, which still survive in numbers, are unchanged descendants of the most ancient Norsemen's sheep and represent a stock that has vanished elsewhere.

Until the mid-nineteenth century the population was usually over 100 people. They pastured a few cows and sheep, cultivated small patches of potatoes, oats and barley, where the soil was deep enough, and caught fish. But sea-birds, especially the plump and juicy, if fishy-flavored, young, were their chief source of meat: thousands of puffins and fulmars and lesser numbers of razorbills, kittiwakes and guillemots were eaten each year, together with large numbers of guillemot eggs. To reach the birds and their nests on the perpendicular cliffs, an incredible skill in rock-climbing, taught from boyhood, was necessary. But the hardships, especially in winter, proved too much, though strenuous efforts were made to preserve the settlement. In 1853, 35 people emigrated to Australia, leaving 78. The numbers remained fairly constant until the nineteen-twenties, but it was more and more a population of the old; and when at last, in 1930, not even a boat's crew could be mustered (there were then only 43 left) the islands were evacuated. Their little deserted hamlet still stands at the head of East Bay, almost habitable, for the houses were ruggedly built.

St Lawrence, Gulf of

A vast gateway to the North American continent, with many islands, and important as a fishing ground. Location *Eastern Canada, between Nova Scotia, Newfoundland and Labrador, at the mouth of the St Lawrence River.* Area *100,000 square miles.* Map *1, G4–H4.*

The Gulf of St Lawrence is roughly pyramid-shaped, with its base lying along the coasts of Newfoundland and Cape Breton to the east, one side following the Labrador coast, and the other side, more irregular, stretching past the Magdalen Islands to the tip of Gaspé Peninsula. At its apex, where the mighty St Lawrence River begins, is the large island of Anticosti. A western arm called Chaleur Bay extends on the south side of Gaspé Peninsula.

Although the interior of the lands surrounding the Gulf may be densely forested – and, in the south, even fertile – the Gulf is basically the home of ice and ice water, for the Arctic Current down the Labrador coast creeps into it by way of Belle Isle Strait and there have been times when its entrances (Belle Isle in the northeast and Cabot Strait in the east, with the narrow Strait of Canso between Nova Scotia and Cape Breton Island) have been completely blocked. Ice water has been called the dominant factor in its shore environment. The chill wind arising from ice makes the coasts treeless; since they are high, rough and rocky, they have a particularly forbidding appearance. At the extreme south, on the little French island of St Pierre, 19 miles from the coast of Newfoundland, the forests of evergreens that sprawl upon the ground are less than knee-high, resembling tree growth at its extreme limit on high mountains. Sprinkled among the miniature and misshapen forests are laurels and golden-rod, only two to three inches high, but full of blossom.

Apart from Anticosti, Prince Edward and Magdalen islands, the Gulf contains numerous smaller ones, mainly along the north shore. Fogs are very frequent and the navigation season is from the middle of April to early December, as for the rest of the year large, drifting sheets of ice make the passage of ships hazardous.

The shallow, undersea plateaus and cold water make excellent breeding grounds for fish, especially cod and herring, and the lobsters are among the best in the world.

It was in 1497 that John Cabot, exploring for England, discovered the coasts of Newfoundland and Nova Scotia. About 1534 Jacques Cartier, the French navigator, reached Gaspé Peninsula. He discovered Cabot Strait from the west and studied the coast of Labrador, noting specially the fjord-like indentations, which are due to the fact that the Gulf lands have sunk several thousand feet in comparatively recent times. He then proceeded by way of the Magdalen group to Prince Edward Island. The Gulf was beginning to freeze up and so he turned home; but in August, 1535, he at long last entered the "Rivière du Canada. . . grand, large et spacieux" – the St Lawrence River.

Today, the Gulf is the gateway of one of the greatest man-made inland waterways, the St Lawrence Seaway. This tremendous joint Canadian-United States project, completed in 1959, turned the modern metropolis of Toronto, on Lake Ontario, into a seaport, opened the way from the Atlantic directly to the Great Lakes of the American Midwest and is providing cheap hydro-electric power for both countries.

St Lawrence Island

A barren, volcanic island, site of ancient Eskimo culture. Location *Near the entrance of Norton Sound, Bering Sea, western Alaska.* Dimensions *90 miles long, 8–32 miles wide.* Map 5, *D2.*

Discovered by Vitus Bering in 1728, St Lawrence Island is treeless and covered with snow for most of the year; all the vegetation is of the tundra type. The Island's rugged terrain rises to 2,070 feet, and it is inhabited by Eskimos whose occupations are walrus hunting, whaling and fox trapping. The two centers of population are Savoonga in the north and Gambell in the northwest of the Island.

The main activity of the Eskimos centers around the herds of walrus, which appear along the coast with the first drift ice in the autumn; they are seen in varying numbers all through the winter, whenever there is open water along the coast. But the main herds arrive during March and April, when several hundred are killed by the natives from their large skin boats, called *umiaks*.

During the walrus season the old Eskimo hunters, captains of these skin boats, gather upon the hill by the sea every morning at daybreak to watch for walrus on the drift ice. Walrus-hunting in the ancient Eskimo manner – Eskimo culture on St Lawrence has been traced back at least 2,000 years – is an adventurous sport. Whenever walrus are sighted, the boat crews are awakened within minutes, and while the men get their hunting gear together – rifles, harpoons, seal pokes and skin ropes – the women and children lift the large skin boats from their racks and bring the outboard motors and dog teams down to the beach. The dogs are brought along to pull the meat and blubber to the boat when an animal is shot on a floe, or to pull it on to the ice when it is shot in the water. The boats have ivory runners so that they can easily be hauled across icefields and floes.

Walrus were once abundant in Arctic waters at high latitudes and had a circumpolar distribution; but they have been gradually exterminated in many areas and now appear in considerable numbers only along the Siberian coast, on St Lawrence Island, at Point Hope in Alaska and on the northwest coast of Greenland. They are dangerous animals; the Eskimos of St Lawrence describe how the walrus squeezes a seal to death between his front flippers and then butchers it with his tusks.

St Pierre and Miquelon

An archipelago in French possession, an important fishing base. Location *Off southern Newfoundland.* Area *93 square miles.* Map *1, J4.*

The 4,900 people who live on the two Atlantic islands of St Pierre and Miquelon, separated by a 15-mile channel from Newfoundland, constitute a French enclave in an Anglo-Saxon world, and at the same time the last remnant of the vast colonial empire which France once held in America. Most of them are descended from Norman settlers and are Roman Catholic.

Both islands are rugged masses of granite with a few small streams and lakes, a thin covering of soil and not much vegetation. Miquelon, the westerly, is also the larger: it consists of Great and Little Miquelon, which were once separated by a navigable channel but since 1783 have been joined by a mudbank. St Pierre has an excellent harbor which the Gulf Stream keeps free of ice all the year round and the town is an important fishing center, lying close to the Grand Banks, with fish salting, drying and canning its principal industries: the entire economy depends on the cod catches, though Miquelon has some slate and other deposits.

Fishing lasts from May to October and is engaged in by the crews of over 500 vessels. About two thirds are fitted out in the islands, while the rest sail across the Atlantic from St Malo, Cancale and other French coastal towns. The resident population is almost doubled during the season.

Breton and Basque fishermen already used the archipelago in the sixteenth century; but permanent settlements were not established until the French were ejected from Acadia (Nova Scotia) in 1763. Occupation, however, began in 1660 and in 1700 the islands were fortified. There was a long see-saw struggle for their possession in the eighteenth century; in 1778 the British destroyed the settlements; five years later the islands were restored to France only to be captured and depopulated again by the British in 1793. France recovered them in 1802, lost them again next year, and regained them when the Treaty of Paris (1814) confirmed French sovereignty. During the Prohibition years in the United States, St Pierre had a highly profitable time, for bootleggers and smugglers used it as a convenient base. When France capitulated in the Second World War, the islands came under the authority of the Vichy government; but 16 months later, in December, 1941, a Free French force landed and captured them. Under United States pressure, however, the old regime was restored. In 1946 St Pierre and Miquelon became part of the French Union and are represented in the French National Assembly and Senate.

Fog-ridden, often wrapped in mist for days, the islands – except during the fishing season – are a peaceful backwater. It is not surprising that the population is decreasing; young people are lured by the opportunities of Canada, and there is a slow exodus that seems unlikely to stop.

St Vincent, Cape

A headland on the Atlantic, identified with several naval battles. Location *Southwest Portugal.* Map *7, A7.*

Cape St Vincent was regarded by the classical geographers Marinus of Tyre and Ptolemy as the westernmost point of Europe – though in reality this distinction belongs to Cape Roca, farther north. Jutting into the Atlantic, 60 miles west of Faro, Cape St Vincent is the site of a remarkable lighthouse standing on the top of a 175-foot cliff – a lighthouse built within the framework of a sixteenth-century monastery. Nearby are the ruins of a town which Prince Henry the Navigator built in the fifteenth century and which included his richly endowed school for navigators and an observatory. This *Villo do Iffante*, or Crown Prince's Town, grew out of a naval arsenal; it was the place to which the great inspirer of exploration and discovery retired in 1438, and in which he died in 1460.

Of the many naval engagements fought off the Cape, that of 1797 between a British fleet consisting of 15 ships-of-the-line and 5 frigates and a Spanish fleet of 26 sail-of-the-line and 12 frigates was perhaps the most famous.

The British squadron was under the command of Admiral Sir John Jervis and a contemporary record related: "...The superiority of naval skill, displayed in this celebrated action, struck all Europe with astonishment..." Indeed, it was a signal victory, as a result of which Jervis was made Lord St Vincent – while the youthful Nelson had first made his mark by his daring action in taking on in his small ship the largest ship then afloat, the *Santissima Trinidad*.

Sakhalin

A long, narrow island, once shared by Japan and Russia, now belonging entirely to the USSR. Location *Off the east coast of Siberia, between Tatar Strait, the Sea of Japan and the Sea of Okhotsk.* Area *29,700 square miles.* Map *4, F1.*

Sakhalin, some 560 miles long and 17–140 miles wide, is dominated by two parallel mountain ranges which rise to 6,604 feet at Mount Nevelskoi in the eastern range. Between them stretches the central valley of the Tym and Pronai rivers. The climate is subarctic with the mean temperature around freezing point; there are extensive forests with some agriculture in the central valley and the Susunai Valley in the south, where grain, potatoes, vegetables, beans, sugar beet and rice are grown. There are important coal deposits at Aleksandrovsk, Uglegorsk, Sinegorsk and Gornozavodsk; there is oil at Okha, and there are paper and pulp mills and fish canneries in the south. The island has extensive railroads, a network of highroads and some coastal shipping for communications. Most of the towns are along the coast: Aleksandrovsk and Okha in the north, Uglegorsk, Kholmsk and Korsakov in the south, Dolinsk and Yuzhno-Sakhalinsk in the Susunai Valley. The population – estimated at about 500,000 – is for the most part Russian, with some Ainu and Gilyaks in the south and Tungus and Nanai in the north. The Japanese population was largely repatriated after the Second World War.

Visited first in 1644 by Poyarkov, the Russian explorer, Sakhalin was colonized by the Japanese in the late eighteenth century; the Russians established their first military fort at Korsakov in 1853. The joint Japanese-Russian control ended in 1875 when Sakhalin became entirely Russian and was developed as a penal settlement. In 1905, after the Russo-Japanese War, Japan obtained the southern half of the island, called Karafuto; the northern half was also occupied by Japan from 1920 to 1925. At the end of the Second World War, Sakhalin passed entirely into the possession of the Soviet Union and was joined with the Kurile Islands to form an *oblast* or province.

At the end of the nineteenth century punishment by death was restricted to only one place in the vast Russian Empire – the penal settlement of Sakhalin. Between April and October, when the Siberian coast was free of ice, ships would sail from Vladivostok, bearing on board their mixed cargoes of thieves, nihilists, murderers and anarchists, destined – even after their sentences had expired – to remain on Sakhalin for the rest of their lives as "colonists." Their prisons were without locks or bars – for there was little chance of reaching freedom if they escaped.

After eight years of good behavior a murderer might be freed of his manacles and be given land to farm. But punishment for any transgression of the severe rules was prompt, cruel and often fatal. Floggings often killed a man with only four strokes of the three-thonged *plet*; habitual offenders were kept in unlit "kennels."

Although some prisoners escaped and terrorized the island's mountainous, forested interior, few got farther. One made his way to America and became a prosperous private detective, but was rearrested during an unwise business trip to Vladivostok and returned to a Sakhalin "kennel." Ten others were rescued from an open boat by an American whaler and landed at San Francisco – but within a year four were in prison and two others dead, one shot during an attempted robbery, the other hanged for murder.

Today Sakhalin has no prisoners, only "pioneers," and at its new city of Komsomolsk, founded in 1932 by 4,000 volunteers of the Young Communist League, there are large shipyards, steelworks and oil refineries – and even a ski school.

Salonika, Gulf of

An inlet of the Aegean, with the important port of Salonika at its head. Location *Northeastern Greece, between Thessaly and Macedonia, Aegean Sea.* Dimensions *70 miles long, 30–50 miles wide.* Map *9, F8–9.*

Bounded on its western side by the coast of northern Greece and on the east by the Chalcidice peninsula, the Gulf of Salonika has a magnificent entrance. On the mainland, mountains rise up; the massive peaks of Olympus, Ossa and Pelion dominate the skyline. On the other side lies the strange three-pronged peninsula with Cape Kassandra facing across to Ossa. Beyond the central prong are the romantic slopes of Mount Athos on the easternmost part of the peninsula.

The Gulf itself is comparatively shallow; no more than a depression or plain (similar to the plain of Larissa) into which the Aegean broke in prehistoric times. The floor of the Gulf shelves gently up towards the land and at its northernmost point it opens out round an easterly bend into the fine bay where the city of Salonika stands. The extensive new harbor testifies to the increasing importance of Salonika, the second city after Athens and the only other city in Greece of any major commercial interest.

The Gulf is subject to much the same winds and weather as the Aegean proper, except that at its northern end, near the city, the summer humidity may be heavy. The cooling northeasterly winds are absent more often than in the open sea. Caiques, coastal craft and fishing vessels of all kinds abound, for the seaborne trade of Salonika is considerable. In a day's sail one may meet modern motor vessels, lateen-sailed fishing craft and slab-sided wooden coasters.

The shores of the Gulf have seen much dramatic history in the making. Salonika, originally called Therma after the nearby hot springs, was renamed in 315 B.C. by Cassander, King of Macedonia, after his wife Thessalonica. From 146 B.C. it became the capital of the Roman province of Macedonia; in the Eastern Empire it was second only to Constantinople in size and importance. The great Roman Via Egnatia linked it both with the Bosporus and with Durazzo (Dyrrhachium) in Albania. The early Christian church of Salonika was the recipient of St Paul's two epistles to the Thessalonians. In 904 A.D. the Saracens occupied it; in 1185, the Sicilian Normans. While the Latin Empire of Constantinople lasted (from 1204 to 1261) its largest fief was Salonika. Baldwin I presented the city to Boniface, his rival, as a sort of bribe, but in 1222 it was seized by the despot of Epirus. Forty-four years later the Greek emperors of Nicaea got possession of Salonika and in 1261 restored it to the Byzantine Empire. The Turks under Sultan Murad I conquered it in 1387; in 1405 it was returned to the Byzantines, then held for seven years (1423–30) by Venice, until Murad II took it again and renamed it Selanik. Sephardic Jews founded a great settlement in Salonika, growing finally to 20 per cent of the population. (Almost the entire Jewish community was wiped out during the Nazi occupation and even their beautiful cemetery was despoiled.)

Here Kemal, the creator of modern Turkey, was born and in 1908 Salonika became the center of the Young Turk revolution. It became Greek after the Balkan Wars of 1912–13. In 1915 the Allies landed at the head of the Gulf and built up a base from which they broke out in 1918 and completed the defeat of the German and Bulgarian armies in the Balkans. From 1941 to 1944 Salonika was held by the Germans and half destroyed; but it has been largely rebuilt, and with its important rail, sea and air communications it is once again the second city of Greece.

Samoa

An archipelago, divided into independent Western Samoa and American Samoa. Location *South Pacific, in Polynesia.* Area *1,207 square miles.* Map *4, H8.*

Samoa is a 350-mile chain, consisting of three large islands, seven smaller ones and several uninhabited islets. The ten main islands are the summits of a submarine range of volcanic origin. The two largest islands – Savaii (703 square miles) and Upolu (430 square miles) – are built up around rugged mountains. Mauga Silisili on Savaii rises to 6,094 feet; Vaaifetu on Upolu to 3,608 feet. Both islands have bases of a succession of great lava flows. Mount Matavanu on Savaii erupted several times between 1905 and 1911 and devastated much of the island.

The climate is tropical but tempered by regular land and sea breezes. The wettest months are from December to March; the north coasts get an average annual rainfall of 120 inches, the south rather more. Except for areas covered by recent lava flows, tropical rain forest and dense vegetation covers the islands. The fauna is scanty; of the few birds about half are peculiar to Samoa; the *manu-mea*, the tooth-billed ground pigeon, represents a rare link with early forms of birdlife.

Samoa is believed to be the chief original Polynesian center in the Pacific. Its hardy seafaring people voyaged to many distant islands. Savaii (originally Savaiki) has been identified with Hawaiki, the legendary home of the New Zealand Maoris.

Jacob Roggeveen, the Dutch navigator, reached Samoa in 1722. Later, Louis Antoine de Bougainville called here; he was so impressed by the superb skill of the islanders in handling their outrigger canoes that he named the group "Navigators' Islands." In 1830 John Williams of the London Missionary Society brought teachers to Savaii. During the nineteenth century Britain, Germany and the United States became interested in the area. In 1899 Britain withdrew and Samoa was divided between Germany and the United States. In the American sector are Tutuila, Aunuu, the three islands of the Manua group, uninhabited Rose Island, and Swains Island, which was annexed by the United States in 1925. The German territory, consisting of Savaii, Upolu, Apolima, Manono and four uninhabited islands, was occupied by New Zealand at the beginning of the First World War. From 1946 to 1961 it was administered by New Zealand as the United Nations Trust Territory of Western Samoa; then, on January 1, 1962, it became independent – the first sovereign independent-state in Polynesia – with Fiame Mataafa as its Prime Minister.

The Samoans – about 141,000 of them – are all of pure Polynesian descent. The majority belong to the Samoan (London Missionary Society) Church, but there are also Roman Catholics, Methodists and Mormons. Missionaries were responsible for all education until recently, when government schools were established for higher grades. Many Samoans speak and write English as well as Samoan, a Polynesian language with a number of dialects. The basis of the social and economic life is the *aiga* or clan, ruled by a *matai*, a head man who may be either a chief or an orator. The Feleti School in American Samoa trains the sons of chiefs. There are about 500 Europeans and 8,000 part-white people in the islands of whom 5,000 are classed as Europeans; they are not subject to *matai* rule, neither have they any share in the communal land.

The main crops are taro, yams, arrowroot, breadfruit, sweet potatoes and fruit. Coconuts (for copra), cacao and bananas are also grown. The plantations, for which the Germans imported Chinese and Pacific island labor, were expropriated by the New Zealand government on behalf of the Samoans. But much of the islands is unsuitable for agriculture; in American Samoa about 70 per cent of the land is densely forested.

American Samoa is classified as an "unorganized and unincorporated American territory" under the control of the United States Department of the Interior. There is a governor, assisted by an advisory legislature or *fono* with a Senate and a House of Representatives.

Pagopago, on Tutuila, with a population of 4,000, is the administrative center for American Samoa. It possesses one of the best harbors in the South Pacific. Apia, on Upolu, is the chief town and only port for overseas shipping in Western Samoa. Nearby is Vailima, for many years the home of Robert Louis Stevenson.

Samothrace

A mountainous Greek island. Location *Northeast Aegean Sea, near the mouth of the Maritsa River, Thrace.* Area *71 square miles.* Map *9, G8.*

Far off the track of most travelers, rarely visited by steamships or cruise liners, the small mountainous island of Samothrace preserves its unspoiled charm. In this northern section of the Aegean it is by far the most distinctive landmark, its steep sides running up to the peak of Mount Phengari (5,249 feet), the highest peak of the Aegean, from which Poseidon, as Homer tells us in the *Iliad*, looked over the plain of Troy.

Samothrace has no real port; its sides are steep and practically unindented. One or two small coves to the south and east are suitable only for small craft or shallow-draft caiques; the open roadstead on the north coast is not always usable because of the prevailing northerly winds. The total population of the island is about 4,000; most of the men are peasant smallholders, fishermen or sponge-divers. The craggy character of the island and its lack of harbors has always made it more isolated than most places in the Greek archipelago and even in classical times it was of little economic or political importance.

The withdrawn, cut-off character of Samothrace, noticeable even today, was the probable reason for the survival, throughout ancient times, of the strange archaic worship of the Cabiri. These were underground gods of fertility whose rites and mysteries – like those of Eleusis – were divulged only to initiates. The origin of the worship has baffled modern scholars just as much as it perplexed the ancients. But the numerous worshippers of the Cabiri endowed the island with the reputation of a sacred place and it was preserved as a free state throughout the Greek internecine struggles.

The ancient capital, Palaeopolis, was situated just below the modern village on the north coast; its walls and temple outlines can be clearly traced. Here was the sanctuary of the mysterious Cabiri, where, inside cyclopean walls that remind one of Mycenae, the initiated took part in the rites of this ancient fertility cult.

The famous winged Nike (Victory) of Samothrace, now in the Louvre, was set up in 306 B.C. by the Greeks to celebrate a naval victory over the Egyptians off Cyprus.

Samothrace, like so many of the Aegean islands, is volcanic in origin and the hot sulphur springs on the north coast have been famous for thousands of years. They still attract a number of visitors from Greece and Turkey.

San Francisco Bay

One of the world's most famous and best-sheltered harbors. Location *Western California, Pacific Ocean.* Dimensions *About 50 miles long, 3-12 miles wide.* Maximum depth *100 feet.* Map *4, M3.*

Running parallel with the Californian coast as part of the great depression continued to the south by the Santa Clara Valley, San Francisco Bay is connected with the Pacific by the narrow Golden Gate. The southern shore of these straits, a narrow, hilly peninsula, is the site of the great city of San Francisco; across the bay to the east lie Berkeley, with its famous university, and such industrial cities as Oakland, Alameda and Richmond. In summer, cold Pacific-current fog lies heavy over the hot coast, seagulls scream overhead and sea lions snort and toss their heads on rocks a few yards offshore.

Sir Francis Drake, the first recorded European visitor, entered the Bay in 1579; it was sighted by Gaspar de Portalá in 1760 and entered again by Juan Manual de Ayala in 1775. Slowly, Spanish mission stations were established around the Bay – reposeful buildings still survive in some parts, carefully preserved as part of the American historical heritage. The first settlement in modern San Francisco was in 1776, when a Spanish presidio and a mission were established by Juan Bautista de Anza.

The neighboring village of Yerba Buena, established a little later, and named after an aromatic vine found growing on the site, became the most important settlement on the Bay; in 1846 it was captured from Mexico by Commodore John D. Sloat, and was renamed "San Francisco" the following year. In 1848 San Francisco was ceded by Mexico, together with the rest of Upper California, to the United States. In 1849 the California gold-rush brought it tremendous prosperity and a good deal of trouble and strife – robbery, white slavery, drug addiction, Tong wars and the rich, ribald life of the Barbary Coast, the harbor district.

The earthquake and disastrous fire of 1906 could not check the development of what has been called the most European city of the United States – a title San Francisco has fully earned, though her artists, her journalists and her beatniks are very much part of the native American scene. The city has also been noted for its generally cosmopolitan character; its famous China-

The Oakland Bay Bridge, San Francisco Bay

town is the largest outside Asia. San Francisco, indeed, is a city of international importance, a fact emphasized in 1945 when it was the home of the conference that drafted the United Nations Charter.

The bridges spanning sections of San Francisco Bay include the Oakland Bay Bridge, opened in 1936, and the Golden Gate Bridge, opened in 1937. These, and others, have greatly facilitated development. By 1939, in fact, the whole area of the Bay was heavily industrialized.

Yerba Buena (formerly Goat Island) is in the Bay, together with Angel and Treasure islands. But the most notable island in the Bay is undoubtedly Alcatraz, site of one of the most famous prisons in the world.

Santa Barbara Islands

A chain of eight islands and many islets, spread over 150 miles. Location *Along the southern California coast, from Point Conception to San Diego.* Map *4, N3.*

The Santa Barbara Islands are divided into a northern and a southern group, each with its own characteristics. The northern group, properly named Santa Barbara, is divided from the mainland by the Santa Barbara Channel (about 20–30 miles wide). It includes San Miguel (about eight miles long) with the reputed burial place of Juan Rodriguez Cabrillo, who discovered the whole archipelago in 1542; Santa Rosa, 17 miles long; Santa Cruz, 23 miles long; and the smallest, Anacapa. The Islands have also been called Channel Islands and in 1938 the Channel Islands National Monument (with a land area of about 1,120 acres and a total land-and-water area of 41.9 square miles) was established on Santa Barbara and Anacapa islands. The herds of basking sea lions, the many thousands of colorful birds, the brilliant flowers and the trees of Santa Cruz have made the Islands a favorite playground for the rich and not-so-rich alike. Fossils of various kinds have been found on some of the Islands.

The southern group (Santa Catalina) is separated from the Californian mainland by the San Pedro Channel and the Gulf of Santa Catalina. Its islands are San Nicholas (about nine miles long, with an airfield); a second Santa Barbara (about a mile and a half long); San Clemente (about 21 miles long, with two military airfields); and the most important, Santa Catalina (about 27 miles long).

Santa Catalina Island is 22 miles from Los Angeles and is part of Los Angeles county, easily reached by 'plane or steamer from Wilmington, the harbor of the great Californian city. There is a daily boat service and the island has become one of the leading resorts in the district, with fine bathing beaches, deep-sea fishing, a million-dollar casino and a golf course. Its principal center is the town of Avalon; the island was largely developed by William Wrigley, the chewing-gum millionaire.

Most of the islands in the group have large sheep ranches. Santa Catalina is proud of its Bird Park, with the thousands of rare tropical birds, and its Marine Gardens, which sightseers visit in glass-bottomed boats.

São Tomé Island

A volcanic island forming, with Principe, an overseas territory of Portugal. Location *Gulf of Guinea, 150 miles northwest of Cape Lopez, Africa.* Area *319 square miles.* Map *6, J6.*

São Tomé, or Saint Thomas, Island was one of the earliest Portuguese settlements in West Africa. The original Portuguese colonists of the late fifteenth century were followed by Spaniards, French and Genoese. The greatest attraction was the lucrative slave trade, in which the Island acted as a clearing house for slaves brought from the continent to await shipment to the Spanish colonies in America.

Shortly after the beginning of the sixteenth century the center of this trade in human flesh shifted to the African mainland as the European settlements developed there and the colonists of São Tomé began to realize the Island's agricultural possibilities. Sugar cane was introduced and by the middle of the century there were 60 highly prosperous sugar factories at work.

The sugar industry, however, collapsed suddenly, following a series of misfortunes: a revolt of the plantation slaves in 1574; the development of the rival Brazilian sugar industry; and the closing of the important markets in the Low Countries at the time of their rebellion against Spain. For nearly 250 years the Island was kept going by the slaving interests and as a victualling station on the Cape route to the east.

In the early nineteenth century agriculture made a spectacular comeback when cocoa and coffee were planted, and a century later nearly one sixth of the world's supply of cocoa came from São Tomé. But by 1908 reports had reached Europe of conditions of near-slavery among the Bantu imported from Angola to work on the plantations. European importers, led by the Quaker firm of Cadbury in Britain, declined to accept any more of the Island's cocoa production. Working conditions improved, but the trade was irrevocably lost to other West African countries.

São Tomé is roughly oval in shape, 30 miles long and 20 miles broad. Volcanic in origin, it rises in the center to 6,640 feet, in the Pico de São Tomé. Much of the higher part of the Island is forested; one of the native trees is the cinchona from which quinine is obtained. Woods also cover the lower slopes where they have not been cleared for coffee plantations, while along the coast the cacao plantations sometimes give way to groves of coconut palms.

The Island has about 56,000 inhabitants, of whom nearly half are African plantation workers from the mainland; the remainder are mostly people of mixed European and African origin.

Sardinia

The second largest island in the Mediterranean, with valuable natural resources and a long, eventful history. Location *West of Italy and south of Corsica.* Area *9,196 square miles.* Map *7, D8.*

Sardinia is 166 miles long and 80 miles wide; lying some 200 miles west of Naples, it is separated from Corsica by the narrow Bonifacio Strait, and is certainly the least well known of the larger Mediterranean islands. Lifting its granite skeleton against the Tyrrhenian Sea, mountainous and volcanic, it is also the least inviting to the casual eye. The Sardinians have been called "dour" by visiting foreigners and "primitive" by their sophisticated Italian neighbors. The craggy cliffs that fall precipitously to the sea on almost all sides, the lack of good ports and the stark nature of much of the interior have always set Sardinia apart from the more fertile and romantic Mediterranean islands, such as Sicily and Majorca. Its beauty is no less for being not so obvious; but travel in the island means more discomfort than elsewhere in the Mediterranean.

The Sardinians are among the most interesting of the Mediterranean peoples. They have been subjected less to admixture of foreign blood than have the people of any other area. Short, stocky, a mixture of agricultural peasants and shepherds, they have a fierce pride. In the mountainous regions such as Barbagia, the shepherds despise the farmers of the valleys. Barbagia is still afflicted with banditry and the sad legacy of the blood feud or vendetta. Italian ethnologists recently made the interesting discovery that the natives of Barbagia have been in continuous revolt against the State for over 2,000 years. Despite many efforts, the Romans were unable to tame them and every country which has since held sovereignty over Sardinia has failed to extend its rule over the Barbagians. Within recent years the Italian Republic lost over thirty *carabinieri* in attempts to eradicate the local vendettas.

To the stranger, however, these mountain people can be hospitable and courteous. Their manners, folk songs, customs and dress are unique even in Sardinia where old-fashioned ways have lingered longer than anywhere else in the Mediterranean. Many of the shepherds still wear short black kilts made of wool with red waistcoats and black coats. In other districts, notably in the north at Oschiri, traditional costume is still worn and the peasant women often have magnificent necklaces and earrings of gold to complement their elaborate dresses.

Cagliari, the most important town and port in the island, lies on the southern coast, at the head of the Gulf that bears its name. The city shows architectural evidence of its many occupations: Romanesque churches dating from the Pisan period; Spanish Gothic from the Aragonese; and eighteenth-century baroque from the suzerainty of the Dukes of Savoy. In summer the climate is almost African and the lagoons on each side of the town shimmer with mirages. About one tenth of the population (about 1,050,000 under the most recent census) live in the capital; the other important centers are Iglesias, Carloforte, Tempio Pausania, Alghero, Olbia, Sassari and Macomer.

Malaria, once the scourge of the island, is almost completely under control; only a few areas of the coastal swampland are still afflicted with the mosquito. As the communications and the industries – particularly mining, for the island is rich in zinc, lead, manganese, lignite, antimony, molybdenum, copper, anthracite, barite, kaolin, talc and steatite – are steadily developed, Sardinian customs and ways of life are changing. It is only in the mountain areas that they survive and even there they are on the decline. Cattle, horses, donkeys and mules are raised in the pasturelands; the donkey is a common form of transport. Stags and wild boars are quite common; the mouflon or wild sheep is still to be found. The Sardinians use the sheep for milk and their sheep's cheese is one of the island's delicacies. There are many cork oaks and the island is the leading Italian producer of cork. There is only one real river in the island, the Tirso, but some of the mountain streams contain excellent trout. The coastal lagoons teem with fish, and tunny are caught in large numbers in the region of Cape Spartivento in the south.

Phoenicians, Carthaginians and Romans ruled the island in pre-Christian times; there was a series of Saracen invasions from the eighth to the eleventh centuries. Genoa and Pisa competed in a series of long and bloody wars for supremacy; from 1720 the island formed, with Savoy, Piedmont and Nice, the Kingdom of Sardinia under the House of Savoy; Liguria was added in 1814, and it was the sovereign of Sardinia who became King of united Italy in 1861. The island fell quickly to the Allies in the Second World War, after Italy's capitulation.

Sargasso Sea

A large tract of comparatively calm water in the midst of clockwise ocean currents, much of it covered by the Sargassum weed. Location *North Atlantic, extending from the West Indies to the Azores.* Map *6, C4.*

More picturesque nonsense has been written about the Sargasso Sea, perhaps, than about any other stretch of water. Jules Verne, in *Twenty Thousand Leagues Under the Sea*, wrote of "trunks of trees, from the Andes or the Rocky Mountains, floated down the Amazon or the Mississippi; numerous spars, the remains of keels or ships' bottoms, side planks stove in and so weighted with shells and barnacles that they could not rise above the surface of the ocean..." The American writer Thomas Janvier wrote of "a vast ruinous congregation of wrecks so far extending that it was as though all the wrecked ships of the world were lying there in a miserable desolate company. . . dead men at their posts on abandoned warships. . . skeletons of slaves still in their shackles. . ." Other writers added their touches by speaking of enormous crabs and gigantic octopods, horrible squid-men, reefs and shoals.

In reality the Sargasso Sea is a calm, sunny region of lazily drifting weeds in the North Atlantic. Columbus ran into it on his first transatlantic crossing, just west of the Azores. The weed increased in abundance until his men began to worry that they were in coastal waters and would run aground. But the bottom was almost three miles under them and they came through easily. The legend of the menace of the Sargassum weed has survived the centuries. Alain Bombard, who sailed alone on a raft across the Atlantic in 1952, was reported to have planned his trip to avoid the Sargasso because it was "a major navigational hazard, a terrible trap where plant filaments and seaweed grip vessels in an unbreakable net."

There is plenty of weed but it floats in relatively small patches with open water in between. Yet the Sargasso Sea is truly remarkable – a huge, slowly rotating eddy, one of the great deserts of the sea.

The large area covered by the weed varies somewhat. In late summer it is a large oval, measuring 1,000 by 2,000 miles; its long axis is more or less east-west. But the Sargasso water system covers a much larger area, with the major Atlantic currents as its boundaries. These give the entire water mass a slow clockwise rotation. Dr John H. Ryther described the Sargasso Sea as a shallow lens of warm water floating on the distinctly colder waters of the main ocean, sharply separated from these colder waters by a zone of rapidly changing temperature. This appears to be unique; and so is the life of the Sargasso.

We do not know where the Sargassum weed comes from. Its name was given to it by Portuguese sailors who thought that its air-bladder floats looked like the small grapes they called *salgazo*. At one time it was thought that it came perhaps from the coastal areas of the West Indies where storms had torn it from its beds. Dr Albert E. Parr, Director of the American Museum of Natural History in New York, made a thorough study of the weeds in the early nineteen-thirties. He found that 90 per cent of them represented two species that are naturally floating and never found attached to rocks. He estimated the standing weed crop at several million tons, far too much to be maintained by castaways from coastal beds. The weeds themselves, adapting themselves to their environment, grow and reproduce by budding; they are vigorously healthy, often showing new leaves and young shoots. The mystery is still unsolved; though the weed must have arrived in the Sargasso Sea a very long time ago, becoming through the slow process of evolutionary adaptation a native of the open waters.

There is little upwelling or mixing to renew its fertility, and so the lazily rotating Sargasso has a rate of plankton production that is only about one third of the average. So there are comparatively few larger marine animals which need plankton to live on. Yet even deserts have their life forms. Almost every clump of drifting weed has its colony of small fish, crabs, shrimps, octopuses and many other creatures, each marvelously adapted to living on and about the weed that gives it sanctuary. If they lost their grip, some would uncontrollably sink into the depths to perish.

In some cases the animals have taken on the appearance of the weed – there are weedlike fish and crabs, sea slugs with folds of skin that enable them to blend perfectly with their surroundings. Some species of worms build houses of lime in which they float with the weeds, taking food from the passing water. There is even one air-breathing inhabitant – *Halobates*, the water strider. This adventurer runs over the sea surface on six long, hairy legs, using the weed as a resting place.

To the depths of the Sargasso mature eels come from Europe, the eastern rivers of the United States and from the Mediterranean countries, to mate and spawn and die; and from the Sargasso the tiny larvae, as transparent as glass and as flat as leaves, set out for their great journeys back to the rivers, where they are caught in their millions and sold as elvers, or "glass eels," for human consumption.

But in spite of all this lively community, the Sargasso Sea is a sparsely populated wilderness, a strange oceanic desert created by the pattern of wind and currents.

Scilly Isles

A small archipelago off western England, famous for

its flowers and rock formations. Location *Cornwall, at the entrance to the English Channel, Atlantic Ocean.* Area *6.3 square miles.* Map *8, C5.*

The Scillies are scattered over an ocean that quickly becomes angry and dangerous. Most of them are bare (or covered with a low scrub) and desolate. All of them, low on the Atlantic, are extensions of the granite of western Cornwall, hard and tough, ready to jag or scrape the bottom off ships; though the bigger islands surround a shallow, gapped lagoon and are themselves partly surrounded by beaches of the whitest sand. All the islands are exposed; and though the climate is mild, flowers for the city markets can be raised only in small plots with windbreaks of stone or of bushes such as euonymus or pittosporum whose waxy leaves resist wind and salt.

There are about 40 islands in the group, five of which are now inhabited: Tresco, which in Cornish means the "Homestead of the Elder Trees;" St Agnes, which is a Norse name meaning "Agni's Ness or Headland;" Bryher, hilliest of the five, meaning in Cornish the "Hill of the Hens;" St Martin's (which was called Brechiek in ancient times); and St Mary's, the largest of the islands and the only one to contain a small town. Long ago the whole group, or most of it, formed a single island, which has been gradually divided and subdivided by a combination of subsidence and erosion. This single ancient island was inhabited; many of the crests and hill tops are capped with bronze-age barrows and burial chambers, half buried in bracken and brambles. On St Mary's, at one point, the four uprights of a burial chamber show clearly in the middle of a road. On the long beach flanking the quay of St Martin's (which many regard as the most attractive of the inhabited islands) little square stone chests of ancient burials are sometimes visible when wind and tide combine to lower the sea level to an unusual degree. Such areas must have been high above the sea, four, three or perhaps only two thousand years ago. The loneliest and in some ways the most magnificent burial place in the Scilly Isles is a tomb overlooking the Atlantic on the highest point of uninhabited White Island, which enjoys an orchestra of seals, wind and waves.

Some of the other islands were once inhabited: Tean, named after an obscure Celtic saint or hermit; St Helen's, where the ruins of an ancient Celtic monastery of beehive huts are hidden under the scrub; and Samson, where the Celtic missionary of the sixth century, St Samson of Dol, may have lived for a while in retreat. On smaller islands, neither inhabited nor habitable, kitchen-middens of limpet-shells and fish-bones of the prehistoric era have been found.

There still are left the rocks, the innumerable crags and jags, few of which can be dignified by the name of islands; above all, the grim assembly of the Western Rocks, dark with swaying weed, which have accounted for many of the worst wrecks around the British Isles. Though wrecks are no longer so common, the five graveyards of the inhabited islands all have their memorials, English, German or of other nationalities, to the dead of Scillonian storms, fogs and reefs.

Any suspicion that the group as a whole or the individual islands are scenically dull or monotonous would be quite wrong. The light is superb, reflected from a huge bowl of sky; colors are clearly revealed; sandy lanes and paths wind among the granite. There are downs, little valleys and a variety in the native vegetation from bluebells to yellow lichens and the brown acres of autumnal bracken. The tide ebbs, and the whole shape of the islands changes as the beaches extend and the sand flats appear. The tide returns, and the islands are again afloat on the enormous ocean.

Flower plots and hedges add pattern to the landscape; there are scattered bulb fields, and a great subtropical garden maintained behind windbreaks of pine at Tresco Abbey. The houses – most of them low cottages of granite – blend into the landscape. Despite centuries of occupation and a present population of nearly 2,000, despite farmers, old cars, visitors and motor-launches, the predominant impression made by the Scillies – especially the Off Islands (as the inhabited islands, except St Mary's, are called) – is one of an intermediacy, wild and free, between the air and the water.

Scoresby Sound

A deep inlet and fjord system of Greenland. Location *Eastern Greenland, Greenland Sea.* Length *About 200 miles.* Map *5, D11.*

First charted and explored by William Scoresby, junior, in his *Baffin* in 1822, when he "ventured to name this capacious inlet in honor of my father," Scoresby Sound is an immense water system. From its mouth, the Sound extends about 70 miles to the east but from the mouth to the end of the northwestern arm the distance is almost three times as great. Numerous fjords branch off to west-southwest, west and northwest to the edge of the Greenland icecap, and many glaciers debouch into it.

Scoresby found along the coasts remains of ancient Eskimo habitations, a few white hares, numerous insects (mainly mosquitoes) and several species of butterflies, together with reindeer and a bee's nest. He also discovered a new species of mouse, named *Mus groenlandica*, numerous birds and about 40 species of plants. He found strange currents and tides which made steering extremely difficult.

Basalts and schists line the often steep walls of the Sound, which also contains Milne Land, an island about 70 miles long and 25 miles wide, rising to 6,234 feet, and several smaller islands. On the north side of the mouth of the Sound there is the small settlement of Scoresby.

Sea Islands

A chain of low-lying islands in the Atlantic. Location *Between the mouths of the Santee and St John rivers, off the coast of South Carolina, Georgia and Florida.* Map *1, E10.*

The Sea Islands look from the air like huge flat boats moored alongside an immensely long dock – for causeways and bridges connect all the important ones to the mainland. On the Atlantic side they are fringed with sandy beaches upon which the long breakers roll; landward they are marshy except where the Intracoastal Waterway cuts through them. Some are forested and some have been set aside as refuges for wildlife and state parks. A few have popular resorts; a number are uninhabited. Those who live on them the year round divide their time between fishing and farming.

The Spaniards came to the Sea Islands first, setting up missions and garrisons. But they had to yield to the English who, in turn, departed after the American Revolution. Early in the nineteenth century plantations were established, especially on the South Carolina islands of St Helena and Port Royal, and the famous, delicately long-stapled Sea Island cotton was developed, with rice as a second crop. After the Civil War, newly-freed slaves were given land confiscated from its Southern owners; the Sea Islands of Carolina still have a largely Negro population. About 40 years ago the boll weevil devastated the cotton fields, and a more varied farming system, including corn, peanuts, potatoes and poultry, was gradually developed. Sea Island shrimps and oysters are also now shipped in great quantities to the mainland.

The principal islands in South Carolina are Folly, James, Johns, Edisto, Daufuskie, Hilton Head, Hunting, Kiawah, Wadamalaw, Ladies, Parris, Port Royal and St Helena islands. St Helena is one of the largest of the Sea Islands; lying between St Helena and Port Royal sounds, it is about 15 miles long and 3–5 miles wide. A highway connects it to Ladies Island in the west; this continues to Port Royal Island and the mainland; another bridge leads to Hunting Island in the east. St Helena was discovered and named by Spanish explorers early in the sixteenth century. Port Royal is another important island in the group, about 13 miles long and 7 miles wide, linked to the mainland by railway and highway bridges. Its two main centers are the town of Port Royal, a well-known tourist and fishing center (mainly for shrimps) and an excellent harbor, and Beaufort, a year-round tourist and resort place, the second oldest town in South Carolina. Founded in 1711, Beaufort was held by the Union forces from November, 1861, to the end of the Civil War; today, with a good harbor, it is prosperous with canning, processing and shipping shrimps and oysters. It has many fine old buildings, among them an arsenal built in 1795. Burton and Seabrook villages are also on Port Royal; the Intracoastal Waterway passes to the east and south of the Island. Parris is just south of Port Royal; just over five miles long, it is occupied by the training camp of the United States Marine Corps. Originally it was the scene of an unsuccessful settlement by Jean Ribaut and his French Huguenot companions in 1562.

The Sea Islands which form part of Georgia

are named Tybee, Wilmington, Skidaway, Ossabaw, St Catherines, Sapelo, St Simons, Jekyll and Cumberland. Of these, Cumberland is the largest in the entire chain, about 23 miles long and 1–5 miles wide. St Simons, lying off the coast, at the mouth of the Altamaha River, is about 13 miles long and 3–7 miles wide, with its resort village connected by a causeway to the mainland. On the west coast is the Fort Frederica National Monument, established in 1945, which includes the ruins of the English fort built between 1736 and 1754 by James Oglethorpe. Not far away is the scene of the Battle of the Bloody Marsh in which the English under Oglethorpe routed the Spanish invaders, who fell into a disastrous ambush. It was after this battle (July 7, 1742) that the Spaniards gave up their effort to regain the Sea Islands; it also had a decisive effect in the struggle for the control of the present-day territory of the southeastern United States. Jekyll, another of the Georgia Sea Islands, about 7 miles long and 1–2 miles wide, is still covered with virgin forest. In the days of the great plantations it was used as a winter resort; since 1947 it has been a State Park.

Florida's share in the Sea Islands is Amelia, between the mouths of St Marys and Nassau rivers, about 20 miles northeast of Jacksonville. About 15 miles long and 4 miles wide, it forms part of Nassau county; the salt marshes separating it from the mainland are bridged by road and railroad. It was first settled by white men in 1735 under Oglethorpe. In 1783 it became part of Spanish East Florida and in 1821, when Spain ceded Florida to the United States, it passed into American hands. Like most of the other Sea Islands, it was captured by Federal forces in 1862. Its northern part is occupied by the Fort Clinch State Park and a lighthouse.

Selvagens

A group of small, rocky, barren islets with surrounding reefs. Location *Atlantic Ocean, about 180 miles south of Madeira.* Map *6, F3.*

In winter the lonely Selvagens or Salvage Islands, half way between the Canary Islands and Madeira, are deserted save for prowling crabs, occasional lizards, and an abundance of cockroaches, mice, rabbits and sea-birds. Night and day their wild, melancholy cries fill the air: squeaks, groans, hiccups from petrels (the tiny Storm Petrel, which also purrs in its burrow, and the larger Frigate Petrel, with a white underside), and piercing, bloodcurdling screams from both Great and Little shearwaters. These are all mid-ocean species which come here in thousands from their roamings and have to nest in relays – so keen is competition for the suitable burrow – or scuffle despondently among fleshy, daisy-flowered *Mesembryanthemums* which, in places sparsely, elsewhere in dense carpets, cover the jagged lava rocks.

Centuries of such bird life have left deep deposits of guano, which accumulates, paradoxically, only where the climate is so dry that few plants can survive. The lack of water is the problem of the Selvagens, the chief reason why they have never been settled (though a penal colony was once tried by the Portuguese, who own them). Nonetheless, guano is valuable and each summer it is quarried with picks and shovels, broken, shifted, sacked and carried to the piles down by the water's edge where each month it is collected by a boat from Madeira. It is a rough life for the guano harvesters, who live in tents or caverns in the lava, get up at dawn, and have little to eat except salt fish – or fresh when it can be caught – with rice, olive oil, dried food and young sea-birds. Then comes winter, the last men pack up, and wild nature takes possession again for a few months.

Seychelles

An archipelago in the Indian Ocean. Location *700 miles northeast of Madagascar.* Area *About 156 square miles.* Map *10, C6.*

The Seychelles, numbering 92 islands and islets, are in the center of a huge submerged bank, extending over about 12,000 square miles, and have an average depth of 150–200 feet of water around them. The principal islands of the group are Mahé (56 square miles), Praslin (9,700 acres), Silhouette (4,900 acres), La Digue (2,500 acres), Curieuse (900 acres), Félicité (689 acres), North Island (525 acres), St Anne (500 acres), Providence (500 acres), Frigate (700 acres), Denis (340 acres), Cerf (290 acres), and Bird or Sea

Cow Island (160 acres). The dependencies include the Amirantes, Alphonse, Bijoutier, St François, St Pierre, the Cosmoledo group, Astove, Assumption, Coëtivy, Aldabra and the Farquhar Islands with a total area of about 156 square miles. The population is about 42,000.

Though only four degrees south of the equator, the islands are refreshed by the southeast trade winds in winter (from May to November) and the northwest monsoons in the summer. The rainfall is fairly heavy, about 90 inches in the year, most of it falling between November and April. The climate is healthy, with a low death-rate and a high, steady birth-rate.

Extremely fertile, the islands produce coconuts, cinnamon, patchouli and vanilla. They are, however, rugged and mountainous, rising to 2,993 feet in the Morne Seychellois on Mahé and are supposed to be the peaks of the legendary Gondwana continent of the Mesozoic era. Aldabra, one of the dependencies, about 630 miles from Mahé, is famous for its gigantic land tortoises; the unique double coconut, *Coco de Mer*, grows in Mahé, and in even larger quantities in Praslin.

The population is largely descended from European settlers and their African slaves – together with the descendants of liberated slaves who were brought to the Seychelles from Mauritius in the eighteenth century. They are Roman Catholics and speak French or a Creole patois.

When the Portuguese discovered the archipelago in 1505 it was uninhabited. It remained for over 200 years a pirates' base, until the French occupied it in 1742. In 1794 the Seychelles were captured by a single British ship and were finally assigned to Great Britain in 1810. By Letters Patent in 1903 they were erected into a separate colony. They are governed by a Governor assisted by an Executive Council of four *ex officio* members and four unofficial members appointed by the Government together with a Legislative Council, partly elected and partly appointed.

Shetland Islands

The northernmost archipelago of the British Isles, consisting of one large and over 100 small islands and islets. Location *Scotland, about 55 miles northeast of the Orkneys.* Area *550.5 square miles.* Map *7, E3.*

The *Ultima Thule* of the ancient geographers, which they spoke of as the northernmost land of the world, is most plausibly to be identified with the Shetlands; for beyond Muckle Flugga, one mile north of Unst, there lies nothing but the Arctic ice.

Scandinavian in background and tradition – Norse was spoken on Foula up to the beginning of the nineteenth century – the Shetlands still cling to their hearty traditions, of which Up-Helley-A', the New Year fire festival, is only one example. The Shetlanders inhabit a group of islands, islets and skerries which show, in more pronounced form, many of the features which characterize the Orkneys. Split by the long salt-water voes (bays or creeks), they can boast of no land more than three miles from the sea. Relatively isolated, even in the age of air travel, they are self-sufficient, depending more than their southern neighbors on fishing, crofting and the Shetland sheep.

Though more windswept than the Orkneys, with fewer trees, with a position 100 miles farther north, giving a longer summer day and a more spectacular view of the Northern Lights, the Shetlands gain the same advantage from the North Atlantic Drift, which governs their wet, warm climate.

Only 29 of the Islands are inhabited and the total population is less than 30,000. The most northerly of the group lie farther north than some parts of Greenland. Mainland, the largest island, accounts for 378 square miles of the total area, as well as for the majority of the people. More than 4,000 live in Lerwick, the capital, where the old houses still face the sea and the main street follows what was once the natural coastline.

To the ornithologist and archeologist, the Shetlands are of great interest. The great promontory of Hermaness, on Unst – to which, with Foula, the great skua has returned as a British breeding species – has been designated a nature reserve. So has Noss, where Shetland ponies are bred and where the great rock wall of the Noup, alive with sea-birds of almost every breed, offers a striking sight. Fair Isle is famous for hand-knitted hosiery and Unst for the finest of the Shetland woolen work.

Archeologically, the Shetlands are unique in possessing Jarlshof, one of the most remarkable sites in Europe. Here, beneath the ruins of the sixteenth-century house at Sumburgh – called "Jarlshof" because it was described thus by Walter Scott in *The Pirate* – the living quarters of three separate civilizations have been excavated, the earliest dating back more than 2,500 years. Second in interest only to Jarlshof – which lies incongruously on the verge of the Shetland airport – is the Pictish broch on Mousa island, a circular tower 45 feet high, the finest example of its kind in the British Isles.

Yet above all it is their remoteness and the Scandinavian background that combine to make the Shetlands unique in Britain. Foula is probably the loneliest inhabited island in Britain, while Unst, Yell, Trondra, Bressay, Whalsay and Papa Stour carry in their very names mystery and majesty.

Sicily

The largest Mediterranean island, an autonomous region of the Republic of Italy. Location *Between southwest Italy and Cape Bon, Africa.* Area *9,831 square miles.* Map *7, E9.*

A triangular island of many moods and many faces, separated from the mainland by the narrow Strait of Messina, Sicily varies immensely from one part to another, geologically, climatically and even socially. About 180 miles long and 120 miles wide, it combines many types of scenery, from mountainous uplands to fertile plains, and has played a vital part in Mediterranean civilization from as far back as the eighth century B.C.

The long, hot coastline of the south, with its ports of Agrigento, Porto Empedocle, Sciacca and Mazara del Vallo, is more backward and primitive than the north, where the modern harbor of Palermo dominates its noble bay. Both north and south coasts differ again from the east, where there are fewer harbors and where the influence of ancient Greece is still apparent. Syracuse, one of the finest and most beautiful harbors of Sicily, still shows evidence of its classical past in the famous Greek theater, and in the ruins of temples and private buildings. Messina, devastated in the terrible earthquake of 1908, has been rebuilt as a modern commercial city – resembling Catania with its busy harbor backed by eighteenth-century buildings of volcanic stone.

The people of Sicily are a mixture of many races. In places there is strong evidence of Moorish blood (the Moors occupied the island for 263 years), while in certain villages there are pockets of Greek and Albanian stock. Normans, Germans, British and French have all at one time dominated the island's affairs and this is apparent not only in the architecture but in the appearance of many of the inhabitants. Sicily is one of the few places in the Mediterranean where a Celtic type with red hair and blue eyes is to be found – often in the same district or village where others betray their Saracen origin by their looks and mannerisms. The Sicilian dialect itself shows marked and curious differences from Italian and is almost incomprehensible to the mainlanders. And equally mysterious, though far more widespread, is the organization of the Mafia, which grew from a patriotic underground organization, the resistance of the underprivileged against the rich, into a world-wide criminal conspiracy that has spread its tentacles wherever Italians live, from Egypt to the United States.

With its fertile plains, its fine natural harbors and its gentle climate, Sicily has always attracted the attention of whatever power was dominant in the Mediterranean. The original inhabitants, the Sikels, were soon dispossessed of the more desirable harbors by the Phoenicians, whose main colony was at Panormus (Palermo). Then came Carthaginians at Lilybaeum (Marsala) and Drepanum (Trapani), followed by the Greeks, whose many colonies included Syracuse, Catania, Zancle (Messina), Gela and Selinus. The Peloponnesian War largely centered around these colonies and it was the disastrous Athenian expedition to Syracuse that ultimately led to the collapse of the Attic empire. The whole of the island became a Roman colony in 241 B.C. and passed to Byzantium in 535 A.D. After the fall of Rome, Goths and Vandals also occupied Sicily for a while. Then came the Saracens, to be dispossessed in turn by the Normans in the eleventh century. Germans, Angevins and Aragonese in succession made the island part of their domains until, in 1738, it came under the Bourbons of Naples, forming the Kingdom of the Two Sicilies. It was in Sicily that Garibaldi hoisted the flag of

Italian unity in 1860, freeing the island from Bourbon misrule, and next year it became part of Italy.

It never fully yielded to the Fascist regime, and when in July, 1943, the Allies made their landings from North Africa it was occupied after less than a month of sharp fighting. It was used as a springboard for the invasion of Italy itself. After the war Sicily was given considerable administrative autonomy under the Republican constitution of 1947; but its economic problems are still one of the major tasks of post-war Italy and most of its population of over 4,000,000 still live in appalling poverty.

But light industry, mining and drilling for oil may one day make Sicily the richest island in the Mediterranean. Until then it depends largely on agriculture and fishing. It produces excellent wines, among them the famous Marsala. Olives, almonds, figs and peaches are also grown.

Singapore

An important strategic and commercial center. Location *Off the southern tip of the Malay Peninsula.* Area *224 square miles.* Map *10, H6.*

Singapore is the name given both to the island at the tip of the Malay Peninsula – to which it is joined by a causeway over Johore Strait – and to the great city and thriving port on the island's south coast. The total population of one of the youngest states in the world is more than 1,500,000, of which nearly 1,000,000 live in the city proper. City of the Lion (Singapura) is an appropriate symbol of this creation of Sir Stamford Raffles (1781–1826), who in 1819 persuaded the East India Company to buy what was then mere jungle and swamp – though there had been a prosperous port here in the thirteenth and fourteenth centuries, until it was sacked by the Javanese around 1377. Raffles himself spoke of it as a "child of my own. But for my Malay studies I should have hardly known that such a place existed. Not only the European but the Indian world was ignorant of it." Its acquisition gained Britain access to the China coast, shortened the Far Eastern voyage by 1,000 miles and restricted Dutch influence to the Indonesian archipelago. The cutting of the Suez Canal and the building of a large naval base in Johore Strait made it a strategic outpost of great importance and prompted an excess of confidence which was to prove sadly illusory when the Japanese swept down in the Second World War. Two of Britain's great battleships, the *Prince of Wales* and the *Repulse,* were sunk off the coast of Malaya, and after a brief, bitter struggle Singapore fell to the invader in February, 1942, not to be regained until the end of the Pacific War.

The occupation was deeply humiliating to the former white rulers and undoubtedly paved the way to independence. This was achieved in 1959, after 140 years of British colonial rule. An agreement signed in London in April, 1957, provided for the constitution of a state with full internal self-government and the creation of a Singapore citizenship; with a Malayan-born head of state, representing the Queen, a cabinet of nine members presided over by a Prime Minister and a fully elected Legislative Assembly of 51 members. The British Commissioner remains responsible for defense and other external affairs other than cultural and commercial matters.

Singapore is a predominantly Chinese city with a considerable intermingling of Tamils, Pakistanis, Sikhs, Indonesians and Eurasians. From the tufted islets of Keppel Harbour to the wild but picturesque heights of Fort Canning, it is a handsome place of wide streets, green lawns and large white buildings. There are also adventurous modernities, such as the Cathay "skyscraper," and several post-war housing developments. But most of Singapore city is violently overcrowded, the arcaded streets loaded with Chinese ideograms, the small rooms of the houses subdivided into even smaller; a city of the Chinese death-house and the hideous Hindu temple, of monsoon drains and tri-shaws, of open-air eating places and warring secret societies – a city where mah-jong and opium exist side by side with cricket and the Club. Its suburbs, Tanglyn or Katong, tend to be limpidly genteel, with bougainvillea and frangipani surrounding white verandas.

The island, 27 miles long and 14 miles wide, is mostly low-lying. There is little agriculture, and the principal industries are rubber milling and manufacture and tin smelting.

Skagerrak

An inlet of the North Sea, an important Scandinavian navigational route. Location *Between Norway and Jutland (Denmark).* Dimensions *150 miles long, 80–90 miles wide.* Maximum depth *Over 2,000 feet.* Map *7, E4–F4.*

The Skagerrak runs in a northeasterly direction from the North Sea, terminating in Oslo Fjord to the north, and in the Kattegat to the south. Its major importance lies in being a shipping route to Oslo and Copenhagen and as the entrance to the Baltic. It is free of ice and navigation is possible at all seasons of the year, which makes the Skagerrak of vital interest to all the Scandinavian countries.

On the Norwegian coast the scenery is most impressive, with high cliffs falling sheer to the sea and the mountains behind them shining in the brisk northern air. The comparatively low coast of Denmark is less striking but has a pleasant beauty in spring or summer with green fields, farmhouses and cottages set in an ordered landscape.

The tidal system of the Skagerrak is determined by the third of the North Sea tides, the comparatively weak movement which runs up the Strait of Dover along the Norwegian coast. It is nullified to some extent in the Skagerrak by the outward flow of fresh water from the Baltic, and the salinity of the area is considerably lower than that of the North Sea. The chief navigational danger is the squalls which descend in winter with terrific force from the Norwegian mountains.

It was off the entrance of the Skagerrak that the most momentous sea battle of the First World War was fought – the Battle of Jutland, in 1916.

Skye

The largest of the Inner Hebrides, famous for its rugged scenery and Jacobite associations. Location *Inverness, Scotland.* Area *670 square miles (including adjoining small islands).* Map *8, C2.*

The Cuillin Hills dominate Skye by reputation, though topographically they fill only one small southwestern corner of the island; their name has become almost synonymous with the "winged isle," "the misty isle" and the various other titles given to Skye. The island is separated from the Scottish mainland by the narrow Sound of Sleat, Loch Alsh and the Inner Sound. It is separated from the Outer Hebrides by the Little Minch and the Sea of the Hebrides.

Skye is deeply indented by sea-lochs and inlets, and no point is more than five miles from the coast. Portree, on the east coast, protected by the island of Raasay, is the capital and principal town. Although still the headquarters of a fishing fleet, it lives largely (as does the rest of the island) on the prosperous summer business of showing visitors where Prince Charlie or Flora Macdonald landed, sheltered or rested and on providing for the mountaineers who visit the Cuillins.

Relics of the bloody feuds fought by the Macdonalds and the Macleods and other clans are scattered throughout the island. There are Dunvegan Castle with its Fairy Flag, Prince Charlie's Cave, Flora Macdonald's grave, and many others. But most visitors come to Skye to take a quiet shudder at "the most savage scenery in Britain." In the north rises the fantastic mass of rock pinnacles, towers and spires known as the Quirang, while a few miles to the south lies the Storr, 2,360 feet high, with its isolated 160-foot black obelisk known as the Old Man of Storr.

The Black Cuillins, different in geological history as in color from the Red Cuillins lying to the east across Glen Sligachan, are the only British range whose summits are accessible only to those who scramble or climb. The main ridge, eight miles long, never drops below 2,500 feet and culminates in Sgur Alasdair, 3,309 feet high; its complete traverse, first made in 1911, involves three recognized rock-routes and some 10,000 feet of ascent and descent. Climbing in the Cuillins started in the eighteen-sixties, and throughout the last third of the nineteenth century provided climbers who had learned their craft on the Continent with the only virgin summits in the British Isles. The last, Sgur Coire an Lochain, was not climbed until 1896.

The unique quality of mountaineering in the Cuillins is given by the texture of the gabbro rock, its roughness, "absurdly and painfully adhesive," allowing apparently impossible routes to be negotiated comparatively easily. For the mountaineer, the glory of the Cuillins lies not only in the genuine mountain character of the peaks but also in the great seascapes spread out below, the sight of the distant Hebrides, and the fine foregrounds of Loch Brittle and Loch Coruisk.

Skye has little cultivable land but a moist and mild climate; the chief occupations of its 10,000 inhabitants are cattle and sheep raising and fishing. There are marble quarries and some oats, potatoes and turnips are grown. At Boreraig Castle, the seat of the Macleods, there was once a famous bagpipers' school, run by the MacCrimmons, the hereditary pipers of the Macleod clan.

Society Islands

Two clusters of volcanic and coral islands forming a chain about 140 miles long. Location *French Establishments in Oceania, South Pacific.* Area *About 650 square miles.* Map *4, K8.*

Forming two main groups, the Society Islands can be divided into the Windward Islands (Îles du Vent, or Archipel de Tahiti), which include Tahiti, Moorea, Maiao, Mehetia and Tetiaroa; and the Leeward Islands (Îles sous le Vent), which consist of Raiatea (the largest), Huahine, Bora-Bora, Maupiti, Tahaa, Mopihaa, Motu Iti, Scilly Island and Bellingshausen Island. Populated by Polynesians, the main products of the Islands are breadfruit, copra and pandanus; rum, sugar, mother-of-pearl and vanilla are also exported and Makatea produces phosphates.

Discovered by Samuel Wallis in 1767, they were visited by Louis de Bougainville in the following year and by Captain James Cook for the first time in 1769. Cook was accompanied by members of the Royal Society and the Islands were named in their honor. English missionaries settled in the Islands in 1797 and were followed by the French. A French protectorate was established in 1843 and the group became a colony in 1880, having earlier become a base for traders and whalers. On Tahiti, the administrative capital of French Polynesia has been established, and the territory is represented in the French National Assembly and Senate in Paris. The population is about 50,000.

By the time Captain Cook visited the Islands for the third time, in 1777, native life had changed considerably in the group. "A stone hatchet," Cook wrote, "is at present as rare a thing amongst them as an iron one was eight years ago, and a chisel of bone or stone is not to be found. . . our iron tools. . . may now be considered as having become necessary to their comfortable existence. . . they cannot (ever) be restored to that happy mediocrity in which they lived before we discovered them . . ."

Socotra

A large island, the insular section of the Mahri sultanate of Qishn and Socotra. Location *150 miles off Cape Guardafui, Indian Ocean.* Area *1,400 square miles.* Map *10, C5.*

In spite of its remoteness from all the main centers of civilization, Socotra (also spelled Sokotra and Soqotra) is in many ways a meeting place of several continents, ages and cultures. Its small area has survived the subsidence (long ago in geological time) of the great primeval continent which embraced present-day Africa, the Middle East, southern Asia and the northwestern part of the Indian Ocean. The early contacts of the island with both Asia and Africa are shown by its flora and fauna which have affinities with both continents. There are no indigenous mammals, but the island has a breed of wild ass that must have been imported from Africa. On the other hand, the small humpless cattle, the sheep and the goats are evidently Arabian imports.

The cultural history of the island also shows varied foreign influences. Greek traders in classical times called it the isle of Dioscorides – perhaps from the Sanskrit name meaning "the island abode of bliss." In later centuries the inhabitants were at one time Christians – in the thirteenth century Abulfeda described them as "Nestorian Christians and pirates" though the island was rather a station of the Indian corsairs who harassed the Arab trade with the Far East. In the late Middle Ages they became Mohammedan. When, in the middle of the seventeenth century, the Carmelite P. Vincenzo visited the island, he found that the people still called themselves Christians and had a strange mixture of

Jewish, Christian and pagan rites. *All* the women were called Maria. The present inhabitants consist of the mixed Arabian, Indian and African people of the lowland coastal districts and the more truly indigenous natives who dwell chiefly on the plateaus and mountains that occupy the central part of the island. The total population is estimated at 8,000, only a fraction of that of earlier times when Arab writers estimated that they could muster 10,000 warriors.

The Socotrans offer something of a puzzle to ethnologists, who have discovered two distinct physical types, both probably of Semitic origin, suggesting that the Socotrans are the descendants of two Mediterranean races that intermarried many centuries ago. They vary from short, round-headed people with long noses and thick lips to tall, fair-complexioned, thin-lipped people with straight noses and black hair. The Socotran language is easier to identify, since it is related to the Mahri tongue spoken on the Arabian mainland by the people of Qishn, a sultanate of the Hadhramaut with which Socotra is linked politically. (The Sultan of Qishn actually resides on Socotra.) Both languages are probably descended from a common ancestor, perhaps the tongue of the ancient kingdom of Sheba in southwestern Arabia.

The people are chiefly herdsmen, but there is some agriculture, especially in the rich alluvial soil along the coast and in the fertile valleys dividing the plateaus and hills. Aloes, "dragon's blood" (a red, resinous plant product used by photo-engravers), myrrh and frankincense are among the chief crops; some millet, cotton and tobacco are also grown. There is a good yield of dates which form the main part of the native diet. But the chief product of the island, exported in some quantity, is *ghee*, or clarified butter, obtained from the milk of cattle and goats. Socotra also has a number of fishermen and pearls are found on the banks off Abd el Kuri, an uninhabited island some miles to the west.

The seafarer approaching from the north finds a varied coastline, consisting partly of low-lying plains with scattered palm trees and bushes and partly of steep limestone cliffs, edging an undulating plateau 1,500–2,000 feet high which covers much of the island, rising to over 4,500 feet in the center in the wooded Haggier Mountains. But there is no protected harbor and in the monsoon season the island is avoided by local craft, as a boisterous wind may easily drive an Arab dhow ashore. It was the lack of a suitable anchorage that caused the island to be abandoned by one after another of the European interests which sought to establish control of the Indian Ocean for trade and conquest. Albuquerque, in 1506, contemplated setting up a depot there to be used as a base for his scheme to give Portugal mastery of the entrance to the Red Sea; but after a second visit in 1508 he abandoned the project. A hundred years later the British East India Company found it equally impracticable to set up a factory there, and plans to acquire the island in the eighteen-thirties as a coaling station were also discarded when Aden was occupied. The only European to have found the island of practical use as a base was the notorious pirate Captain Evory at the end of the seventeenth century, who set up his temporary headquarters sometimes at Perim and sometimes at Socotra.

Socotra has been under British protection since 1866, when a treaty was concluded with the Mahri Sultan of Qishn; during the Second World War a British garrison was posted on the island.

Sogne Fjord

A many-branched inlet of the North Sea, Norway's largest fjord. Location *Western Norway.* Dimensions *112 miles long, 3 miles wide.* Maximum depth *Over 4,000 feet.* Map *8, F2.*

Throughout its length, from the bold outer coast, Sogne Fjord is one of the most beautiful and scenically varied of Norway's fjords. As one sails up this magnificent waterway, the *fjeld* or highland on either side increases from around 2,000 feet at the seaward end to over 5,000 feet in the interior. Many streams and waterfalls cascade down the steep flanks of precipitous cliffs. Some of these are fed by the great icefield of the Jostedalsbre, which is in the mountains on the northern side of the Sogne; others have their source in the wild Horungene group to the east.

Except where the shores of Sogne Fjord are steepest, forests cling to the slopes, often surmounted by great rocky precipices and bluffs

The settlement of Flam in the Sogne Fjord

that are usually snow-covered, except at the height of the summer. Arable land is scarce and the population sparse except in some of the broad tributary valleys. In these inner branch fjords there is often a surprisingly luxuriant, almost southern, vegetation. Apart from a variety of crops, fruit growing flourishes and in places there is even a little tobacco grown. There are exceptionally fine birch trees and oaks, which supply the timber for the native woodcrafts.

Because of the steepness of the shores of Sogne Fjord, few roads have been built along it, but there are several important routes leading from the heads of the branch fjords and many good hotels on the shores, reached by the frequent steamship service. Sogne is also crowded with fascinating Viking traditions; the district is noted for having its own dialect.

Solomon Islands

A chain of volcanic islands extending for 900 miles. Location *Southwest Pacific, 1,500 miles north of Sydney.* Area *16,000 square miles.* Map *4, F7–8.*

Except for traders and officials, few people visit the clustered islands of the Solomons. Strung out between the Bismarck Archipelago and the New Hebrides, the larger islands – such as Guadalcanal – rise to high peaks covered with tropical forest; others are mere atolls with enclosed lagoons.

Most of the Islands comprise a British Protectorate, which includes Choiseul, Guadalcanal, Malaita, New Georgia, San Cristobal, Savo, Santa Isabel, the Santa Cruz Islands, the Shortland Islands, and many islets. Guadalcanal, the largest island of the British Protectorate (2,500 square miles), is built up around a volcanic, mountainous backbone; its highest point is Mount Popomansiu (8,000 feet). Rennell Island, 120 miles southeast of the main group, is a typical raised coral atoll, almost level at about 400 feet above the sea; Ontong Java or Lord Howe Island is a low coral atoll. The capital is Honiara, on Guadalcanal.

Bougainville – the largest of the Solomons – and Buka are governed by Australia, under a United Nations mandate.

The climate in the Solomons is hot and humid throughout the year, though from May to October cooler, drier southeast winds bring some relief. From December to March the winds are mainly northwesterly; rainfall varies from 120 inches annually on the windward sides of the higher islands to 70 inches at Honiara. The greater part of the larger islands is covered by tropical rain forest, mixed with various hardwoods and kauri pine. The only fairly large savanna area is along the north coast of Guadalcanal, whose fauna includes wild dogs, native pigs and large rats; some of the other larger islands are infested with crocodiles in their swamplands. There are many varieties of birds – parrot, kingfisher, hawk, hornbill and the rare long-tailed pigeon on Guadalcanal.

Alvado de Mendaña, voyaging west from Peru, was the first to sight Santa Isabel, in 1567. Abel Tasman discovered Ontong Java in 1642. The main archipelago was rediscovered by Captain Philip Carteret in 1767, after which many European navigators visited it. During the second half of the nineteenth century thousands of natives were recruited for labor on the sugar plantations of Queensland and Fiji; in 1893 Britain proclaimed a protectorate over the southern islands of the group. In 1900, the northern Solomons (Choiseul, Santa Isabel and Ontong Java), which were then in German possession, were transferred to Britain. Early in 1942, the Japanese occupied the Solomons, but eight months later the Allied counter-offensive began, pushing northwards, and after bitter fighting – especially on Guadalcanal – most of the archipelago was regained.

The Solomon Islanders are mostly Melanesians, with some Polynesians on several of the Islands. The population is about 114,000, of which less than 1,000 are Europeans and a few hundred Chinese and Indians. The Islanders are famous for their gondola-shaped canoes, often inlaid with pearl-shell and built with grace and care. Shell money is still the currency for traditional purposes – such as the purchase of a bride – on Malaita, Guadalcanal and San Cristobal. More than 40 different languages and dialects are spoken in the Islands with pidgin English as the *lingua franca*. Since the nineteenth century Christian missionaries have been at work among the former headhunters and cannibals; but deep-rooted superstitions and beliefs still survive, even among the converts.

The produce of the Islands includes bananas, breadfruit, coconuts, sweet potatoes, taro and yams; copra is sold to Chinese and European traders. On Malaita the coastal people barter fish for the vegetables which the bush-dwellers grow. Most of the coconut plantations which were destroyed during the Second World War are back in production. In 1952 cocoa was introduced; rice is being cultivated extensively on Guadalcanal, and coffee is also grown.

Southampton Island

A large, bleak island at the entrance to Hudson Bay. Location *Eastern Keewatin district, Northwest Territories.* Area *16,936 square miles.* Map *1, C1.*

Southampton Island is separated from the Canadian mainland by Roes Welcome Sound on the west, and from the Melville Peninsula in the north by Repulse Bay and Frozen Strait. East of it, Foxe Channel, leading to Foxe Basin, separates it from southern Baffin Island. Roughly triangular, its southern coasts are indented by the deep Bay of God's Mercy and by South Bay. The main settlement, Coral Harbour, is at the head of South Bay. East Bay, Duke of York Bay and Ell Bay, on the eastern and western coasts, are smaller.

The Island was discovered by Thomas Button in 1613 during his voyage across the northern part of Hudson Bay when he entered Roes Welcome Sound. Robert Bylot and William Baffin sighted it again in 1615, sailing east along the coast to Frozen Strait, and put a party ashore near Cape Comfort, to which they gave its name; they also named Seahorse Point for the large number of walruses in the area. Within five years of the discovery of Hudson Bay by Henry Hudson, both the east and west coasts of Southampton Island were observed, though it was believed to be part of the mainland. Luke Foxe saw it in 1631 and named it after the Earl of Southampton.

In 1742 Middleton landed some men on the west coast, described the coastal area and also observed the high land in the center of the Island. Sailing north through Roes Welcome Sound he discovered Repulse Bay and could see along Frozen Strait to the east coast – being the first to establish that Southampton Island was a true island. Edward Parry in 1821 and Captain George F. Lyon in 1824 made some further explorations; these were extended in the second half of the nineteenth century, when whaling started in northern Hudson Bay. Stations were established on the coast of Southampton Island. In 1903 members of the Canadian Government expedition, led by A. P. Low, spent some time on Southampton Island and so did the Fifth Thule Expedition in 1922 under K. J. V. Rasmussen. A permanent trading post was set up two years later at Coral Harbour by the Hudson's Bay Company and exploration was extended inland. In 1929-30 G. M. Sutton studied the bird life of the Island; T. H. Manning traveled extensively in 1933-36, studying the geographical features and wild life. In more recent years Canadian Government scientists have paid numerous visits to the Island.

Southampton offers a remarkable contrast between the rugged uplands of the interior and east coast and the flat lowlands of the rest of the Island, due to the two basically different rock formations. The uplands form part of the Canadian Shield and consist of crystalline rock, chiefly mica-gneiss and granite of the Precambrian period, while the rest is horizontally bedded limestone of the Paleozoic age. The uplands form a plateau ranging from 1,300 feet to 1,750 feet in height, while the vertical cliffs on the east coast rise to 1,500 feet. The eastern part of the plateau, towering above Foxe Channel, is the highest and most picturesque.

The surface is cut by swift streams in deep, gorge-like valleys, some of which are over 1,000 feet deep. Most of the rivers rise in the interior of the uplands. The Boas River, flowing south, ends its course at the Bay of God's Mercy; the Kirchoffer and Ford rivers in South Bay. The Cleveland River flows north into Duke of York Bay. There are several minor rivers – including Mathiassen Brook – flowing through deep gorges, rapids and waterfalls, entering Foxe Channel in a series of spectacular cataracts. The upper level of the plateau is a gently rolling, featureless expanse of rock without lakes or much vegetation. To the south, the plateau slopes gradually and merges into the lowlands extending along the south coast. The western boundary of the plateau is clearly defined by a sharp escarpment 600–1,000 feet high, overlooking the lowlands that fringe the west coast.

In the southeast the Bell Hills, a ridge of crystalline rock, extend about 40 miles from Gore Point to Seashore Point on the Bell Peninsula. Their average height is 600–700 feet with Mount Minto over 1,000 feet. In the southwest the Munn Hills rise to about 500 feet, standing out sharply above the limestone plain surrounding them.

The only permanent white settlements are at Coral Harbour and Munn Bay on the south coast. Two years after its foundation, Anglican and Roman Catholic mission churches were built at Coral Harbour; in 1950 a school was established by the Canadian Government. Munn Bay, five miles to the west, has a Royal Canadian Mounted Police station and a meteorological observation post. Northeast of Munn Bay there is an airfield built during the Second World War, connected with the only road on the whole Island.

The Eskimo and mixed population numbers over 200, most of whom live near Coral Harbour, while a few have camps at Expectation Point and Duke of York Bay.

The earliest of the present inhabitants are Aivilik Eskimos whom whalers brought over from the mainland about 1908. Later some Okomiut Eskimos arrived from Coats Island. But Southampton Island has been inhabited for at least 2,000 years, as some 1954 archeological excavations established. The earliest known inhabitants were the Sadlermiut Eskimos, a strange and primitive group, descendants of the Dorset Eskimos, probably the last survivors of an ancient culture. They had little contact with the other tribes; Captain George F. Lyon, the first European to describe them, met a party of Sadlermiuts in 1824. The other Eskimos regarded them with contempt because they led a stone-age existence, still chipping their weapons and knives out of stone. During the winter of 1902–03 whalers brought some disease to Southampton Island which wiped out the tribe – except for one woman and four children. These were removed to the mainland to live with another tribe, but four years later only two of the children were living and all trace of them was lost.

South Georgia

A barren, mountainous island, one of the Falkland Island Dependencies. Location *South Atlantic, about 800 miles east of the Falkland Islands.* Area *1,450 square miles.* Map *6, E11.*

About 100 miles long and 20 miles wide, South Georgia lies about 1,200 miles east of Cape Horn; a bleak, snow-covered mass of rock for most of the year. But in early November the bare rock patches on the mountainsides grow larger, the gorges begin to gush with torrents from the melting snows, brilliant green mosses, burnets and grey tussock grasses burst into life on the lower slopes and in the harbor at Grytviken, the only village of the island, all is activity. Whaling is the most important industry of South Georgia where, during the Antarctic summer, as many as 20 whales a day are brought in to be cut up and turned into oil.

The island's snowy peaks rise to 8,000 feet, their slopes furrowed with deep gorges which are filled with glaciers. Geologically, South Georgia consists of gneiss and argillaceous schists with no trace of fossils, which shows that, like the

Falklands, it is a surviving fragment of some greater land mass now vanished – most probably a former extension of the Andean system.

South Georgia was claimed for Great Britain in 1775 by Captain James Cook. It is an inhospitable place, though if it were not for its damp, foggy climate it would be well suited for cattle or sheep farming. In 1882 a German expedition was stationed at Royal Bay, on the southeast coast, to observe the transit of Venus. Its members found the flora surprisingly rich, collecting 13 flowering plants, mostly the same as in the Falklands, but one allied to a form found in distant New Zealand. Of its fauna, the huge chocolate-colored birds that waddle like ungainly geese near the coast are the most remarkable. In summer they toil away from volcano-shaped nests, turn into the wind, run a few steps, open giant scimitar wings and leap into the air – only to tumble back to earth an instant later. A noble spectacle, for these are the young of the Wandering Albatross, *Diomeda exulans*, the largest of all sea-birds, the greatest flyer of all living creatures. Here they hatch and here they learn to fly until each year in June they soar away, not to touch land again, sometimes for several years.

South Georgia's year-round population is about 250, but during the whaling season it swells to over 700. It has one truly prominent and permanent inhabitant – for here is buried Sir Ernest Shackleton, one of the greatest of all Antarctic explorers.

South Orkney Islands

A barren archipelago, part of the British Antarctic Territory. Location *Northeast of Palmer Peninsula, Antarctica.* Area *400 square miles.* Map *3, G7.*

Like the other islands in the British Antarctic Territory, the South Orkneys are formed by the high peaks of the Scotia Arc – the southern continuation of the Andes that curves across the Antarctic Ocean as a submarine ridge to re-emerge in the ranges of the Palmer Peninsula, or Graham Land, as it is known in Britain. They were discovered in 1821 jointly by George Powell in the tiny sealing sloop *Dove* and by the American Nathaniel Palmer. During the next 80 years, crews of other sealing vessels landed on them from time to time. In 1903–04 the Scottish National Antarctic Expedition in the *Scotia* wintered at Laurie Island, where they established a weather station which the Argentine Government has maintained to the present day. There is now also a British weather station on Signy Island. The other two islands in the group are Coronation and Powell with a number of surrounding rocks – among them the Inaccessible Islands.

The South Orkneys are a cluster of jagged peaks rising steeply out of the ocean and covered in a mantle of ice. During most of the year the sky is completely overclouded and the average temperature is well below freezing point. Despite an abundance of breeding petrels, penguins and seals, the Islands form part of the cold desert of the Antarctic and only a few mosses and lichens cover the areas which become snow-free in summer.

In December, 1959, Argentina, Australia, Belgium, Britain, Chile, France, Japan, New Zealand, Norway, South Africa, the Soviet Union and the United States signed a treaty on scientific co-operation in the Antarctic. This suspended all territorial claims and disputes in the area for 30 years. In accordance with the provisions of this treaty, the South Orkneys were incorporated into the British Antarctic Territory, a new British colony which came into being on March 3, 1962, and which includes the former Falkland Island Dependencies lying south of latitude 60° South and between longitude 20° and 80° West.

South Shetland Islands

A chain of mountainous, ice-capped islands, part of the British Antarctic Territory. Location *South of South America, off the northern tip of Palmer Peninsula, Antarctica.* Map *3, F7.*

The South Shetlands spread from west to east, forming a fringe along the north shore of the Palmer Peninsula. Like the South Orkneys, they rise on the Scotia Arc. They were first sighted by William Smith of the English brig *Williams* in 1819. Smith paid another visit to the group eight months later, landed on King George I Island and claimed it for England; he also gave the whole chain its present name. In 1820 Edward Bransfield was sent out in the *Williams*

rdeen fishing village, Hong Kong

to survey the Islands, which had attracted the attention of American and British sealers.

The most famous of the group is Deception Island, which contains one of the finest natural harbors in the world. The Island is a volcano, and its crater wall has been breached by the sea to form a broad, sheltered lagoon some four miles across and nearly 600 feet deep, called Port Forster. In 1828 and 1842 voyagers reported steam from numerous vents, but in 1904 Otto Nordenskjöld found no evidence of volcanic activity. Deception has been used by whalers for many years and today is the site of a weather station and base manned by the Falkland Island Dependencies Surveys, which have several other bases among the Islands.

The South Shetlands also include Smith (or James), Low (or Jameson), Snow, Livingston, Greenwich, Robert, Nelson, Elephant and Clarence islands, and a number of rocks. Although they are almost devoid of land plants, their vast sea-bird populations – chiefly penguins and petrels – are of great interest to naturalists. On Deception Island, volcanic heat makes it possible for these birds to nest earlier than is usual so far south, and also allows the growth of a scanty moss flora.

Spanish Main

The coastal regions and offshore islands of Spanish America. Location *Between Panama and the mouth of the Orinoco River, northern South America.* Map *2, E5–G4.*

The Spanish Main is less a geographical area than an historical tradition and a romantic idea. Properly speaking, it is the northern coast of South America, stretching westward from the mouth of the Orinoco to the Isthmus of Panama or a little farther; the *main*-land bordering the Caribbean Sea. But the term is more often applied to the curving chain of islands that form the northern and eastern boundaries of the Caribbean, starting from Mosquito, near the Isthmus, and including Jamaica, St Domingo and the Leeward and Windward islands, continuing to Trinidad and the coast of Venezuela in South America.

Here, against the backdrop of blue water and palm-fringed lagoons, the struggle between Spain and Britain for the supremacy of the high seas unfolded in the sixteenth and seventeenth centuries. The fast ships of the British pirates swooped down on the stately but clumsy Spanish treasure galleons. Some of their captains were patriots who fought less for gain than for the glory of their Queen (though they did not despise gold and silver); others were cut-throats and treacherous scoundrels who would just as readily rob their own countrymen as the subjects of His Most Catholic Majesty. Later, in the second half of the seventeenth century, Spain with her weakening power would rather put up with the lawless adventurers known as the "Brothers of the Coast" and the "Buccaneers" than co-operate with foreign governments to suppress them. Several of the Caribbean islands became useful and practically impregnable bases for the pirates of the Spanish Main. Jamaica was full of the so-called "private men-of-war" whose doings are prominent in the correspondence of the early governors, who were not uncommonly their associates. Not all those sailing the Spanish Main were pirates: some contented themselves with smuggling, a most profitable trade, as Spain denied her colonists the right of trading with foreigners yet could not supply their needs herself.

Captain Kidd, Captain Avery (or Every), Bartholomew Roberts, John Martel, Edward Teach ("Blackbeard"), James Fife, Oliver La Bouche, Thomas Cocklyn, Edward England – these are only some of the pirate captains whose exploits made the Spanish Main a legendary area of high adventure, sudden treachery, incredible daring – and buried treasure. Most of them came to a bad end though a few survived to enjoy their ill-gotten wealth. And they left a body of legend behind that has supplied innumerable writers with material for books about "pirates and blue water."

Spitsbergen

A large Norwegian archipelago. Location *Between Greenland and Franz Josef Land, Arctic Ocean.* Area *23,658 square miles.* Map *5, F9–10.*

Spitsbergen is one of the most interesting of the polar archipelagos – and not only because Soviet

Maddalena Bay, Spitsbergen

and Western coal-mining industries operate there in close proximity. Visitors to the islands have remarked that the yellow poppies grow taller than the polar willows, which seldom exceed three inches from root to crown.

The principal islands of the archipelago are West Spitsbergen, Northeast Land, Barents Island, Edge Island and Prince Charles Foreland. Bear Island, farther south, and a few islands on the eastern side of the group – Hopen, Kvitoya and Kong Karls Land – are included, together with Spitsbergen proper, in the Norwegian possession of Svalbard.

Spitsbergen's name came from its sharp peaks, which rise to 5,633 feet in Mount Newton, on West Spitsbergen. The Stubendorff Range is particularly impressive. Many of the peaks, however, are flat-topped from the passage of ice. The islands are flanked to the west by a branch of the warm North Atlantic Drift, so that navigation is possible for more than half the year.

Spitsbergen has featured in many epics of exploration and served as base for several flights to the North Pole by balloon, plane and dirigible. Discovered by the Vikings in 1194 (according to the *Landmabok*, it was rediscovered by the Dutch explorer Willem Barentsz in 1596. In due course, it attracted whalers, sealers and walrus hunters from many countries.

Early in this century Americans, British, Scandinavians, Dutch and Russians became interested in Spitsbergen's coal deposits. Uninhabited, the islands were a no man's land for the adventurous. In 1920, however, nine nations agreed to Norway's taking possession, subject to the islands remaining unfortified and to the signatories being given certain rights in exploiting the mineral resources. Russia adhered to the treaty some years later. In 1925 Norway took over Spitsbergen officially, and today she and the Soviet Union operate coal mines there. (During the Second World War the population was evacuated to England and the mines were set on fire to deny them to the Germans.) There is a Norwegian governor who periodically visits the Soviet settlements by dog-team or cutter, according to the season. The Russian population is around 1,500, the Norwegian 2,000. Most of the Norwegian miners sign on for a year or two to make money, as wages are high in the Arctic. The annual coal production is about 380,000 tons.

Coal mining remains the principal industry, but there are other mineral deposits and sealing, whaling and fishing are also important.

There are large numbers of waterfowl, especially the eider duck, but land animals – blue and white fox, reindeer and polar bear – have been hunted almost to extinction, and are now protected. About 130 species of Arctic vegetation are found near the shores, and on the tundra of the interior.

Staffa

A small, uninhabited island, famous for its many basaltic caves. Location *Inner Hebrides, Argyll, Scotland.* Map *8, C3.*

Fingal's Cave has been celebrated in the poems of Wordsworth and Scott, the paintings of Turner and the music of Mendelssohn, and was ceremoniously visited by Queen Victoria in 1847. It is one of the many basaltic caves of Staffa, with an entrance rising to an archway 227 feet long, supported by immense basaltic columns; the crown of the arch is 66 feet above the sea, which is 25 feet deep at low tide. Fingal was a mythological hero of Gaelic legend, father of Ossian who, in turn, was purported by Macpherson to have written the long epic poem *Fingal* (1762) narrating the hero's adventures – and the cave was fabled to have been one of his homes.

The astonishing cave had little more than local publicity until 1772 when Sir Joseph Banks, the naturalist, was driven into the Sound of Mull by bad weather while sailing to Iceland. He visited Staffa, just seven miles west of Mull, and spread the news of the cave. Two years later, the indefatigable Thomas Pennant visited Scotland and printed Banks's description in his *Tour of Scotland*. Since then, only the worst of weather has kept visitors away.

Staffa, uninhabited, has numerous other caves – the Boat Cave, the Clam Shell Cave and Mackinnon's Cave – piercing the cliffs that rise from the flat northeast angle of the island to a height of some 140 feet in the southwest. None, however, compares with Fingal's cave, which is approached either by boat or across a Giant's Causeway similar to its namesake in Northern Ireland.

There is a base of conglomerate tuff above which the sea rises and falls with the steady, relentless rhythm of the Atlantic. Above this, forming the vertical and parallel walls of the cave, rises the columnar basalt, a mass of pentagonal or hexagonal pillars, arranged in a colonnade, black, with white chalk accretions in places. Above this is the amorphous basalt, roofing the huge cavern, 400 feet wide, about 60–70 feet high and carved more than 200 feet into the cliff-face.

The great cave arouses a wonder that no familiarity or routine round of visitors can spoil.

Staten Island

A large island, comprising Richmond borough of New York City and Richmond county of New York State. Location *Close to New Jersey shore, Bay of New York; five miles southwest of the Battery, Manhattan Island.* Area *57 square miles (with small adjacent islands).* Map *1, F7.*

Separated from the New Jersey mainland on the north by Kill van Kull and by Arthur Kill on the west, Staten Island is about 14 miles long and seven miles wide. The Bayonne and the Goethals Bridge and the Outerbridge Crossing connect it with New Jersey; on the east the Lower Bay and the Narrows divide it from Brooklyn on the western extremity of Long Island. A ferry terminal on the northeastern shore at St George services the ferryboats to Manhattan and Brooklyn, while the various communities of Staten Island are connected by railroad.

Staten Island's chief towns are St George, Stapleton and Port Richmond, with New Dorp, Tompkinsville, Tottenville and West New Brighton as lesser centers. Except for a range of hills extending about six miles from St George to the southwest (nowhere more than about 400 feet high) and a smaller east-west ridge in the north, the Island is generally flat and level. Along the east shore there are several bathing beaches and amusement resorts; there is a thinly inhabited, swampy region in the west, but otherwise the Island is mainly residential with a few semi-rural communities. It has several large parks, including La Tourette, Silver Lake, Marine and Wolfes Pond. The industries are mainly concentrated in the north, with shipbuilding and repairing, lumber milling, printing and oil refining as the most important; there are also soap, fertilizer, asphalt, paper and lead factories; dyes, clothing, dental equipment and various building materials are also produced.

St George, Tompkinsville, Clifton and Stapleton form the port region in the northeast; the first free port in the United States was established here in 1936.

Staten Island was visited by Henry Hudson in 1609 and was named Staaten Eylandt by the Dutch. The first permanent community was established in 1661, a previous settlement having been destroyed by the Indians. In 1898 Staten Island was incorporated into New York City as Richmond borough. Today it has a population of about 200,000.

There are many historical monuments and sites on Staten Island. Fort Wordsworth, on the Narrows, opposite Fort Hamilton in Brooklyn, was originally established in 1663; Billopp (or Conference) House, built before 1688, was the site of Lord Howe's negotiations with Continental patriots in 1776; the Church of St Andrew was built in 1708. A quarantine station, a Federal marine hospital and a home for retired seamen are also on the Island.

Stewart Island

A volcanic island of New Zealand. Location *20 miles south of South Island.* Area *About 660 square miles.* Map *4, G11.*

Stewart Island lies in the Pacific, some 20 miles south of South Island, New Zealand. It has a population of just over 500, which makes it one of the more sparsely populated islands of the Pacific; but it is popular as a summer resort with New Zealanders who really want to "get away from it all," and who have only to cross the Foveaux Strait to reach it.

Chiefly composed of low mountains (Mount Anglem, 3,200 feet, is the highest peak), Stewart Island produces granite, frozen fish, and some tin and feldspar. Its chief town is Oban (formerly Half-moon Bay) in the northeast; in the south is Port Pegasus.

Discovered in 1808 by the British, Stewart

Island was bought from the Maoris in 1864. With nearby Ruapuke Island and the Mutton Bird Islands, it forms a separate county of New Zealand.

Suez Canal

The most important waterway between Europe and the East. Location *Egypt, between the Mediterranean and the Red Sea.* Dimensions *107 miles long, 197 feet wide.* Maximum depth *42.5 feet.* Map *10, B2.*

One of the principal waterways of the world, crossing the isthmus between Asia and Africa and obviating the long passage round the African continent, the Suez Canal has been called the lifeline between east and west. It is the main route by which the oil of the Persian Gulf reaches Europe and one of the major achievements of nineteenth-century engineering. Ferdinand de Lesseps, a French diplomatist and member of the French consular service, conceived the idea of building the Canal after reading the memoirs of Lapère, an engineer who had accompanied Napoleon on his expedition to Egypt and whom the Emperor had commissioned to survey the area with a view to the construction of such a canal. Lapère's survey led him to believe that there was a difference of nearly 30 feet in the levels of the Mediterranean and Red seas – a conclusion which, coupled with Napoleon's defeat at the Battle of the Nile, led to the abandonment of the plan. De Lesseps, however, backed by better scientific knowledge, was convinced that the project was practicable.

A canal linking the two seas was not, in fact, a novelty even in Napoleon's time; one had actually existed in the fourteenth century B.C., and possibly much earlier. At that time, the head of the Red Sea extended as far north as the Bitter Lakes, and it was not so very difficult for the Pharaohs, using slave labor, to cut a canal from this point to join the River Nile. Seagoing vessels were able to unload their cargoes into vessels of lighter draught which could ferry them up the Nile and then, through the easterly arm of the Nile Delta, into the Mediterranean. Another canal, following a different course and linking Cairo with the Red Sea near the modern town of Suez, was built by the Arabs in the seventh century A.D. Neither of these early ventures attempted to cut through the isthmus itself, and the credit for first conceiving this idea seems to belong to Harun-al-Rashid, Caliph of Bagdad, who was dissuaded from attempting it only when his ministers pointed out that the Christian fleets from Byzantium would thus gain access to the coasts of Arabia.

The history of the Suez Canal is a complex web of intrigue, international rivalry and – on several occasions – near-bankruptcy. From the beginning, the British were against the idea. Lord Palmerston, who was then Prime Minister, was particularly hostile to it, being unable to see any advantage to his country in the project. He actively distrusted the presence of French influence in Egypt, and thought that England as a great commercial power would be drawn by her interest in the canal traffic into a more direct interference in Egypt, which he wanted to avoid.

In 1854 the Compagnie Universelle du Canal Maritime de Suez was constituted and in 1859 the work commenced; the first laborers began to dig their trench through the sand at Port Said. Labor troubles developed quickly – Britain and other countries protested strongly against the employment of forced labor. The work was finally completed with the aid of mechanical dredgers by which the greater part of the canal was cleared. Utilizing the already existing lakes, such as Lake Menzela, and aligning the Canal so that it passed through the shallow depressions which now form Lake Timsah and the Bitter Lakes, the work was completed in 1869. The Canal was formally opened on November 16, with Verdi's *Aida* specially composed in honor of the great event; the first to make the passage was the Empress Eugénie of France aboard the royal yacht.

In spite of the early British hostility to the plan, the Canal's importance to a great maritime nation quickly became obvious. It remained for Benjamin Disraeli to conclude in 1875 one of the most spectacular achievements of his career when he borrowed $20,000,000 from the Rothschilds and bought from the bankrupt Khedive of Egypt his 177,000 shares – making Britain owner of nearly 50 per cent of the company. In 1888 the Suez Canal Convention was signed, by which it was agreed that the Canal should "always be free and open, in time of war as in time of peace, to every vessel of commerce or of war, without distinction of flag." Two world wars were to see the terms of the Convention disregarded, since the prevention of German ships from having access to the Canal became an essential part of British and Allied policy.

In the nineteen-fifties the rising tide of Egyptian nationalism identified the ownership of the Canal with the presence of British military bases in the country, and although the Convention was due to run until 1968, the dethronement of King Farouk brought to a head the strong agitation for the abrogation of both the Anglo-Egyptian Treaty and the Canal concession. Things came to a head in 1956 when President Nasser expropriated the Canal. Israel, which had been engaged in a prolonged dispute with Egypt, launched an attack in the Sinai Peninsula and Britain and France sent troops into the Nile Delta area. The military action was stopped by the intervention of the United Nations and some of the two Western powers' allies – notably the United States – and by strong opposition within Britain and France themselves. The Egyptians had blocked the Canal by sinking ships, but after a few months it was cleared again, and gradually relations between Egypt and the Anglo-French allies returned to normal.

Since its inception the Canal has been greatly widened and it is now possible for large vessels to pass each other at almost every point. It is also navigable at night; the banks are lined with powerful floodlights. The steady drift of desert sand remains a major problem and constant dredging is necessary to keep the Canal in a good navigable state. The future of the Canal depends almost entirely on the ability of the Egyptian government to maintain and improve it.

Sulu Archipelago

A group of islands, part of the Philippines. Location *Between Mindanao and Borneo.* Area *1,086 square miles.* Map *4, B6.*

The long chain of the Sulus extends over 200 miles southwest from Basilan Island, near Mindanao, to within 25 miles of the northeast coast of Borneo, forming Sulu province (population over 250,000) of the Philippine Republic. There are almost 400 islands and uncounted rocks, reefs and islets in the group.

Jolo or Sulu Island is the biggest of the Archipelago, occupying 345 square miles with a population of about 116,000; it is also the chief island and capital of Sulu province. About 37 miles long and 12 miles wide, it narrows to a quarter of that width in its center. The mountains rise to 2,664 feet and jungle covers much of the surface; but its fertile areas produce rice, cassava, coconuts and fruit. Here is the principal home of the Moros, the fierce race of pirates who were said to have been subdued in 1876 by the Spaniards – but who still risked an occasional raid as late as 1957. With its offshore islands (Pata, Cabucan, Capual) and islets, it forms the Jolo Group. Jolo, the chief town, lies on the northwest coast. Jolo exports large quantities of mother-of-pearl, hemp and fruit and exquisite pearls.

The Pangutaran Group of the Archipelago consists of coral islands and includes Panducan, North Ubian and Usada; the largest is Pangutaran itself (36.7 square miles, about 11 miles long) and the group lies about 25 miles northwest of Jolo.

The Samales Group, east of Jolo and south of Basilan, has a total area of about 50 square miles and consists of Tongquil, Simisa, Balanguingui and other islands.

The Tawitawi Group has a population of around 40,000 and is about 40 miles off the northeast coast of Borneo and 60 miles southwest of Jolo. Tawitawi, its largest island, has an area of 229 square miles; it rises to 1,800 feet and has only a handful of people living on it. Most of the population in the group are on the small offshore islands, on Bilatan, Bongao, Kinapusan, Sanga Sanga, Simunul, South Ubian and Tandubas. The islands produce coconuts, rice and fruit and have some manganese deposits. Under the 1947 pact with the Philippines, a United States naval base has been set up in the group.

The Tapul Group of the Sulu Archipelago has an area of about 90 square miles and a population of about 47,000. It stretches between Jolo and Tawitawi. Tapul Island is 10.5 square miles; Lugus, Lapac, Cabingaan and Taluc are also in the Group, of which the largest is Siasi (29.6

Native canoes in the Sulu Archipelago

square miles), 25 miles southwest of Jolo, with a population of almost 13,000.

Sibutu Island (39 square miles) is the westernmost of the Archipelago, 20 miles southwest of Tawitawi across the Sibutu Passage. The group bearing the name of its main island, Sibutu, includes nearby Tumindao Island and several other islets. Sibutu was inadvertently omitted from the 1898 Spanish-American treaty, but two years later was ceded (together with Cagayan Sulu Island) to the United States.

In 1899 the sultanate of Sulu was formally recognized in a treaty with the American Government; it ended in 1940 when the reigning sultan ceded the Sulus to the Philippines.

Sumatra

The sixth largest island in the world. Location *Greater Sunda Islands, Indonesia.* Area *163,557 square miles.* Map *10, H6.*

Extending for 1,110 miles and 280 miles wide, lying astride the equator, Sumatra is the third largest island of the East Indies and forms part of the Indonesian Republic. The Barisan Mountains run in an almost straight line down its western coast, so close to the sea that there are virtually no lowlands on that side of the island. With dozens of peaks rising above 6,000 feet, many of them active volcanoes – the highest point, 12,487 feet, is the volcano Mount Kerinchi or Indrapura – with numerous lakes and mud volcanoes, with vast forests and grasslands (ranging from tropical to temperate in their fauna and flora), this is a land of great scenic beauty. Here live many of the wild animals for which Sumatra is famous: the Sumatran elephant, considered by some a distinct species; the Sumatran rhinoceros with its two horns, unlike the one-horned species of nearby Java; the enormous ox-like banteng; the royal and clouded tigers; tapirs; orangutans; and the siamsang, largest of the gibbons and found only on Sumatra. All this is combined with a teeming bird, reptile and insect life.

The great Sumatra Lowlands lie east of the mountains. There are almost continuous swamps and sandbanks along the east coast, except for a stretch of 150 miles in the northernmost part. The mouths of the rivers are usually barred by low-lying islands and the streams meander so tortuously through the waterlogged areas that it is almost impossible to say where the sea ends and the land begins. This coast is largely a huge, interwoven series of deltas.

Sumatra is constantly growing in area because the rivers carry so much sediment. This natural reclamation is helped by the immense growth of mangroves in the swamps and by the sand and ocean silt which is washed up to the low-lying shoreline from the very shallow sea. This oozing, mangrove-ridden region is almost uninhabitable, though there are some Sumatrans who manage to live by fishing; and along the lower reaches of some important rivers (the Musi and the

Jambi or Djembi on whose banks, but well upstream, stand Palembang and Jambi, two important cities), a few villages on stilts exist precariously.

The primary value of the east coast is that the island's many navigable rivers form here the watery highways that lead to seaports, which are often at a considerable distance from the sea. Palembang is more than 56 miles from salt water along the crooked course of the Musi River. Bengat, Jambi and Pelalawan are also some distance upstream from the low east coast. All the rivers here have wide drainage areas and most settlements are along them. Navigation is sometimes difficult in the lower reaches because of the wide mudbanks and the unexpected changes in the depth of water, caused by the tides and the irregular flow of the streams. Between the eastern coastal quagmires and the western mountain ranges extends one of the largest and most valuable agricultural regions of the East Indies. Parts of it are utterly wild and jungle-covered while others are laid out in great plantations. Most of them still await more intense development.

The Hindu kingdom of Sri Vijaya, with its capital at Palembang, reached its golden age in the eighth century when it ruled the Malay Peninsula and a large part of Indonesia. It fell in the fourteenth century to the Arab invasion from Java. As in so many parts of the East Indies, the Portuguese were the first European visitors; then came the Dutch (in 1596), who gradually gained mastery over all the native states, with Achin being the last to submit. Near the end of the eighteenth and in the early nineteenth centuries there was a short British occupation. After the Japanese occupation in the Second World War, most of Sumatra (with the exception of two small eastern and western sections) was included in the original Republic of Indonesia; in 1946 the Dutch sponsored the formation of South Sumatra and East Sumatra as independent states, but after four years the whole island was absorbed into Indonesia.

The most advanced among the Sumatran people are the Achinese, devout Mohammedans who occupy the northern coastal regions and who did not surrender to the Dutch until 1910; within the framework of the Indonesian Republic they have once again asserted their spirit of independence. In the west live the coastal Malays, identical with the people of the Malay Peninsula; in the southwest are the Palembangese, similar to the Javanese; and in the center of the island the Menangkabaus, who still trace descent in the female line, though they are now Mohammedans. North of these is the country of the Bataks, cannibals until recently and still mostly pagan, while scattered in the forest are a few primitive tribes, the Kubus and the Bayo-Alas. But perhaps the most fascinating of all Sumatra's peoples are the Orang-Laut – the sea people – who live in scattered communities along the east coast. Sturdy and strong, they are the direct descendants of the fierce pirates who formerly almost controlled these waters. Known also as the Sea Gypsies, they are nautical nomads and they number probably between 10,000 and 12,000.

Sumatra has large oil and coal fields, gold and silver mines and valuable camphor, ebony and ironwood forests; it produces rubber, copra, palm oil and resin, with coffee, tea, pepper and sugar as plantation crops. The chief towns and centers are Benkulen, Jambi, Kutaraja, Medan, Padang, Palembang, Sibolga and Telukbetung.

Sydney Harbour

The best harbor on the east coast of Australia. Location *Pacific Ocean, New South Wales, Australia.* Area *About 22 square miles.* Map *4, F10.*

Sydney Harbour begins with a narrow passage out of the Pacific, a mile wide between bold rocks and tawny grass. Once inside this rocky gate, one can sail for ten miles or so up a broad fairway between shores so indented with bays, coves and branches that the total coastline of Sydney Harbour is nearly 200 miles long; a winding circuit of low hills on which natural woodlands have been preserved as public parks. Here and there, the dark foliage is interrupted by the red tiles of the suburbs.

The Harbour runs south from the Pacific, parallel with the coast, and along the narrow peninsula which divides it from the thundering sea beaches lie the more expensive districts of Sydney. Here the bays are fringed with old mansions and the gardens of many more that

Sydney Harbour Bridge

have long since gone to make room for modern houses and apartment buildings; with long terraces, high lawns, old trees and, underneath stone walls, bathing-pools and yacht anchorages. Farther up the fairway are the grassy shores of the Domain, the principal park of the city, and Sydney Cove, where the first settlement in Australia was established; here, the narrow, winding streets climb from the quays to a lofty skyline. A little west from this, the great steel of the Harbour Bridge spans the green water – 1,650 feet long, it was built in 1932 to connect the city with its northern suburbs. Beyond the Bridge are warehouses, factories, silos, docks, engineering works and the busy estuaries of two rivers, the Lane Cove and the Parramatta.

Every day the surface of the great Harbour is alive with rowing-boats and launches, pinnaces, lighters and tugs, moving among the liners, freighters and warships at anchor in the stream or berthed along the quays. At weekends it mirrors the white canvas of fleets of sailing craft. At night its waves reflect the rows of golden rectangles which are the windows of the long, low ferry steamers.

Tahiti

A large island in Oceania, capital of the French Establishments. Location *Windward Group, Society Islands, South Pacific.* Area *402 square miles.* Map *4, K9.*

Tahiti is the largest and most important island of French Oceania. Shaped like an hour-glass, its eastern and western halves are joined by the narrow isthmus of Taravao. The larger portion, Tahiti Nui (Big Tahiti) is also known to the Tahitians as the Land of the Golden Haze; the smaller is called Little (Iti) Tahiti or Taiarapu. Among the many artists who have been attracted by the beauty of Tahiti is Paul Gauguin, who arrived there in 1891 and stayed for most of the 12 remaining years of his life.

The mountains of Tahiti are of singular beauty, rugged and sharply pointed like those of Rarotonga in the Cook Islands, but higher. The loftiest, Orohena, reaches 7,618 feet; lower but even more spectacular is Le Diadème (4,362 feet), whose name is derived from the pointed ridge crests, towering above the lowlands.

Tahiti was discovered in 1767 by Captain

Samuel Wallis, commanding H. M. S. *Dolphin*, who called it King George III Island and hoisted the British flag. A year later, Louis Antoine de Bougainville, unaware of this, annexed it in the name of the King of France and called it La Nouvelle Cythère, partly in tribute to the beauty of the Tahitian girls, but mainly, no doubt, because Tahiti was thought to be the best place from which to observe the transit of Venus across the disk of the sun, due to take place in 1769. The Royal Society of London sent a scientific expedition for this purpose, which traveled in H. M. S. *Endeavour*, commanded by James Cook, then a lieutenant of the Royal Navy. Cook named the Society Islands in honor of the Royal Society.

The next important event in Tahiti's history was the fateful visit in 1788 of the *Bounty*, on her mission to collect breadfruit plants for the British plantations in the West Indies. In 1791 H. M. S. *Pandora* arrived in search of the *Bounty*'s mutineers and removed the 11 who had had the temerity to stay behind when Fletcher Christian moved on to Pitcairn Island. In 1787 the London Missionary Society established a staff in Tahiti, who from this center carried out their work throughout eastern Polynesia.

For 40 years there was no interference with Tahiti's independence under its native rulers who, whether King or Queen, bore the dynastic title of Pomare. But when, in 1838, the Tahitians drove away some newly arrived French Roman Catholic missionaries, the French admiral Du Petit Thouars arrived and under threat of bombardment exacted an indemnity from the celebrated Queen Pomare IV (who reigned from 1827 to 1877). She also had to re-admit the French missionaries and allow them to preach their faith freely.

The harassed ruler later sought British protection, but the British Government declined to intervene. In 1842, Du Petit Thouars returned and extorted from the Queen's ministers (in her absence from Papeete, the capital) the acceptance of a French protectorate. Queen Pomare refused to acknowledge this until 1847 and withdrew in the meantime to the island of Raiatea. She died in 1877 after a troubled reign, and three years later her son and successor, fifth and last of his name, was forced to make full cession of his kingdom to France.

Since then innumerable tourists have traveled to the "Island of Venus" and much of its original charm has faded or become commercialized.

Tampa Bay

A large arm of the Gulf of Mexico, divided into two parts. Location *Western Florida.* Dimensions *About 25 miles long, 7–12 miles wide.* Map *2, D1.*

Tampa Bay, with the cities of Tampa and St Petersburg on its shores, is dissected by several peninsulas. The Pinellas Peninsula on the west (on which St Petersburg stands) provides the partial shelter important for the safety of shipping, while another peninsula in the center of the Bay divides the northern part into Hillsboro Bay on the northeast (about 10 miles long and 4–6 miles wide) and Old Tampa Bay on the northwest (about 15 miles long and 4–12 miles wide). Old Tampa Bay is spanned by bridges which connect the central peninsula with the western shore. Tampa is at the northern end of Hillsboro Bay, where the Hillsboro River enters the Bay.

Tampa Bay has played an important part in American history. It was here that Pánfilon de Narváez landed on the west coast of Florida in 1528, taking possession of the land in the name of Charles V of Spain. The Indians were hostile or indifferent, and in September, 1528, Narváez was drowned along the Gulf shore. Only five of his expedition survived to reach Mexico. Eleven years later, in May, 1539, Don Hernándo de Soto made the second landing and discovered Juan Ortix, one of Narvaez's unfortunate companions, who had been saved by the daughter of a chief from being massacred. But the Indians were still hostile and wily, and as De Soto's party made its painful way up the peninsula, there were many attacks on them. In 1549 Father Luis Cancer de Barbastro and his companions anchored somewhere near Tampa Bay; the Dominican father was put ashore and was promptly done to death by the Indians within sight of his companions. The remainder of the party went back to Mexico.

It was not until 1823 that the city of Tampa – or rather, Fort Brooke, as the settlement was originally called – was established; it became one of Florida's chief depots for supplies during the long Indian wars. In 1837 a treaty was signed with the Indians and they began to assemble near Fort Brooke, to be evacuated to New Orleans. But the evacuation never took place, because the Seminoles wanted to take their Negro slaves with them, and the war dragged on.

During the Civil War Tampa was used as a blockade point and in the Spanish-American War it was an important embarkation base for the United States forces. Today, with a population of over 150,000, it is a port of entry with a fine harbor; the city's modern development began in the late eighteen-eighties when railroads were constructed and the cigar industry was developed.

Tasmania

A large island, forming (with offshore islands) a state of the Commonwealth of Australia. Location *Between the Indian Ocean and the Tasman Sea, 150 miles south of Victoria, Australia.* Area *26,215 square miles.* Map *4, E11.*

Abel Tasman, in 1642, first saw the island which was to perpetuate his name, though for many years it bore the name he gave it: Van Diemen's Land. He approached it from the west, running before a boisterous wind, only seven weeks after leaving Mauritius. Rounding the South Cape, he landed a party at Blackman's Bay in early December and set sail again after planting a Dutch flag on what he believed to be part of the Australian mainland.

Tasman's party suspected the presence of human beings, but it was not until 130 years later that Europeans first encountered the inhabitants. The second visitor to the island, a young French officer, panicked when some naked Tasmanians approached his landing party, and ordered his men to fire. This unfortunate incident was the start of continuous hostility between white men and the natives. In 1804, the year after the first permanent settlement of Europeans was established (a British penal colony on the Derwent estuary, opposite the site where Hobart, the capital, now stands), another party of aborigines was shot down without provocation by a group of Englishmen.

The systematic extermination of the Tasmanians reduced their numbers by 1835 from some thousands to about 200, who were transported to Flinders Island at the eastern end of Bass Strait, which separates Tasmania from Australia. Only there, under a humane administration, was something learned of them and their way of life. They were nomads who only rarely built themselves the most primitive shelters and seldom wore clothing, although they knew the use of fire. They ate what they could find: large and small animals, grubs, shellfish, fruit or seeds. Their only weapons were primitive wooden clubs and spears. With a very dark brown skin and black, curly hair, they had heavy brows, short, broad noses, thick lips and very large teeth. The size of their brain cavity was smaller than that of any other existing people. An inordinate fear of death led to a complicated system of taboos, although they held no other formal religious beliefs. Only 40 of them survived to be transferred to a new home in Tasmania (at Oyster Bay in the southeast) in 1847, and the last of their bewildered race died in 1876.

The country in which modern European civilization has so decisively replaced a palaeolithic culture is a roughly triangular island, with a plateau averaging 2,000 feet in height at its center. Similar blocks lie in the northeast and along the east coast, and the whole island is a continuation of the mountain system running down the east coast of Australia. The ridge joining Tasmania to the mainland was submerged long ago and this caused the preservation of animal and plant species (as well as humans) more primitive than those in Australia, although the wild life is similar; it includes marsupials such as the kangaroo and wombat, and egg-laying mammals such as the duck-billed platypus, which are to be found only in this part of the world. The Tasmanian wolf and the Tasmanian devil are also found here and there are many poisonous snakes.

The central plateau slopes down on the western side of the island to form a peneplain rich in minerals and covered with eucalyptus forest. In the river valleys of the east, hard fruits, apricots and hops are grown, while in the northwest and northeast soils of volcanic origin favor dairying and potato-growing. Sheep are raised on the

The island of Thera

central plateau. Though part of the southwest is still unexplored, the extensive development of hydro-electricity from the lakes of the central plateau, the substantial metallurgical, paper and textile industries, the modern towns and cities, with a population of about 350,000, make it difficult to believe that 200 years ago the people of the island were living in the Old Stone Age.

Thera

The southernmost of the Cyclades, famous for its volcanic tuff. Location *Cyclades, Greece, Aegean Sea.* Area *31 square miles.* Map *9, G10.*

The eastern and southern shores of Thera form a crescent, embracing a great circular bay which is bordered by the islands of Therasia and Aspro on the west and northwest. The whole island is part of a volcanic crater about 12 miles long and three miles wide; the bay has largely filled the crater, which is over 1,000 feet deep. Thera rises to 1,858 feet in the peak of Prophet Elias, a quiescent volcano which once, in prehistoric times, blew the island to pieces, leaving only the fragments which form Thera and Therasia today.

Later eruptions (the last severe one occurred in 1866) raised a new peak from the sea bed which forms a small island in the center of the bay. This is still puffing smoke, and the sea is often full of large lumps of pumice floating on the surface, some in the softest shade of pink, others streaked with red, still others showing traces of cobalt on a background of pale green. There is only one small section of the bay where a ship can anchor: just below the town of Thera, on the western shore, where a small ledge juts out. Even here, only shallow-draught vessels are secure; larger ones must tie up at buoys moored several hundred yards away, or make fast to the sheer cliff sides. Thera itself is 900 feet above the landing stage and its white houses and towers straggle along a knife-edge precipice. It is a dazzlingly white town – houses, shops, streets and pavements are all whitewashed and reflect the brilliant Mediterranean light.

With a population of just under 10,000, Thera produces a famous wine and grows cotton, wheat, tobacco, barley and vegetables.

Settled by the Dorians from Laconia, Thera joined Crete in colonizing Cyrene in 631 B.C. and became a tributary to Athens in 427 B.C. In the Middle Ages it was part of the Venetian duchy of Naxos and was taken by the Turks in 1537. Its old name, Santorin or Santorini, originated in the name of its patron saint, St Irene.

Tierra del Fuego

A large archipelago separated from the mainland of Argentina by the Strait of Magellan. Location *The southern tip of South America, between the Atlantic, Antarctic and Pacific oceans.* Area *27,476 square miles.* Map *6, D11.*

Tierra del Fuego, the "Land of Fire," one of the bleakest and stormiest island groups in the world, comprises the large island of Tierra del Fuego (about 18,000 square miles); the smaller but still considerable Navarino, Hoste, Clarence, Santa Inés and Desolation islands, with Staten Island, off the southeast coast across Le Maire Strait, sometimes included in the group; and numberless small islands, islets and isolated rocks within a maze of inlets and channels. At the southernmost point Cape Horn rises on Horn Island.

The great system of the Andes stretches through the western part of the archipelago, though its peaks are comparatively low – Mount Sarmiento rising to 7,500 feet and Mount Darwin to 7,005 feet. In the eastern section extends the Patagonian plateau (Tierra del Fuego is sometimes considered part of Patagonia).

Lashed by storms, with one of the highest rainfalls in the world (which turns to snow on the mountains), the islands are still not too harsh to allow human habitation. Sheep and cattle are bred and cereals are grown. The population is mostly concentrated on the main island and numbers about 10,000 in the entire archipelago. The Fuegian aborigines are among the most primitive in the world; the Onas, Alikulufs and Yahgans still live largely in the Stone Age.

The archipelago was discovered by Ferdinand Magellan in 1520, and named "Land of Fire" either because of fires lit by the natives along the coasts or because of the flames of volcanoes now extinct. It was more than three centuries before the islands were completely surveyed – chiefly by Philip Parker King (1826–28) and Robert Fitzroy (1831–36); the latter expedition, in the *Beagle*, was accompanied by Charles Darwin.

The frontier of Chile and Argentina runs through Tierra del Fuego island from Cape Espiritu Santo in the north, lying on the Strait of Magellan, to Beagle Channel in the south. Argentina possesses 7,750 square miles of the main island (the eastern part) and Staten Island, and Chile the rest of the archipelago. There is still a dispute between the two countries over the three small islands of Pietón, Lennox and Nueva, at the mouth of Beagle Channel.

The Argentina section, including Staten Island, forms the Territory of Tierra del Fuego, with a total area of 7,996 square miles and a population of just over 5,000. Sheep raising is the most important productive activity in the Territory. Its mineral resources are still only partly exploited, though there is gold in the rivers and beach sands with huge quantities of guano, not to mention lignite, copper, zinc, nickel and iron ores. Whaling and sealing, and fishing for mackerel and sardines, yield a rich sea-harvest along the coast. There is plenty of virgin timber – mainly pine, cypress, and oak. There are meat packing plants at Rio Grande and fish canneries and sawmills at Ushuaia, the capital. Trade is mostly in wool, meat, the fur of nutria and seal, and in lumber.

The Magallanes province of Chile, which includes the islands of Tierra del Fuego with numerous other archipelagoes and islands and a narrow strip of the mainland, has a population of about 50,000, but only one tenth of that number live in the Tierra del Fuego group. They are mostly Indians who live by sheep farming and lumbering.

Timor

The largest, most easterly, of the Lesser Sundas, divided between Indonesia and Portugal. Location *525 miles northwest of Darwin, Australia.* Area *13,071 square miles.* Map *4, C8.*

Timor is a rugged, mountainous, scrub or grass-covered island, 300 miles long, 10-16 miles wide, with a population of well over 800,000. It lies in deep water, a little to the west of the 100-fathom line, on the edge of the shallow Arafura Sea, which extends southeast to northern Australia. Though part of the East Indian volcanic chain, Timor has no active volcanoes, only a few hot springs. Its highest point is Mount Ramelau in the center, which rises to 9,678 feet.

Because the prevailing wind is a dry, easterly wind from the arid plains of northern Australia, Timor – like Ombai, Flores and other nearby islands – has a much drier climate and a less luxuriant vegetation than the islands farther west; it has few streams and no important rivers. The rainy season lasts from January to March and the annual rainfall is about 58 inches. Excellent sandalwood grows, though there are no true forests; coconut and eucalyptus trees form the woodlands. The fauna consists of cuscus, monkeys, deer, civet cats, snakes and crocodiles; a noted breed of hardy ponies is exported.

The bulk of the population is Papuan mixed

with Malayan, Polynesian and other elements; there is a great diversity of physical types. The people are still divided into many hostile tribes, speaking about 40 different Papuan and Malayan languages or dialects. Headhunting has not been entirely suppressed.

The Portuguese probably visited Timor before the Spaniards arrived in 1522. A few years later the Portuguese settled on the island, and the Dutch, coming in 1613, became their bitter rivals and expelled them from Kupang. During the eighteenth century the two powers were in frequent conflict; in 1859 their boundaries were at long last settled by treaty. This was replaced by an agreement signed at Lisbon in 1893, which also established arbitration for disputes. In the Second World War the Japanese occupied Timor early in 1942; afterwards the western part of the island was incorporated in Indonesia.

The colony of Portuguese Timor has an area of more than 7,000 square miles and a population of about 440,000. It occupies the eastern half of the island and the Oc-Cusse exclave in the Indonesian section. This is a territory of some 310 square miles, on the north coast, bordered by the Savu Sea, and has valuable sandalwood forests and coconut groves with rice plantations. Pante Macassar, its chief town and port, is on Ombai Strait and has an airport. The Portuguese colony also includes the offshore islands of Atauro, also known as Pulo Cambing or Kambing – a hilly island of 72 square miles with a population mainly occupied in fishing – and Jaco, uninhabited, about five square miles in area, off the eastern tip of Timor, in the Timor Sea. The chief port and capital of the colony is Dili, or Dilly, which has soap, perfume and pottery industries, and exports cotton, coffee, hides, rice, sandalwood, wheat and wool. Its population is about 2,000.

Indonesian Timor has an area of nearly 6,000 square miles and a population of over 400,000. Its capital is Kupang, a port with a bunker station, exporting copra, hides, pearls, sandalwood and trepang. Its airport is an important link in the Java-Australian route.

The Timor Sea, between Timor and the north coast of Australia, is a shark-infested arm of the Indian Ocean, with a width of about 300 miles, merging to the northwest with the Arafura Sea.

Tobago

A noted tourist resort. Location *West Indies, 22 miles north-northeast of Trinidad.* Area *116.24 square miles.* Map *2, J4.*

Christopher Columbus discovered Tobago in 1498 on his third voyage. Dutchmen from Zeeland settled on the island in 1632, after an attempt to colonize it from Barbados had failed in 1618. It remained a much-contested island, establishing something of a record in changing hands no less than a dozen times between Britain, France, the Netherlands and James, "the Viking Duke" of Courland – until in 1814 it became finally and lastingly British. It was amalgamated with Trinidad in 1888 to form a Crown Colony.

Defoe took Tobago for his model in describing Robinson Crusoe's island – though Alexander Selkirk, the original of Crusoe, was actually marooned on Juan Fernandez in the South Pacific, some 3,000 miles away. Tobago, indeed, would have been a far more pleasant place for the five long years. It has a pleasant tropical climate with a dry season from December to June and the average temperature is 80° F. Its natural beauty has attracted many visitors – its beaches are served by boats from Port of Spain, Trinidad, and its airport, Crown Point, near the southwestern tip, is within easy jet-distance from New York or London. Tobago has several excellent anchorages. A low ridge, rising to 1,890 feet, crosses the island, which has several large virgin forests, mostly of hardwood.

The population makes a living from cacao, copra, sugar cane and tobacco, and from enthusiastic tourists.

Tonga-Kermadec Trench

A deep rift in the floor of the Pacific containing some of the deepest places in the world's oceans. Location *East of the Tonga and Kermadec archipelagoes, running south of Samoa.* Length *1,500 miles.* Maximum depth *Over 35,000 feet.* Map *4, H8–10.*

A canyon deeper than seven Grand Canyons, in length equal to the distance from New York to Havana, the Tonga-Kermadec Trench (discovered in 1895) is one of the major, though hidden, features of the Pacific Ocean. The average depth of the Pacific is 13,215 feet, but in the Tonga-Kermadec Trench, and in the Marianas, Japan, Philippine and other trenches, the sea floor drops suddenly 30,000 feet or more in a deep furrow. Similar trenches, though much less deep, occur in the Atlantic and Indian oceans, lying like the Pacific trenches just off the edge of the continental shelf, usually alongside a chain of islands. Here the lighter rock of which the continents are composed suddenly thins out, and the heavier rock, typical of the great ocean basins and of the deeper layers of the earth's crust, comes close to the surface.

While the older, shallower trenches of which we know are full of accumulated sediment, the deepest trenches are bare and rough-walled; so young that no sediment has had time to settle in them, except perhaps for some small quantities of dust from nearby active volcanoes.

Scientists believe that the rock of the earth's crust is in circulation on the most gigantic, continental scale. Deep down, as heat accumulates – for rock is a poor conductor – the crust begins to rise to the surface in a slow convection current rather like that in heated asphalt or jam.

When it reaches the surface, it spreads slowly and, being no longer surrounded by the insulating earth, cools. With the release of pressure it may also change structurally into a lighter and different kind of rock. Meanwhile, below, cool rock is being drawn in on all sides to take the place of the hot rock that has risen – and to take the place of this rock, yet cooler rock is drawn from above. In this way a complete circulation is established over a vast period of time, with long intervals of stability when the hot rock has reached the surface and cooled and the cool rock, which has descended, has not had time to heat up.

Such great circulation cycles seem to correspond with the great periods of mountain building and continent formation, and also with the earth's geological ages.

Ocean trenches are believed to be the outward manifestations of descending currents, where masses of rock are being brought together, buckled, folded and forcibly dragged downwards. Various tests seem to prove this theory. The temperature of the rock in these trenches is about half the normal temperature at such depths – which would be expected if the down currents were of cold rock. This downward pull will eventually be released at the end of the geological cycle, but by that time the trenches will be full of sediment, so a vast thickness of sediment will rise high in the air to form a range of mountains where each of the trenches now lies.

Meanwhile, today, the stresses and strains deep beneath the trenches are enormous; rock is being sheared, melted and faulted. Adjacently there are always belts of young active volcanoes, where this molten rock is forcing through the crust. Most of the deep earthquakes of the world also originate beneath the trenches.

Torres Strait

A shallow, island-dotted stretch of sea. Location *Between the south coast of New Guinea and the north coast of Cape York Peninsula, Australia.* Width *About 95 miles.* Map *4, D8.*

The Torres Strait, discovered in 1606 by Luis Vaez de Torres, the Spanish navigator, on his voyage around New Guinea, connects the Arafura Sea with the Coral Sea. At the southwestern end, Endeavour Strait leads from it into the Gulf of Carpentaria, while on the northeast the Great Northeast Channel branches off into the Gulf of Papua of the Coral Sea.

Scene of numerous shipwrecks, the Strait contains the Torres Islands, the northernmost group of the New Hebrides. There are several hundred of them, scattered over 20,000 square miles of sea. They include Prince of Wales Island (75 square miles), Hiu (10 square miles), Tegua, Toga and Lo, with other hilly, volcanic isles, some of them of striking beauty, and a good many tiny uninhabited coral islets barely showing above the water. They form part of Queensland, Australia, although geographically and ethnologically they are more closely associated with New Guinea. There has been a steady decline in the population of the Islands, which began at the end of the nineteenth century when great beds of valuable pearl oysters were discovered. The Islands were invaded by hundreds of adventurers – white, Japanese, Filipino, Malay, Papuan, South Sea Islanders – and the natives,

Land's En

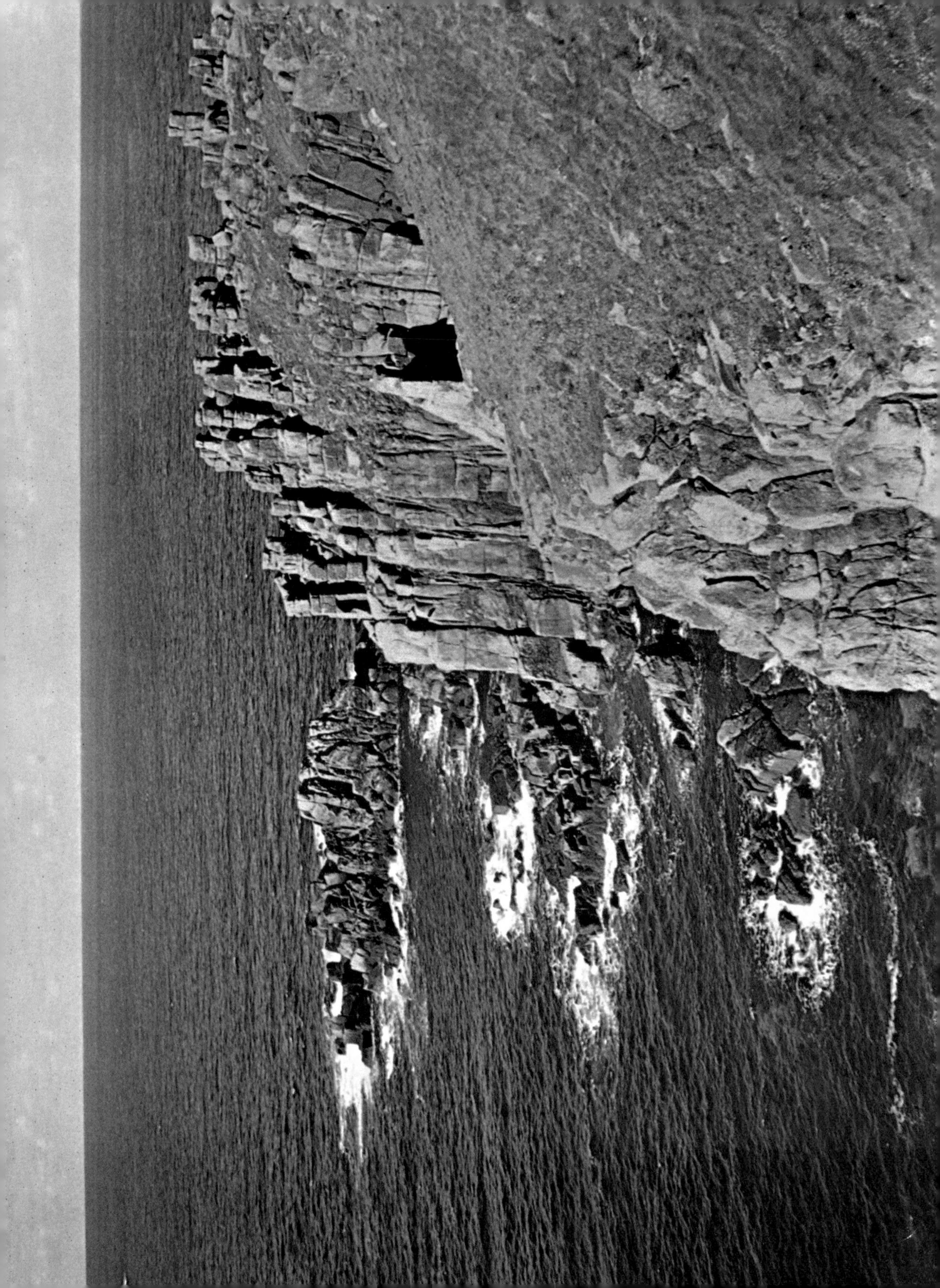

until then notable for their fine physique, were reduced to semi-slavery and overworked as divers (often to premature death), until the Queensland government stepped in. Since the end of the Second World War there are signs of the decline being halted; the population is now about 4,000.

Tortuga Island

An island near Haiti, formerly notorious as a haunt of pirates. Location *Caribbean Sea.* Area *70 square miles.* Map *2, F2.*

Of the three Tortuga islands in the world – one in the Gulf of California, a second off the coast of Venezuela and the third near Haiti – the last is the biggest and most important. All three have been named after the turtles that infested them.

The Haitian Tortuga was one of the earliest refuges of French and English freebooters in the seventeenth century. There are also relics on the Island of a vanished race, the Arawaks, whose broken pottery is found more abundantly on Tortuga than anywhere else in the West Indies.

Though rugged and roadless, the Island is well-populated (about 13,000 people live on it), except at the wooded western end, where wild boar are still to be found. The Atlantic coast of the Island is so sheer that in some places fishermen have to use ropes to get down to their boats. There are no good harbors, but the fishing villages – Boucan Guepès, La Vallée, Pointe-à-Oiseaux, Cayonne and Basse-Terre (the buccaneers' capital) – offer adequate anchorages. The present capital is Palmiste, in the uplands; nearby are the ruins of the palace to which Pauline Bonaparte Leclerc retired with her court in 1802 to escape the ravages of malaria and yellow fever on Haiti.

Only bananas and subsistence crops are grown on Tortuga, which dozes sleepily in the reflected glory of its boisterous past.

Trinidad

One of the world's most important sources of asphalt. Location *West Indies, Atlantic Ocean, ten miles off the Venezuela coast.* Area *1,863.82 square miles.* Map *2, J4.*

Trinidad is almost square in shape, with promontories to the north of and south its western coast that enclose the Gulf of Paria. These ridges, forming the northern and southern spurs of the island, are continuations of mountain chains on the mainland of Venezuela. Port of Spain, the capital of Trinidad, is on the Gulf and is one of the most important towns in the West Indies.

Discovered by Columbus in 1496, Trinidad remained a Spanish possession until the British captured it at the end of the eighteenth century. The island's history matches its exotic, tropical nature; for many years, Trinidad was one of the haunts of the buccaneers, and Port of Spain had the reputation of being one of the wildest, most unruly ports in the Caribbean. The Spanish occupation is still reflected in much of the architecture of the city although this has been tempered by Victorian and Edwardian houses and hotels and overlaid in recent years by American-style office buildings and shops. During the summer the town and harbor are often stiflingly hot, with a high degree of humidity, for the trade winds do not blow as far as Trinidad. The offshore winds from Venezuela, though they provide a working breeze for the island schooners, are themselves hot and moisture-laden.

The people of the city are as colorful as their surroundings. Negroes predominate among the inhabitants, and there are several thousand Chinese. The white population is a mixture of British, French, Spanish and Portuguese. In a brief walk through the town's main streets, one meets almost every conceivable blend of color and racial feature. The prevailing note is gaiety and the famous calypsos of Trinidad (often pointed comments on the social and political scene) reflect the mood of sharp but good-humored vigor that is so noticeable in the island. In the evenings, when a cool breeze from the mountains descends, the sound of the steel bands with their plangent vibratory drumming is heard. Empty oil drums, specially tempered to give the required pitch, are the basis of a steel band, and competitions are held annually during the festival of Mardi Gras.

Combining rich agriculture with the production of asphalt and oil, Trinidad has suffered less than any other island in the West Indies from economic problems. The soil is fertile and many varieties of tropical fruit and plant grow in abundance. Sugar cane is the main crop, but

ftsund Strait, Lofoten Islands

Trinidad also exports cocoa, coffee, indiarubber and timber, as well as having a monopoly of Angostura bitters. Asphalt remains, however, its most important product and the great Pitch Lake is one of the world's most important sources of supply. At first sight it reminds one of a scene from Dante's Inferno: the great pool, about 114 acres in area, heaves and steams in the center, and the air about it quivers. Around the edge, the asphalt is comparatively hard, but the strong tropical sun at midday gives it the texture of a newly-tarred road. The Lake is something over three miles in circumference and the acrid smell of pitch hangs in the air. In places the asphalt bulks itself in heavy muscular ridges which move slowly towards the sea, and the tropical rainstorms leave pools of water in the Lake's hollows and depressions. The asphalt which now goes to surface the roads of the world was first used by buccaneers to caulk and coat their craft.

Tristan da Cunha

An isolated volcanic island group in the South Atlantic. Location *Roughly halfway between South Africa and South America.* Area *40 square miles.* Map *6, G9.*

Tristan da Cunha is a volcanic group discovered in 1506 by the Portuguese admiral Tristão da Cunha, after whom the principal island, as well as the group, was named. The islands, which include Gough Island, Inaccessible Island and Nightingale Island, are roughly halfway between South Africa and South America, and about 1,600 miles south-southwest of St Helena.

British and American sealers set up temporary headquarters here from about the middle of the eighteenth century. In 1816 the group was annexed by Britain, and a garrison was placed on the principal island. The following year the garrison was withdrawn, but Corporal William

The volcano on Tristan da Cunha

Glass, with his wife and two children, elected to stay behind. They were later joined by others, forming the nucleus of a contented, though isolated, community.

In 1942, a British meteorological and radio station was set up on the main island, and in 1948 a South African company was given permission to establish a fishing and canning industry.

Then, in October, 1961, disaster struck. The dormant volcano in the middle of Tristan da Cunha island erupted unexpectedly, and the islanders were hastily evacuated to Nightingale Island, 18 miles away. A Dutch liner took them on to Cape Town, and from there they were taken to Britain and housed for the time being in a disused army camp. Two months later, as the eruption continued and there seemed no prospect of Tristan da Cunha becoming habitable again in the foreseeable future, the British government arranged permanent homes for the islanders in former Royal Air Force married quarters at Calshot, near Southampton.

Trobriand Islands

A small volcanic island group under Australian administration. Location *Territory of Papua, southwest Pacific.* Map *4, E8.*

The Trobriands lie about 100 miles off the northeast coast of the mainland of Papua. They consist of four main islands, of which Kiriwina is the largest, and several smaller ones. The Australian government station is at Losuia, on Kiriwina.

The Islands are of coral formation; they are very fertile and thickly inhabited. The Islanders are skilful wood carvers, and all their houses are richly decorated with carvings of birds, fishes and animals. Unlike the dug-outs used almost everywhere in Papua and New Guinea, the Trobriand canoes are built of planks, with the seams sewn and caulked.

The Islands produce yams, pearl shell, pearls and sea cucumbers. The Islanders are not cannibals – and, so far as is known, have never been. They practise white magic, including various forms of rain-making, and use charms and incantations for the cure of illness and to encourage growing crops.

During the Second World War, the Trobriands were used as an Allied base from 1943 onwards. Today, apart from representatives of the Australian government and members of the Methodist mission, the only settlers are a few traders who deal in copra, bêche-de-mer and pearls found in the lagoons. The native population is about 10,000.

Trucial Coast

The southernmost section of the Persian Gulf, once notorious as the Pirate Coast. Location *From the Oman Promontory to the base of Qatar Peninsula.* Length *About 350 miles.* Map *10, C3.*

The low-lying coast of Trucial Oman is protected by a maze of shoals, small islands and reefs. The many shallow inlets of the mainland provided natural harbors for the small, fast dhows of the Jawasmi, as the pirates of this area were collectively called. During the eighteenth century, they confined themselves to boarding local vessels. Later, they came under the influence of the fanatical Wahabi sect (who consider themselves the only true Moslems and among whom it was formerly held virtuous to kill not only infidels but also any Moslems who did not belong to the sect).

The advantages of the Wahabite religious dogma were keenly felt by the Jawasmi, and piracy developed from a way of making a living into an article of faith. The pirates became bolder, and the turn of the century saw the beginning of a reign of terror which lasted virtually unchecked until 1819. British destruction of the principal Jawasmi stronghold in 1810, following attacks against vessels of the East India Company, caused only a temporary lull in their depredations.

Finally, in 1819, a joint expedition organized by the British and the Sultan of Muscat systematically reduced every fortress along the notorious coast and sank or burned every pirate ship. A truce between Britain and the local sheiks was signed in 1820 and was made perpetual in 1853; all the local rulers bound themselves to abstain from piracy. The coast was named after this truce. A final treaty was signed in 1892.

The treaties also attempted to put an end to

slave trading, for many years the second staple industry of the southern shore. Slaves were brought to the Gulf by the thousand from East Africa, for Arabian, Persian and Turkish purchasers. Slaving, however, is no longer a profitable trade, though it still survives. Piracy is almost unknown and although British naval patrols still keep an eye open, the dark, swift dhows of the sinister Jawasmi no longer lie in wait in the southern shallows, and the tankers pass majestically on their way with their precious cargoes for Europe or America.

Truk

A group of 57 volcanic islands, a major Japanese base in the Second World War. Location *Eastern Caroline Islands, western Pacific.* Area *39 square miles.* Map *4, E6.*

The Truk islands were discovered and colonized by the Spaniards who – as with so many of their Pacific possessions – sold them to Germany in the eighteen-nineties. At the end of the First World War they became a Japanese mandated territory under the League of Nations. The Japanese, ignoring the terms of the Mandate, fortified them – chopping off the tops of two mountains and dredging deep channels – and they became one of their major naval and air bases in the Pacific, serving as one of the main springboards of the Japanese advance south and east in the early months of the Second World War. Though the base was repeatedly attacked by American planes, heavily damaging or destroying shore installations and shipping, and was shelled by a British task force in June, 1945, it was by-passed in the American landings in the Marianas to the north and did not surrender until September, 1945.

Apart from the volcanic islands, there are many small coral islands, forming a dangerous triangle-shaped reef occupying about 140 square miles. The two largest volcanic islands are Tol (9 square miles, rising to 1,483 feet) and Moen (8.5 square miles); next in importance are Fefan, Dublon, Udot, Uman and Kuop (two miles south, but generally included in the group). Dublon is the headquarters of the district government; it was between Dublon and the neighboring Uman and Fefan that the Japanese base established its main anchorage.

The islands produce copra and dried bonito; their pre-war population, estimated at 16,000, has been reduced to around 10,000. The group is now under United States administration.

Tuamotu Islands

A scattered group of about 80 small coral atolls in French Oceania. Location *South Pacific.* Area *330 square miles.* Map *4, L9–M9.*

The Tuamotus, or Low Archipelago, are scattered over a vast area of more than 140,000 square miles of ocean, east of Tahiti. Discovered by the Spanish in 1606, they were annexed by France in 1881 and are administered from Tahiti.

Without the coconut palm, human life could not survive on most of these low, waterless rings of coral, which have a total population of a little over 5,000. From coconut palms the Islanders obtain food and drink, building materials and utensils, even a medium of exchange. The trunks are used for house posts, beams and rafters, for dug-out canoes, and for fuel. The leaves make excellent thatch or, dried and bunched, efficient torches for lighting the way at night or attracting fish on the reefs. They can be woven into baskets, carriers, mats and screens; the midribs are used for fences and walls; the basal sheath – like coarse sacking – for wrapping material or straining-muslin. In the center of the crown of leaves there is the young unopened bud which can be eaten cooked as a vegetable or raw as a salad – the world-famous "mountain cabbage." The sap from the young flower-stalks can be fermented into toddy or distilled into the arrack drunk on festive occasions.

The coconuts themselves, when young, tender and green, provide what may be the only drinkable liquid on an atoll – coconut milk – while the flesh is a delicate cream. When ripe, this cream turns into hard, nutritious flesh from which a rich oil can be compressed – useful in cooking, for anointing the hair and body or for burning in lamps. The inner shell, dried and cleaned, can be shaped into an infinite variety of vessels – bowls, pitchers, flasks, spoons, cups, forks, scoops – as well as into implements such as fishhooks and arrow points. Even the surrounding husk is useful, for its fiber is made into rope and string for fishlines, nets, cord to bind house-frames and fences and to tie on arrow-heads, etc. Finally, dried and smoked, the coconut meat becomes copra, used by the civilized world as a source of oil for making margarine and other purposes. No wonder that every coconut palm, even on the uninhabited islands, probably has its owner, and that wealth is reckoned in numbers of trees.

Some of the Tuamotus have another source of wealth in pearl-diving. Holding a 16-pound weight tied to a rope, with a basket also on its end, the diver plunges 120 feet down for a 2½-minute stay under water, during which time he collects up to a dozen shells before ascending to the surface. Seventy dives a day is not bad, it is said – a hundred may drive one mad. But over-fishing has reduced the size of the shells brought up and diminished the number of pearls found.

Tyrrhenian Sea

A large arm of the Mediterranean with many bays and gulfs. Location *Between the west coast of Italy and the islands of Corsica, Sardinia and Sicily.* Map *9, C9.*

Taking its name from Tyrrhenus, legendary founder of the Etruscan kingdom, the Tyrrhenian is one of the most interesting areas of the Mediterranean. It was over this sea that the Etruscans ruled until their defeat by the Romans.

The Tyrrhenian is crossed by a number of shipping lanes – from Algeria and Marseilles to Naples and from Marseilles and Genoa for ships bound east through the Strait of Messina. Naples and Palermo are the principal ports. Since the establishment of docks at Palermo and facilities for large modern oil tankers, the volume of traffic to Sicily has increased greatly. From Palermo a steady traffic runs to England with fruit, especially oranges and lemons.

Few rivers of importance drain into the Tyrrhenian; the Tiber is almost the only major one.

For most seasons of the year this is a gentle sea. The principal winds are the tramontana, an offshore wind blowing from the mountains behind the Italian coastline, and the sirocco, a southerly wind which blows mainly in spring and summer. The sirocco can be extremely hot by the time it reaches the Tyrrhenian, as well as humid from the moisture absorbed on its passage over the southern Mediterranean. During a sirocco the Gulf of Gioia, to the east of the Lipari Islands, can be a dangerous area, the wind descending in squalls off the mountains of Sicily and Calabria and the current from the Strait of Messina pushing up an ugly sea. Westerly winds, known to the Italians as *libeccio*, can also blow strongly over the Tyrrhenian and are usually coupled with the passage of a cyclonal depression moving eastward over the Mediterranean. In winter the strongest wind comes from the north-east, the gregale; it can raise a heavy sea in only a few hours. When it blows, the water banks up in the large Bay of Palermo and a dangerous swell results, even inside the modern harbor.

In summer the Tyrrhenian is often an area of cloudless calm for days on end, but electrical storms are quite frequent. These build up over the land and can be detected by the mounting cumulo-nimbus clouds that rise like fantastic baroque cathedrals above the hot coastline. Off the western coast of Italy they hurl themselves seaward with amazing speed, causing damaged sails and broken masts even among the experienced local fishermen.

The Sea is at its deepest in the southeast between Sicily and Naples, in the area of the volcanic Lipari Islands. Coastal fishing plays an important part in the economy of all the islands and of the Tyrrhenian coastline. Flying fish, gunnard, mullet, wrasse and squid are caught; there are several tunny fisheries, especially off Sicily; and the Tyrrhenian swordfish is among the best eating in the Mediterranean.

Ushant

A small, barren island, the westernmost point of France. Location *Off the coast of Brittany, Atlantic Ocean.* Dimensions *5 miles long, 2 miles wide.* Map *8, C5.*

Ushant, or Ouessant, has an area of 3,850 acres. Almost entirely granitic, its steep, rugged coasts are accessible only in a few places; frequent fogs make it a danger to navigation. A channel about 14 miles wide separates it from the coast of Finistère.

The rocky shore of Ushant

A breed of small black sheep is raised on the island and potatoes and cereals are grown. The population is about 2,200; the men are mostly pilots and fishermen, while the women tend the fields. The port of Lampaul is on the southwestern side; a lighthouse, at its northwest point, marks the entrance to the English Channel.

Ushant was attacked and laid waste by the English in 1388; in 1597 it was made a marquisate, the title being held by René de Rieux de Sourdéac, governor of Brest. Ushant has always guarded the approaches to the French naval base of Brest, frequently giving France a tactical advantage during naval battles with Britain.

On July 27, 1778, an indecisive battle was fought off Ushant between the French and British fleets – the first major sea battle in European waters of the American War of Independence.

Vancouver Island

The largest island off the western coast of America. Location *British Columbia.* Area *13,049 square miles.* Map *4, M2.*

Vancouver, separated from the southwest coast of British Columbia by Queen Charlotte Strait, Johnstone Strait, Haro Strait, the Strait of Georgia and Juan de Fuca Strait, became a separate Crown Colony under the administration of the Hudson's Bay Company as early as 1849. The Oregon Treaty of 1846 had defined the boundary between Canada and the United States along the forty-ninth parallel of latitude; but as a result of the discovery of gold along the Fraser River, and the consequent wild rush of prospectors, a separate colony of "New Caledonia" (later renamed British Columbia) was founded in 1858. In 1866 the older region of Vancouver Island was added to it. The Island's name commemorates the great British navigator, Captain George Vancouver, whose explorations and chartings of the coastline began in 1792.

Vancouver Island is rugged and heavily forested, like the mainland of British Columbia. Its northern half is mountainous and some of the grandest alpine scenery is found in Strathcona Provincial Park in the central region. Here is the Forbidden Plateau from which the loftier peaks rise – Golden Hinde (7,219 feet, the highest on the Island), Elkhor (7,200 feet) and others. Small glaciers and permanent snowfields – the Comox and Cliffe glaciers and the Aurole snowfield among them – cling to the flanks of the mountains. Victoria Peak (7,095 feet) lies to the northwest and outside Strathcona Park. Towards the southeastern end of the Island the mountains are much lower, seldom exceeding 3,000 feet, and many are rather flat-topped.

There are several long, deep fjords on the west coast, of which Nootka Sound, Quatsino Sound and the so-called Alberti Canal are the most important. The fjords and the numerous lakes in the interior follow in general the rectangular pattern of those on the mainland coast; they have been attributed to the effects of crustal fracture and pre-glacial and glacial erosion. Geologically, the Island forms part of the Coast Range mountains. Coal, copper and gold are found in valuable quantities: the Zeballos gold mine at the head of Esperanza Inlet, north of Nootka Island, was discovered early in 1934 and has been one of British Columbia's, and Western Canada's, best producers of gold. Forestry is another important industry.

Esquimault Bay has a naval dockyard, which is equipped with one of the largest dry docks in the world. Nearby is the city of Victoria, capital of British Columbia. It has a mild climate and a fine situation, looking south across Juan de Fuca Strait, which is a reminder of early Spanish activities. From its historic origin as one of the earliest British colonies and as a fur-trading port in 1843 under the Hudson's Bay Company, Victoria rose to become the principal commercial town of the province, though by 1886 it was eclipsed by the mainland city of Vancouver.

Vancouver Island's population is over 150,000.

Victoria Island

The third largest island in the Canadian Arctic Archipelago. Location *Southwest Franklin district, Northwest Territories, Canada.* Area *80,340 square miles.* Map *5, A6–B6.*

Victoria Island, about 425 miles long and 350 miles wide, lies immediately north of the Canadian mainland, with Banks Island to the northwest, Prince of Wales Island to the northeast, and King William Island to the southeast.

It was first seen in 1826 from the mainland side of Dolphin and Union Strait by Dr John Richardson, on Sir John Franklin's second expedition. He named it Wollaston Island. In 1838 Peter Warren Dease and Thomas Simpson observed another part of its south coast from Kent Peninsula, and called it after young Queen Victoria, who had succeeded to the throne in the previous year. In 1839 they explored the south coast by boat from Cape Colborne for about 100 miles to the west. The exploration of the south coast was completed by Dr John Rae in 1851, during the search for the unfortunate Franklin expedition. He covered by sledge and boat the whole distance from Prince Albert Sound in the west to Point Polly on the east. Here he was within a few miles of discovering the answer to the Franklin tragedy, but ice in Victoria Strait prevented him from crossing to King William Island.

In 1850 an expedition led by Captain R. Collinson was sent to search for Franklin from Bering Strait. During the winter of 1850–51, sledge parties explored the west and north coasts of Victoria Island from Prince Albert Sound to Wynnicet Bay. In 1851–52, Collinson made almost exactly the same voyage, spending the winter in Walker Bay. In 1852 he sailed south round the Island to Cambridge Bay, and in the spring of 1853 he traveled by sledge a short distance past the farthest point reached by Rae – but also failed to cross the strait to King William Island where Franklin and his men had perished.

In 1905 Lieutenant Godfred Hansen of the Amundsen Expedition, wintering on King William Island, traveled up the east coast as far as Cape Nansen. The rest of the north coast was mapped by Storker T. Storkerson of Vilhjalmur Stefansson's Canadian Arctic Expedition during two sledge journeys in 1915 and 1917. The *Polar Bear* of Stefansson's expedition spent two winters off the west coast, the first at Armstrong Point (1915–16), the second in Walker Bay (1916–17). Stefansson Island, off the northeast peninsula of Victoria Island, though seen by Storkerson in 1917, was not put on the maps until photographed by the Canadian Air Force in 1946–47.

A geological reconnaissance by air was carried out by Dr A. L. Washton in 1938–41, over the southern part of the Island. In 1949 he was joined by A. E. Porgild and J. L. Jeness, who studied the Island's botany and geography. In 1947–49 five landings were made by Canadian Air Force planes to take magnetic observations.

Victoria Island consists largely of flat-bedded Paleozoic sediments interrupted by two arches of Precambrian rock. There is a well-defined upland belt stretching from the west coast (Prince Albert Sound and Walker Bay) to the north coast between Glenelg Bay and Hadley Bay. The other arch outcrops in the Richardson Islands off the south coast and turns inland from Wellington Bay, but is much less distinctive. The

Big Cinnamon Bay, in the Virgin Islands

eastern part is very low, rising gradually towards the northwest, reaching about 1,000 feet northeast of Prince Albert Sound. The northeastern peninsula has steep cliffs on the western side. The topography of Wollaston Peninsula is more varied, with some hills rising to 1,700 feet. There are a few small and unimportant hills in the east – the exception being Mount Pelly, about seven miles northeast of Cambridge Bay, which forms a very prominent landmark, being the highest point (675 feet) in the lowlands.

Outcrops of bedrock are found in some parts of the Island, but are mostly covered with drift material, mainly of glacial origin.

The Precambrian upland consists of Proterozoic sedimentary and volcanic rocks, forming tilted tabular blocks with sharp edges and flat or gently sloping tops. The highest and most rugged are south and east of Glenelg Bay, rising to about 2,500 feet. Copper is found in Prince Albert Sound and around Minto Inlet. Northwest of the upland there is a rolling plateau about 1,000–1,500 feet in height, divided into two slightly inclined areas by two rivers rising near the edge of the upland, flowing first north, then east into the head of Richard Collinson Inlet. The river mouths are flat and sandy.

The population of Victoria Island is about 350. Eskimos frequent the southern part and occasionally visit the north. There are three settlements: on Holman Island (in King's Bay, Amundsen Gulf); on Read Island, off the southwest coast; and at Cambridge Bay, on the southeast coast.

Virgin Islands

A group of about 100 small islands, divided between the United States and Great Britain. Location *West Indies.* Area *About 192 square miles.* Map *2, H2.*

Spread over 60 miles of ocean, between the Virgin Passage on the west and Anegada Passage on the east, the Virgin Islands form the westernmost part of the Lesser Antilles, though geographically they belong to Puerto Rico and the Greater Antilles. With a pleasant, equitable climate – there are generally two dry and two wet seasons, and the heat is tempered by the northeast trade winds – they produce sugar cane, sea-island cotton, tobacco, coconuts, limes and vegetables.

Columbus came upon this delightful island cluster in 1494, on his second voyage, and named them for St Ursula, the legendary British princess who was martyred at Cologne with 11 of her companions (though tradition increased this number to a more impressive 11,000 by misreading a medieval manuscript).

The names of some of the Islands – Rum, Dead Man's Chest, Fallen Jerusalem, Salt Water, Money Rock – are enough to indicate how far from the lofty principles of their holy patroness their inhabitants fell in the seventeenth century, when the Virgin Islands were a favorite resort of pirates and buccaneers.

The Virgin Islands were first colonized by the Dutch; the Danish West Indies Company established its first permanent settlement on St Thomas in 1672. Eight years later, Negro slaves were introduced to work on the sugar plantations, which became very prosperous. In 1754 some of the Islands were formed into the colony of the Danish West Indies. Tortola was originally settled by the Dutch but passed into British possession in 1666; the Danish-held islands were acquired by the United States (after negotiations which had begun more than 50 years previously) in 1917 – for a bargain price of $25,000,000.

The British Virgin Islands have an area of 59 square miles and a population of 7,600. They number about 32, including Tortola (the largest), Virgin Gorda, Anegada and Jost van Dykes; only 11 in the group are inhabited. There is a small airfield on Beef Island; a daily launch service connects them with St Thomas, in the American part of the group. The principal exports are livestock, fish, charcoal, vegetables and fruit; rum is distilled on a small scale. The Islands are governed by an Administrator assisted by an Executive Council, of which two members are chosen by the unofficial members of the Legislative Council. The capital is Road Town, on the southeast coast of Tortola.

The American Virgin Islands have an area of 132 square miles and a population of 31,000. St Thomas, St Croix and St John are the principal islands; the capital, Charlotte Amalie, on St Thomas, has one of the finest harbors in the West Indies, with a large coaling and oil refuelling station. Universal suffrage was introduced in 1936 and the Islands are on their way to self-government.

Viscount Melville Sound

A large section of the east-west passage through the Arctic Archipelago. Location *Western Franklin district, Northwest Territories, Arctic Ocean.* Dimensions *250 miles long, 100 miles wide.* Map *5, B6–7.*

Viscount Melville Sound is an arm of the Arctic Ocean and is an important section of the long-sought Northwest Passage. It leads between Banks, Victoria and Prince of Wales islands on the south and Melville and Bathurst islands on the north. To the west, McClure Strait branches off to the Beaufort Sea, while Barrow Strait and McClintock Channel connect it on the east and southeast. The Sound is navigable only under favorable weather conditions during late summer.

When Sir Robert McClure discovered the western part of the great Sound during his voyage of 1850–53, he found the natives on the shores far from friendly. "... Great was my surprise upon approaching the land," he wrote, "to find instead of being greeted with the usual friendly signs that two savages with gesticulations the most menacing, having bended their bows with arrows on their strings, and one with a large knife which he brandished most significantly, waved us off. Taking no heed of these hostile demonstrations, we pulled in. They retreated yelling furiously..."

Sir Robert named the Sound after Henry Dundas, third Viscount Melville, suppressor of the Canadian rebellion of 1837. He managed to extract some vague information from the Eskimos about an earlier party of explorers who had built a house and then moved inland; but it was never discovered who they were, and some experts today believe that the story was traditional, dating from the time of the earliest discoveries in the New World.

Wash, The

A shallow inlet of the North Sea. Location *Between Lincolnshire and Norfolk, on the east coast of England.* Dimensions *20 miles long, 15 miles wide.* Map *8, D4.*

A squarish inlet of the sea, 12 miles across at the mouth, the Wash has for centuries been silting up with sediment carried down from the land by the four rivers that flow into it – the Witham, the Welland, the Nene and the Great Ouse. Since Roman times, men have been progressively reclaiming new areas of silt accretions to add to the area of the fertile Fens. There was a sharp setback at the time of the dissolution of the monasteries by Henry VIII, but since the Dutchman Vermuiden's work in the seventeenth century the process has been resumed. But it is piecemeal reclamation of small areas of saltings nearest the existing sea wall; there will be no dramatic dam building here, as there has been in Holland, for the Wash has a rise and fall of 18 feet between low and high tide.

The sands and channels in the Wash are constantly shifting. As it is impossible to enter the mouths of any of the four rivers at low tide, it is inadvisable to run for the Wash in a northeast gale.

An important shellfish industry is carried on from King's Lynn and Boston, with shrimps, mussels and cockles as the chief catch. Few white fish are caught, owing to the enormous number of seals, which rest on the exposed sandbanks at low water and swim after fish at high tide.

Weddell Sea

A broad inlet of the South Atlantic. Location *Between Palmer Peninsula and Coats Land, Antarctica.* Area *About 770,000 square miles.* Map *3, F8.*

The coastal ice-cliffs of the inner portion of the Weddell Sea have not yet been delineated, so that its area cannot be established definitely. Neither the Weddell Sea nor the somewhat smaller Ross Sea on the other side of Antarctica are deep gulfs, but coastal "shelf" seas lying over the Weddell and Ross shelves. Along the inner limit of the Weddell Sea, the line of great ice-cliffs stretches for some 450 miles; it forms the terminal front of the Weddell or Filchner Ice Shelf, fed in part from the continental ice-sheet of the interior. It has been thought – though it has not been fully proved – that a continuous depression by way of this Shelf westwards to the Ross Shelf Ice and Sea may mark a major belt of subsidence, or rift-zone, across the continent.

The Weddell Sea has generally been considered very difficult for navigation because of the amount and movement of its pack ice. James Weddell, the sealer who discovered it in 1823, sailed south to latitude 74°15′ and found relatively good conditions. He named it originally "Sea of King George IV." In 1904 W. S. Bruce in the *Scotia* discovered Coats Land on the east side; in 1912 W. Filchner found the Leopold Coast. Sir Ernest Shackleton's *Endurance* was crushed in the pack ice in 1915, and his party subsequently made their epic escape to Elephant Island.

During the International Geophysical Year, four stations were established at the head of the Sea: Halley Bay, the Royal Society base (since taken over by the Falkland Islands Dependencies Survey), on Caird Coast; "Shackleton," the Trans-Antarctic Expedition's base on the Weddell Ice Shelf; "General Belgrano," an Argentine base on the Weddell Ice Shelf; and "Ellsworth," the American base, also on the Weddell Ice Shelf, which was later transferred to Argentina.

West Indies

A vast chain of islands, spreading in a huge crescent of over 2,500 miles. Location *Off Central America, from Florida to the coast of Venezuela, separating the Atlantic from the Caribbean.* Area *About 72,000 square miles.* Map *2.*

The West Indies form perhaps the most picturesque and varied archipelago in the world; the islands range in size from the 44,000 square miles of Cuba to rocks less than an acre in extent. They stretch in a long curve from the southeast coast of Florida to the northern shore of South America, enclosing the Caribbean Sea and lying across the trade routes to the Panama Canal.

The name "West Indies" is due to the fact that when Christopher Columbus discovered them he believed he had reached India by a western route. The archipelago has also been called the Antilles, after Antilla, or Antiglia, a mythical country which was believed to exist in the west and which is shown on ancient charts about 200 leagues west of the Azores.

Jamaica, Cuba, Hispaniola (or Haiti) and Puerto Rico form the Greater Antilles, and the semicircle of smaller islands (Leeward Islands, Windward Islands, Trinidad and Tobago, Barbados and the Dutch and Venezuelan islands off the northern coast of Venezuela) form the Lesser Antilles.

Cuba, an independent republic with the Isle of Pines as a dependency, is by far the largest of the West Indian islands. Next in size is Hispaniola, divided between Haiti, in the west, and the Dominican Republic.

The British sphere of interest in the West Indies extends over the Bahamas, Barbados, Jamaica (with the Turks and Caicos Islands and the Cayman Islands), Trinidad and Tobago, the Windward Islands (which consist of Grenada, St Lucia, Dominica, St Vincent and the Grenadines) and the Leeward Islands (Antigua, Barbuda, Redonda, St Kitts, Nevis, Anguilla, Montserrat and the British Virgin Islands).

The two American dependencies are Puerto Rico and the Virgin Islands of the United States (St Thomas, St Croix, St John and some neighboring islets).

Guadeloupe (with its dependencies Marie-Galante, Les Saintes, Désirade and Saint-Barthélemy) and Martinique are French. Curaçao and its dependencies are Dutch. St Martin is owned jointly by the Dutch and French. Margarita is Venezuelan.

Most of the West Indies are volcanic in origin, but some are of coral formation. Many of the almost landlocked harbors are craters of extinct volcanoes. The islands are peaks of a submerged range of mountains, the Caribbean Andes, which early in the Tertiary period formed a link between North and South America. The discovery in Georgia and Carolina of fossilized remains of animals still surviving in South America, and the traces found in Guadeloupe of the Megatherium – a giant prehistoric animal that could not have existed within the narrow limits of a comparatively small island – seem to prove this. In the Tertiary period, the Isthmus of Panama was probably a group of islands, of which at least one (now represented by Ancon Hill, overlooking Panama city) was of volcanic origin. The subsidence which caused the present physiographic state of the Antilles was probably gradual. The first result was the formation of a large island occupying the site of Cuba, Jamaica, Haiti and Puerto Rico; this has been demonstrated by soundings and the distribution of flora and fauna. The bird known in Jamaica as the "Green Tody," for instance, is found in all four of these islands but nowhere else.

There are petroleum and manjak deposits in Barbados and Trinidad; the famous Pitch Lake in Trinidad provides an additional source of wealth in its seemingly inexhaustible asphalt. Bauxite is worked in Jamaica. Many of the islands have mineral springs and sulphur deposits.

The climate as a whole is healthy for Europeans throughout the year, especially during the northeast trade winds season in winter. The rainy season usually starts in June and lasts until the end of the year, with a break in August or September; but days without sunshine are rare and it is usually possible to predict rain. The nights are beautiful, the moon and stars shining with a tropical brilliance. The hurricane season is from August to October; but the hurricanes do not come without a warning fall in the barometer, and notice of their approach is signalled from stations of the United States Weather Bureau in the larger islands. Serious damage or loss of life are infrequent, though in 1950 and 1951 the Leeward Islands and Jamaica were badly hit. Volcanic eruptions have been confined in modern times to Mont Pelée in Martinique and the Soufrière in St Vincent.

The 15,000,000 people who live in the West Indies are a cosmopolitan mixture of English, Spanish, Portuguese, French, Dutch, Danish and American colonists and their descendants; of Negroes, East Indians and Chinese. The larger islands, when discovered, had a gentle, timid native population, the Arouagues or Arawaks, while the smaller islands were peopled by Charaibes or Caribs. The Arawaks were soon exterminated; but the Caribs were for many years a source of resistance and trouble. There are still families of almost pure-blooded Caribs in Dominica and a few in St Vincent.

Soon after the European occupation of the islands there was a desperate shortage of labor, and slavery was adopted by the Spaniards. The first slaves were imported by them to work the mines of Hispaniola before 1503. In 1517 Charles V gave the monopoly of the slave trade to a Flemish courtier, from whom it passed to Genoese merchants and then to the Portuguese.

Sir John Hawkins began slave trading in 1562 and Sir Francis Drake followed in 1568. Near the end of the sixteenth century the Dutch took up the trade and in 1662 and 1672 English "African Companies" were formed to conduct the traffic. In 1688 the African slave trade was thrown open to all Englishmen and at the end of the seventeenth century 25,000 Negroes were being imported annually in English ships to the English colonies. In 1713 the South Sea Company obtained the infamous *Asiento*, or contract to supply Spanish America with slaves, pledging itself to pay duty for every slave it brought to the Spanish West Indies while the King of Spain was to receive a quarter of the profits. The monopoly did not pay, and when the Spanish king demanded his share in 1739 this led to war; although the Treaty of Aix-la-Chapelle in 1748 renewed the contract for four years, it was finally annulled in 1750.

The slave trade was abolished in 1807, but slavery continued in the English colonies until 1834. The French colonies abolished slavery in 1848, the Dutch West Indies in 1863 and Puerto Rico in 1873. St Thomas held out until 1876. Slaves were gradually emancipated in Cuba, though total abolition was not achieved until 1886.

After the total abolition of slavery, shortage of labor became acute. There was intermittent Indian immigration. In 1853 Chinese were introduced into Trinidad and in 1854 some arrived in Jamaica. Many Chinese remained and are chiefly engaged in retail trade.

The origins of the white population of the West Indies are extremely varied. In the days of slavery, each slave owner was obliged to employ a certain number of white servants to serve in the militia; Cromwell sent many Irish prisoners to Nevis and Montserrat; Barbados received an influx of Royalists during the Commonwealth. In 1685, after the battle of Sedgmoor, hundreds of the followers of Monmouth, tried at the Bloody Assizes, were sent to Barbados by Judge Jeffreys. After the American Revolution, many loyalists emigrated to the West Indies with their slaves; Jamaica and the Bahamas were particularly favored. In the nineteenth century many Portuguese from Madeira and elsewhere settled in the islands; in 1840 Germans were imported into St Lucia. In Cuba there are descendants of old Spanish families and immigrants from Spain. And, of course, a considerable American population lives in the West Indies, mainly in Puerto Rico, though also in the British islands. The term "creole," which is commonly believed to apply only to people of colored descent, actually means anyone born in the West Indies, even if his parents are white. The term is even applied to animals and produce; for example, a creole cow, a creole dog or creole corn are familiar terms.

The chief languages of the West Indies are English, French and Spanish; there are a great many *patois* forms, such as *papiamento*, a mixture of Spanish, Portuguese and Dutch, which is spoken in Curaçao.

The West Indies have all achieved independence or considerable autonomy within the last 50 years.

Whales, Bay of

An inlet of the Antarctic Ocean. Location *Ross Shelf Ice, Antarctica.* Map *3, D9.*

Discovered by Sir James Clark Ross in 1841, visited by C. E. Borchgrevink in 1899, by Captain Robert Falcon Scott in 1901 and by Sir Ernest Shackleton (who gave it its name) in 1907, the Bay of Whales has been described as the strangest bay in the world. It is a break in the great Ice Barrier, and the ring of ice around it is 100 feet or more in height.

It was here that Roald Amundsen set up his winter camp in 1910, before starting off with

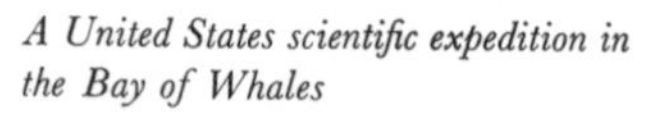

A United States scientific expedition in the Bay of Whales

four companions, four sledges and four teams of 13 dogs for the South Pole on October 19, 1911 – and it was to this base camp that they returned, triumphant, having been away for 99 days and having covered 1,860 miles. Amundsen did not find the Bay a particularly inviting place, being surrounded on all sides by the towering ice walls of the Barrier.

The greater part of this giant glacier is constantly on the move, slowly but unceasingly sliding down to the sea, where huge chunks break off into slowly floating icebergs. But Amundsen discovered that in the 68 years since it was first seen by Sir James Ross, this part in the Bay of Whales had been stationary – which meant that the glacier must be grounded here. It meant also that he could safely set up his winter camp on top of the ice shelf overlooking the Bay of Whales, 60 miles farther south than Scott and so that much nearer to his objective, the South Pole.

Roosevelt Island and Little America are just south of the Bay, which has become a crossroads of Antarctic exploration.

White Sea

A large inlet of the Barents Sea. Location *Northern Europe, USSR.* Area *36,680 square miles.* Map *7, J3.*

The White Sea has been called Russia's "snow-covered back door;" it played a vital part in the Second World War, when it was one of the main routes through which Allied aid could reach the hard-pressed Soviet Union. The "Murmansk Run," which often brought tragic losses in men and ships, was kept up until other, more practical, approaches were made available by Allied progress.

The White Sea is about 365 miles long. Its mouth – in the north – opens into the Barents Sea between the capes of Svyatoi Nos on the west and Kanin Nos on the east. A strait connects the Barents Sea with the main body of the White Sea; this *gorlo*, to use the Russian term, is 100 miles long and 30–35 miles wide. The main basin of the White Sea is flanked by rocky, deeply indented shores on the west, while the eastern shores are flat and marshy. Its chief bays are Kandalaksha (in the northwest), Onega (in the south) and Dvina (in the southeast), the two latter being the estuaries of the Onega and Northern Dvina rivers. The Mezen River empties into Mezen Bay, an inlet in the north.

Except in its center, the Sea freezes over between November and May – which is one reason why Russia has always sought more southerly ports than Archangel, Belomorsk, Kandalaksha, Kem, Mezen and Onega, which are the White Sea's main harbors. There is plentiful fishing (mainly cod and herring), with seal herds on the Solovetskiye Islands, near the entrance of Onega Bay. Russia's main lumber exports are shipped from the coasts of the White Sea.

The White Sea-Baltic Canal starts at Belomorsk in Onega Bay, continues south along the lower stretch of the Vyg River, which has been canalized, through Lake Vygozero, and crosses a 246-foot-high watershed with 19 locks to Lake Onega at Povenets. This section is 140 miles long. The Canal continues across Lake Onega, the Svir River, Lake Ladoga and the Neva River to Leningrad. Built in 1931–32, the Canal was badly damaged in the Second World War, and was repaired and reopened in 1949. It is frozen during the winter.

Whitsunday Islands

A small island group in the Coral Sea. Location *Between the Great Barrier Reef and Cape Conway Peninsula, off the east coast of Queensland, Australia.* Area *38 square miles.* Map *4, E9.*

Captain James Cook discovered and named the Whitsunday Islands in June, 1770.

Lying in calm water protected by the Great Barrier Reef, they are as lofty and spectacular as the fjords of Norway – but with sunny skies, sparkling blue seas and coral reefs. The Islands themselves are the tops of coastal mountains that protrude above sea level, which rose about half a million years ago and drowned great stretches of coastline, including the canyons that became Sydney Harbour. The coral gardens that surround each island are technically called fringing reefs. They are built up by coral polyps that have drifted in the sea and colonized the rocks fringing the half-sunken mountains.

In the patches of rain forest on some of the Islands, incubator birds build their vast pyramids, as in Papua; there are vast flocks of snowy Nutmeg Pigeons, so named because they live principally on wild nutmegs. Along the reefs, tiger sharks cruise sleekly and stone fish lie camouflaged among dead coral fragments. The stone fish is armed with a series of hollow spines that project upwards from its back. These connect with poison-ducts that discharge venom of great virulence if the fish is trodden upon. It sometimes kills, but most victims escape with an incapacity lasting a month or so, sometimes necessitating skin grafts. However, if the coral is explored in moderately heavy-soled shoes, there is no risk.

The main products of the Islands are trochus shells and fish. In recent years they have become popular as vacation resorts.

Wight, Isle of

A large island off the south coast of England. Location *The English Channel.* Area *147 square miles.* Map *8, D5.*

The Isle of Wight is roughly diamond-shaped, nearly 23 miles long from east to west, and nearly 14 miles wide. It is part of the former rim of chalk downs surrounding the lowland area in which lies the New Forest. On the promontory at the western end of the island are three chalk cliffs, about 100 feet high, known as the Needles. The Isle of Wight is separated from the mainland by the Solent in the northwest and by Spithead in the northeast.

In Regency and Victorian times the Isle became a popular resort, and in 1825 steam packets began to ply between Portsmouth, on the mainland, and Ryde. Alfred Tennyson lived on the island for some years, and Queen Victoria's seaside home, Osborne House, is near the yachting center of Cowes, on the Solent, where the famous annual yachting regatta is held. The climate of the island is very mild, and even in winter sheltered spots, such as Ventnor, are popular resorts.

Apart from the tourist trade, the inhabitants are principally engaged in sheep-rearing and dairy farming.

Windward Islands

A group of islands consisting of the French-owned Martinique and the British Windward Islands. Location *Lesser Antilles, West Indies, between the Leeward Islands and Venezuela.* Area *1,249 square miles.* Map *2, H4–J3.*

The Windward Islands form a crescent across the lower half of the Caribbean Sea. Flying south from the small airfield of St Lucia, one crosses the channel to St Vincent, the green shoulders and high peak of the volcano Mount Soufrière providing a striking landmark; its last major eruption was in 1902. All the Islands are the summits of a submerged mountain chain and have a volcanic history.

Beyond St Vincent the Grenadines are spread like shining dots on the sea, the rich green of their vegetation framed by the white of beaches and breakers where the long rollers of the Atlantic come to rest. In the south of the group lies Grenada itself, with its capital, St George, at the southwestern corner of the island. Martinique, between Dominica and St Lucia, is an overseas department of France.

The Islands' flora is especially rich and varied. Almost every variety of tropical plant and fruit grows in abundance, together with vegetables and fruit which have been imported at one time or another from the cooler climate of Europe. But despite extensive cultivation, about one third of the land area of the Windwards is still dense forest.

St Lucia possesses the finest harbor, one of the best in the West Indies: the port of Castries on the western coast, a large natural bay with a narrow entrance, completely sheltered from the northeasterly trade winds. Sugar and rum, cocoa, arrowroot and cotton, the standard products of the Islands, are shipped from here.

The climate is tropical but the prevailing winds keep the Islands reasonably cool even in summer. Tropical rainstorms burst with sudden violence to disappear again as quickly as they came, leaving everything fresh and steaming. Of the larger islands, St Lucia is perhaps the most beautiful, its mountains, especially the famous Pitons, rising sheer from the sea, their peaks veiled in cloud.

One of the Pitons on St Lucia,
Windward Islands

Wrangel Island

A tundra-covered Arctic island. Location *West Chukchi Sea, 85 miles off northeast Siberia, USSR.* Area *1,740 square miles.* Map *5, E3–4.*

Wrangel Island was discovered in 1867 by Thomas Long, commander of an American whaling vessel. He named it after the Russian navigator Baron Ferdinand Petrovich von Wrangel, who had sought the island unsuccessfully during his Arctic expedition of 1820–23, having heard of it from Siberian natives. For some years, it was believed to be part of the mainland, and was not discovered to be an island until George Washington De Long of the United States Navy explored it in 1879–81.

Vilhjalmur Stefansson visited Wrangel Island in 1921, with a view to claiming it for Great Britain. In 1924 the Soviet Union claimed it and two years later established the first permanent colony there – a trading post and meteorological station on the south coast. Apart from this station, Wrangel Island is uninhabited.

Wrath, Cape

A high, rugged promontory on the coast of Scotland. Location *Northwest extremity of Scotland, 10 miles west-northwest of Durness.* Map *8, D2.*

Cape Wrath, which the Norsemen called *hverta*, a turning point, is a spectacular landmark on the Scottish coast. Composed of gneiss rock rising in a sheer pyramid from the water's edge, it is 363 feet high. Its precipitous sides afford striking examples of the action of waves. The cliffs glow with a strange roseate hue, due to the many veins of rich pink pegmatite. The color is further enhanced by the luxuriant growth of primroses (*Primula scotia*).

The view from Cape Wrath extends past Far-Out Head in the east at the mouth of the Kyle of Durness to Strathy Point, 36 miles away. Far beyond it, to the left, the cliffs of Hoy may be seen. On a clear day Stack Skerry and Sule Skerry, the lonely island of North Rona, the Butt of Lewis and the mountains of Harris are visible.

The lighthouse on Cape Wrath was built in 1828; it is 65 feet high.

Yap

An island group, formerly an important Japanese air and naval base. Location *Caroline Islands, western Pacific.* Area *85 square miles.* Map *4, D6.*

A cluster of four large and ten small volcanic islands, the Yap group lies 275 miles northeast of Palau. Fertile and wooded, they are surrounded by a 16-mile-long reef. Rull is the largest (ten miles long, three miles wide, rising to 984 feet), with Tomil, Map and Rumung making up the larger group. Tomil Harbor provides an excellent anchorage on the southeast coast of the island.

The islands were claimed by Spain in the sixteenth century and remained under Spanish rule until Germany bought them in 1899. In 1918 they became part of the Japanese Mandated Islands. Japan turned them into fortified bases, and they served her well in the Second World War. Today they are administered by the United States and form an important communication center with two radio stations and a cable station. Their produce is mainly copra and dried bonito.

Yap has long been known for its unique currency: large stones from a quarry on Pelew, 225 miles to the southwest. A round, flat stone about a foot across corresponded roughly to a silver dollar. With a hole drilled in the center of each stone, several of them could be carried to market. The larger the stone, the greater its value. The huge millstone 12 feet in diameter was the equivalent of a $1,000 note; the hole drilled in it was large enough to hide the plumpest chief.

It was not felt necessary to shift the heavier stones, weighing tons, whenever something was bought or sold. The stones were left in their original positions, in the gardens or courtyards of the original owners; they were treated as real estate and simply transferred in the name of the new proprietor. The Yaps had no written language, the contract was purely verbal; but it was perfectly binding. Many rich men had their wealth scattered all over the islands. They had, of course, the right to visit their property, to inspect it, sit in the center hole and enjoy to the full the pride of ownership.

Yap is in the path of tropical hurricanes. Tidal waves, too, occur not infrequently. Sometimes

The stone money of Yap

they were so violent that several of the huge stones were washed into the lagoons. Once the hurricane had passed, the huts been repaired, the dead buried, the Yaps went in search of their lost currency. They found the stones at the bottom of the lagoon, clearly visible in the beautifully transparent water. But once their whereabouts had been established, no one dreamed of salvaging them. The money, the wealth, was still there; solid enough to draw yams or other food, clothes and building materials against it.

Today dollars have become accepted currency, at least in the purchase of American stores. But in internal trade, stone money is still supreme.

Yellow Sea

An arm of the Pacific Ocean between China and Korea. Location *North of the China Sea.* Dimensions *400 miles long, 400 miles wide.* Map *4, C2–D3.*

With a reputation both romantic and sinister, the Yellow Sea, or Hwang Hai as the Chinese call it, is also doomed. At least, geologists have calculated that in about 24,000 years it will have disappeared entirely, just as the inland seas west of Shantung have already become dry land. Its navigation is already much obstructed by the shifting sandbanks as well as by the dense fogs in which these shallow waters are often wrapped. The Chinese restrict the term "Yellow Sea" to the portion discolored by the alluvial deposits and call the marine waters that preserve their natural purity the "Black Sea."

The best natural harbors of the Yellow Sea are on the rocky peninsulas – Dairen and the naval base of Port Arthur on the Liaotung Peninsula (the Strait of Chihli, between the Liaotung and Shantung peninsulas, connects the Yellow Sea proper with the Gulf of Chihli and the ports of Chefoo and Tsingtao on the Shantung Peninsula). Other ports are Lienyün, Tientsin, Hulutao and Yingkow in China and Chinnampo and Chemulpo (Inchon) in Korea.

The Shantung is the largest peninsula in North China (13,570 square miles) and is well supplied with harbors and many offshore islands. The Liaotung (6,950 square miles) is next in size, and is also fringed with numerous islands.

During winter the water temperature of the Sea near the coastline of China reaches freezing point. Large schools of fish migrate south seasonally, spending the whole winter in the warm regions of the East China Sea.

The rivers which empty into the Yellow Sea include the Hwai, the Yellow, the Pai, the Liao and Yalu rivers of China and the Taedong and Han of Korea.

Zante

The southernmost main island of the Ionian Archipelago. Location *Off northwest Peloponnesus, Greece.* Area *157 square miles.* Map *9, F9.*

With Ithaca and Levkas to the north, Zante forms part of the protective crescent of islands guarding the entrance to the Gulf of Patras. Unlike the other two islands, though, Zante is rich and fertile. Its large central plain, shielded on the west and east by hills, is a garden of vines, with here and there the yellow of cornfields breaking the prevailing green. Even the hills are covered with olive and orange groves, figs and vines, rising in carefully tended terraces.

From Mount Skopos (1,600 feet), the highest point, situated at the northern end of Zante, the island falls away from the silver limestone of the peak in graduated folds of cultivated land. Only on the western coast does the land drop sheer into the sea in precipitous cliffs. Next to Corfu, Zante is the richest of the Ionian Islands, though its prosperity is constantly threatened by the menace of earthquakes. The most recent, in 1954, caused considerable loss of life and widespread destruction; the town of Zante itself, which lies in a small bay on the east coast, was devastated, suffering the worst damage since 1893.

Because of its position commanding the southern approaches to the Gulf of Patras, Zante has constantly changed hands and has been occupied by the prevailing sea power of the time. Tradition attaches it to Ithaca as a dependency of Odysseus; both Achaea and Arcadia sent colonists to it in historical times. Athens built a naval base on Zante late in the fifth century B.C., Macedon conquered it in 211 B.C., and in 191 B.C. it came under Roman rule. Gaiseric, King of the Vandals, laid it waste in the fifth century A.D.; then it was ruled in turn by the Normans of Sicily, by the Venetians, French, Russians and British. In 1864 it was finally ceded to Greece by Britain, with the other Ionian Islands. All these successive occupations have left their mark on the architecture, language and customs of the 42,000 people who live on Zante today. Many Italian words crop up in the local dialect and the aristocracy of the island proudly claim Venetian descent.

Zanzibar

A British protectorate, famous for its production of cloves. Location *Off the east coast of Africa, Indian Ocean.* Area *1,020 square miles (including Pemba Island and adjacent islets).* Map *10, B7.*

Originally colonized by Bantu settlers from the mainland, Zanzibar for hundreds of years formed part of the loosely held Persian or Arab empire of Zanguebar or Zenj, until this was destroyed by the Portuguese. The explorers and traders of Portugal in the early sixteenth century took the great cities of Kilwa, with its 300 mosques, Mombasa, Malindi and Mukdishu, colonizing the entire coast. A century later the Portuguese, harried by Turkish pirates and the frequent raids of the fierce Zimba tribesmen from the interior, were driven south to Mozambique, while Zanzibar, Pemba and the coastal provinces fell under the sway of the Imam of Oman.

The Imams had little time to look after their African possessions, for they were too busy fighting wars or quelling rebellious border tribes at home; gradually, the governors they appointed became more and more independent until, like the Masrui family in Mombasa, they defied their overlords and refused to pay tribute. Sultan-bin-Ahmed, who became Imam in 1791, was a stern man and began putting things in order until he was killed in a skirmish at sea. But his successor, Seyyid Said-bin-Sultan, though only 13 years old when he succeeded, survived 25 years of continuous warfare until at last he established order throughout his country. Then he turned his attention to Africa. He landed at Mombasa, subdued the Masrui and sailed on to Zanzibar in 1828. Here, enchanted by the peace and beauty of the island, his kingdom secure, he decided to end his days. Clove and coconut plantations were established at his orders (they still bring the island much of its wealth today); aqueducts were constructed to bring fresh water to the town; palaces, mosques and beautiful white houses were built – and in 1833 Zanzibar was declared capital of the entire Sultanate. The city flourished and its harbor was filled with merchant ships of every nation.

However, British opposition to slavery, which clashed strongly with Arab ideas, exercised a strong pressure upon the Sultanate. In 1822 the sale of slaves to Christians was forbidden. In 1842 the slave trade was officially abolished. Reforms continued after Said's death in 1856, when Zanzibar became an independent Sultanate, separate from Muscat and Oman, until in 1897 the legal status of slavery was finally abolished. This meant that the older slaves were thrown on their own resources and found that they had to work or starve; for a while there was considerable disorder with stealing and murder daily occurrences.

In 1890 Britain established a protectorate over Zanzibar. Swamps were drained, roads built, rats killed, food inspected in the markets, streets swept daily; a hospital and an abattoir were built and the local people (many of them descendants of slaves) were made to bury their dead instead of throwing them on the beach.

Today Zanzibar has a population of about 300,000. The Protectorate includes the islands of Zanzibar and Pemba, a coastal strip from Vanga to Ras Kiamboni (Dick's Head) on the mainland and the islands of Lamu, Manda, Patta and Siu. The islands still produce a large percentage of the world's supply of cloves and clove oil – the average annual export totals almost $10,000,000 in value – while chilies, oil cake, coir fiber, sea shells, seaweed and frozen lobsters are also exported. Rice and casava are grown extensively for local consumption. Primary and secondary schools provide free education, with training colleges for men and women primary teachers. Almost 400 miles of motor roads have been built; there is a civil airdrome close to the city of Zanzibar, with daily services to Tanganyika and Kenya.

Zeeland

A Dutch province, consisting of a stretch of mainland and six islands. Location *Southwest Netherlands, between the southern arm of the Maas River estuary, North Brabant, Belgium and the North Sea.* Area *650.7 square miles.* Map *8, E5.*

Apart from the mainland section along the Belgian frontier, Zeeland spreads over six large islands: Walcheren, North and South Beveland, Schouwen-Duiveland, Tholen and Sint Philipsland. All of them lie below the high tide mark, protected from the rage of the sea by a line of high sand dunes, which nature built up on their seaward edges, and from the waters of the wide estuaries behind and between them by man-made sea walls. In the tidal surge of February, 1953, the greater part of this area was flooded, with terrible loss of life and damage to farm land. The fight to dry out these islands must rank as one of man's greatest battles against the sea. In 1958, in order to prevent any recurrence of such a disaster, the Dutch embarked on the most ambitious of their land reclamation projects to date: the damming of the mouths of the four Zeeland estuaries (in effect, the mouths of the Rhine and the Maas) in order to turn them into freshwater lakes instead of fiercely tidal arms of the sea. Preliminary work began in 1960 and will take about ten years; the construction of the projected dams will make the damming of the shallow and nearly tideless Zuider Zee seem an elementary piece of engineering.

In the Middle Ages Zeeland was a bone of contention between the Counts of Holland and Flanders. It was annexed to Holland in 1323 by Count William III and united with the remainder of the country during the reign of Stadholder William III (1672–1702). Walcheren was flooded by the Allies during the Second World War to cut off the escape of the German forces in the Low Countries.

Zuider Zee

A former lake, now split by land reclamation into the the Ijsselmeer and the Waddenzee. Location *Northern and central Netherlands.* Area *Originally 80 miles long, now much reduced.* Map *8, E4–5.*

The great scoop into the land which was known as the Zuider or Zuyder Zee dates only from the thirteenth century. Before that, the Frisian Islands, now far off shore, were linked by a continuous coastline and on the site of the Zuider Zee there were forests inhabited by bears and wolves. Then, a lake (called Flevo Lacus by Tacitus), connected with the sea by a river, was gradually enlarged as the sea filtered through the low, sandy coastline into the even lower country beyond, and became transformed into marshes and finally into an inland sea which was notorious for its dangerous winding channels. Numerous sandbanks spread in all directions, leaving between them narrow passages suitable only for flat-bottomed, narrow-beamed barges. Some of the enormous sandbanks were covered by only two or three feet of water.

Then, in 1920, the Dutch began to reclaim their lost land from the sea. Work began on building enormous polders, or artificial islands, and this work has continued almost without interruption for more than 40 years. The Ijsselmeer Dam (the Dutch call it Afsluitdijk) which stretches for 19 miles from Den Oever in northern Holland to within a mile and a half of Zurich (Friesland) was completed in 1932, with navigation locks and drainage sluices at both ends and a roadway running along its top. Having cut off the sea from the Zuider Zee, the Dutch pro-

Dam-building in the Zuiderzee

ceeded to reclaim the land. The islands of Urk, Schokland and Wieringen were all incorporated in the newly drained territories with only Marken remaining an island – for the time being. The sea areas reclaimed include the Beemster Polder, 27.7 square miles in area, with Purmerend, its chief town, on the southeastern side – this is actually one of the oldest polder areas, drained in 1612; the North-East Polder, 185 square miles, on the west coast of Overijssel province with which the islands of Urk and Schokland have been incorporated; the Eastern Flevoland Polder, drained in 1957 and the largest at the present time; and the Wieringermeer Polder, 80 square miles, joining the former Wieringen Island to the mainland. This area was flooded at the end of the Second World War, but has been once again reclaimed. Only 30 miles north of Amsterdam, its chief town is Medemblik. The main towns on the Ijsselmeer are Amsterdam (on the Ij or Y inlet), Enkhuijzen, Hoorn, Harderwijk and Stavoren. Reclamation work still continues.

The other main section of the former Zuider Zee is the Waddenzee which, until the Ijsselmeer Dam was built, formed the northern part and lay between the West Frisian Islands and the mainland of northern Holland.

Gazetteer

Gazetteer

Abashiri Bay Inlet of the Sea of Okhotsk in E Hokkaido, Japan; 30 m. long, 10 m. wide. Formerly also Shari Bay.

Abukir Bay Inlet of the Mediterranean in NW Lower Egypt; *c.* 160 sq. m. Scene of battle of the Nile (1798) in which Nelson defeated Napoleonic fleet. Also spelled Aboukir and Abu Qir.

Acklins Island (or Acklin Island) S Bahama Islands, SE of Crooked Island; 50 m. long, 1–13 m. wide.

Adak Island One of the Andreanof group, Aleutian Islands, SW Alaska; 30 m. long, 3–20 m. wide.

Adam's Bridge Chain of shoals between India and Ceylon, in the Indian Ocean; 18 m. long. Also called Rama's Bridge.

Addu Atoll Southernmost group of the Maldive Islands, in the Indian Ocean.

Adelaide Island Antarctica, off W coast of Palmer Peninsula; 59½ m. long, 17½ m. wide.

Adelaide Peninsula Northwest Territories, extending 60 m. N into Arctic Ocean, S of King William Island.

Adélie Coast Section of Wilkes Land, Antarctica, on the Indian Ocean; 150,000 sq. m.

Admiralty Gulf Inlet of Timor Sea in NE Western Australia; 35 m. long, 30 m. wide.

Admiralty Inlet Fjord of Lancaster Sound in NW Baffin Island, Northwest Territories; 230 m. long, 2–20 m. wide. One of the world's longest fjords.

Admiralty Island SE Alaska, in the Alexander Archipelago; 1,664 sq. m.

Admiralty Sound S extension of the Strait of Magellan in W coast of main island of Tierra del Fuego; 50 m. long, 10 m. wide at entrance.

Adonara Island of the Solor group, Lesser Sundas, Indonesia, in Flores Sea; 200 sq. m. Also spelled Adunara and Adoenara.

Adventure Bay Inlet of the Pacific between central Chonos Archipelago and Guamblin Island, S Chile; *c.* 20 m. long, *c.* 30 m. wide.

Aegean Islands Islands off Asia Minor, N of the Dodecanese, forming an administrative division of Greece; 1,506 sq. m. Also applied generally to all the islands of the Aegean Sea.

Aegina Island in the Saronic Gulf, E central Greece; 32 sq. m. Struck first Greek coins, and was of great commercial importance until defeat by Athens (459 B.C.).

Afognak Island S Alaska, between Shelikof Strait and Gulf of Alaska; 43 m. long, 9–23 m. wide.

Akimiski Island Northwest Territories, in James Bay, opposite mouths of Ekwan and Attawapiskat rivers; 898 sq. m.

Akpatok Island Northwest Territories, in Ungava Bay; 551 sq. m.

Akte E prong of the Chalcidice peninsula, Greece, on the Aegean Sea; 30 m. long, 5 m. wide. Rises to 6,670 ft in Mt Athos. Also known as Akti, Hagion Oros and Ayion Oros.

Akutan Island One of the Krenitzin group, Fox Islands, Aleutian Islands, SW Alaska; 19 m. long, 15 m. wide.

Aland Islands Archipelago of Finland, in the Baltic, at the entrance to the Gulf of Bothnia; 572 sq. m. Comprise *c.* 6,500 islands and rocks, 80 of them inhabited; largest is Aland (285 sq. m.).

Alaska Current Branch of the Aleutian Current in the Gulf of Alaska; flows counterclockwise.

Alaska Peninsula SW Alaska, between Bering Sea and Pacific; 500 m. long.

Alava, Cape Westernmost point of continental U.S., NW Washington, on the Pacific.

Albatross Bay Inlet of the Gulf of Carpentaria in W Cape York Peninsula, N Queensland, Australia; 23 m. long, 10 m. wide.

Albay Gulf Inlet of the Philippine Sea in SE Luzon, Philippines; 30 m. E-W, 5–13 m. N-S.

Albemarle Sound Arm of the Atlantic in NE North Carolina; 50 m. long, 5–15 m. wide.

Alcatraz Rocky island in San Francisco Bay, W California; site of "The Rock," U.S. Federal prison for recidivists.

Aldabra Island Outlying dependency of the Seychelles, in the Indian Ocean; largest atoll of the Seychelles (21 m. long, 8 m. wide), enclosing 50-sq.-m. lagoon.

Alderney, Race of Strait between Alderney island and Cape La Hague, France; dangerous tidal races.

Alenuihaha Channel Territory of Hawaii, between Maui and Hawaii; *c.* 23 m. wide.

Aleutian Current Cold current of the N Pacific, formed by union of Japan and Okhotsk currents; eastward-flowing. Also called Subarctic Current.

Aleutian Trench Submarine depression of the N Pacific, S of the Aleutian Islands; greatest depth over 24,000 ft.

Alexander I Island Antarctica, off W coast of Palmer Peninsula, in Bellingshausen Sea; *c.* 205 m. long, *c.* 45–85 m. wide.

Alexandra Land Westernmost island of Franz Josef Land, in the Arctic Ocean; 70 m. long, 10–30 m. wide.

Algoa Bay Inlet of the Indian Ocean in S Cape Province, South Africa; 15 m. long, 50 m. wide at mouth.

Almadies, Cape Westernmost point of Africa, at tip of Cape Verde, Senegal.

Almirante Montt Gulf Inlet of the Pacific in S Chile, N of Muñoz Gamero Peninsula; 20 m. long, *c.* 8 m. wide.

Along Bay Arm of Gulf of Tonkin between mainland of N Vietnam and Catba Island; *c.* 20 m. long, 5–10 m. wide. Also spelled Allong, Halong and Dalong.

Alor Islands Group of the Lesser Sundas, Indonesia, across Ombai Strait from Timor; 1,126 sq. m. Consist of 2 islands: Alor (or Ombai, 810 sq. m.) and Pantar.
Als Island in the Little Belt, Denmark; 121 sq. m. Belonged to Germany until 1920 plebiscite.
Alsten Island Mountainous island, N central Norway; 59 sq. m. Contains Seven Sisters (peaks), celebrated in legend.
Alta Fjord Inlet of Norwegian Sea, N Norway; 20 m. long, 7–11 m. wide. Sometimes called Alten Fjord.
Alvarado Lagoon Sotavento lowlands, Veracruz, SE Mexico; 20 m. long, up to 3 m. wide.
Amager Island in the Oresund, Denmark; 25.1 sq. m. Part of Copenhagen is in N.
Amakusa Islands Island group in East China Sea, Japan, off W coast of Kyushu; 341 sq. m. Comprise *c.* 70 islands and islets.
Amakusa Sea NE arm of East China Sea, between Nomo Peninsula and Shimo-jima, Japan.
Amami-gunto N island group of Ryukyu Islands, between East China Sea and Philippine Sea; 498 sq. m., *c.* 200 m. long. Extensive fishing. Anglicized as Amami Islands. Formerly sometimes called Hokubu-shoto.
Amami-O-shima (sometimes O-shima) Largest island of Amami-gunto group; 333 sq. m. Chief products silk textiles and sugar.
Ambergris Cay Island in the Caribbean Sea, N British Honduras; 25 m. long, 5 m. wide.
Amboina (or Ambon) Island in the Moluccas, Indonesia; 314 sq. m. Opposed Indonesian independence; led brief revolt against state of Indonesia in 1950. Sometimes spelled Amboyna.
Amchitka Island Rat Islands, SW Alaska; 40 m. long, 2–5 m. wide. Site of U.S. air base in Second World War.
Amchitka Pass Sea passage in the Aleutian Islands, SW Alaska, between the Rat and Andreanof islands; 60 m. wide. Steamer route from N Pacific to Bering Sea.
Amin Divi Islands (or Amindivi Islands) N group of Laccadive Islands, India, in the Arabian Sea.
Amirantes (or Amirante Isles) Archipelago in Indian Ocean; 100 m. long N-S; outlying dependency of the Seychelles.
Amlia Island Andreanof Islands, SW Alaska; 46 m. long, 3–9 m. wide.
Amund Ringnes Island Sverdrup Islands, Northwest Territories, in the Arctic Ocean; 1,764 sq. m.
Amundsen Gulf Arm of the Arctic Ocean, Northwest Territories, opening off Beaufort Sea; 250 m. long. Westernmost section of the Northwest Passage.
Amundsen Sea Part of the S Pacific off the coast of Antarctica, W of Ross Sea. Explored and named by Nils Larsen, 1929.
Anadyr Gulf Inlet of NW Bering Sea, NE Siberia; includes Anadyr Bay and Krest Gulf. Whaling ground.
Ana María, Gulf of Caribbean inlet of E Cuba; shallow sea fringed by reefs; *c.* 20 m. N-S.
Anambas Islands Group in Indonesia, in South China Sea, between Borneo and Malay Peninsula; comprise 3 islands surrounded by numerous islets. Largest is Jemaja (or Djemadja), 15 m. long, 10 m. wide.
Ancud, Gulf of Inlet of the Pacific between Chiloé Island and the Chile mainland; *c.* 40 m. W-E, 30 m. N-S.
Andaman Sea Arm of Indian Ocean between Lower Burma, Thailand, Sumatra, and Andaman and Nicobar islands; 300,000 sq. m., 600 m. long N-S, 400 m. wide. Mean depth 2,850 ft.
Andoy Northernmost island of the Vesteralen group, N Norway, within the Arctic Circle; 150 sq. m. Sometimes called Anda or Anna.
Andreanof Islands Group of the Aleutian Islands, SW Alaska.
Andros Northernmost island of the Cyclades, Greece, in the Aegean Sea; 145 sq. m.
Andros Island W Bahama Islands; 1,600 sq. m. Has only river in the Bahamas: Goose River.
Anegada Bay Inlet of the Atlantic, Argentina; 50 m. wide with the adjoining Unión and San Blas bays.
Anegada Passage Channel in the West Indies between the Atlantic and the Caribbean; *c.* 40 m. wide.
Angel de la Guarda Island Barren, uninhabited island in Gulf of California, NW Mexico; 330 sq. m. Seasonal fishing base. Sometimes called Angel de la Guardia.
Angel Island Largest island in San Francisco Bay; *c.* 1½ m. long. Former site of quarantine station and immigration station; during Second World War internment camp for enemy nationals.
Angeln Peninsular region of NW Germany; 330 sq. m.; traditional home of the Angles.
Anglesey (or Anglesea) Island in the Irish Sea, NW Wales; 275.1 sq. m. Linked with mainland by two bridges.
Angmagssalik Island SE Greenland; 25 m. long, 12–20 m. wide.
Aniva Gulf Inlet of Sea of Okhotsk, Russian SFSR; 65 m. wide, 50 m. long.
Anjouan Island (or Johanna Island) One of the Comoro Islands, in Mozambique Channel; 138 sq. m. Former notorious slave market.
Annette Island Gravina Islands, SE Alaska; 20 m. long, 7–10 m. wide. Tsimshian Indian reserve.
Anson Bay Inlet of Joseph Bonaparte Gulf of Timor Sea in Northern Territory, Australia; 21 m. long, 15 m. wide.
Antalya, Gulf of (or Gulf of Adalia) Inlet of Mediterranean Sea in SW Turkey; 130 m. wide, 50 m. long.
Anticosti Island Gulf of St Lawrence, E Quebec; 140 m. long, 30 m. wide; main industry lumbering.
Antifer, Cape Headland, N France, on English Channel. Terminus of submarine cable to England.
Antigua Island in the Leeward Islands; 108 sq. m. Sugar cane and sea-island cotton.
Antilles Current N branch of North Equatorial Current, North Atlantic.
Antioche, Pertuis d' Inlet of Bay of Biscay, W France; 24 m. long, 16 m. wide; contains small islands.
Antongil Bay Inlet of Indian Ocean on NE coast of Madagascar; 40 m. long, 20 m. wide.
Anvers Island Largest island of Palmer Archipelago in the S Pacific; 35 m. long, 24 m. wide; rises to 9,412 ft. Sometimes called Antwerp Island.
Anxious Bay Inlet of Great Australian Bight, South Australia; 42 m. long, 13 m. wide; opens into 2 lagoons.
Aoba Volcanic island, New Hebrides; *c.* 95 sq. m. Sometimes called Leper Island.
Apalachee Bay Bight of the Gulf of Mexico, NW Florida; *c.* 30 m. wide. Wildlife refuge on coast.

Arabat Tongue Narrow spit of land in E Crimea; *c.* 70 m. long.
Arafura Sea Part of the Pacific, merging W with Timor Sea. Contains Aru Islands.
Aran Island Island in the Atlantic, off W coast of County Donegal, Ireland; 4 m. long, 3 m. wide; lighthouse at NW end.
Aransas Bay Inlet of Gulf of Mexico, S Texas; *c.* 25 m. long, *c.* 5 m. wide. Traversed by Gulf Intracoastal Waterway.
Araruama Lagoon Tidewater lake on SE coast of Brazil, connected by channel with open Atlantic; 22 m. long. Saltworks.
Arauco Gulf Inlet of the Pacific, S central Chile. Submarine coal deposits.
Araya Peninsula NE Venezuela, in the Caribbean; 45 m. long E-W, up to 11 m. wide.
Ards, The Peninsula in E County Down, Northern Ireland, between Irish Sea and Strangford Lough; *c.* 20 m. long, 5 m. wide.
Arfersiorfik Fjord, W Greenland. Extends E from Davis Strait to edge of inland icecap; 95 m. long, 1–15 m. wide.
Argolis, Gulf of Inlet of Aegean Sea in E Peloponnesus, Greece. 20 m. wide, 30 m. long. Formerly called Gulf of Nauplia or Nauplion.
Argolis Peninsula E Peloponnesus, Greece, in Aegean Sea; 45 m. long, 12–20 m. wide.
Arguin Bay Sheltered inlet of W Mauritania; well-known fishing ground.
Ariakeno-umi Gulf of Amakusa Sea, Japan; 20 m. long N-S, 17 m. wide E-W.
Aristazabal Island Hecate Strait, W British Columbia; 149 sq. m., 28 m. long, 10 m. wide.
Arkticheski Institut Islands (or Arkticheskiy Institut) Group in Kara Sea of Arctic Ocean, Russian SFSR.
Arnhem Bay Inlet of Arafura Sea, Arnhem Land, Northern Territory, Australia; 20 m. E-W, 15 m. N-S.
Arran Island in the Firth of Clyde, Scotland; 165.8 sq. m. Deer forests.
Arsuk Fjord SW Greenland, 65 m. SE of Frederikshaab; 20 m. long.
Arta, Gulf of (or Ambracian Gulf) Large Ionian inlet in W central Greece; 20 m. long, 5–10 m. wide.
Artemision, Cape N extremity of Euboea, Greece, on Aegean Sea. Scene of naval battle between Greeks and Persians, 480 B.C.
Aru Islands (or Aroe Islands) Group in the S Moluccas, Indonesia, in Arafura Sea; 3,306 sq. m. Comprise 5 main islands fringed with *c.* 80 islets. 5 main islands sometimes considered as being one, divided by 4 narrow channels, called Tanabesar. Also spelled Arru.
Arve Prinsen Island W Greenland, at head of Disko Bay; 29 m. long, 6–19 m. wide.
Arzew, Gulf of Wide inlet of the Mediterranean, NW Algeria; 30 m. wide, 10 m. long.
Asid Gulf Arm of Visayan Sea, Philippines. Deeply indents S coast of Masbate island; *c.* 40 m. E-W, *c.* 20 m. N-S.
Asinara, Gulf of Inlet of Mediterranean Sea, NW Sardinia; 40 m. wide. Fisheries.
Assateague Island Narrow barrier island off Atlantic shore of Maryland and Virginia; 35 m. long; abundant wildlife.
Assumption Island (also Assomption) Outlying dependency of the Seychelles, one of the Aldabra group. Of coral origin.
Astrolabe Bay NE New Guinea, N of Huon Peninsula. Site of Madang harbor.
Atacama Trench Submarine depression in South Pacific Ocean off W coast of South America. Greatest depth Richards Deep, 25,049 ft.
Atchafalaya Bay Arm of the Gulf of Mexico, S Louisiana; *c.* 21 m. long NW-SE, 10 m. wide.
Atka Island Andreanof Islands, SW Alaska; 65 m. long, 2–20 m. wide; rises to 4,852 ft in Korovin Volcano.
Atsumi Peninsula Central Honshu, Japan, between Atsumi Bay and Philippine Sea; 20 m. long, 5 m. wide.
Attu Island Westernmost of the Aleutian Islands, largest of the Near Islands; 30 m. long, 8–15 m. wide. Rugged, barren. Occupied by Japanese in Second World War; now important link in N Pacific defense system.
Audierne, Bay of W France, on Bay of Biscay; 24 m. wide, *c.* 5 m. long.
Aulatsivik Island Off NE Labrador; 12 m. long, 9 m. wide; mountainous, rising to 3,100 ft.
Aurlands Fjord S arm of Sogne Fjord, W Norway; *c.* 20 m. long.
Australes, Iles Outlying dependencies of Madagascar in S Indian Ocean. Comprise Kerguelen Islands, Crozet Islands, St Paul Island, Amsterdam Island and Adélie Coast.
Austrian Sound Strait of Arctic Ocean in E Franz Josef Land; 70 m. long, 10 m. wide.
Austvagoy Largest of the Lofoten Islands, in the Norwegian Sea, N Norway; 203 sq. m., 33 m. long, 11 m. wide. Sometimes spelled Ostvagoy or Ostvaagoy.
Avacha Bay Sheltered inlet of Pacific Ocean on SE coast of Kamchatka Peninsula.
Avalon Peninsula SE Newfoundland, connected with mainland by a 4-mile isthmus; 110 m. long, up to 60 m. wide, *c.* 4,000 sq. m. Most densely populated part of Newfoundland (population *c.* 125,000).
Avery Island One of Five Islands, S Louisiana; salt dome (alt. *c.* 200 ft) in sea marshes and swamps. Bird sanctuary and Jungle Gardens, with many rare plants.
Awaji-shima Island, Hyogo prefecture, Japan, between Harima Sea and Osaka Bay; 228 sq. m. Roughly triangular.
Axel Heiberg Island Largest of Sverdrup Islands, Northwest Territories, in the Arctic Ocean; 13,583 sq. m., 220 m. long, 20–100 m. wide; coastline indented with deep fjords. Surface consists of plateau rising to over 6,000 ft in NE.
Azuero Peninsula W central Panama, on Pacific Ocean, forming W side of Gulf of Panama. 60 m. wide, 50 m. long.

Baba, Cape NW Turkey, on the Aegean Sea; westernmost point of Anatolian mainland and hence of the continent of Asia.
Babar Islands Group of the S Moluccas, Indonesia, in Banda Sea. Consist of 1 large island (Babar) surrounded by 5 islets; 314 sq. m.
Babelthuap Volcanic island, largest of Palau group, W Pacific; 143 sq. m.
Babuyan Islands Volcanic group in Luzon Strait, Philippines. Rice, fishing.

Bachan (or Batjan) Island, N Moluccas, Indonesia, in Molucca Passage; 913 sq. m. Also spelled Batyan.
Badung Passage (or Badoeng Passage) W arm of Lombok Strait; 20 m. long, 8–20 m. wide.
Bahía Blanca Bay of Atlantic Ocean, Argentina; 40 m. long, 33 m. wide at mouth.
Bahiret el Biban Coastal lagoon of SE Tunisia; *c.* 20 m. long, 5 m. wide; sheltered by narrow sand bar.
Baidarata Bay (or Baydarata Bay) Inlet of Kara Sea, NW Siberian Russian SFSR; 115 m. long, 34 m. wide.
Bailey Islands 11-m. chain of volcanic islands, southernmost group of Bonin Islands, W Pacific. Formerly called Coffin Islands.
Baillie Hamilton Island Northwest Territories, at N end of Wellington Channel; 17 m. long, 7–11 m. wide.
Baird Inlet W Alaska, between mouths of Yukon and Kuskokwim rivers; 70 m. long, 1–18 m. wide.
Bakka Bay Inlet of Atlantic, NE Iceland, on E side of Langanes peninsula; 15 m. long, 20 m. wide at mouth.
Balabac Island Palawan province, Philippines; 125 sq. m.
Balabac Strait Connects Sulu Sea and South China Sea between Balabac Island and North Borneo; 30 m. wide.
Baldwin Peninsula NW Alaska; extends 45 m. NW, N of Seward Peninsula; 1–12 m. wide.
Ballantyne Strait Arm of the Arctic Ocean, Northwest Territories, between Prince Patrick Island and Brock and South Borden islands; 80 m. long, 35–60 m. wide.
Ballenas, Canal de las Channel in Gulf of California, NW Mexico, between Lower California and Angel de la Guarda Island; *c.* 55 m. long, 10–15 m. wide.
Balleny Islands Glaciated volcanic group N of Antarctica, 150 m. off Victoria Land. Discovered 1839 by John Balleny, British sealer.
Banderas Bay Pacific inlet, W Mexico, just N of Cape Corriente; 27 m. long, *c.* 25 m. wide.
Banggai Second largest island of Banggai Archipelago, Indonesia; 112 sq. m.
Banggai Archipelago Indonesia, in Molucca Sea; 1,222 sq. m. Comprises Banggai, Peleng (largest island of group) and *c.* 100 islets.
Banggi (or Banguey) Island in South China Sea, off N tip of Borneo; 23 m. long, 15 m. wide.
Bangka (or Banka) Island, Indonesia, in the Java Sea, off SE coast of Sumatra; 140 m. long, 70 m. wide; irregular shape. One of principal tin-producing centers of world.
Bangka Strait Between Bangka and Sumatra; 10–20 m. wide.
Banks Island 1. Island in Hecate Strait, W British Columbia; 388 sq. m.
2. Island, Northwest Territories; westernmost of the Arctic Archipelago, in the Arctic Ocean; *c.* 26,000 sq. m.
Banks Peninsula E South Island, New Zealand; 30 m. E-W, 17 m. N-S.
Bantry Bay Inlet of the Atlantic, SW coast of County Cork, Ireland; 21 m. long, 4 m. wide. One of Europe's best natural anchorages.
Banyak Islands (or Banjak Islands) Group in Indonesia, off W coast of Sumatra. Numerous small islands, largest Tuangku (or Toeangkoe), 20 m. long, 6 m. wide.
Banzare Coast Part of Wilkes Land, Antarctica, on Indian Ocean.
Baranof Island SE Alaska, in Alexander Archipelago; 1,607 sq. m. Former headquarters of Russian fur-trading.
Barents Island Island in Spitsbergen group, in Barents Sea; 514 sq. m. Largely uncharted.
Barnegat Bay Arm of the Atlantic, E New Jersey; extends *c.* 30 m. along coast. Forms part of Intracoastal Waterway.
Barrow, Point Northernmost point of Alaska, on Arctic Ocean. Starting point of Sir Hubert Wilkins' flight across North Pole.
Barrow Strait Arm of the Arctic Ocean, Northwest Territories; 150 m. long, 40–70 m. wide.
Bartlett Trough Broad-floored depression in Caribbean Sea between Jamaica and Cayman Islands; 22,788 ft deep. Sometimes called Cayman Deep.
Basilan Island Philippines, off SW tip of Mindanao; 494 sq. m. With onshore islets forms Basilan Islands.
Basse-Terre Island forming W half of Guadeloupe; 364 sq. m.
Bass Strait Channel between coasts of Victoria and Tasmania; 30,000 sq. m.; mean depth 230 ft. Discovered 1798 by George Bass.
Bataan Peninsula Mountainous peninsula, S Luzon, Philippines. Shelters Manila Bay from South China Sea; 30 m. long, 20 m. wide, rising to 4,700 ft in Mt Bataan.
Batam Island, Riouw Archipelago, Indonesia, in South China Sea; *c.* 180 sq. m.
Batanta Island belonging to Netherlands New Guinea, in Dampier Strait; *c.* 30 m. long, 5 m. wide.
Bathurst, Cape Northernmost point of Canadian mainland, Northwest Territories, on Beaufort Sea.
Bathurst Inlet Inlet of Coronation Gulf, Northwest Territories; 150 m. long, 3–65 m. wide.
Bathurst Island Parry Islands, Northwest Territories, in the Arctic Ocean; 7,272 sq. m.
Batu Islands (or Batoe Islands) Group in Indonesia, off W coast of Sumatra, in Indian Ocean; 463 sq. m. Comprise 3 large islands surrounded by many islets.
Bay Islands Archipelago in Honduras, Caribbean Sea; 144 sq. m.
Beagle Channel Strait in Tierra del Fuego, separating main island from others of the group; 150 m. long, 3–8 m. wide.
Behm Canal Natural channel, SE Alaska, almost circling Revillagigedo Island, which it separates from the mainland; 120 m. long.
Beijerland (or Beierland) Island, SW Netherlands, S of Rotterdam; 16 m. long, 9 m. wide. Sometimes spelled Beyerland; also called Hoeksche Waard.
Belaya Zemlya Northeasternmost group of Franz Josef Land, in Arctic Ocean. Comprises 5 islands.
Belcher Channel Arm of the Arctic Ocean, Northwest Territories, between Cornwall Island and Devon Island; 70 m. long, 30–40 m. wide.
Belcher Islands Group in E part of Hudson Bay, Northwest Territories; 1,096 sq. m. Largest Flaherty Island. Small Eskimo population.
Belle Isle, Strait of N entrance to Gulf of St Lawrence, between Newfoundland and Labrador; 60 m. long, 10–15 m. wide. Strong tidal current.
Bellot Strait Arctic channel, Northwest Territories; 30 m. long, 2–8 m. wide.

Bely Island (or Belyy Island) Kara Sea, just N of Yamal Peninsula; 40 m. long, 28 m. wide.
Bengkalis Island in Strait of Malacca, Indonesia, just off E coast of Sumatra; 42 m. long, 12 m. wide; swampy and low.
Benguela Current Cold current of S Atlantic Ocean, moving N along W coast of Africa S of Gulf of Guinea. Brings desert-like aridity to coastal area.
Benin, Bight of Atlantic bay of the Gulf of Guinea, on West African coast.
Ben Sekha, Ras Northernmost point of Africa, on Mediterranean coast of N Tunisia. Lighthouse.
Berhala Strait Channel of South China Sea, Indonesia; 20–60 m. wide.
Bering Island Largest of Komandorski Islands, off Kamchatka Peninsula, in SW Bering Sea; 54 m. long, 22 m. wide.
Biafra, Bight of Inlet of Atlantic on W coast of Africa, innermost bay of Gulf of Guinea; 370 m. wide, 200 m. long.
Biak Largest island of Schouten Islands, Netherlands New Guinea, at entrance to Geelvink Bay; *c.* 50 m. long, 25 m. wide.
Bickerton Island Aboriginal reservation in Gulf of Carpentaria, 6 m. off NE coast of Northern Territory, Australia; 12 m. long, 10 m. wide.
Bigge Island Timor Sea, at NE entrance to York Sound; 14 m. long, 7 m. wide. Barren, composed of quartzite.
Big Island Island, Northwest Territories, off S Baffin Island; 36 m. long, 3–16 m. wide.
Bijagós Islands (or Bissagos Islands) Archipelago in E Atlantic, just off Portuguese Guinea, to which it belongs; *c.* 600 sq. m.; consists of *c.* 15 large islands and numerous islets. Formerly spelled Bijagoz.
Biliran Island Philippines, in Samar Sea; 192 sq. m.
Billiton (also Belitung and Belitoeng) Island in Indonesia, between South China and Java seas; 1,866 sq. m.; almost square in shape. Important tin mines.
Bilugyun Island Lower Burma, off Moulmein; 107 sq. m.
Bimini Islands (or Biminis) String of cays in the Bahama Islands; 8.5 sq. m. Popular tourist resort.
Bintan (or Bintang) Largest island of Riouw Archipelago, Indonesia, in South China Sea; 415 sq. m.
Biscayne Bay Shallow arm of the Atlantic, S Florida; *c.* 40 m. long, 2–10 m. wide; forms part of Intracoastal Waterway.
Bismarck Sea SW arm of Pacific Ocean, NE of New Guinea.
Blake Deep Ocean depth (27,365 ft) in North Atlantic Ocean, N of Puerto Rico.
Blanc, Cap (or Cape Blanc) N Tunisia, on the Mediterranean; often considered to be the northernmost point of Africa, though nearby Ras ben Sekka is in fact.
Blosseville Coast Region on Denmark Strait, SE Greenland. Extends *c.* 300 m. NE-SW. Indented by small bays and fjords.
Blue Hill Bay Inlet of the Atlantic, S Maine, extending inland 20 m.
Blue Mud Bay W inlet of Gulf of Carpentaria, Northern Territory, Australia; 30 m. long, 24 m. wide.
Blying Sound NW arm of Gulf of Alaska, S Alaska. Washes Kenai Peninsula.
Boa Vista Island Easternmost of Cape Verde Islands; 239 sq. m. Roughly circular. Originally called São Christovão.
Bogoslof Island Volcanic islet, Aleutian Islands, SW Alaska. Of recent formation; first appeared in 1796 and shape has been changed several times by eruption.
Bogue Island (or Bogue Banks) Narrow barrier beach, E North Carolina; *c.* 25 m. long.
Bogue Sound Waterway, E North Carolina, sheltered from Atlantic by Bogue Island; *c.* 30 m. long E-W, 2 m. wide.
Bohol One of the Visayan Islands, S central Philippines; 1,491 sq. m.; between Camotes Sea and Mindanao Sea.
Bohol Strait Philippines, between Bohol island and Cebu; 12–25 m. wide.
Bokn Fjord Inlet of North Sea, SW Norway; 13 m. wide at mouth, *c.* 35 m. long. Contains many islands.
Bolivar Peninsula S Texas, extending SW between Galveston and East bays; *c.* 23 m. long.
Bolshevik Island (or Bol'shevik Island) S island of Severnaya Zemlya archipelago in Arctic Ocean; 450 sq. m.; 20 per cent glacier-covered.
Bolshoi Lyakhov Island (or Bol'shoy Lyakhov Island) Largest of Lyakhov Islands, between Laptev and East Siberian seas of Arctic Ocean.
Bombarai Peninsula, Netherlands New Guinea; *c.* 110 m. N-S, *c.* 90 m. W-E, with W projection (50 m. long).
Bombay Harbour Inlet of Arabian Sea, W India; *c.* 10 m. long, 6–8 m. wide; docks and numerous open wharves.
Bon, Cape Headland on Mediterranean coast of NE Tunisia, at tip of Cape Bon Peninsula, which is *c.* 20 m. wide, 50 m. long.
Bonaventure Island E Quebec, in the Gulf of St Lawrence; 2½ m. long. Granted to Captain Duval by George III and still inhabited by his descendants. Bird sanctuary.
Bonavista, Cape Promontory, E Newfoundland; reputed landfall of John Cabot, discoverer of Newfoundland, 1497.
Bonavista Bay E Newfoundland, ending at Cape Bonavista; 40 m. long, 40 m. wide at mouth. Deeply indented coastline.
Bondoc Peninsula S Luzon, Philippines; S tip projects into Sibuyan Sea; *c.* 35 m. long, 12 m. wide.
Bone, Gulf of Large inlet of Flores Sea, Indonesia, indenting S coast of Celebes; 150 m. N-S, 30–90 m. E-W. Also spelled Boni.
Bonifacio, Strait of Between Point Falcone (Sardinia) and Cape Pertusato (Corsica), joining Tyrrhenian and Mediterranean seas.
Boothia, Gulf of Inlet of Arctic Ocean; 250 m. long; lies between Boothia Peninsula and Baffin Island, Northwest Territories.
Boothia Peninsula Northwest Territories, extending N into Arctic Ocean from Keewatin district mainland; 190 m. long, up to 130 m. wide. Formerly called Boothia Felix.
Borden Islands 2 islands, Northwest Territories, in the Arctic Ocean; *c.* 4,000 sq. m.; formerly thought to be a single island.
Borden Peninsula N Baffin Island, Northwest Territories; extends 140 m. N into Lancaster Sound; 40–105 m. wide.
Borgne, Lake Salt-water bay, arm of Mississippi Sound, SE Louisiana; *c.* 27 m. long.

Boris Vilkitski Strait (or Boris Vil'kitskiy Strait) Strait joining Kara and Laptev seas of Arctic Ocean and separating Severnaya Zemlya archipelago from Taimyr Peninsula; 80 m. long, 35–50 m. wide. Also called Vilkitski Strait.

Bougainville Volcanic island, largest of the Solomon Islands, SW Pacific; 3,880 sq. m. Mountainous, rising to 10,170 ft in Mt Balbi.

Bougainville Strait Solomon Islands, SW Pacific; separates Bougainville and Choiseul, joining Coral Sea and Pacific Ocean; 30 m. wide.

Bougie, Gulf of Bay of the Mediterranean, NE Algeria; 27 m. wide; semicircular.

Boularderie Island NE Nova Scotia, off Cape Breton Island; 25 m. long, 2–6 m. wide; coal mined in N.

Boussole Strait Widest strait of the Kuriles, Russian SFSR; 40 m. wide.

Brabant Island Second largest island of Palmer Archipelago, Antarctica, in S Pacific; 29 m. long, 17½ m. wide.

Brac Island Largest of Dalmatian Islands, Yugoslavia, in Adriatic Sea; 152 sq. m. Tourist center. Sometimes spelled Brach.

Branco, Cabo Headland, NE Brazil, on Atlantic Ocean. Together with Pedras Point (32 m. S) it is considered easternmost point of South America.

Bransfield Strait Channel in South Pacific, separating South Shetlands from Palmer Peninsula; *c.* 175 m. long, *c.* 52 m. wide.

Brazil Current Warm current of S Atlantic, branch of South Equatorial Current; flows S along E coast of South America and meets cold Falkland Current.

Breaksea Sound Inlet of Tasman Sea, SW South Island, New Zealand; 20 m. long, 2 m. wide; contains several islets.

Breaksea Spit Dangerous shoal off SE coast of Queensland, Australia, in Pacific Ocean; extends 17 m. from Sandy Cape on Fraser Island.

Brecknock Peninsula W part of main island of Tierra del Fuego, Chile; *c.* 40 m. long. Uninhabited.

Breidi Fjord (or Breida Fjord) Inlet of Denmark Strait, W Iceland; 80 m. long, 40 m. wide at mouth. Contains numerous islets. Also spelled Breidhi or Breidha Fjord.

Breton Sound Arm of the Gulf of Mexico between Louisiana coast and Breton Island; *c.* 20 m. wide.

Brevoort Island Northwest Territories, in the Atlantic, off Hall Peninsula, SE Baffin Island; 25 m. long, 5 m. wide.

Bridgwater Bay Inlet of Bristol Channel, NW Somerset, England; 20 m. wide, 7 m. long.

Bristol Bay Arm of Bering Sea between Alaskan mainland and Alaska Peninsula; 250 m. long, 180 m. wide; shallow.

Bristol Channel Inlet of Atlantic separating Wales and SW England; 85 m. long, 5–43 m. wide. Has highest tidal rise in England.

Broad Sound Inlet of Coral Sea, E Queensland, Australia; 35 m. long, 30 m. wide.

Brock Island Northwest Territories, in the Arctic Ocean, off Borden Islands; 414 sq. m.; 25 m. long, 20 m. wide.

Brodeur Peninsula NW Baffin Island, Northwest Territories. Extends 200 m. N into Lancaster Sound; 45–90 m. wide.

Brownsea Island Scene of first camp of Boy Scout movement; at E end of Poole Harbour, SE Dorset, England; 2 m. long, 1 m. wide.

Bruce Coast Part of coast of Coats Land, Antarctica, on the S Atlantic.

Brunei Bay Inlet of South China Sea in NW Borneo; 16 m. long, 8 m. wide. Forms chief coastal feature of sultanate of Brunei.

Brunswick Peninsula Southernmost part of South American mainland, in S Chile; *c.* 70 m. long.

Bruny Island in Tasman Sea, off SE coast of Tasmania. North Bruny and South Bruny are connected by narrow isthmus; 142 sq. m., 32 m. long, 10 m. wide.

Bubiyan Island Uninhabited island at head of Persian Gulf, belonging to Kuwait; 25 m. long, 15 m. wide.

Buchanan Bay Arm of Kane Basin, E Ellesmere Island, Northwest Territories; 40 m. long, 12–20 m. wide.

Budd Coast Mountainous part of coast of Wilkes Land, Antarctica, on Indian Ocean.

Buena Vista Bay Inlet on N coast of central Cuba; *c.* 30 m. E-W, 6 m. wide; shallow.

Buka Volcanic island in the Solomon Islands, SW Pacific; 190 sq. m.

Buor-Khaya Bay Inlet of East Siberian Sea; 80 m. wide. Also spelled Borkhaya Bay.

Burias Island Philippines, separated from SE Luzon by Burias Pass; 164 sq. m.

Burias Pass Strait in the Philippines, between Burias Island and SE Luzon; *c.* 40 m. long, 8–20 m. wide.

Burin Peninsula S Newfoundland, between Fortune Bay and Placentia Bay; 85 m. long, 20 m. wide.

Burrard Inlet Arm of Strait of Georgia, SW British Columbia; 23 m. long, 1–4 m. wide.

Buru (or Boeroe) Island in the S Moluccas, Indonesia, between Ceram and Banda seas; 3,668 sq. m. Surrounded by coral reefs.

Busuanga Island Largest of the Calamian Islands, Philippines; 344 sq. m.

Bute Inlet Arm of Strait of Georgia, SW British Columbia; 50 m. long, 1–3 m. wide.

Buton (or Boeton) Island between Molucca and Flores seas, Indonesia; 1,759 sq. m. Chief product asphalt.

Buton Bay E coast of Buton; 30 m. long, 20 m. wide.

Buzzards Bay Inlet of the Atlantic, SE Massachusetts, extending to base of Cape Cod peninsula; 30 m. long, 5–10 m. wide.

Byam Martin Channel Arm of Arctic Ocean, Northwest Territories, between Melville and Bathurst islands; 150 m. long, 30–65 m. wide.

Byam Martin Island Byam Martin Channel, Northwest Territories; 30 m. long, 20 m. wide.

Bylot Island Northwest Territories, in the Arctic Ocean, off N Baffin Island; 4,968 sq. m. Consists mainly of ice-covered plateau.

Byrd Deep Ocean depth (28,152 ft) in Antarctic Ocean, off Ross Sea.

Byron, Cape Easternmost point of Australia, E New South Wales.

Cadiz, Gulf of Wide Atlantic inlet, SW Iberian Peninsula; extends *c.* 200 m. from Cape St Vincent in Portugal to Gibraltar.

Caernarvon Bay Inlet of St Georges Channel, Wales;

extends 35 m. N-S between Holy Island and Caernarvon; 20 m. wide.

Cagliari, Gulf of Inlet of Mediterranean, S Sardinia; 28 m. wide. Sometimes called Golfo degli Angeli.

Caicos Islands W group of Turks and Caicos Islands, dependency of Jamaica. Caicos Bank, shoal *c.* 60 m. in diameter, is surrounded by numerous islands including East Caicos, South Caicos and others.

Caicos Passage Channel in the Caribbean separating Mayaguana island from Caicos Islands; *c.* 40 m. wide.

Caird Coast Part of coast of Coats Land, Antarctica, on Weddell Sea.

Calamian Islands (or Calamianes) Group in the Philippines between Palawan and Mindoro; 600 sq. m.

Calauag Bay S arm of Lamon Bay, Philippines; 21 m. long, 4–11 m. wide.

California Current Cold ocean current of N Pacific, branch of Aleutian Current, flowing S along W coast of North America.

Calvert Island SW British Columbia, in Queen Charlotte Sound; 100 sq. m., 20 m. long, 2–10 m. wide.

Camagüey Archipelago Coral reefs off N coast of E Cuba; extend *c.* 150 m. NW-SE and form S flank of Old Bahama Channel.

Cambay, Gulf of Inlet of Arabian Sea, India, between N Bombay and Kathiawar peninsula; 15–120 m. wide, 130 m. long.

Cambridge Gulf SW arm of Joseph Bonaparte Gulf of Timor Sea; 50 m. long, 10 m. wide.

Cambridge Island Off coast of S Chile, at NW entrance of Nelson Strait; 30 m. long, 3–7 m. wide. Sometimes called Almagro Island.

Camden Bay NE Alaska, on Beaufort Sea; 45 m. wide.

Camotes Sea Philippines, leading N to Visayan Sea and S to Mindanao Sea; Camotes Islands in center.

Campana Island S Chile, just NW of Wellington Island; *c.* 50 m. long, *c.* 12 m. wide.

Campeche, Gulf of Inlet of Gulf of Mexico, SE Mexico.

Camranh Bay Inlet of South China Sea, S central Vietnam; T-shaped, 10 m. long, 20 m. wide, closed by neck 1 m. wide.

Canaries Current Cold ocean current in the Atlantic off NW coast of Africa. It is the N hemisphere counterpart of the Benguela Current off SW Africa.

Canarreos, Los Archipelago off SW Cuba, consisting of a chain of numerous keys extending *c.* 60 m. along N and E shores of Isle of Pines.

Canaveral, Cape Seaward extremity of barrier island sheltering Banana River lagoon, E Florida, on the Atlantic. Site of testing ground for guided missiles.

Candia, Sea of (or Sea of Crete) Deepest section of the Aegean Sea, between Cyclades and Crete. Depth over 6,000 ft.

Canigao Channel Philippines, leading from Camotes Sea to Mindanao Sea.

Canterbury Bight Inlet of S Pacific, E South Island, New Zealand; 115 m. wide.

Cape Barren Island Second largest of Furneaux Islands, off NE coast of Tasmania; 172 sq. m.

Cape Cod Bay S arm of Massachusetts Bay, E Massachusetts, on Atlantic coast; *c.* 25 m. wide; enclosed by Cape Cod peninsula.

Cape York Peninsula N Queensland, Australia, between Gulf of Carpentaria and Coral Sea; 280 m. N-S, 150 m. E-W. Largely tropical jungle.

Cardigan Bay Inlet of Irish Sea, W Wales. Extends 65 m. SSW-NNE and is 35 m. wide.

Cariaco, Gulf of Inlet of the Caribbean, NE Venezuela, S of Araya Peninsula; 40 m. long, *c.* 10 m. wide.

Carigara Bay Wide inlet of Samar Sea, N Leyte, Philippines; 20 m. E-W, 9 m. N-S.

Carmarthen Bay Largest inlet of Bristol Channel, S Wales; 27 m. long, 12 m. wide.

Carroll Inlet Long, narrow inlet of Bellingshausen Sea, Antarctica. Extends SE for 30 m. into George Bryan Coast.

Cartagena, Bay of Inlet of Caribbean Sea, N Colombia, just S of Cartagena.

Casco Bay SW Maine, between Cape Elizabeth and Cape Small; 20 m. wide.

Casiguran Sound Inlet of Philippine Sea, between W coast of central Luzon and San Ildefonso Peninsula; 20 m. long, 1–10 m. wide.

Castellammare del Golfo Inlet of Tyrrhenian Sea, W Sicily; 20 m. wide, 11 m. long.

Catanduanes Island in the Philippines, Philippine Sea, off SE Luzon; 552 sq. m.

Catania, Gulf of Inlet of Ionian Sea, E Sicily; 20 m. long, 5 m. wide.

Catba Island (or Cacba Island) Island in Gulf of Tonkin, off N Vietnam mainland; 15 m. long, 13 m. wide.

Cat Cays String of islets, NW Bahama Islands, adjoining South Bimini; 60 m. long.

Cat Island Long, narrow island in the central Bahamas, said to be most fertile of the archipelago; 50 m. long, *c.* 3 m. wide.

Cay Sal Bank Shoal in the West Indies, between Florida and Cuba; *c.* 70 m. long, up to 45 m. wide.

Cazones, Gulf of S Cuba, 45 m. WSW of Cienfuegos; *c.* 30 m. long, up to 10 m. wide.

Cebu Island in the Visayan Islands, Philippines, between Visayan Sea and Mindanao Sea; 1,702 sq. m. Volcanic, but largely overlaid with coral.

Cedros Island NW Mexico, on Pacific coast of Lower California; 134 sq. m. Sparsely inhabited.

Celebes Sea Section of W Pacific Ocean, between Mindanao, Sulu Archipelago, Borneo, Celebes and Sangi Islands; *c.* 400 m. N-S, *c.* 500 m. E-W.

Ceram Island in S Moluccas, Indonesia, between Ceram and Banda seas; 6,622 sq. m., 210 m. long, 45 m. wide. Sometimes spelled Seran and Serang.

Ceram Laut Island group in S Moluccas, Indonesia, off SE coast of Ceram; 100 sq. m.; comprises *c.* 15 islands, largest of which is Ceram Laut, 12 sq. m. Sometimes spelled Serang Laut.

Ceram Sea Part of Pacific Ocean in Indonesia, between Halmahera, Ceram, New Guinea and Sula Islands. Merges with Molucca and Arafura seas. Formerly known as Pitt Passage.

Chalcidice Peninsula, NE Greece, projecting into Aegean Sea from Macedonia; 60 m. long, 30 m. wide; terminates in 3 prongs, each 30 m. long: Kassandra, Sithonia and Akte.

Chaleur Bay Inlet of the Gulf of St Lawrence between Gaspé Peninsula and N New Brunswick; 90 m. long, 15–25 m. wide. It is submerged valley of the Restigouche River, which it receives at head.

Chandeleur Islands Archipelago in the Gulf of Mexico, SE Louisiana; frequented by fishermen, fur trappers.
Chandeleur Sound Arm of Gulf of Mexico between Louisiana coast and Chandeleur Islands; *c.* 20 m. wide.
Chang, Ko Island, S Thailand, in Gulf of Siam; 20 m. long, 5 m. wide.
Changshan Islands 1. (or Miao Islands) Island group in Yellow Sea, China, guarding entrance to Gulf of Chihli. Comprises 15 islands, largest being Changshan Island, 7 m. long, 2 m. wide.
2. Island group in Korea Bay of Yellow Sea, off E coast of Liaotung peninsula.
Chantrey Inlet Bay of Arctic Ocean, Northwest Territories, on E side of Adelaide Peninsula; 100 m. long, 50 m. wide at mouth.
Charco Azul Bay W inlet of Chiriquí Gulf of the Pacific, W Panama; 30 m. wide, 15 m. long.
Charcot Bay Inlet in Antarctica, on N coast of Palmer Peninsula.
Charcot Island Island off W coast of Palmer Peninsula, Antarctica, in the S Pacific; 57 m. in diameter.
Charles Island Northwest Territories, in Hudson Strait; 26 m. long, 1–7 m. wide.
Charlotte Harbor Shallow inlet of the Gulf of Mexico, SW Florida; *c.* 25 m. long, 5 m. wide.
Charlton Island Northwest Territories, at head of James Bay; 113 sq. m., 19 m. long, 9 m. wide. Terminal for ocean-going ships.
Chatham Island Uninhabited island off W coast of S Chile; 35 m. long, *c.* 12 m. wide.
Chatham Sound Channel of Dixon Entrance, W British Columbia, extending N from Porcher Island to mouth of Portland Inlet; 40 m. long, 8–15 m. wide.
Chatham Strait Navigable channel through NW section of Alexander Archipelago, SE Alaska; 210 m. long.
Chaun Bay Inlet of East Siberian Sea, Russian SFSR; 100 m. long, 35 m. wide.
Chauques Islands Archipelago off E coast of Chiloé Island, S Chile; comprises 16 islands.
Chaves Island (also called Santa Cruz Island or Indefatigable Island) Central Galápagos Islands, Ecuador, in the Pacific; 389 sq. m. Circular, of volcanic origin.
Cheduba Island Bay of Bengal, off Arakan coast, Lower Burma; 20 m. long, 15 m. wide.
Cheju Island Island, Korea, between Cheju Strait and East China Sea; 713 sq. m. Extinct volcano.
Cheju Strait Channel connecting Korea Strait with Yellow Sea; *c.* 50 m. wide; contains many islands.
Chelyuskin, Cape Northernmost point of Asiatic continent, at N end of Taimyr Peninsula, on Boris Vilkitski Strait. Originally called Northeast Cape.
Chesha Bay Inlet of Barents Sea, E of Kanin Peninsula; 70 m. wide, 65 m. long.
Chesterfield Inlet Northwest Territories, in Hudson Bay; 140 m. long, 1–10 m. wide.
Chetumal Bay Inlet of Caribbean Sea on E coast of Yucatan Peninsula; 35 m. long N-S, 3–20 m. wide.
Chiba Peninsula Central Honshu, Japan, between Tokyo Bay and Sagami Sea (W) and the Pacific (E); 60 m. long, 20–30 m. wide. Sometimes called Boso Peninsula.
Chichagof Island Alexander Archipelago, SE Alaska; 2,104 sq. m.
Chignecto Bay Inlet of the Bay of Fundy, noted for high tides; 50 m. long, 10 m. wide.
Chignik Bay SW Alaska, on E side of Alaska Peninsula, SW of Kodiak Island; 20 m. long, 18 m. wide at mouth.
Chihli, Gulf of Arm of Yellow Sea, NE China; 300 m. long, 180 m. wide. Connected with Yellow Sea by Strait of Chihli (or Pohai Strait).
Chilkoot Inlet SE Alaska, NNW arm of Lynn Canal; 20 m. long.
Chinchorro Bank Barrier reef in Caribbean Sea, SE Mexico. Extends 28 m. N-S, 4–10 m. wide.
Chinhae Bay Inlet of Korea Strait, S Korea; 20 m. long, 15 m. wide.
Chin Island Island in the Yellow Sea, just off SW coast of Korea; 159 sq. m.
Chios (or Khios) Island in the Aegean, Greece, off Asiatic Turkey; 321 sq. m. One of the places which claimed to be the birthplace of Homer; famous for Homeridae (school of epic poets) in classical times.
Chiquimulilla Canal Coastal lagoon, S Guatemala, separated from the Pacific by low, sandy islands; *c.* 70 m. long.
Chiriquí Gulf Inlet of Pacific Ocean in W Panama, E of Burica Peninsula; 80 m. wide, 15 m. long.
Chiriquí Isthmus W Panama, between Chiriquí Lagoon and Chiriquí Gulf; 45 m. wide.
Chiriquí Lagoon Inlet of Caribbean Sea in W Panama, closed off by Bocas del Toro Archipelago; 32 m. wide, 13 m. long.
Chita Peninsula Central Honshu, Japan, between Ise Bay and Chita Bay; 20 m. N-S, 3–8 m. E-W. Sometimes spelled Tita.
Chocó Bay Indentation of the Pacific coast of W Colombia; 135 m. long.
Choctawhatchee Bay Arm of the Gulf of Mexico, NW Florida; *c.* 30 m. long, 3–5 m. wide; part of Gulf Intracoastal Waterway.
Choiseul Volcanic island, Solomon Islands, SW Pacific; 1,000 sq. m.
Choiseul Sound Inlet in East Falkland Island; *c.* 20 m. long, 2 m. wide.
Chonos Archipelago Island group in the Pacific, off S Chile; extends *c.* 130 m. N-S and consists of over 1,000 islands. Uninhabited except for a few Indians.
Chuginadak Island Largest of the Islands of Four Mountains, Aleutian Islands, SW Alaska; 14 m. long, 3–8 m. wide; rises to 5,680 ft in Mt Cleveland, an active volcano.
Chukchi Peninsula NE extremity of Asia and Siberia, Russian SFSR, at E end of Anadyr Range. Mountainous, severe climate.
Chukchi Sea Part of Arctic Ocean, joined to Bering Sea by Bering Strait; navigable August-September. Also spelled Chuckchee Sea.
Chusan Archipelago (or Chushan Archipelago) Island group in East China Sea, off Hangchow Bay. Main island is Chusan, 22 m. long, 10 m. wide; strong tidal currents and frequent fogs.
Clarence Island Easternmost of the South Shetland Islands, off Palmer Peninsula, Antarctica; 15 m. long, 10½ m. wide.
Clarence Strait 1. SE Alaska, in Alexander Archipelago;

extends 125 m. NW from Dixon Entrance to Sumner Strait.
2. Channel connecting Timor Sea with Van Diemen Gulf, between Melville Island and NW coast of Northern Territory, Australia; 90 m. long, 16 m. wide.
3. Arm of Strait of Hormuz of Persian Gulf, SE Iran; 70 m. long, 5 m. wide.

Clarie Coast Part of coast of Wilkes Land, Antarctica, just W of Adélie Coast, on Indian Ocean.

Clayoquot Sound Inlet of the Pacific, extending *c.* 60 m. along W central coast of Vancouver Island. Has several arms extending inland.

Cleveland Peninsula SE Alaska, extending *c.* 35 m. SW into the Alexander Archipelago.

Coats Island Northwest Territories, in N part of Hudson Bay; 1,544 sq. m.

Cobequid Bay E arm of the Minas Basin, central Nova Scotia; 30 m. long, 6 m. wide.

Cobourg Island (or Coburg Island) Northwest Territories, in Baffin Bay, at entrance of Jones Sound; 22 m. long, 4–14 m. wide. Breeding-ground of large numbers of murres.

Cobourg Peninsula N Northern Territory, Australia, forming SW shore of Arafura Sea; 50 m. long, 25 m. wide. Reserve for native flora and fauna.

Coco, Cayo Coral island off E Cuba, in Old Bahama Channel; 25 m. long, up to 8 m. wide. Low and swampy. Belongs to Camagüey Archipelago.

Coco Channel Seaway connecting Bay of Bengal and Andaman Sea.

Cod Island (or Ogualik Island) NE Labrador; 11 m. long, 10 m. wide. Entire surface covered by Kaumajet Mountains.

Coiba Island SW Panama, in the Pacific Ocean; 20 m. long, 6 m. wide. Sometimes called Quibo Island.

Cold Bay Inlet of N Pacific in SW Alaska Peninsula; 20 m. long, 4–8 m. wide.

Collier Bay Inlet of Indian Ocean in Western Australia, NE of King Sound; 60 m. E-W, 40 m. N-S.

Colorados, Los (or Bajos de Los Colorados) Archipelago off NW Cuba, consisting of a chain of low coral reefs and keys. Extends *c.* 140 m. along the coast from Cape San Antonio. Also called Guaniguanico or Santa Isabel.

Columbia, Cape Northernmost point of Canada, on N Ellesmere Island, Northwest Territories, in the Arctic Ocean.

Columbus Bank Shoal in the Bahama Islands, E and S of Great Ragged Island; *c.* 50 m. long, up to 20 m. wide.

Committee Bay Inlet of the Gulf of Boothia, Northwest Territories, in W side of Melville Peninsula; 130 m. long, 80 m. wide at mouth.

Comorin, Cape Southernmost point of Indian peninsula, in Indian Ocean; rocky headland, with ancient temple which is important Hindu pilgrimage site.

Concepción Bay Inlet of Gulf of California on E coast of Lower California, NW Mexico; 22 m. long, 2–5 m. wide.

Concepción Strait (or Conception Strait) Inlet of the Pacific off S coast of Chile, between Madre de Dios Archipelago and Hanover Island; *c.* 40 m. long, 4–8 m. wide.

Conception Bay Inlet in SW Newfoundland, in S section of Avalon Peninsula; 50 m. long, 20 m. wide at entrance.

Contreras Island Uninhabited island, S Chile, NW of Adelaide Islands; 35 m. long, *c.* 7 m. wide.

Cook Inlet Inlet of the Gulf of Alaska, S Alaska, on W side of Kenai Peninsula; 150 m. long, 9–80 m. wide.

Cook Strait New Zealand, between North Island and South Island; 16 m. wide at narrowest point.

Coorong, The Long, narrow lagoon, SE South Australia, separated from Indian Ocean by sandspit; 80 m. long, 2.5 m. wide, 3–10 ft deep.

Coral Bay Large inlet of SE St John Island, Virgin Islands; fine harbor.

Corfu, Channel of Arm of Ionian Sea between Corfu and Albania and Greek Epirus mainland; *c.* 30 m. long.

Corinth, Isthmus of Greece, connecting Peloponnesus with central Greece, between Gulf of Corinth and Saronic Gulf; 20 m. long, 4–8 m. wide. Crossed by Corinth Canal.

Corio Bay W arm of Port Phillip Bay, S Victoria, Australia; 20 m. long, 12 m. wide.

Corisco Bay Inlet of Gulf of Guinea, bounded by Cape San Juan and Cape Esterias; 35 m. wide, 20 m. long.

Cork Harbour Inlet of the Atlantic on SE coast of County Cork, Ireland, forming one of the best natural anchorages in the world; 8 m. long, up to 6 m. wide.

Cornwallis Island Parry Islands; 2,592 sq. m. Weather station on SE coast.

Cornwall Island Northwest Territories, in the Arctic Ocean; 720 sq. m.

Coro, Gulf of E inlet of Gulf of Venezuela, NW Venezuela; 25 m. long, up to 20 m. wide.

Coronado Bay Bight of the Pacific, S Costa Rica; 60 m. wide, 20 m. long.

Coronation Gulf Arm of the Arctic Ocean separating Victoria Island from Mackenzie district, Northwest Territories; 130 m. long, 50–70 m. wide. Part of the Northwest Passage.

Corpus Christi Bay Arm of the Gulf of Mexico, S Texas; *c.* 25 m. long E-W, 3–10 m. wide.

Cosigüina Peninsula W Nicaragua, between Pacific Ocean and Gulf of Fonseca; 20 m. long, 10–13 m. wide. Sometimes spelled Consigüina; formerly also Cosegüina and Conseguina.

Coulman Island Antarctica, just off Victoria Land; 13 m. long, 16½ m. wide.

Courland Lagoon Large coastal lagoon, Russian SFSR, separated from Baltic by Courland Spit (60-m. sandspit); connected with open sea by Memel Channel; lagoon is 625 sq. m.

Cowal Peninsula, SE Argyll, Scotland; *c.* 30 m. long, up to 15 m. wide.

Cowie Harbour Inlet of Celebes Sea, NE Borneo; 30 m. long, 5–10 m. wide.

Coyuca Lagoon Pacific coast of Guerrero, SW Mexico.

Cres Island Island in the Adriatic, Yugoslavia; 150 sq. m., *c.* 40 m. long.

Creswell Bay Arm of Prince Regent Inlet, SE Somerset Island, Northwest Territories; 45 m. long, 50 m. wide at mouth.

Crimea Peninsula on the Black Sea, projecting 120 m. S; 10,000 sq. m., 200 m. W-E.

Croker Island Island in Arafura Sea, off NE shore of Cobourg Peninsula, Australia; 126 sq. m., 27 m. long, 10 m. wide. Aboriginal reservation.

Cromarty Firth Long, narrow inlet of Moray Firth, Scotland; 18 m. long, 3–5 m. wide.

Crooked Island Passage Deep channel in S central Bahamas, bounded by Samana Island, Crooked Island and Long Island; *c.* 60 m. long.
Cross Sound SE Alaska, between Chicagof Island and the mainland; extends 30 m. NE from Gulf of Alaska to Icy Strait.
Crown Prince Frederick Island Northwest Territories, in the Gulf of Boothia, off NW Baffin Island; 22 m. long, 6 m. wide.
Culebra Gulf Inlet of the Pacific, NW Costa Rica, S of Santa Elena Peninsula; 25 m. wide, 15 m. long. Also called Papagayo Gulf.
Culion Island One of the Calamian Islands, Philippines, between Palawan and Mindoro; 153 sq. m. Government leper colony.
Cumberland Islands Archipelago in Coral Sea between Great Barrier Reef and Repulse Bay, Australia; 60-m. chain of 36 rocky islands and scattered coral islets.
Cumberland Peninsula SE Baffin Island, Northwest Territories; extends *c.* 200 m. E into Davis Strait, up to 150 m. wide. Mountainous, rising to over 8,500 ft.
Cumberland Sound Inlet of Davis Strait, SE Baffin Island, Northwest Territories; 170 m. long, 100 m. wide at mouth.
Cupica, Gulf of Inlet of the Pacific, W Colombia; *c.* 20 m. long.
Currituck Sound Arm of the Atlantic, NE North Carolina and SE Virginia; *c.* 30 m. long, 5 m. wide.
Cutch, Gulf of Inlet of Arabian Sea on W coast of India; 110 m. long, 10–40 m. wide.

Dahlak Archipelago Island group in the Red Sea, off the coast of Eritrea; consists of 2 main islands – Dahlak (*c.* 290 sq. m.) and Norah (*c.* 50 sq. m.) – and 124 smaller islands. Flat, desert and mostly uninhabited.
Dall Island SE Alaska, in the Alexander Archipelago; 43 m. long, 2–8 m. wide.
Damar Islands Group in Banda Sea, S Moluccas, Indonesia. Consist of main island Damar (12 m. long, 10 m. wide; volcanic) and several islets; total area 122 sq. m. Also spelled Danmar and Dammer.
Dampier Strait Channel connecting S end of Jailolo Passage with Pacific Ocean; *c.* 90 m. long, 20–50 m. wide.
Danco Coast NW coast of Palmer Peninsula, Antarctica, between Charcot Bay and Cape Renard.
Danmark Fjord Inlet in NE Greenland; 130 m. long, 1–20 m. wide; extends SW to edge of inland icecap.
Daracya Peninsula SW Turkey, extending 34 m. S into Aegean Sea; 21 m. wide.
Darnley Bay Inlet of Amundsen Gulf, on E side of Parry Peninsula, Northwest Territories; 28 m. long, 20 m. wide at mouth.
Darvel Bay Inlet of the Celebes Sea, NE Borneo; 40 m. long, 30 m. wide.
Davao Gulf Inlet in SE coast of Mindanao, Philippines; 90 m. long, 30–50 m. wide.
Davis Inlet Bay of the Atlantic, E Labrador; 20 m. long, 1 m. wide.
Davis Sea Section of Indian Ocean, off coast of Antarctica, between Shackleton Shelf Ice and West Shelf Ice.
Davis Strait Arm of the Atlantic between SE Baffin Island and SW Greenland; 400 m. long, 180–400 m. wide. Part of sea passage to Arctic Ocean, generally navigable from midsummer until late fall.
Dawson Island Central Tierra del Fuego archipelago, Chile; 55 m. long, 20 m. wide; sheep raising.
Dease Strait Arm of the Arctic Ocean, Northwest Territories, between Coronation Gulf and Queen Maud Gulf; 130 m. long, 12–30 m. wide.
Delagoa Bay Sheltered inlet of Indian Ocean in S coast of Mozambique; 50 m. long, 20 m. wide.
Delmarva Peninsula E United States; extends *c.* 180 m. S from just S of Wilmington, Delaware; greatest width *c.* 70 m.
De Long Fjord Passage of the Arctic Ocean, between N Greenland and offshore islands; 30 m. long, 2–5 m. wide.
Denmark Strait Sea passage between Greenland and Iceland, cut by Arctic Circle; *c.* 300 m. long, 180 m. wide at narrowest point. Icebergs are carried through it by cold East Greenland Current.
D'Entrecasteaux Channel Inlet of Tasman Sea between Tasmania and Bruny.
D'Entrecasteaux Islands Volcanic group in SW Pacific, 25 m. SE of New Guinea; *c.* 1,200 sq. m.
Desolation Island Bleak, uninhabited island in Tierra del Fuego archipelago, Chile; 80 m. long, 10 m. wide.
d'Espoir, Bay Inlet of Hermitage Bay, S Newfoundland: 30 m. long, 4 m. wide at entrance.
Devon Island Northwest Territories, in the Arctic Ocean; 21,606 sq. m. Plateau, ice-covered in E.
Dezhnev, Cape Northeasternmost point of Asia and Siberia, Chukchi Peninsula, on Bering Strait.
Digby Neck Peninsula on Bay of Fundy, W Nova Scotia; 30 m. long, 2 m. wide.
Diligent Strait Arm of Andaman Sea between main group of Andaman Islands and Ritchie's Archipelago.
Dinagat Island Philippines, just off NE Mindanao; 309 sq. m.
Dingle Bay Inlet of the Atlantic, W County Kerry, Ireland; 18 m. wide at entrance, extending 24 m. inland to Castelmaine Harbour.
Dirk Hartogs Island Indian Ocean, 1 m. off W coast of Western Australia; 239 sq. m. Sometimes written Dirk Hartog's Island.
Discovery Bay Inlet of Indian Ocean, SE Australia, between Cape Northumberland and Cape Bridgewater; 45 m. long, 8 m. wide.
Discovery Passage Channel on E coast of Vancouver Island, SW British Columbia; 26 m. long.
Disenchantment Bay SE Alaska, at head of Yakutat Bay; 20 m. long.
Disko Island in Davis Strait, just off W Greenland; 3,312 sq. m. First reached by Eric the Red between 982 and 985.
Disko Bay Inlet of Davis Strait, W Greenland, separating Disko island from the mainland; 120 m. long, 50 m. wide at mouth.
Dixon Entrance Strait in N Pacific between Alexander Archipelago and Queen Charlotte Islands; *c.* 50 m. long, *c.* 50 m. wide.
Djerba Island in the Mediterranean Sea, just off S coast of Tunisia; 197 sq. m. Very fertile and beautiful.
Dmitri Laptev Strait (or Dmitriy Laptev Strait) Strait joining Laptev and East Siberian seas of the Arctic Ocean. 80 m. long, 30 m. wide. Also called Laptev Strait.

The coast of Madeir

Doce Leguas, Cayos de las Coral reefs off Caribbean coast of E Cuba; *c.* 85 m. long NW-SE.
Dolleman Island Antarctica, in Weddell Sea, just off E coast of Palmer Peninsula; 11 m. long.
Dolphin and Union Strait Arm of the Arctic Ocean between Amundsen Gulf and Coronation Gulf, Northwest Territories; 100 m. long, 20–40 m. wide. Forms part of Northwest Passage.
Domel Island Central Mergui Archipelago, Lower Burma, Andaman Sea; 25 m. long, 2–6 m. wide.
Dominica Largest of the Windward Islands, West Indies; 29 m. long, 16 m. wide.
Dominica Passage Channel in Lesser Antilles, West Indies; *c.* 20 m. wide.
Donegal Bay Inlet of the Atlantic, Ireland, between counties Donegal, Leitrim and Sligo; 25 m. long, 21 m. wide at mouth.
Dornoch Firth Inlet of Moray Firth; 22 m. long, 9 m. wide at mouth.
Doubtful Sound Inlet of Tasman Sea, SW South Island, New Zealand; 20 m. long, 2 m. wide.
Douglas Island SE Alaska, between Admiralty Island and mainland; 18 m. long, 3–7 m. wide. Site of famous Treadwell mine.
Dove Bay NE Greenland; 50 m. wide at mouth, extending *c.* 50 m. inland. Inland icecap descends to E shore.
Drake Passage Antarctic strait off South America between Cape Horn and South Shetland Islands; *c.* 500 m. long, 400 m. wide; joins South Pacific and South Atlantic.
Drammen Fjord NW arm of Oslo Fjord, SE Norway; 20 m. long, 1–3 m. wide. Also called Drams Fjord.
Drin Gulf Inlet of the Adriatic in NW Albania; 20 m. wide, 10 m. long.
Dulce, Golfo (or Osa Gulf) Inlet of the Pacific in S Costa Rica, between Osa Peninsula and the mainland; 30 m. long, *c.* 10 m. wide.
Dumaran Island Philippines, just off NE coast of Palawan; 126 sq. m.
Duncan Canal Inlet in S coast of Kupreanof Island, Alexander Archipelago, SE Alaska; 30 m. long, 2 m. wide.
Duncan Passage Channel connecting Bay of Bengal and Andaman Sea between main group of Andaman Islands and Little Andaman Island.
Dundas Strait Channel connecting Timor Sea with Van Diemen Gulf between Melville Island and Cobourg Peninsula, Australia; 40 m. long, 18 m. wide.
Dundee Island Antarctica, off E tip of Palmer Peninsula; 13 m. long, 8 m. wide.
Dusky Sound Inlet of Tasman Sea, SW South Island, New Zealand; 25 m. long, 12 m. wide. Contains several islands.
Dvina Bay SE inlet of White Sea in N European Russian SFSR; 80 m. wide, 65 m. long. Formerly also called Archangel Bay.

East Australian Current Tasman Sea of Pacific Ocean, flowing S along SE coast of Australia. Forms part of counterclockwise circulation of Tasman Sea.
East Cape 1. Easternmost point of New Guinea, at N side of entrance to Milne Bay.
2. Easternmost point of New Zealand proper, NE North Island.
Eastern Shore Tidewater region along E shore of Chesapeake Bay including all of Maryland and Virginia E of the bay.
East Greenland Current Cold ocean current of N Atlantic, rising in Arctic Ocean and flowing S and SW along E coast of Greenland. Carries many icebergs.
East Korea Bay Wide inlet of Sea of Japan in N Korea; 100 m. long, 50 m. wide. Formerly also called Broughton Bay.
East Siberian Sea Section of Arctic Ocean, bounded W by New Siberian Islands, S by N coast of NE Siberia, E by Wrangell Island, N by edge of continental shelf.
Ebrié Lagoon Ivory Coast, West Africa; flanked by narrow spit and linked with ocean by channel; 70 m. long.
Eclipse Sound Arm of Baffin Bay, N Baffin Island, Northwest Territories; 60 m. long, 40 m. wide.
Edge Island One of the Spitsbergen group, in Barents Sea of Arctic Ocean; 1,942 sq. m. Large icefield along SE coast; interior of island uncharted.
Edremit, Gulf of NW Turkey, inlet of Aegean Sea; 20 m. wide, 27 m. long.
Edward VII Peninsula Antarctica, extending NW from Marie Byrd Land into Ross Sea.
Efate Most important island of New Hebrides, SW Pacific; 50 m. long, 20 m. wide. Formerly called Sandwich Island.
Egede and Rothe Fjord Inlet of Denmark Strait, SE Greenland; 65 m. long, 5–10 m. wide. Extends to edge of inland icecap. Also called Sermilik.
Eglinton Island Parry Islands, Northwest Territories, in the Arctic Ocean; 504 sq. m.
Eights Coast Antarctica, along S shore of Bellingshausen Sea.
Elcho Island Arafura Sea, off Napier Peninsula of Arnhem Land, Australia; 30 m. long, 7 m. wide. Aboriginal reservation.
Elephant Island E South Shetland Islands, off Palmer Peninsula, Antarctica; 25 m. long, 13 m. wide.
Eleuthera Island Central Bahama Islands, between Great Abaco Island and Cat Island; 164 sq. m.
Ellef Ringnes Island Sverdrup Islands, Northwest Territories, in the Arctic Ocean; 4,266 sq. m.
Ellice Island Northwest Territories, in Beaufort Sea of Arctic Ocean; 24 m. long, 4–11 m. wide.
Ellis Island SE New York, in Upper New York Bay. Former chief immigration station of U.S.; now detention station for deportees.
Emerald Island Northwest Territories, in Ballantyne Strait of Arctic Ocean; *c.* 20 m. long, 5–10 m. wide.
Encounter Bay Inlet of Indian Ocean, SE South Australia; 20 m. E-W, 6 m. N-S.
Endeavour Strait Channel of Torres Strait, N Queensland, Australia; 30 m. long, 10 m. wide. Opens into Gulf of Carpentaria.
Enggano (or Engano) Island in the Indian Ocean, off SW coast of Sumatra; 171 sq. m.
English Company's Islands 50-m. chain of islands in Arafura Sea, parallel with NE coast of Arnhem Land, Australia. Comprise 4 rocky islands and several islets.
Epi Volcanic island, New Hebrides, SW Pacific; 141 sq. m. Formerly called Tasiko.
Erikub Uninhabited atoll in the Ratak Chain of the

Valletta harbor, Malta

Marshall Islands, w central Pacific; c. 20 m. long. Comprises 14 islets. Formerly Chatham Islands.
Eriskay Island in the Outer Hebrides, Scotland; 3 m. long, 1½ m. wide. Prince Charles Edward, the Young Pretender, first landed on Scottish soil here in 1745.
Erromanga Island in the New Hebrides, sw Pacific; c. 345 sq. m. Has extinct volcanoes and savannas.
Eschscholtz Bay SE arm of Kotzebue Sound, NE Seward Peninsula, NW Alaska; 30 m. long, 7–16 m. wide. Sometimes spelled Escholtz.
Esperanza Inlet w coast of Vancouver Island, British Columbia; separates Nootka Island from Vancouver Island; 22 m. long.
Etolin Island Alexander Archipelago, SE Alaska, between Prince of Wales Island and mainland; 30 m. long, 10–22 m. wide.
Etolin Strait w Alaska, extending SE-NW between Kuskokwim Bay and Bering Sea; 60 m. long, 30–50 m. wide.
Euboea Largest Greek island in the Aegean Sea; 1,457 sq. m. In ancient times chief cities were Chalcis and Eretria.
Euboea, Gulf of (or Gulf of Evvoia) Arm of Aegean Sea between Euboea and mainland of Greece. Consists of 50-m. N section and 30-m. S section joined by Euripos at Chalcis. Formerly called Talanti Channel or Atalante Channel in N section and Egripo Channel or Euripos Channel in S section.
Eureka Sound Arm of the Arctic Ocean, Northwest Territories, between Axel Heiberg Island and Ellesmere Island; 180 m. long, 8–30 m. wide.
Exmouth Gulf Inlet of Indian Ocean, NW Western Australia; 55 m. N-S, 30 m. E-W.
Exploits, Bay of Inlet of Notre Dame Bay, E Newfoundland; 30 m. long, 2–6 m. wide.
Exuma Group of islands in the central Bahamas; 100 sq. m.
Exuma Sound Deep Atlantic channel in the central Bahamas; c. 100 m. long, c. 40 m. wide.
Eyja Fjord Inlet of Greenland Sea, N Iceland; 40 m. long, 2–8 m. wide.
Eyre Peninsula S South Australia, between Great Australian Bight and Spencer Gulf; 200 m. N-S; triangular, with base of 250 m.; rises to 1,000 ft.

Faddei Island (or Faddey Island) One of Anjou group of New Siberian Islands; c. 40 m. in diameter.
Faitsilong Archipelago Group of islands and islets, N Vietnam, in Gulf of Tonkin.
Faitsilong Bay Arm of Gulf of Tonkin, N Vietnam, between mainland and Faitsilong Archipelago; c. 20 m. long, c. 10 m. wide.
Fakarava Atoll of the Tuamotu Islands, second largest of the group, S Pacific. Its lagoon is 32 m. long, 10 m. wide. Formerly called Wittgenstein Island.
Falkland Current Cold ocean current of South Atlantic, flowing N along E coast of Argentina to meet the Brazil Current.
Falkland Sound Strait separating East and West Falkland Islands; c. 50 m. long, 1½–20 m. wide.
False Bay Inlet of the Atlantic, sw Cape Province, South Africa, 12 m. S of Cape Town; 20 m. long, 18 m. wide at mouth.
Falster Island in the Baltic Sea, separated from S Zealand (Denmark) by Storstrom strait; 198 sq. m. Very fertile.
Farallon Islands 2 groups of islets in the Pacific, forming part of San Francisco city and county. Waterless, rocky. Bird refuge. Only Southeast Farallon is inhabited. Also called Farallones.
Farasan Islands Low, sandy archipelago in the Red Sea, off Asir coast. Belong to Saudi Arabia. Comprise 2 large and many smaller islands; largest is 35 m. long. Sometimes spelled Farsan and Farisan.
Faxa Bay Inlet of the Atlantic, sw Iceland; 30 m. long, 50 m. wide at mouth.
Fergusson Island Largest of the D'Entrecasteaux Islands, 30 m. SE of New Guinea; 518 sq. m.; volcanic, with hot springs.
Fernandina Island (or Narborough Island) w Galápagos Islands, in the Pacific Ocean; 245 sq. m. Volcanic origin.
Fidalgo, Port Bay on E shore of Prince William Sound, S Alaska; 25 m. long, 2 m. wide.
Findlay Islands Group of 4 islands, Northwest Territories, in the Arctic Ocean; Lougheed Island is the largest.
Fire Island (or Fire Island Beach) Narrow barrier beach off S shore of Long Island, SE New York; c. 30 m. long. Sometimes called Great South Beach.
Fitzwilliam Strait Arm of the Arctic Ocean, Northwest Territories, between Melville Island and Prince Patrick Island; 60 m. long, 15–40 m. wide.
Flensburg Firth Baltic estuarine inlet forming Danish-German border; c. 30 m. long.
Fletcher Islands Bellingshausen Sea, off Eights Coast, Antarctica; comprise McNamara and Dustin islands.
Fleurieu Peninsula Name sometimes given to peninsula S of Adelaide, South Australia; 33 m. long, 22 m. wide.
Flinders Bay Inlet of Indian Ocean, sw Western Australia; 24 m. E-W, 8 m. N-S.
Flinders Island Largest of Furneaux Islands, in Bass Strait, off NE coast of Tasmania; 802 sq. m.
Flinders Passage Channel of Coral Sea breaking through Great Barrier Reef off E coast of Queensland, Australia; 21 m. long, 7½ m. wide.
Flores Island, Lesser Sundas, Indonesia, between Flores Sea and Savu Sea; 5,511 sq. m. Mountainous, with many volcanic peaks; dry climate, unlike most Indonesian islands.
Flores Sea Part of the Pacific Ocean between Java Sea and Banda Sea; c. 150 m. wide.
Florida One of the Solomon Islands, sw Pacific; 20 m. long, 10 m. wide; volcanic.
Florida, Straits of Passage between Florida Keys (N) and Cuba and Bahama Islands (S and SE); up to 90 m. wide. Connects Gulf of Mexico with Atlantic.
Florida Current Warm ocean current of North Atlantic, forming first section of Gulf Stream system. Flows N along SE coast of United States.
Fogo Island in Leeward group of Cape Verde Islands, in the Atlantic; 184 sq. m. Has active volcano, Cano Peak (9,281 ft).
Fogo Island Island just off E Newfoundland; 100 sq. m.
Folda Fjord of the North Sea, N Norway; 8 m. wide at mouth, divides into North Folda (36 m. long) and South Folda (24 m. long). Sometimes spelled Folla; sometimes called Foldenfjord.

Fonseca, Gulf of Sheltered inlet of the Pacific in Central America; *c.* 700 sq. m., 20 m. wide at mouth.
Formosa Strait Arm of the Pacific Ocean between Chinese mainland and Formosa, linking East and South China seas; 100 m. wide at narrowest point.
Fortune Bay Inlet of the Atlantic, s Newfoundland; 80 m. long, 40 m. wide at entrance.
Four Mountains, Islands of Group of 5 small, uninhabited islands of the Aleutians, sw Alaska. Volcanic; noted for fog and strong sea currents.
Foveaux Strait New Zealand, between s tip of South Island and Stewart Island; 20 m. wide.
Foxe Basin Arm of the Atlantic, Northwest Territories, between Melville Peninsula and Baffin Island; 300 m. long, 200–250 m. wide.
Foxe Channel Arm of Hudson Bay, Northwest Territories, between Melville Peninsula and Southampton Island (w) and Foxe Peninsula of Baffin Island (E); 200 m. long, 90–200 m. wide.
Foxe Peninsula sw Baffin Island, Northwest Territories, extending 150 m. w into Foxe Channel; 50–100 m. wide.
Fox Islands Easternmost group of the Aleutian Islands, sw Alaska, extending *c.* 300 m. sw from Alaska Peninsula.
Foyle, Lough Inlet of the Atlantic between County Donegal, Eire, and County Londonderry, Northern Ireland; 20 m. long.
France, Ile de Island in Greenland Sea, off NE Greenland; 20 m. long, 3–6 m. wide. Almost entirely glaciated.
Franklin Bay Inlet of Amundsen Gulf, on w side of Parry Peninsula, Northwest Territories; 30 m. long, 25 m. wide at mouth.
Franklin Strait Arm of the Arctic Ocean between Boothia Peninsula and Prince of Wales Island, Northwest Territories; 110 m. long, 20–60 m. wide.
Franz Josef Fjord (or Franz Joseph Fjord) Inlet of Greenland Sea, E Greenland; 125 m. long, 1–20 m. wide. Extends several arms to edge of inland icecap.
Frederick E. Hyde Fjord Inlet of Arctic Ocean, N Greenland; 120 m. long, 2–10 m. wide.
Frederick Sound SE Alaska, between Kupreanof Island and mainland; extends 50 m. E-W.
Frederik Hendrik Island Netherlands New Guinea, off s coast of New Guinea island, in Arafura Sea; *c.* 110 m. long, *c.* 55 m. wide; swampy.
Frenchman Bay Inlet of the Atlantic Ocean in s Maine. Extends *c.* 20 m. inland.
Friz Strait (or Vries Strait) s Kuriles, Russian SFSR; 24 m. wide.
Frobisher Bay Inlet of the Atlantic in SE Baffin Island, Northwest Territories; 150 m. long, 20–40 m. wide.
Frohavet Section of the North Sea off coast of Norway, N of entrance to Trondheim Fjord.
Fro Islands Group of small islands in North Sea, 20 m. off coast of Norway; extend in 20-m. chain parallel to coast.
Froward Cape Southernmost point of American mainland, at tip of Brunswick Peninsula, Chile.
Frozen Strait Arm of Foxe Channel, Northwest Territories, between Melville Peninsula and Southampton Island; 50 m. long, 12–20 m. wide.
Fuerteventura Second largest of the Canary Islands; 666 sq. m. Suffers from drought. Sometimes spelled Forteventura.
Fukae-shima Largest and southernmost island of Gotoretto group, Japan, in East China Sea; 129 sq. m. Sometimes spelled Hukae-sima, Fukaye Shima and Fukai.
Furneaux Islands Group in Bass Strait, off NE coast of Tasmania.
Fury and Hecla Strait Arm of the Arctic Ocean between Baffin Island and Melville Peninsula, Northwest Territories; 100 m. long, 10–20 m. wide. Rarely navigable because of ice.
Fyn Second largest island of Denmark, between s Jutland and Zealand; 1,149 sq. m. Also spelled Fyen.

Gabès, Gulf of Inlet of central Mediterranean in E and SE Tunisia; 60 m. long, 60 m. wide.
Gabriel Channel Narrow strait in central Tierra del Fuego, Chile, connecting Admiralty Sound and Strait of Magellan; 30 m. long.
Gaeta, Gulf of Inlet of Tyrrhenian Sea in s central Italy; 65 m. long, 20 m. wide.
Gallipoli Peninsula (ancient Chersonesus Thracica) Turkey, extending 55–60 m. sw between Gulf of Saros (Aegean) and the Dardanelles; 3½–13 m. wide.
Galo Fjord Inlet of the Baltic in E Sweden; 27 m. long, 1–10 m. wide.
Garofalo Whirlpool in the Strait of Messina, just off NE Sicily, identified with the Charybdis of ancient legend.
Gaspé Bay Inlet of the Gulf of St Lawrence, E Quebec, at E end of Gaspé Peninsula.
Gaspé Peninsula E Quebec, extending into the Gulf of St Lawrence; 150 m. long, 60–90 m. wide. Heavily wooded, uninhabited interior; settlements on coast.
Gastineau Channel SE Alaska, between Douglas Island and mainland; 20 m. long, with 16-ft tide; navigable.
Gazelle Peninsula NE New Britain, Bismarck Archipelago, sw Pacific; 50 m. wide, separated from rest of island by isthmus *c.* 20 m. wide.
Geelvink Bay Deep inlet of the Pacific, Netherlands New Guinea, bounded w by Vogelkop peninsula; 200 m. E-W, 200 m. N-S.
Geelvink Channel Strait of Indian Ocean between Houtman Abrolhos and w coast of Western Australia; 70 m. long, 30 m. wide.
Genkai Sea NE arm of East China Sea; 36 m. E-W, 28 m. N-S.
Genoa, Gulf of N section of Ligurian Sea, Italy, enclosed by Riviera di Levante and Riviera di Ponente.
Geographe Bay Inlet of Indian Ocean, sw Western Australia; 40 m. wide at mouth, 10 m. N-S.
Geographe Channel Strait of Indian Ocean between w coast of Western Australia and Bernier Island; 50 m. long, 21 m. wide.
Geographical Society Island King Oscar Archipelago, E Greenland, in Greenland Sea, at mouth of Franz Josef Fjord; 55 m. long, 21 m. wide.
George Bay Inlet of the Gulf of St Lawrence, NE Nova Scotia, at E end of Northumberland Strait; 20 m. long, 20 m. wide. Forms sw shore of Cape Breton Island.
George Bryan Coast Antarctica, along s shore of Bellingshausen Sea.
George V Coast Antarctica, between Victoria Land and Adélie Land.
George Land Island, w Franz Josef Land, w of British

Channel; 80 m. long, 15–30 m. wide. Formerly called Prince George Land.

George VI Sound Antarctica, separating Alexander I Island from base of Palmer Peninsula.

Georgia, Strait of Channel between mainland of British Columbia and Vancouver Island; 150 m. long, 20–40 m. wide. Connects Queen Charlotte Sound with Puget Sound and Juan de Fuca Strait.

Germania Land Peninsula in NE Greenland, extending 40 m. E into Greenland Sea; ice-free.

Gibraltar, Strait of Passage connecting the Atlantic and the Mediterranean, between Spain and Africa; *c.* 36 m. long, 8–27 m. wide.

Gilford Island SW British Columbia, at E end of Queen Charlotte Strait; 159 sq. m.

Gioia, Gulf of Inlet of Tyrrhenian Sea, S Italy, between Cape Vaticano and Strait of Messina; 25 m. long, 10 m. wide.

Gizhiga Bay NW arm of Shelekhov Gulf of Sea of Okhotsk; 160 m. wide, 90 m. long.

Godthaab Fjord Inlet of Davis Strait, SW Greenland; 70 m. long, 2–20 m. wide; arc-shaped.

Golden Bay Inlet of Tasman Sea, N South Island, New Zealand; 20 m. wide. Also called Massacre Bay.

Gonaives, Gulf of W coast of Haiti; *c.* 75 m. wide.

Gonâve, Ile de la Island in the Gulf of Gonaives, belonging to Haiti; 254 sq. m.

Goodenough Island Volcanic island, D'Entrecasteaux Islands, Territory of Papua, SW Pacific; 20 m. long, 15 m. wide. Formerly called Morata.

Good Friday Gulf Arm of the Arctic Ocean between Amund Ringnes Island and Axel Heiberg Island, Northwest Territories; 70 m. long, 35–60 m. wide.

Goose Land Peninsula on W coast of S island of Nova Zemlya, Russian SFSR; 50 m. wide, 20 m. long.

Goto-retto Island group, Japan, in East China Sea; 249 sq. m., extending in 60-m. chain. Sometimes Goto Islands.

Graham Bell Island Easternmost island of Franz Josef Land, in the Arctic Ocean; 45 m. long, 25 m. wide.

Graham Island Largest of the Queen Charlotte Islands, W British Columbia, in the Pacific; 2,485 sq. m. Inhabitants mostly Haida Indians.

Grand Bahama Island One of Bahama Islands, in the NW part of the group; 75 m. long, up to 15 m. wide. Sometimes called Great Bahama Island.

Grand Canary One of the Canary Islands, Spain. Most important of the group, attracting many tourists; 592 sq. m.

Grande, Bahía Inlet of the Atlantic, Argentina; 140 m. N-S, *c.* 45 m. W-E.

Grande Comore Island Largest and westernmost of Comoro Islands, in Mozambique Channel of Indian Ocean; 442 sq. m.

Grande-Terre Island forming E half of Guadeloupe; 218.63 sq. m. Limestone formation.

Grand Manan Island Bay of Fundy, SW New Brunswick; 16 m. long, 7 m. wide. Popular resort.

Gravina Islands Part of Alexander Archipelago, SE Alaska. Largest islands of group are Gravina, Annette and Duke.

Great Abaco Island N Bahama Islands; *c.* 100 m. long, up to 14 m. wide. Adjoined NW by Little Abaco Island.

Great Australian Bight Wide bay of Indian Ocean indenting S coast of Australia; 720 m. E-W, 220 m. N-S. Contains several islands.

Great Bahama Bank Shoal in the Bahamas, SE of Florida; *c.* 350 m. long, between Cuba and Andros Island.

Great Barrier Island Volcanic island, New Zealand, 55 m. NE of Auckland; 110 sq. m. Forms breakwater for Hauraki Gulf.

Great Belt Strait connecting the Kattegat with the Baltic Sea; *c.* 40 m. long, *c.* 10 m. wide.

Great Channel Seaway connecting Indian Ocean with Andaman Sea and Strait of Malacca.

Great Inagua Island Southernmost and one of the largest of the Bahama Islands. Large, shallow lake on island abounds in bird life.

Great Koldewey Island in Greenland Sea, NE Greenland, at mouth of Dove Bay; 55 m. long, 2–5 m. wide.

Great Natuna (also Bunguran and Boengoeran) Largest of Natuna Islands, Indonesia; 40 m. long, 25 m. wide.

Great Northeast Channel Passage of Coral Sea connecting Torres Strait with Gulf of Papua; *c.* 100 m. long, 20 m. wide.

Great Northern Peninsula (or Petit Nord Peninsula) N section of Newfoundland; 170 m. long.

Great South Bay Arm of the Atlantic, SE New York, extending *c.* 45 m. from inlet near Rockaway Beach to Moriches Bay.

Greely Fjord Arm of the Arctic Ocean, W Ellesmere Island, Northwest Territories; 130 m. long, 1–15 m. wide.

Greenland Sea S section of Arctic Ocean off NE Greenland, N of Iceland; contains much polar drift ice.

Grenada Southernmost of the Windward Islands, West Indies; *c.* 120 sq. m.

Grenadines Archipelago in S part of Windward Islands, West Indies; extend in 60-m. chain.

Grenville Channel W British Columbia, separating Pitt Island from the mainland; 55 m. long, 1 m. wide.

Groote Eylandt Largest island in Gulf of Carpentaria, 25 m. off coast of Northern Territory, Australia; 950 sq. m. Aboriginal reservation.

Guacanayabo, Gulf of Shallow inlet of the Caribbean in S coast of Cuba; *c.* 60 m. wide, 60 m. long.

Guadalcanal Volcanic island, Solomon Islands, SW Pacific; 2,500 sq. m. Mountainous, rising to 8,000 ft in Mt Popomansiu.

Guadalupe Island NW Mexico, in the Pacific, *c.* 150 m. off coast of Lower California; 102 sq. m.

Guadeloupe Passage Channel in the Leeward Islands, bounded by Montserrat, Antigua and Guadeloupe; *c.* 35 m. wide.

Guafo Gulf Inlet of the Pacific, S Chile, connecting the Pacific and the Gulf of Corcovado; 30 m. wide.

Guam Largest and southernmost of the Marianas Islands, W Pacific; 216 sq. m. Inhabitants mostly Chamorros; belongs to United States.

Guanahacabibes Peninsula Westernmost part of Cuba, extending *c.* 45 m. E from Cape San Antonio; unhealthy and sparsely populated.

Guayaquil, Gulf of Pacific bay, SW Ecuador. One of the largest inlets on the W coast of South America; *c.* 110 m. wide at mouth, *c.* 50 m. long.

Guimaras Island Philippines, off SE coast of Panay; 223 sq. m.

Guimaras Strait Channel between Visayan Sea and Panay Gulf, Philippines; *c.* 80 m. long, 7–16 m. wide.
Guinea Current Warm ocean current of North Atlantic, flowing E along coast of West Africa, in Gulf of Guinea.
Guldborg Sound Strait between Lolland and Falster islands, Denmark.
Gwatar Bay Inlet of Arabian Sea, at S end of Iran-Pakistan border; 20 m. long, 10 m. wide.
Gyda Bay SW arm of Yenisei Gulf of Kara Sea; 60 m. long, up to 20 m. wide.

Hafun, Ras Easternmost headland of Africa, at tip of Hafun peninsula, Somali Republic.
Hainan Strait South China Sea, joining Gulf of Tonkin and South China Sea proper, separating Luichow Peninsula and Hainan; 50 m. long, 10–15 m. wide.
Haitan Island (or Hai-t'an Island) China, in East China Sea, at N entrance to Formosa Strait; 17 m. long, 10 m. wide.
Halifax Bay Inlet of Coral Sea, E Queensland, Australia; 50 m. long, 15 m. wide.
Hall Basin Channel in the Arctic between NE Ellesmere Island and NW Greenland; 40 m. long, 30 m. wide.
Hall Island 1. Northwest Territories, in the Gulf of Boothia, near W entrance of Fury and Hecla Strait; 40 m. long, 6 m. wide.
2. S Franz Josef Land, in Arctic Ocean; separated from Wilczek Land by Austrian Sound; 25 m. long, 25 m. wide.
Hall Peninsula SE Baffin Island, Northwest Territories. Extends 150 m. SE into Davis Strait; 100 m. wide at base.
Halmahera Largest island of the Moluccas, Indonesia, consisting of 4 peninsulas separated by 3 bays; *c.* 6,870 sq. m. Also spelled Hamaheira or Halmahaira; also called Jailolo, Djailolo, Jilolo or Gilolo.
Hamilton Inlet Bay of the Atlantic, SE Labrador; 50 m. long, 25 m. wide.
Hammamet, Gulf of Inlet of the central Mediterranean, off NE coast of Tunisia; 25 m. long, 50 m. wide.
Hangchow Bay Inlet of East China Sea, Chekiang province, China; 100 m. long, 70 m. wide at mouth. Famous for Hangchow Bore tidal phenomenon.
Hano Bay Inlet of the Baltic, S Sweden; 35 m. long, 15 m. wide.
Hanover Island Island off coast of S Chile; 40 m. long, 5–22 m. wide; uninhabited.
Hardanger Fjord Inlet of the North Sea, SW Norway; *c.* 80 m. long.
Hardwicke Bay Inlet of Spencer Gulf, South Australia; 33 m. long, 20 m. wide.
Hare Bay Inlet, NE Newfoundland; 20 m. long, 10 m. wide at entrance.
Harima Sea E section of Inland Sea of Japan; *c.* 50 m. long, 40 m. wide.
Harris S part of the Lewis with Harris island, Outer Hebrides, Scotland; 13 m. long, 10 m. wide; connected to the larger N part by 1-m.-wide isthmus. Famous for tweeds. Sometimes known as the Isle of Harris.
Hatteras Island E North Carolina: name sometimes given to 40-m. section of the Outer Banks lying between Pamlico Sound and the Atlantic.
Hauraki Gulf Inlet of S Pacific in N North Island, New Zealand; 34 m. E-W, 26 m. N-S.
Hawke Bay Inlet of S Pacific, E North Island, New Zealand; 50 m. long, 35 m. wide.
Hawkesbury Island W British Columbia, in Douglas Channel; 159 sq. m.
Hayes Peninsula NW Greenland, extending *c.* 100 m. into Baffin Bay and Smith Sound; *c.* 200 m. wide.
Hazen Strait Arm of the Arctic Ocean, Northwest Territories, between South Borden and Melville islands; 60 m. long, 50 m. wide.
Heard Island Sub-Antarctic island in S Indian Ocean; *c.* 25 m. long, 10 m. wide. Volcanic, rising to *c.* 11,000 ft in Big Pen Peak. Largely covered by snow and glaciers.
Hearst Island Weddell Sea, off E coast of Palmer Peninsula, Antarctica; 37 m. long, 10½ m. wide.
Hebrides, Sea of the (or Gulf of the Hebrides) Arm of the Atlantic between the Inner Hebrides and the S Outer Hebrides; *c.* 30 m. wide.
Hecla and Griper Bay Inlet of the Arctic Ocean, N Melville Island, Northwest Territories; 85 m. long, 25–60 m. wide.
Helena Island Parry Islands, Northwest Territories, just off N Bathurst Island; 23 m. long, 8 m. wide.
Hel Peninsula N Poland, extending SE into the Baltic and separating Puck Bay from the Baltic; 21 m. long, up to 2 m. wide. In 17th century was series of islands.
Herendeen Bay Inlet of Bristol Bay of Bering Sea, SW Alaska; 20 m. long.
Hermitage Bay Inlet of the Atlantic, S Newfoundland; 30 m. long, 10 m. wide at entrance.
Hermit Islands Coral group, Bismarck Archipelago, Territory of New Guinea; comprise *c.* 5 islands on reef 12 m. long, 10 m. wide.
Hervey Bay Inlet of the Pacific, SE Queensland, Australia; 50 m. long, 35 m. wide.
Hibiki Sea S arm of Sea of Japan, between SE coast of Honshu and small islands forming E boundary of Tsushima Strait.
Hierro (or Ferro) Smallest and westernmost of the Canary Islands; 107 sq. m. Anciently thought to be the end of the world.
Hiiumaa (or Khiuma) Second largest island of Estonia, in Baltic Sea; 373 sq. m. Poor, sandy soil.
Hinchinbrook Island 1. S Alaska, in the Gulf of Alaska, at mouth of Prince William Sound; 22 m. long, 4–13 m. wide.
2. Coral Sea, just off E coast of Queensland, Australia, within Great Barrier Reef; 152 sq. m.
Hinghwa Bay (or Hsing-hua Bay) Inlet of Formosa Strait, China; 20 m. wide, 15 m. long.
Hinlopen Strait Passage of the Arctic Ocean extending between West Spitsbergen and Northeast Land of Spitsbergen group; 100 m. long, 7–30 m. wide. Receives several glaciers.
Hinnoy Largest island of the Vesteralen group, Norway, in the North Sea; 849 sq. m. Sometimes spelled Hindoy.
Hiroshima Bay Inlet of Inland Sea of Japan; 20 m. N-S, 15 m. E-W.
Hitra Island in North Sea, central Norway, separated from mainland by Trondheim Channel; 218 sq. m. Formerly called Hitteren.
Hiuchi Sea (or Bingo Sea) Central section of Inland Sea of Japan; *c.* 60 m. E-W, *c.* 35 m. N-S.

Hiva Oa (or Hivaoa) Second largest of Marquesas Islands, S Pacific; c. 60 m. in circumference. Volcanic.
Hizen Peninsula Japan, in East China Sea; branches into 3 peninsulas: Sonogi, Nomo and Shimabara. Joined to mainland by neck c. 30 m. wide; major section of peninsula is c. 50 m. long.
Hobbs Coast Antarctica, along the coast of Marie Byrd Land.
Hochstetter Foreland Peninsula, NE Greenland, on Greenland Sea; 75 m. long, 20–25 m. wide. Generally ice-free.
Hokkaido Northernmost and second largest of the 4 main islands of Japan; c. 29,600 sq. m. Sometimes called Hokushu.
Holberg Inlet N arm of Quatsino Sound, N Vancouver Island; 21 m. long, 1 m. wide.
Holy Island (or Lindisfarne) Island in the North Sea, just off the E coast of Northumberland, England. Site of first establishment of Celtic Christianity in England. Lindisfarne Gospels written here.
Home Bay Inlet of Davis Strait, E Baffin Island, Northwest Territories; 40 m. long, 50 m. wide at mouth.
Honduras, Gulf of (or Bay of Honduras) Wide inlet of the Caribbean on coasts of Honduras, Guatemala and British Honduras.
Honghai Bay Shallow inlet of South China Sea in Kwangtung province, China; 25 m. wide.
Honshu Largest and most important island of Japan; c. 88,000 sq. m.
Hood Canal W arm of Puget Sound, W Washington; c. 75 m. long; narrow, curved.
Hooker Island S Franz Josef Land, in Arctic Ocean; 20 m. long, 15 m. wide.
Hormuz, Strait of (or Strait of Ormuz) Channel connecting Persian Gulf with Gulf of Oman of Arabian Sea; 40–60 m. wide.
Hoste Island Tierra del Fuego archipelago, Chile; c. 90 m. long.
Hotham Inlet Arm of Kotzebue Sound, NW Alaska; 50 m. long, 5–20 m. wide.
Houtman Abrolhos Archipelago in Indian Ocean, 35 m. off W coast of Western Australia; extends c. 50 m. N-S and comprises 3 coral groups: Wallabi Islands, Easter Islands and Pelsart Islands. Sometimes called Houtman Rocks and Abrolhos Islands.
Howe Sound Inlet of the Strait of Georgia, SW British Columbia; 26 m. long, 1–10 m. wide.
Hoyo Strait Japan, connecting Iyo Sea with Philippine Sea; c. 60 m. long, c. 35 m. wide. Sometimes called Bungo Strait.
Huna Bay Inlet of Greenland Sea, NW Iceland; 65 m. long, 2–40 m. wide.
Hunter Island NE Queen Charlotte Sound, SW British Columbia; 129 sq. m.
Huon Gulf NE New Guinea, bounded by Huon Peninsula and coast of Morobe district; 80 m. wide, 65 m. long.
Huon Peninsula NE New Guinea, between Astrolabe Bay and Huon Gulf; 60 m. wide.
Hvar Island Adriatic Sea, S Croatia, Yugoslavia; 120 sq. m.
Hydra Island, Greece, in the Aegean Sea; 20 sq. m. Played important part in Greek war of independence.
Hyuga Sea N arm of Philippine Sea, forming wide bight in E Kyushu, Japan; c. 75 m. wide.

Icaria (or Ikaria) Island in the Aegean, Greece; 99 sq. m. Here Icarus fell into the sea in Greek mythology.
Ice Bay Inlet of the Indian Ocean, Antarctica, between Enderby Land and Queen Maud Land; 30½ m. long, 26 m. wide.
Icy Strait SE Alaska, between Chichagof Island and the mainland; c. 40 m. long.
Igaliko Fjord Inlet of the Atlantic, SW Greenland; 35 m. long, 1–3 m. wide.
Ilha Grande Bay SE coast of Brazil, 70 m. W of Rio; 30 m. wide, 15 m. long.
Iligan Bay Inlet of Mindanao Sea, Philippines, in N central Mindanao; 30 m. long, 30 m. wide.
Illana Bay Inlet of Moro Gulf in SW coast of Mindanao, Philippines; 40 m. long, 50 m. wide at mouth.
Imbros Largest island of Turkey, in Aegean Sea, off coast of Gallipoli Peninsula; 108 sq. m.
Inagua Southernmost islands of the Bahamas, comprising Great Inagua Island and Little Inagua Island; 560 sq. m.
Independence Fjord Inlet of Greenland Sea in NE Greenland; 80 m. long, 8–15 m. wide. Extends to edge of inland icecap, where it receives Academy Glacier.
Indispensable Strait Solomon Islands, SW Pacific; 40 m. wide.
Inglefield Gulf Inlet of N Baffin Bay, NW Greenland; 60 m. long, 10–20 m. wide. Extends to edge of inland icecap, where it receives several glaciers.
Ingrid Christensen Coast Antarctica, on the Indian Ocean.
Inside Passage Natural waterway off coast of British Columbia and Alaska, through the Alexander Archipelago; c. 950 m. long. Follows channels and straits sheltered from Pacific storms.
Investigator Islands Chain in Great Australian Bight, 4 m. off W coast of Eyre Peninsula; 40 m. long. Comprise Flinders Island, Pearson Island and Waldegrave Island.
Investigator Strait Channel of Indian Ocean forming SW entrance to Gulf St Vincent, South Australia; 60 m. long, 35 m. wide.
Ionian Islands Island group in the Ionian Sea, off W coast of Greece. Largest islands are Corfu, Leukas, Cephalonia and Zante.
Iriomote-jima Volcanic island of Sakishima group in the Ryukyus, between East China Sea and Philippine Sea; 144 sq. m.
Irish Sea Arm of the Atlantic separating Ireland from Great Britain; 40,000 sq. m., 130 m. long, 130 m. wide, mean depth 200 ft.
Irminger Sea Section of North Atlantic off SE Greenland. Irminger Current, part of North Atlantic Current, flows N and W past S coast of Iceland.
Isabela Island (or Albemarle Island) Largest of the Galápagos Islands, in the Pacific; 2,249 sq. m. Volcanic.
Isafjardardjup (or Isafjardhardjup) Inlet of Denmark Strait, NW Iceland, on NW coast of Vestfjarda Peninsula; 50 m. long, 1–12 m. wide.
Ise Fjord N Zealand, Denmark; 20 m. long.
Is Fjord Inlet of the Arctic Ocean, W West Spitsbergen;

70 m. long, 8–20 m. wide. Extends several arms and receives several glaciers.

Ishikari Bay Inlet of Sea of Japan in W Hokkaido, Japan; 50 m. long, 30 m. wide. Also called Otaru Bay.

Ishinomaki Bay Inlet of the Pacific Ocean in N Honshu, Japan; 25 m. E-W, 10 m. N-S. Contains hundreds of islets.

Islands, Bay of Inlet of the Gulf of St Lawrence, W Newfoundland; 20 m. long, 10 m. wide at mouth.

Islay Island of the Inner Hebrides, Scotland, most southerly of the Hebrides; 233.7 sq. m. including Oversay, small island off SW end.

Iturup Island Largest and most important of the Kurile Islands, Russian SFSR; 2,587 sq. m.

Iviza Smallest of the chief Balearic Islands, in the W Mediterranean; 221 sq. m. with adjacent islets.

Iwo Jima Largest and most important of the Volcano Islands, W Pacific; *c.* 8 sq. m. Site of Japanese air base in Second World War; occupied by U.S. forces in March, 1945, after heavy fighting.

Iyo Sea SW section of Inland Sea of Japan, between SW coast of Honshu and NW coast of Shikoku.

Izmit, Gulf of Narrow inlet at E end of Sea of Marmara, NW Turkey; 45 m. long.

Izu Peninsula Central Honshu, Japan, between Suruga Bay and Sagami Bay; 40 m. long, 10–20 m. wide.

Izu-shichito Island group, Japan, between Philippine Sea and Pacific; 116 sq. m. Group extends in 300-m. chain N-S. Volcanic. Sometimes called Izu-shoto.

Jaffna Lagoon Separates Jaffna Peninsula from Ceylon proper; *c.* 50 m. long, 10 m. wide.

Jaffna Peninsula Northernmost part of Ceylon, separated from Ceylon proper by Jaffna Lagoon and from India by Palk Strait; *c.* 55 m. long, up to 15 m. wide. After Colombo area, the most densely populated section of Ceylon.

Jailolo Passage (or Djailolo Passage) Channel connecting Ceram Sea with the Pacific; *c.* 100 m. wide.

Jakobshavn Ice Fjord Inlet of Disko Bay, W Greenland; 25 m. long, 3–6 m. wide. Receives Jakobshavn Glacier at head.

Jamaica Channel Caribbean Sea, separating Jamaica from Hispaniola; 120 m. wide.

Jambeli Channel SW Ecuador, on the coast of Guayas province, linking Gulf of Guayaquil with Guayas River estuary; *c.* 50 m. long, 7–20 m. wide.

James Bay S arm of Hudson Bay, between NE Ontario and NW Quebec; 275 m. long, 135 m. wide; very shallow; contains several islands.

James Ross Strait Arm of the Arctic, Northwest Territories, between King William Island and Boothia Peninsula; 110 m. long, 30–40 m. wide.

Japan, Sea of Arm of the Pacific between Japan and the mainland of Asia; 1,000 m. long, 500 m. wide.

Japan Current Warm ocean current originating in the Philippine Sea, then entering East China Sea and flowing N along E shores of Formosa and S Ryukyu Islands; here it forks, main stream moving N along E shores of Kyushu, Shikoku and Honshu, then E past Aleutian Islands and S along coast of North America. Offshoot, known as Tsushima Current, enters Sea of Japan through Korea Strait, flowing N along W shores of Kyushu and Honshu.

Japan Trench Submarine depression in North Pacific, extending in a curve from Bonin Islands to the Kuriles; deepest part is Tuscarora Deep (27,929 feet) in the N.

Japen Islands (or Jappen Islands) Group belonging to Netherlands New Guinea, in Geelvink Bay; 10,907 sq. m. Comprises 3 islands; largest is Japen, *c.* 100 m. long, *c.* 15 m. wide. Also spelled Yapen and Yappen.

Jardines Bank Shoal off S Cuba; extends *c.* 70 m. E from Isle of Pines.

Jardines de la Reina Archipelago of coral reefs off Caribbean coast of E Cuba; *c.* 85 m. long NW-SE. Comprises more than 400 keys.

Jardinillos Bank E continuation of Jardines Bank, off S Cuba; *c.* 25 m. long.

Java Sea Part of the Pacific between Borneo and Java; *c.* 600 m. E-W, *c.* 200 m. N-S.

Java Trench Submarine depression in Indian Ocean off S coast of Java, contains greatest depth of Indian Ocean (24,440 ft).

Jenny Lind Island (or Lind Island) Northwest Territories, in Queen Maud Gulf, off SE Victoria Island; 17 m. long, 10 m. wide.

Jens Munk Island Northwest Territories, at head of Foxe Basin, off NW Baffin Island; 45 m. long, 17 m. wide.

Jersey Largest and southernmost of the Channel Islands; 44.9 sq. m.

Jervis Inlet NE arm of Malaspina Strait, SW British Columbia; 51 m. long, 1–8 m. wide.

Jigüey Bay Shallow inlet of Old Bahama Channel, E Cuba, between Cayo Romano and Cuba; *c.* 30 m. long, 6 m. wide.

Jintotolo Channel Philippines, connecting Visayan Sea with Sibuyan Sea; 20 m. wide.

Jiquilisco Bay Inlet of Pacific Ocean, SE Salvador; 25 m. long, 1–2 m. wide.

Johnstone Strait SW British Columbia, joining Queen Charlotte Strait with Strait of Georgia and separating Vancouver Island from mainland; 70 m. long, 2–3 m. wide.

Johore Strait (or Tebrau Strait) Arm of Singapore Strait between Singapore and Johore, at S tip of Malay Peninsula; 30 m. long, ¾–3 m. wide.

Joinville Island Antarctica, off NE tip of Palmer Peninsula; 36 m. long, 17½ m. wide.

Jolo Island (or Sulu Island) Chief island of the Sulu Archipelago, Philippines, between Sulu Sea and Celebes Sea; 345 sq. m.

Jones Sound Arm of Baffin Bay, Northwest Territories, between Ellesmere Island and Devon Island; 250 m. long, 15–60 m. wide.

Jorge Montt Island Uninhabited island off coast of S Chile, just NE of Nelson Strait; 28 m. long, 25 m. wide.

Joseph Bonaparte Gulf Arm of Timor Sea, N Australia; 225 m. E-W, 100 m. N-S. Divides into Cambridge Gulf and Queen's Channel.

Juan de Fuca Strait SW British Columbia and NW Washington, between Vancouver Island and the Washington mainland; *c.* 100 m. long, 11–17 m. wide.

Juan Stuven Island Uninhabited island off coast of S Chile; *c.* 20 m. long.

Judge Daly Promontory NE Ellesmere Island, Northwest Territories, on Kennedy Channel; 100 m. long, 10–48 m. wide.

Jura Island of the Inner Hebrides, Scotland; 28 m. long, 8 m. wide.
Jutland (also Cimbric Peninsula) Peninsula of N Europe comprising continental Denmark and part of N Germany.

Kabaena Island, Indonesia, off SE coast of Celebes; 338 sq. m.
Kachemak Bay Arm of Cook Inlet, SW Kenai Peninsula, S Alaska; 40 m. long, 20 m. wide.
Kagoshima Bay Inlet of East China Sea, S Kyushu, Japan; *c.* 45 m. long, 13 m. wide.
Kai Islands (or Kei Islands) Group in the S Moluccas, Indonesia, in Banda Sea; 555 sq. m. Also called Key Islands and Ewab Islands.
Kaipara Harbour N North Island, New Zealand; 40 m. long, 5 m. wide. Connected with Tasman Sea by passage 5 m. wide.
Kaiwi Channel Territory of Hawaii, between Molokai and Oahu islands; 20 m. wide.
Kalmar Sound Strait of the Baltic between SE Sweden and Oland island; 85 m. long, 4–14 m. wide.
Kamchatka Gulf Inlet of the Pacific on E coast of Kamchatka Peninsula; 85 m. wide.
Kamchatka Peninsula Large peninsula of NE Siberia, separating Sea of Okhotsk from Bering Sea and Pacific Ocean; 104,200 sq. m.
Kamishak Bay S Alaska, on W side of mouth of Cook Inlet; 20 m. long, 45 m. wide at mouth.
Kanaga Island Andreanof Islands, Aleutian Islands, SW Alaska; 30 m. long, 4–8 m. wide; rises to 4,416 ft at Kanaga Volcano.
Kandalaksha Bay Northwesternmost and deepest section of White Sea, between Kola Peninsula and Karelia; 130 m. long, 60 m. wide, 1,115 ft deep.
Kandavu (or Kadavu) Southwesternmost of the Fiji islands, SW Pacific; 157 sq. m. Volcanic.
Kane Basin Expansion of sea passage between Lincoln Sea of Arctic Ocean and the Atlantic. Lies between Ellesmere Island and NW Greenland; 110 m. long, 50–120 m. wide.
Kangaroo Island South Australia, in the Indian Ocean, 27 m. S of Yorke Peninsula; 90 m. long, 33 m. wide. Structurally part of Mount Lofty Ranges on mainland.
Kangean Islands Indonesia, in Java Sea; 258 sq. m. Comprise 3 islands surrounded by *c.* 60 islets; largest is Kangean (188 sq. m.).
Kangerdlugssuak (or Kangerdlugssuaq) Inlet of Denmark Strait, SE Greenland; 45 m. long, 3–9 m. wide. Extends to edge of inland icecap and receives several large glaciers.
Kanghwa Island Korea, in Yellow Sea, at mouth of Han River; 163 sq. m. Sometimes spelled Kangwha and Kanghoa.
Karaburun Peninsula Turkey, extending into the Aegean between the Gulf of Smyrna and Chios island; 60 m. long, 15 m. wide.
Karaginski Island (or Karaginskiy Island) SW Bering Sea, Kamchatka oblast, Russian SFSR; 775 sq. m.
Karakelong Largest island of Talaud Islands, Indonesia; *c.* 380 sq. m.
Karamea Bight Inlet of Tasman Sea, NW South Island, New Zealand; 65 m. long, 15 m. wide.
Kara Sea Section of Arctic Ocean off Russian SFSR. Mostly not over 650 ft deep.
Karimata Islands Indonesia, in Karimata Strait, off SW coast of Borneo. Comprises 2 large islands, Karimata and Serutu (or Seroetoe), and *c.* 60 islets.
Karimata Strait Channel connecting Java Sea with South China Sea; *c.* 125 m. wide.
Karimun Islands (or Karimoen) Group of the Riouw Archipelago, Indonesia, in South China Sea. Largest island of group is Kundur (or Koendoer), 18 m. long, 10 m. wide.
Karkar Volcanic island, Territory of New Guinea, 9 m. NE of New Guinea, in the SW Pacific; 140 sq. m. Active volcano. Formerly Dampier Island.
Karkinit Gulf Shallow inlet of Black Sea between the Crimea and the Ukrainian mainland; 65 m. long, 15–50 m. wide.
Karl Alexander Island N Franz Josef Land, in the Arctic Ocean; 22 m. long, 10 m. wide.
Karpas Peninsula NE promontory of Cyprus; *c.* 50 m. long, 10 m. wide at base.
Karrats Fjord Inlet of Baffin Bay, W Greenland; 70 m. long, 3–17 m. wide.
Karskiye Vorota Strait joining Barents and Kara seas of Arctic Ocean; 30 m. wide, 20 m. long. Also called Kara Strait.
Kasaan Bay Inlet of Clarence Strait, E Prince of Wales Island, SE Alaska; 35 m. long, 2–8 m. wide. Few inhabitants, mostly Haida Indians.
Kassandra Westernmost of the 3 arms of the Chalcidice peninsula, on the Aegean; 30 m. long, 5 m. wide.
Kathiawar Peninsula of W India, extending into Arabian Sea between Gulf of Cutch and Gulf of Cambay; *c.* 23,000 sq. m.
Kauai Fourth largest of Hawaiian Islands; 551 sq. m. Geologically oldest of the group.
Kauai Channel Territory of Hawaii, between Kauai and Oahu; 55 m. wide. Formerly called Kaieiewahe Channel.
Kebao Island Triangular island in Gulf of Tonkin, N Vietnam; 15 m. long, 10 m. wide.
Keku Strait SE Alaska, extending between Kupreanof and Kuiu islands, in Alexander Archipelago; 40 m. long.
Kemp Coast Antarctica, E of Enderby Land, on the Indian Ocean.
Kenai Peninsula S Alaska, extending 150 m. into Gulf of Alaska. Mountainous, inhabited by Kenai Indians.
Kenmare River Deep inlet of the Atlantic between County Cork and County Kerry, Ireland. Extends 28 m. inland, 2–6 m. wide.
Kennedy Channel Sea passage in the Arctic between Ellesmere Island and NW Greenland; 80 m. long, 16–24 m. wide.
Kent Peninsula Northwest Territories, on Dease Strait. Extends 105 m. into Coronation Gulf; 7–29 m. wide.
Keppel Bay Inlet of the Pacific, E Queensland, Australia; 30 m. long, 12 m. wide.
Kerch Peninsula E section of the Crimea, between Sea of Azov and Black Sea; 60 m. long, 20–30 m. wide. Arid, with some irrigated agriculture.
Kerch Strait Shallow channel connecting Sea of Azov and Black Sea and separating Kerch Peninsula of Crimea from Taman Peninsula; 25 m. long.

Kermadec Deep Ocean depth (30,928 ft) of South Pacific Ocean, E of Kermadec Islands.

Keta Lagoon SE Ghana, closed off by sandspit from Gulf of Guinea; 32 m. long, 2–7 m. wide.

Khatanga Gulf Inlet of Laptev Sea of Arctic Ocean, Russian SFSR, at mouth of Khatanga River; 175 m. long.

Kiaochow Bay Sheltered inlet of the Yellow Sea, Shantung province, China; 200 sq. m.

Kii Channel Strait connecting Osaka Bay and Harima Sea of Inland Sea of Japan with Philippine Sea; *c.* 30 m. N-S, *c.* 35 m. E-W.

Kii Peninsula S Honshu, Japan, between Kii Channel and Kumano Sea; 80 m. E-W, 60 m. N-S.

Kilbrannan Sound (or Kilbrennan Sound) Arm of Firth of Clyde, Scotland; *c.* 25 m. long, 3–10 m. wide.

Killinek Island Northwest Territories, at SE entrance of Hudson Strait, off N extremity of Labrador; 20 m. long, 2–9 m. wide.

King Channel Arm of the Pacific in Chonos Archipelago, S Chile; *c.* 50 m. long.

King Christian Island Northwest Territories, off Ellef Ringnes Island, in Maclean Strait; 17 m. long, 9 m. wide.

King Frederik VI Coast Coast region of SE Greenland.

King George Bay Inlet in West Falkland Island; *c.* 20 m. long, 2–7 m. wide.

King George Island South Shetland Islands, off Palmer Peninsula, Antarctica; 37½ m. long, *c.* 14 m. wide.

King George Islands Group consisting of 15 small islands and islets in Hudson Bay, Northwest Territories; covers area *c.* 30 m. long, 20 m. wide.

King Island 1. Largest of the Mergui Archipelago, Lower Burma, in the Andaman Sea; 170 sq. m.
2. Bass Strait, 55 m. off NW coast of Tasmania; 425 sq. m.

King Oscar Archipelago Group of islands in Greenland Sea, E Greenland, between Franz Josef Fjord and King Oscar Fjord.

King Oscar Fjord Inlet of Greenland Sea, E Greenland; 90 m. long, 8–15 m. wide.

King Sound Inlet of the Indian Ocean, N Western Australia; 40 m. E-W, 80 m. N-S.

Kintyre Peninsula of S Argyll, Scotland; 42 m. long, up to 10 m. wide.

Kiriwina Largest of Trobriand Islands, Territory of Papua, SW Pacific; 30 m. long, 10 m. wide.

Kiska Island Rat Islands, Aleutian Islands, SW Alaska; 20 m. long, 2–7 m. wide.

Kisseraing Island Central Mergui Archipelago, Lower Burma, in the Andaman Sea; 20 m. long, 10 m. wide.

Knight Inlet Arm of Queen Charlotte Strait, opposite Vancouver Island; 75 m. long, 1–4 m. wide.

Knight Island S Alaska, in Prince William Sound; 25 m. long, 2–9 m. wide.

Knight Island Passage S Alaska, forming SW entrance to Prince William Sound; 20 m. long, 3–5 m. wide.

Knik Arm N arm of Cook Inlet, S Alaska; 30 m. long, 2–6 m. wide.

Knivskjellodden Low cape, northernmost point of Europe, on Barents Sea of Arctic Ocean, in N Norway. Also spelled Knivskjelodden; also called Knivskjerodden (Knivskjaerodden).

Knox Coast Section of Wilkes Land, Antarctica, on Indian Ocean.

Kobbermine Bay Inlet of Atlantic, SW Greenland; 20 m. long, 1–10 m. wide.

Koje Island Korea, sheltering Chinhae Bay; 147 sq. m.

Kola Gulf Ice-free inlet of Barents Sea, NW Kola Peninsula; 50 m. long, ½ m. wide.

Kola Peninsula N European USSR, between Barents and White seas; 250 m. long, 150 m. wide; consists of granite, gneiss and other crystalline formations.

Kolguyev Island Barents Sea, Russian SFSR, 50 m. off mainland; 1,350 sq. m.

Kolombangara Volcanic island, New Georgia, Solomon Islands, in the SW Pacific; 20 m. long, 15 m. wide. Sometimes spelled Kulambangra.

Kolyuchin Bay Inlet of Chukchi Sea, N Chukchi Peninsula, NE Siberia; 37 m. long.

Komandorski Islands (or Commander Islands) Group in SW Bering Sea, Russian SFSR. Comprise Bering Island, Medny Island and 2 islets. Foggy; frequent earthquakes.

Komodo Island in the Lesser Sundas, Indonesia, between Flores Sea and Sunda Strait; *c.* 184 sq. m.

Kompong Som Bay Inlet of Gulf of Siam, SE Cambodia; 35 m. long, 15–20 m. wide.

Komsomolets Island N island of Severnaya Zemlya archipelago, in the Arctic Ocean; 3,570 sq. m.; 65 per cent covered by glaciers.

Kong Karls Land (also King Charles Islands or King Karl Islands) Group consisting of 3 islands and several islets in Barents Sea of Arctic Ocean; 128 sq. m. Part of Svalbard (Norwegian possession).

Korcula Island Dalmatian island in the Adriatic, S Croatia, Yugoslavia; 107 sq. m. Also spelled Korchula.

Korean Archipelago Name sometimes given to island groups and islands off SW coast of Korea.

Korea Strait Channel connecting Sea of Japan with East China Sea; *c.* 110 m. wide.

Kos Second largest island of the Dodecanese, Greece, in the Aegean. Hippocrates born here.

Kos, Gulf of (also Gulf of Cos, Gulf of Kerme and Ceramic Gulf) Aegean Sea, SW Turkey, N of Resadiye Peninsula; 60 m. long, 18 m. wide.

Kosciusko Island Alexander Archipelago, SE Alaska; 25 m. long, 5–12 m. wide.

Kotelny Island (or Kotel'nyy Island) Largest of the Anjou group of New Siberian Islands; 100 m. long, 60 m. wide.

Kotor, Gulf of Winding inlet of the Adriatic, SW Yugoslavia. Good harbor.

Kotzebue Sound Arm of Chukchi Sea on N side of Seward Peninsula, NW Alaska; 100 m. long, 70 m. wide.

Kra, Isthmus of Neck of land between Gulf of Siam and Pakchan River estuary, S Thailand, connecting Malay Peninsula with Asian mainland; 25–30 m. wide at narrowest point.

Krasnaya Armiya Strait Strait joining Kar and Laptev seas of Arctic Ocean; 90 m. long, 5–10 m. wide.

Krk Island Largest of Yugoslav islands, in N Adriatic, NW Croatia; 165 sq. m. Formerly part of Istria.

Kronotski Gulf (or Kronotskiy Gulf) Inlet of the Pacific, Kamchatka Peninsula, Russian SFSR.

Kronotski Peninsula Kamchatka Peninsula, Russian SFSR, separating Kronotski Gulf from Kamchatka Gulf; 50 m. wide.

Kruzenshtern Strait (or Krusenstern Strait) Kurile Islands, in the main group, between Lovushki Islands and Raikoke Islands, Russian SFSR; 31 m. wide.
Kruzof Island SE Alaska, in the Alexander Archipelago; 23 m. long, 8 m. wide.
Kuiu Island SE Alaska, in the Alexander Archipelago, between Kupreanof Island and Baranof Island; 65 m. long, 6–23 m. wide.
Kumano Sea N arm of the Philippine Sea, S Honshu, Japan; *c.* 80 m. long.
Kunashir Island Southernmost and second largest of main Kurile Islands chain, Russian SFSR; 1,548 sq. m. Volcanic.
Kunisaki Peninsula NE Kyushu, Japan, between Suo Sea and Beppu Bay; 24 m. N-S, 18 m. E-W.
Kupreanof Island SE Alaska, in Alexander Archipelago; 52 m. long, 20–30 m. wide.
Kupreanof Strait S Alaska, between Raspberry Island and Kodiak Island; 20 m. long, 2–3 m. wide.
Kuria Muria Bay Inlet of the Arabian Sea on coast of SE Oman; 80 m. wide. Contains Kuria Muria Islands.
Kusadasi, Gulf of Inlet of the Aegean, W Turkey; 25 m. wide, 19 m. long.
Kuskokwim Bay SW Alaska, NW of Bristol Bay; 100 m. long, 100 m. wide at mouth.
Kvaenang Fjord Inlet of the Norwegian Sea, N Norway; 45 m. long, 1–12 m. wide.
Kvichak Bay NE arm of Bristol Bay, S Alaska; 50 m. long, 30 m. wide.
Kvitoya Island in Svalbard (Norwegian possession), in Barents Sea of Arctic Ocean; 102 sq. m.
Kwajalein Largest atoll of the Marshall Islands, W central Pacific; 6 sq. m. Consists of 97 islets on lagoon. Japanese base in Second World War, captured by U.S. in 1944.
Kwangchow Bay Inlet of South China Sea, China, at NE base of Luichow Peninsula.
Kyparissia, Gulf of Inlet of the Ionian Sea, SW Peloponnesus, Greece; 35 m. wide, 10 m. long. Formerly Gulf of Arcadia.
Kythera (or Kithira) Island in the Mediterranean, at mouth of Gulf of Laconia, Greece; 108½ sq. m.
Kyushu Island of Japan, between East China Sea and Philippine Sea, just S of Honshu; 13,770 sq. m. Sometimes spelled Kiushiu and Kyusyu.

Labrador Current Cold ocean current flowing S along coast of Labrador and E Newfoundland.
Labrador Sea Section of the North Atlantic between Labrador and SW Greenland.
Labuk Bay Inlet of Sulu Sea, NE Borneo; 30 m. long, 20 m. wide.
Laconia, Gulf of Inlet of the Ionian Sea, SE Peloponnesus, Greece; 35 m. wide, 30 m. long. Formerly Gulf of Marathonisi.
Lady Franklin Bay Inlet of Robeson Channel, NE Ellesmere Island, Northwest Territories; 25 m. long, 6–10 m. wide.
Lagonoy Gulf Inlet of Philippine Sea in SE Luzon; *c.* 50 m. E-W, *c.* 20 m. N-S.
Laguna Madre Narrow, shallow lagoon along coast of Gulf of Mexico, NE Mexico and S Texas. Extends *c.* 120 m. S from Corpus Christi Bay to mouth of Rio Grande, where it is interrupted for *c.* 40 m. by the delta, then continues *c.* 100 m. further.
Lamon Bay Arm of the Philippine Sea, Philippines, bounded on the W by the E coast of Luzon; *c.* 50 m. long, *c.* 25 m. wide.
Lampung Bay (or Lampoeng Bay) Inlet of Sunda Strait, Indonesia, at S end of Sumatra. Also spelled Lampong Bay.
Lanai Island in the Territory of Hawaii, *c.* 7 m. W of Maui; 141 sq. m.
Lancaster Sound Arm of Baffin Bay, Northwest Territories, extending W between Devon Island and Baffin and Somerset islands; *c.* 200 m. long, 40 m. wide.
Lands Lokk Island in the Arctic Ocean, Northwest Territories, off NW Ellesmere Island; 20 m. long, 8 m. wide.
Langanes Peninsula of NE Iceland; extends 30 m. NE into Greenland Sea.
Langeland Island of Denmark, in the Baltic, between Fyn and Lolland islands; 110 sq. m.
Langkawi Island Strait of Malacca, Malaya, main island of Langkawi group; 203 sq. m.
Langoy Island in the North Sea, N Norway, in the Vesteralen group; 332 sq. m.; important fisheries.
Lanzarote One of the Canary Islands, Las Palmas province, Spain; 307 sq. m.
La Paz Bay Sheltered deep-water inlet of the Gulf of California, NW Mexico; 50 m. long, *c.* 20 m. wide.
La Pérouse Strait Strait joining Sea of Japan and Sea of Okhotsk; 26 m. wide. Sometimes called Soya Strait.
Laptev Sea Section of the Arctic Ocean, Russian SFSR, bounded S by the coast of E Siberia.
Lars Christensen Coast Antarctica, on the Indian Ocean. Extends from Bjerk Peninsula to Sandefjord Bay.
Larsen Bay S arm of Uyak Bay in W Kodiak Island; 20 m. long.
Laurie Island South Orkney Islands, in the S Atlantic; 110 m. long, 1–3 m. wide.
Lavongai Volcanic island, Bismarck Archipelago, Territory of New Guinea, in the SW Pacific; *c.* 460 sq. m.
Leopold and Astrid Coast Antarctica, on the Indian Ocean.
Leti Islands (or Letti Islands) Group in the S Moluccas, Indonesia, in the Banda Sea; *c.* 290 sq. m.
Leukas (or Levkas) Island of the Ionian group, Greece, in the Ionian Sea; 114 sq. m. Sometimes identified with the ancient Ithaca.
Lévrier Bay Inlet of the Atlantic, W Mauritania, between Cap Blanc Peninsula and the mainland; 28 m. long, up to 20 m. wide.
Lewis with Harris Largest and northernmost island of the Outer Hebrides, Scotland; 825.2 sq. m.
Leyte One of Visayan Islands, E central Philippines, between Luzon and Mindanao; 2,785 sq. m. Mountainous, rising to 4,426 ft.
Leyte Gulf Large inlet of Philippine Sea between Leyte and Samar, Philippines; scene of U.S. naval victory over Japan (October 1944).
Liaotung, Gulf of N arm of Gulf of Chihli, SW Manchuria, between Liaotung peninsula and mainland; 100 m. long, 60 m. wide.
Lifu Coral island, largest of Loyalty group, SW Pacific; *c.* 40 m. long, 10 m. wide; roughly semicircular.

Lim Fjord Strait, N Jutland, Denmark, connecting North Sea with Kattegat; *c.* 110 m. long. Until 1825 W section consisted of series of fresh-water lakes.
Limmen Bight Indentation in NE coast of Northern Territory, Australia, in Gulf of Carpentaria, between Groote Eylandt and Sir Edward Pellew Islands; 85 m. NW-SE.
Lincoln Sea Section of the Arctic Ocean, off NE Ellesmere Island and NW Greenland.
Lindenows Fjord Inlet of the Atlantic in SE Greenland, extending 35 m. to edge of inland icecap; 1–3 m. wide.
Lingayen Gulf Inlet of South China Sea in central Luzon, Philippines; *c.* 35 m. long, 26 m. wide at entrance.
Lingga Island, Lingga Archipelago, Indonesia, in South China Sea; *c.* 360 sq. m.
Lingga Archipelago Island group in Indonesia, in South China Sea, off E coast of Sumatra; 842 sq. m. Generally low, and of coral formation.
Linnhe, Loch Inlet on W coast of Scotland, between Inverness and Argyll; 35 m. long, 1–5 m. wide.
Lisianski Inlet Narrow inlet, SE Alaska, on NW coast of Chichagof Island; 25 m. long.
Little Andaman Island Southernmost of the Andaman Islands, Bay of Bengal, separated from the main group by Duncan Passage; 26 m. long, 16 m. wide.
Little Bahama Bank Shoal in NW Bahamas, N of Grand Bahama Island; *c.* 150 m. long, *c.* 50 m. wide.
Little Belt Strait connecting the Kattegat with the Baltic Sea, Denmark; *c.* 30 m. long, ½-*c.* 20 m. wide.
Little Inagua Island S Bahama Islands, just NE of Great Inagua Island; *c.* 10 m. long, up to 10 m. wide. Almost uninhabited.
Liverpool Coast Region on Greenland Sea, Greenland; extends 80 m. N from mouth of Scoresby Sound. Noted for dangerous currents.
Livingston Island South Shetland Islands, off Palmer Peninsula, Antarctica; 32½ m. long, *c.* 4–16 m. wide.
Lizard, The Promontory on the English Channel, SW Cornwall, England. S extremity (Lizard Point or Lizard Head) is the southernmost point of Great Britain.
Lleyn Peninsula Wales, between Cardigan Bay and Caernarvon Bay of Irish Sea; *c.* 30 m. long, 5–15 m. wide.
Loks Land Island, Northwest Territories, off SE Baffin Island, in Davis Strait; 20 m. long, 15 m. wide.
Lolland (or Laaland) Island, Denmark, in Baltic Sea, separated from S Zealand by Smaalandsfarvand strait; 479 sq. m.
Lomblem (also Kawula or Kawoela) Largest of the Solor Islands, Lesser Sundas, Indonesia, between Flores Sea and Savu Sea; 499 sq. m. Irregular shape.
Lombok Strait Channel connecting Indian Ocean with Java Sea, between Bali and Lombok; 50 m. long, 20–40 m. wide. Forms part of dividing line between Australian and Asian fauna.
Londonderry Island Tierra del Fuego, Chile, in the Pacific; 27 m. long.
Long Island Volcanic island, Territory of New Guinea, SW Pacific; 160 sq. m.
Long Island Sound Sheltered arm of Atlantic, between Long Island and mainland, New York and Connecticut; *c.* 90 m. long, 3–20 m. wide.
Long Strait (or De Long Strait) Strait joining East Siberian and Chukchi seas and separating Wrangell Island from the mainland; 85 m. wide.
Lopez Bay S arm of Lamon Bay, Philippines, between Alabat Island and S Luzon; 36 m. long, 3–11 m. wide.
Lougheed Island Largest of Findlay Islands, Northwest Territories, in the Arctic Ocean; 504 sq. m.
Louise Island Queen Charlotte Islands, W British Columbia, in Hecate Strait; 105 sq. m.
Louisiade Archipelago Territory of Papua, SW Pacific, 125 m. SE of New Guinea. Comprises *c.* 10 volcanic islands and many coral reefs.
Louis Philippe Peninsula Extreme N tip of Palmer Peninsula, Antarctica, in the S Pacific; extends *c.* 70 m. NE from Charcot Bay and Sjögren Fjord. Sometimes called Trinity Peninsula.
Lower California Peninsula, NW Mexico, separating the Gulf of California from the Pacific; *c.* 760 m. long, 30–150 m. wide.
Lübeck Bay SW arm of Mecklenburg Bay of Baltic Sea, N Germany; *c.* 20 m. long, *c.* 10 m. wide.
Luce Bay Inlet of Irish Sea, S Wigtown, Scotland; 20 m. long, 19 m. wide at mouth.
Luichow Peninsula China, on South China Sea, between Kwangchow Bay and Gulf of Tonkin; 90 m. long, 30–45 m. wide.
Luitpold Coast Part of Coats Land, Antarctica, on Weddell Sea.
Luster Fjord N arm of Sogne Fjord, W Norway; *c.* 30 m. long, 2 m. wide. Also spelled Lyster.
Lützow-Holm Bay Bay on Indian Ocean, Antarctica, bordered by Prince Olav Coast, Prince Harald Coast and Cook Peninsula; 113 m. wide, 96 m. long.
Luzon Largest and most important island of the Philippines, at N end of archipelago; 40,420 sq. m.
Luzon Strait Channel connecting South China Sea and Philippine Sea, between Formosa and Luzon.
Lyakhov Islands S group of New Siberian Islands between Laptev and East Siberian seas; 2,660 sq. m.
Lyell Land Peninsula, E Greenland, on King Oscar Fjord; 35 m. long, 15–28 m. wide.
Lyngen Fjord Inlet of Norwegian Sea, N Norway; 60 m. long, 2–5 m. wide.
Lynn Canal N arm of Chatham Strait and Stephens Passage, SE Alaska; 90 m. long, 7–12 m. wide.
Lyse Fjord Narrow SE arm of Bokn Fjord, SW Norway; extends 25 m. NE from Hogs Fjord.

Macajalar Bay Inlet of Mindanao Sea in N Mindanao, Philippines; 17 m. long, 20 m. wide at mouth.
McArthur, Port Harbor in NE Northern Territory, Australia, in Gulf of Carpentaria; 25 m. long, 10 m. wide. Formed by Sir Edward Pellew Islands and mainland.
McCauley Island W British Columbia, in Hecate Strait; 108 sq. m.
Macclesfield Bank Group of coral reefs, China, in South China Sea. Comprises over 20 shoals in area 75 m. long, 33 m. wide.
McClintock Channel Arm of the Arctic Ocean, Northwest Territories, between Victoria and Prince of Wales islands; 170 m. long, 65–130 m. wide.
MacClintock Island S Franz Josef Land, in Arctic Ocean; 20 m. long, 15 m. wide.

McCluer Gulf Inlet of Ceram Sea in NW New Guinea, between Vogelkop and Bombarai peninsulas; *c.* 150 m. E-W, *c.* 15–50 m. N-S. Sometimes called Telok Berau.
McClure Strait Arm of the Beaufort Sea of the Arctic, Northwest Territories, extending W from Viscount Melville Sound; 170 m. long, 60 m. wide.
MacKenzie Bay Antarctica, on the Indian Ocean, along Lars Christensen Coast; 61 m. long, 87½ m. wide.
Mackenzie Bay Inlet of the Beaufort Sea of the Arctic Ocean, Northwest Territories, at mouth of Mackenzie River delta; 100 m. long, 120 m. wide at mouth.
McKinley Sea Marginal sea of the Arctic Ocean, off N Greenland.
Mac-Robertson Coast Antarctica, on the Indian Ocean, between William Scoresby Bay and Cape Darnley.
Madame Island (or Isle Madame) Island in the Atlantic, E Nova Scotia, S of Cape Breton Island; 12 m. long, 9 m. wide.
Madura Island of Indonesia, in Java Sea, just off NE coast of Java, across Madura Strait; 1,762 sq. m.
Maewo Volcanic island in the New Hebrides, SW Pacific; *c.* 135 sq. m. Formerly called Aurora Island.
Mafia Island E Tanganyika, in Indian Ocean; 170 sq. m. Identified with the island of Menuthias, which was mentioned in the oldest sailing guide to the East African coast, and was visited by tourists from the Mediterranean some 1,400 years before the discovery of America.
Magdalena Island S Chile, off coast of Aysén province; *c.* 40 m. in diameter.
Magdalen Channel (or Magdalen Sound) S arm of Strait of Magellan in Tierra del Fuego, Chile.
Magdalen Islands (or Îles Madeleine) Group in the Gulf of St Lawrence, E Quebec; 102 sq. m. Comprise 9 main islands and numerous islets.
Mageroy Island, N Norway, in Barents Sea of Arctic Ocean; 106 sq. m. On N coast is Knivskjellodden, northernmost point of Europe.
Mainland Largest island of the Shetlands, Scotland; 406.5 sq. m. Has been identified with Ultima Thule.
Maio One of Cape Verde Islands, easternmost of the Leeward group, in the Atlantic Ocean; 104 sq. m. Formerly spelled Mayo.
Majorca Largest of the Balearic Islands, Spain, in the Mediterranean; 1,405 sq. m.
Makhir Coast Section of coast of Somali Republic on Gulf of Aden.
Malaita Volcanic island in the Solomons; 1,572 sq. m., 115 m. long, 15 m. wide. Most populous of group (*c.* 40,000 inhabitants).
Malaspina Strait Arm of Strait of Georgia, SW British Columbia, between Texada Island and mainland; 40 m. long, 3–5 m. wide.
Malay Archipelago Term used for island group between Malay Peninsula and Indochina (NW) and Australia and New Guinea (SE). Includes islands of Indonesia and the Philippines (and sometimes New Guinea). Also called East Indies.
Malekula Second largest of New Hebrides, SW Pacific; 45 m. long, 23 m. wide. Volcanic.
Malta Channel Strait between SE Sicily and the Maltese Islands, Mediterranean; *c.* 60 m. wide.
Maltese Islands Archipelago in the central Mediterranean comprising Malta, Gozo and several smaller islands; 121.8 sq. m. Generally called Malta.
Mandalya, Gulf of Inlet of Aegean Sea, SW Turkey; 23 m. long, 21 m. wide.
Manfredonia, Gulf of Inlet of Adriatic Sea, S Italy; *c.* 30 m. long, *c.* 15 m. wide.
Mangole (or Mangoli) Island in the Sula Islands, N Moluccas, in the Molucca Sea; 72 m. long, 10 m. wide.
Mangueira, Lagoa da Shallow lagoon, S Rio Grande do Sul, Brazil, separated from open Atlantic by sand bar; 60 m. long, 8 m. wide.
Manila Bay Landlocked inlet of South China Sea, SW Luzon, Philippines, sheltered W by Bataan Peninsula; *c.* 35 m. wide, *c.* 30 m. long. One of the world's best harbors.
Mannar, Gulf of Inlet of Indian Ocean between S Madras and Ceylon; 80–170 m. wide, *c.* 100 m. long. Also spelled Manaar and Manar.
Mansel Island Northwest Territories, in Hudson Bay, off N Ungava Peninsula; 62 m. long, 4–30 m. wide. Reindeer reserve since 1920.
Manus Largest of Admiralty Islands, Bismarck Archipelago, Territory of New Guinea; 633 sq. m. Also called Admiralty Island.
Maré Coral island, southernmost of Loyalty group, SW Pacific; *c.* 22 m. long, 18 m. wide.
Margarita Island NE Venezuela, in the Caribbean; 444 sq. m. Horseshoe-shaped, consists in fact of 2 islands joined by sand spit.
Marguerite Bay Inlet of Antarctica, on W coast of Palmer Peninsula, S Pacific.
Mariager Fjord Inlet of the Kattegat, E Jutland, Denmark; *c.* 25 m. long.
Marinduque Island in the Philippines, betweens Luzon and Mindoro; 346 sq. m.
Marion Island Sub-Antarctic island in S Indian Ocean, just SW of Prince Edward Island; 13 m. long, 8 m. wide. Annexed by South Africa, 1947.
Markham Sound Strait of the Arctic, S Franz Josef Land; 50 m. long, 10 m. wide.
Marroquí, Point Southernmost point of European mainland, S Spain, on Strait of Gibraltar. Generally considered dividing point between Mediterranean and Atlantic. Also called Tarifa Point.
Marsh Island Low, marshy island, S Louisiana, between Gulf of Mexico and Vermilion and West Cote Blanche bays; 21 m. long, 2–10 m. wide.
Martinique Passage Channel in the Windward Islands, between Dominica and Martinique; *c.* 25 m. wide.
Marudu Bay Inlet of South China Sea, N Borneo; 30 m. long, 15 m. wide.
Masbate One of Visayan Islands, Philippines; 1,262 sq. m. One of chief gold-bearing areas of the Philippines.
Mascarene Islands Group of islands in Indian Ocean, consisting of Réunion, Mauritius and several others.
Masira Bay (or Bahr al Hadri) Inlet of Arabian Sea, extending 100 m. **SW** from Masira (island) to Ras Madraka (cape).
Masoala Peninsula Madagascar, on NE coast; 40 m. long, 30 m. wide (at widest point).
Masset Inlet Central Graham Island, W British Columbia; 20 m. long, 2–8 m. wide, connected with Dixon Entrance by 25-m.-long Masset Sound.

Masson Island Island in Shackleton Shelf Ice, off Queen Mary Coast, Antarctica; 13 m. long, 10½ m. wide.
Matagorda Bay Inlet of Gulf of Mexico; *c.* 50 m. long, 3–12 m. wide.
Matagorda Island Low, sandy island, S Texas, between San Antonio and Espiritu Santo bays and the Gulf of Mexico; 36 m. long, 1–4 m. wide.
Matamanó, Gulf of (or Ensenada de la Broa) Inlet of the Gulf of Batabanó, W Cuba; *c.* 30 m. long, 15 m. wide.
Matapan Peninsula Central of the 3 peninsulas of S Peloponnesus, Greece; 28 m. long.
Matochkin Shar Strait of the Arctic Ocean connecting Barents and Kara seas; separates N and S islands of Novaya Zemlya; 60 m. long, 1–2 m. wide.
Matty Island Northwest Territories, in James Ross Strait, between Boothia Peninsula and King William Island; 20 m. long, 15 m. wide.
Maui Second largest of the Hawaiian Islands, separated from Hawaii by Alenuihaha Channel; 728 sq. m.
Mayaguana Passage Channel of the Atlantic between Mayaguana island and cays off E Acklins Island, S Bahamas; *c.* 25 m. wide.
Mayotte Island Easternmost of the Comoro Islands, in Mozambique Channel of Indian Ocean; 25 m. long, 10 m. wide.
Mecklenburg Bay Bight of the Baltic, N Germany, between Fehmarn island and Darss peninsula; 55 m. wide.
Medny Island (or Mednyy Island) Second largest of Komandorski Islands, in SW Bering Sea; 34 m. long, 4 m. wide.
Meighen Island Sverdrup Islands, Northwest Territories, in the Arctic Ocean; 360 sq. m.
Melanesia One of the 3 main divisions of the Pacific islands; includes Fiji islands, New Caledonia, Loyalty Islands, New Hebrides, Solomon and Santa Cruz islands, Admiralty Islands, Louisiade and Bismarck archipelagoes and D'Entrecasteaux Islands.
Melbourne Island Northwest Territories, in Queen Maud Gulf, E of base of Kent Peninsula; 18 m. long, 10 m. wide.
Melrakkasletta Peninsula of NE Iceland, extending into Greenland Sea between Axar Fjord and Thistil Fjord; 25 m. long. At tip is Rifstangi cape, northernmost point of Iceland.
Melville Bay Broad inlet of Baffin Bay, NW Greenland. Receives several large glaciers.
Melville Island Largest of the Parry Islands, Northwest Territories, in the Arctic Ocean; 16,503 sq. m.
Melville Peninsula Peninsula on Canadian mainland, Northwest Territories, just N of the Arctic Circle; extends N between Gulf of Boothia and Foxe Basin; 250 m. long, 70–135 m. wide.
Mendol Island in the Strait of Malacca, just off E coast of Sumatra, Indonesia; 12 m. long, 10 m. wide. Also called Mendor, Pendjalai and Penjalai.
Mentawai Islands (or Mentawei Islands) Volcanic group off W coast of Sumatra, in the Indian Ocean, Indonesia; 2,354 sq. m. They consist of *c.* 70 islands, of which largest is Siberut.
Merino Jarpa Island Island off W coast of Aysén province, S Chile; 33 m. long, 3–12 m. wide.
Merritt Island E Florida, between Indian River Lagoon and Banana River Lagoon; *c.* 30 m. long, up to 7 m. wide.
Messenia, Gulf of Inlet of Ionian Sea between Cape Akritas and Cape Matapan, S Peloponnesus, Greece; 35 m. long, 30 m. wide. Sometimes called Gulf of Messene, and formerly called Gulf of Korone and Gulf of Kalamata.
Messenia Peninsula Peninsula on Ionian Sea, SW Peloponnesus, Greece; at S tip is Cape Akritas; 20 m. long, 15 m. wide.
Meta Incognita (also Kingait) Peninsula of SE Baffin Island, Northwest Territories, extending SE into the Atlantic; 170 m. long, 30–80 m. wide.
Mezen Bay (or Mezen' Bay) Inlet of White Sea, Russian SFSR, W of Kanin Peninsula; 55 m. long, 60 m. wide.
Micronesia One of 3 main divisions of Pacific islands; includes Caroline, Marshall, Marianas and Gilbert islands.
Middle Caicos (also Grand Caicos) Largest island of Turks and Caicos Islands (dependency of Jamaica); 72.8 sq. m.
Midway Atoll and 2 islets halfway across N Pacific; 2 sq. m. Battle of Midway (June 3–6, 1942) was one of decisive battles in the Second World War.
Mill Island Northwest Territories, in Hudson Strait, at S end of Foxe Channel; 20 m. long, 14 m. wide.
Milne Bay New Guinea, easternmost bay of the island; 30 m. long, 15 m. wide.
Minas Basin Central section of deep inlet of Bay of Fundy; 24 m. long, up to 25 m. wide. Connected to Bay of Fundy by Minas Channel.
Minas Channel Inlet in N central Nova Scotia connecting Bay of Fundy with Minas Basin; 24 m. long, 10–14 m. wide.
Minch, The (also North Minch) Strait of the Atlantic between Lewis with Harris (Outer Hebrides) and Scottish mainland; *c.* 35 m. wide.
Mindanao Second largest island of the Philippines; 36,537 sq. m. Lies at S end of the group.
Mindanao Sea S Philippines; opens E to Philippine Sea, W to Sulu Sea and N to Visayan Sea; *c.* 170 m. E-W.
Mindanao Trench Submarine depression in North Pacific, off NE Mindanao; greatest depth 35,948 ft. Also called Philippine Trench.
Mindoro Island in the Philippines, between Mindoro Strait and Tablas Strait; 3,759 sq. m.
Mindoro Strait Philippines, separating Mindoro from Calamian Islands; *c.* 50 m. wide.
Minicoy Island Southernmost of the Laccadives, in the Arabian Sea.
Minorca Second largest of the Balearic Islands, Spain, in the W Mediterranean; 271 sq. m.
Minto Inlet Arm of Amundsen Gulf, Northwest Territories, in W Victoria Island; 75 m. long, 8–25 m. wide.
Mirabella, Gulf of (also Gulf of Merabello) Inlet of the Aegean in E Crete; 20 m. wide, 15 m. long.
Mirim Lake Shallow tidewater lagoon, S Brazil and E Uruguay, separated from Atlantic by marshy bar; 110 m. long, up to 25 m. wide.
Misima Volcanic island in the Louisiade Archipelago, Territory of Papua, SW Pacific; 100 sq. m.
Mississippi Sound Arm of the Gulf of Mexico, between coast and series of narrow islands; connected with Mobile Bay through Grants Pass; *c.* 80 m. long, 7–15 m. wide.
Mitkof Island Alexander Archipelago, SE Alaska, be-

tween Kupreanof Island and mainland; 24 m. long, 7–17 m. wide.
Moa Largest of the Leti Islands, s Moluccas, Indonesia, in Banda Sea; 169 sq. m.
Mohéli Island One of main islands of Comoro group, in Mozambique Channel of Indian Ocean; 112 sq. m.
Moller, Port Bay on Alaska Peninsula, sw Alaska; 20 m. long, 10 m. wide.
Molokai Island, Territory of Hawaii; 259 sq. m.
Molucca Passage Channel in Indonesia connecting Molucca Sea and Ceram Sea with the Pacific; *c.* 150 m. wide.
Molucca Sea Section of the Pacific between Celebes and Buru, Indonesia.
Mompog Pass Channel in the Philippines, connecting Tayabas Bay (s Luzon) with Sibuyan Sea; *c.* 40 m. long, 11 m. wide.
Mona Roman name for island sometimes identified with Isle of Man, sometimes with Anglesey.
Mona Passage Strait leading from the Atlantic to the Caribbean between Puerto Rica and Hispaniola; *c.* 75 m. wide.
Montague Island s Alaska, on w side of entrance of Prince William Sound; 50 m. long, 5–12 m. wide.
Montague Sound Inlet of Timor Sea, Western Australia, between Cape Voltaire and Bigge Island; 20 m. long, 30 m. wide.
Montague Strait Strait forming entrance to Prince William Sound from Gulf of Alaska.
Monte Bello Islands Coral group in the Indian Ocean, off NW coast of Western Australia; surrounded by coral reef. Largest is Barrow Island.
Montijo Gulf Inlet of the Pacific, w central Panama; 20 m. long, 15 m. wide.
Moraleda Channel Strait of the Pacific, s Chile; separates Chonos Archipelago from mainland; *c.* 80 m. long.
Moray Firth Inlet of the North Sea, NE Scotland; 78 m. wide between Kinnairds Head and Duncansbay Head; 21 m. wide between Lossiemouth and Tarbat Ness, where it is sometimes held to begin.
Moresby Island One of Queen Charlotte Islands, w British Columbia, in the Pacific; 1,060 sq. m.
Moreton Bay Inlet of the Pacific in SE Queensland, Australia; 65 m. N-S, 20 m. E-W.
Mornington Island 1. Uninhabited island, Trinidad Gulf, off s Chile, w of Wellington Island; 28 m. long, *c.* 8 m. wide.
2. Northernmost and largest of Wellesley Islands, Gulf of Carpentaria, off Queensland, Australia; 40 m. long, 15 m. wide; uninhabited.
Moro Gulf Inlet of Celebes Sea in s coast of w Mindanao, Philippines.
Morotai One of the Molucca Islands, in N part of group; 50 m. long, 25 m. wide. Formerly also called Morty.
Morris Jesup, Cape (or Cape Morris K. Jesup) Northernmost point of land in the world, at N extremity of Greenland, on the Arctic Ocean.
Morrosquillo, Gulf of Inlet of the Caribbean, N Colombia; 20 m. long, *c.* 8 m. wide.
Mors Largest island in Lim Fjord, NW Jutland, Denmark; 140 sq. m.
Mosquito Coast (or Mosquitia) Undeveloped coastal region of Central America, on the Caribbean. Part belongs to Honduras, part to Nicaragua. Consists of tropical forested lowland with marshy shore. Name comes from Mosquito Indians, chief inhabitants.
Mosquito Gulf Bight of the Caribbean in w central Panama; 80 m. wide, 10 m. long.
Motovka Gulf Inlet of Barents Sea, Russian SFSR, between Rybachi and Kola peninsulas; 35 m. long, 4–8 m. wide.
Mouchoir Passage Strait in the West Indies separating Mouchoir Bank (shoal) from the Turks Islands; *c.* 60 m. long.
Mounts Bay Inlet of the English Channel in sw Cornwall, England, between Land's End and Lizard Head; 21 m. long, 10 m. wide.
Moyo (also Mojo) One of the islands of Indonesia, off N coast of Sumbawa; 20 m. long, 9 m. wide.
Mozambique Current Warm current flowing sw from Indian Ocean through Mozambique Channel; s part also called Agulhas Current.
Muchalat Inlet w arm of Nootka Sound in Vancouver Island, sw British Columbia; 24 m. long.
Muckle Flugga Northernmost of the Shetland Islands, just N of Unst; site of the North Unst Light.
Muna (also Moena) Island of Indonesia, between Molucca and Flores seas, off SE Celebes; 659 sq. m.
Muñoz Gamero Peninsula Chilean Patagonia, sw of Puerto Natales, on Strait of Magellan; 80 m. long, *c.* 30 m. wide. Mountainous, rising to 5,740 ft in Mt Burney.
Muravyev-Amurski Peninsula s Maritime Territory, Russian SFSR, extending 25 m. ssw into Peter the Great Bay. Also spelled Murav'yev-Amurskiy.
Murman Coast N shore of Kola Peninsula, on Barents Sea; *c.* 200 m. long; ice-free. Sometimes called Norman Coast.
Mussau (or St Matthias Islands) Island group of the Bismarck Archipelago, Territory of New Guinea, sw Pacific. Comprises 2 volcanic islands: Mussau (*c.* 160 sq. m.) and Emirau (20 sq. m.); and several coral islets.
Mutsu Bay Inlet of Tsugaru Strait, N Honshu, Japan; 25 m. long.
Mytilene Channel Arm of the Aegean between Lesbos and Turkish mainland; 30 m. long, 10 m. wide.

Nachvak Fjord Inlet of the Atlantic in NE Labrador, at the foot of Cirque Mountain; 30 m. long, 3 m. wide.
Nagai Island One of Shumagin Islands, sw Alaska; 32 m. long, 1–11 m. wide.
Namhae Island Korea, in Cheju Strait, almost joined to s coast of mainland; 115 sq. m. Almost divided into two, and has three peninsulas.
Nams Fjord Inlet of North Sea, central Norway; 22 m. long, *c.* 2 m. wide. Sometimes called Namsen Fjord.
Nansen Sound (or Fridtjof Nansen Sound) Arm of the Arctic Ocean between Axel Heiberg Island and Ellesmere Island, Northwest Territories; 90 m. long, 10–35 m. wide.
Nantucket Sound Channel of the Atlantic Ocean between Cape Cod and Nantucket Island and Martha's Vineyard; *c.* 30 m. long, *c.* 25 m. wide.
Napier Peninsula NE Arnhem Land, N Northern Territory, Australia; 20 m. long, 6 m. wide.

Nassau Bay NE New Guinea, opening on Huon Gulf. Allies landed here in 1943 to capture nearby Japanese base.
Nassau Gulf Tierra del Fuego, between Navarino Island and Wollaston Islands; *c.* 60 m. long, 15 m. wide.
Natewa Bay E Vanua Levu, Fiji, separating E peninsula from rest of island; 35 m. long, 10 m. wide.
Natuna Islands (also Natoena Islands) Group in Indonesia, between Borneo and Malay Peninsula, in South China Sea. Comprise Great Natuna (largest), North Natuna Islands and South Natuna Islands (2 small groups). Mostly low and wooded.
Navarino Island Tierra del Fuego, Chile, across Beagle Channel from main island of Tierra del Fuego; 955 sq. m.
Navy Board Inlet Arm of Lancaster Sound, N Baffin Island, Northwest Territories; 70 m. long, 6–18 m. wide.
Ndeni (or Santa Cruz) Volcanic island of the Santa Cruz group, Solomon Islands, SW Pacific; 35 m. long, 15 m. wide.
Near Islands Westernmost group of the Aleutian Islands, SW Alaska; uninhabited except Attu (largest).
Negro Bay Inlet of Indian Ocean, Somali Republic, at mouth of Nogal Valley; 30 m. long, 5 m. wide.
Negros Fourth largest of the Philippines, in the Visayan Islands, between Panay and Cebu islands; 4,905 sq. m. Sugar cane and rice.
Nellie Juan, Port Bay in S Alaska, on E side of Kenai Peninsula; 30 m. long, 3 m. wide.
Nelson Island W Alaska, across Etolin Strait from Nunivak Island; 42 m. long, 20–35 m. wide.
Nemuro Strait Channel between E Hokkaido, Japan, and Kunashir Island, Kurile Islands; connects Sea of Okhotsk with the Pacific; 60 m. long, 10–30 m. wide.
New Georgia Volcanic island group of the Solomon Islands, SW Pacific; *c.* 2,000 sq. m. Largest island of group is New Georgia, 50 m. long and *c.* 20 m. wide.
New Georgia Sound SW Pacific, in the Solomon Islands; *c.* 310 m. long, extending from Shortland Islands to Florida and Savo islands.
New Siberian Islands Archipelago, Russian SFSR, between Laptev and East Siberian seas; 11,000 sq. m. Few inhabitants, sparse tundra; mammoth fossils have been found.
Nias Volcanic island in Indonesia, off the W coast of Sumatra; 1,569 sq. m.
Nicholas Channel Strait off the NW coast of Cuba; *c.* 100 m. long.
Nicoya, Gulf of Inlet of the Pacific, W Costa Rica, between Nicoya Peninsula and the mainland; *c.* 50 m. long, *c.* 10 m. wide.
Nicoya Peninsula Largest peninsula of Costa Rica; 75 m. long, 20–30 m. wide.
Nine Degree Channel Channel in the Laccadives, India, in the Arabian Sea; divides Minicoy Island from the Laccadives proper.
Niue Coral island in S Pacific, belonging to New Zealand; *c.* 100 sq. m. Sometimes called Savage Island.
Nootka Island SW British Columbia, off W coast of Vancouver Island, in the Pacific; 206 sq. m.
Nordenskjöld Coast E coast of Palmer Peninsula, Antarctica, between Sjögren Fiord and Drygalski Bay; *c.* 61 m. long.
Nord Fjord Inlet of the North Sea, W Norway, 70 m. long, 1–3 m. wide. Receives glacier streams from the Jostedalsbre at its head.
Nord Islands Island group running parallel to the coast of W Norway for *c.* 30 m., in North Sea.
Nordre Isortoq Fjord of Davis Strait, SW Greenland; 85 m. long, 1–3 m. wide.
Nordre Strom Fjord Inlet of Davis Strait in W Greenland; 110 m. long, 1–16 m. wide. Extends to edge of inland icecap.
Normanby Island Volcanic island of the D'Entrecasteaux Islands, Territory of Papua, SW Pacific; *c.* 400 sq. m.
Northbrook Island SW Franz Josef Land, in the Arctic Ocean; 20 m. long, 12 m. wide.
Northeast Land Island of Spitsbergen group, in Barents Sea; 5,710 sq. m. Almost completely glaciated.
Northeast Providence Channel Strait of the Atlantic, Bahama Islands, NE of the Great Bahama Bank; *c.* 110 m. long.
North Island One of 2 main islands of New Zealand; 44,281 sq. m. It is the smaller of the two, but the more populous.
North Pacific Current (also North Pacific Drift) Warm ocean current formed by convergence of Japan and Okhotsk currents.
Norths Coast Part of Wilkes Land, Antarctica, on the Indian Ocean.
North Stradbroke Island Pacific Ocean, off coast of Queensland, Australia, S of Moreton Island; 123 sq. m. Also called Stradbroke Island.
North Uist One of the islands of the Outer Hebrides, Scotland; 118 sq. m.
Northumberland Strait Channel of the Gulf of St Lawrence; separates Prince Edward Island from New Brunswick and Nova Scotia; 200 m. long, 9–30 m. wide.
Northwest Providence Channel Channel in the Bahamas between Little Bahama Bank and Great Bahama Bank; *c.* 130 m. long. Connects Straits of Florida with Northeast Providence Channel.
Norton Bay NE arm of Norton Sound, W Alaska, on S side of base of Seward Peninsula; 30 m. long, 20 m. wide.
Norton Sound Arm of Bering Sea, W Alaska, on S shore of Seward Peninsula; 130 m. long, 90 m. wide.
Norwegian Bay Arm of the Arctic Ocean, off SW Ellesmere Island, Northwest Territories; *c.* 100 m. long, 90 m. wide.
Norwegian Current Terminal branch of the North Atlantic Current, in the Norwegian Sea.
Norwegian Sea Section of the Atlantic Ocean off the coast of Norway; separated from the open Atlantic by submarine ridge. Usually ice-free, because of warm Norwegian Current.
Nossi-Bé (or Nosy-Bé) Island in the Mozambique Channel, just off NW Madagascar; 115 sq. m. Volcanic in origin.
Noto Peninsula Central Honshu, Japan, between Sea of Japan and Toyama Bay; 45 m. long, 6–17 m. wide.
Notre Dame Bay Inlet of the Atlantic, E Newfoundland; 50 m. long, 55 m. wide at entrance.
Nottingham Island Hudson Strait, Northwest Territories, between Ungava Peninsula and Southampton Island; 441 sq. m.

Novaya Sibir Island Easternmost of the Anjou group of the New Siberian Islands, Russian SFSR; 75 m. long, 35 m. wide. Also spelled Novaya Sibir' Island.
Nuevo, Golfo Inlet of the Atlantic, Argentina, S of Valdés Peninsula; 40 m. W-E, 30 m. N-S.
Nûgssuak (or Nûgssuaq) 1. Peninsula of W Greenland; extends into Davis Strait from inland icecap; 110 m. long, 18–30 m. wide. Also spelled Nugsuak.
2. Peninsula of NW Greenland, on Baffin Bay; 30 m. long, 1–4 m. wide.
Nuhu Chut Largest of the Kai Islands, S Moluccas, Indonesia, in the Banda Sea; 241 sq. m. Also spelled Nuhu Tjut and Noehoe Tjoet; also called Great Kai.
Nuhu Rowa One of the Kai Islands, S Moluccas, Indonesia, just W of Nuhũ Chut; 30 m. long, 10 m. wide. Also called Little Kai; also spelled Noehoe Rowa.
Nuka Bay S Alaska, on SE coast of Kenai Peninsula; 20 m. long, 1–7 m. wide.
Numfor (or Noemfoor) Island of the Schouten group, Netherlands New Guinea, at entrance to Geelvink Bay; 14 m. long, 21 m. wide.
Nunarssuit Island off SW Greenland, off S side of mouth of Kobbermine Bay; 20 m. long, 3–9 m. wide. Formerly called Desolation Island.
Nunivak Island W Alaska, in the Bering Sea, separated from mainland and Nelson Island by Etolin Strait; 56 m. long, 40 m. wide. Treeless, with heavy fogs.
Nushagak Bay SW Alaska, on N shore of Bristol Bay; 50 m. long, 4–20 m. wide.
Nyuts Archipelago Island group in Great Australian Bight, off South Australia; consists of 40-m. chain. Largest of group is St Peter Island.

Oahu Third largest of the Hawaiian Islands; 589 sq. m.
Oates Coast Section of Antarctica, W of Victoria Land.
Obi Islands (or Ombi Islands) Group of the N Moluccas, Indonesia, in Ceram Sea. Consist of Obir (or Obira, 52 m. long, 28 m. wide), and small offshore islands.
Observatory Inlet Narrow arm of Portland Inlet, W British Columbia; 45 m. long, 1–4 m. wide.
Ofot Fjord Inlet of Vest Fjord, N Norway; 45 m. long, 3–6 m. wide.
Okhotsk Current Cold ocean current flowing S from Bering Sea along E Kurile Islands, Hokkaido and N Honshu to meet Japan Current in the Pacific.
Oki-gunto Island group, Japan, in Sea of Japan, off SW Honshu; 145 sq. m. Also called Oki Islands and Oki-no-shima.
Okinawa Largest island of the Okinawa Islands; 467 sq. m.
Okinawa Islands Central group of the Ryukyu Islands, between East China Sea and Philippine Sea; 579 sq. m. Stretch in a 70-m. chain.
Oktyabrskaya Revolyutsiya Island (or Oktyabr'skaya Revolyutsiya Island) Central island of the Severnaya Zemlya archipelago, in the Arctic Ocean; 5,400 sq. m. Almost half covered by glaciers.
Oland Island in the Baltic, separated from mainland of SE Sweden by Kalmar Sound; 519 sq. m.
Old Bahama Channel Strait off N coast of Cuba, S of Great Bahama Bank; *c.* 100 m. long, 15 m. wide.
Oman, Gulf of NW arm of the Arabian Sea; 350 m. long, 200 m. wide between Ras al Hadd and Gwatar Bay.
Ombai Strait Channel between Timor and Alor Islands, joining the Banda and Savu seas. Also called Matua Strait.
Omura Bay Landlocked gulf of the East China Sea in W Kyushu, Japan; 20 m. long, 8 m. wide.
One and a Half Degree Channel Seaway of the Indian Ocean, between Haddummati and Suvadiva atolls of the Maldive Islands; *c.* 55 m. wide.
Onega Bay S inlet of the White Sea, W of Onega Peninsula, NW European USSR; 100 m. long, 30–50 m. wide.
Onega Peninsula White Sea, between Onega Bay and Dvina Bay; 80 m. long, 15–60 m. wide.
Onekotan Island (or Onnekotan Island) One of N main Kurile Islands group, Russian SFSR; 121 sq. m.
Onslow Bay Bight of the Atlantic between capes Lookout and Fear, SE North Carolina; *c.* 100 m. long, 25 m. wide.
Ontong Java Atoll of the Solomon Islands, SW Pacific; comprises 4 islands on reef 30 m. long, 20 m. wide. Also called Lord Howe Island.
Oregon Inlet Channel connecting Pamlico Sound with the Atlantic, North Carolina, running through the Outer Banks.
Oreos Channel Arm of the Aegean, between Euboea and the Greek mainland; 20 m. long, 2–4 m. wide.
Oresund Strait connecting the Kattegat with the Baltic, between Zealand and Sweden; 87 m. long, average 17 m. wide; minimum depth 23 ft. Also known as The Sound.
Ormoc Bay Inlet of the Camotes Sea in W Leyte, Philippines; 13 m. E-W, 16 m. N-S.
Orosei, Gulf of Inlet of the Tyrrhenian Sea in E Sardinia; 31 m. wide, 8 m. long.
Orust Island in the Skagerrak, SW Sweden, separated from mainland by narrow channel; 133 sq. m.
Osaka Bay E arm of the Inland Sea of Japan, between Awaji-shima and S coast of Honshu; 35 m. long, 20 m. wide.
Osa Peninsula S Costa Rica, on the Pacific; 35 m. long, 10–15 m. wide.
Oster Fjord Inlet of the North Sea in SW Norway; *c.* 20 m. long; separates Osteroy from mainland.
Ostero Second largest of the Faeroe Islands; 111 sq. m.
Osteroy Island, SW Norway, NE of Bergen; 127 sq. m. Separated from mainland by Sor and Oster fjords.
Osumi Peninsula S Kyushu, Japan, between Kagoshima and Ariake bays; 45 m. long, 20 m. wide.
Osumi Strait Channel connecting East China and Philippine seas, between Tanega-shima and S coast of Kyushu; 35 m. long, 20 m. wide. Formerly also Van Diemen Strait.
Otranto, Strait of Channel connecting Adriatic and Ionian seas; *c.* 43 m. long.
Ottawa Islands Group of 24 small islands in Hudson Bay, off NW Ungava Peninsula, covering area *c.* 70 m. long, 50 m. wide.
Otway Sound Inlet of the Strait of Magellan, Chile, between Brunswick Peninsula and Riesco Island; 50 m. long, 12–20 m. wide.
Outer Banks Chain of sandy barrier islands extending along the North Carolina coast. Also called The Banks.

Oyster Bay Inlet of the Tasman Sea formed by E coast of Tasmania, Freycinet Peninsula and Schouten Island; 17 m. long, 14 m. wide.

Padang Island of Indonesia, in the Strait of Malacca, just off E coast of Sumatra; 35 m. long, 18 m. wide.
Padre Island Barrier island, S Texas, between Laguna Madre and the Gulf of Mexico; *c.* 115 m. long, generally under 2 m. wide.
Pag Island, W Croatia, Yugoslavia, in the Adriatic; 114 sq. m. Separated from mainland by Velebit Channel.
Pagi Islands Group of the Mentawai Islands, Indonesia, off W coast of Sumatra; consist of North Pagi (25 m. long, 17 m. wide), South Pagi (42 m. long, 12 m. wide) and many islets. Sometimes spelled Pagai.
Paita Bay Inlet of Pacific, NW Peru; 5 m. long, 30 m. wide.
Palawan Westernmost of the large islands of the Philippines, between the Sulu Sea and the South China Sea; 4,550 sq. m. Formerly also called Paragua.
Palk Strait Inlet of the Bay of Bengal between S Madras and the N coast of Ceylon; 85 m. long, 40–85 m. wide.
Palliser Bay Inlet of Cook Strait, North Island, New Zealand; 20 m. long, 10 m. wide.
Palma (also La Palma) One of the Canary Islands, in NW part of group; 281 sq. m.
Palmas, Cape Headland, SE Liberia, marking W limit of Gulf of Guinea.
Palmer Archipelago Island group of Antarctica, off NW coast of Palmer Peninsula, SW of the South Shetlands.
Palmer Peninsula Part of Antarctica, extending *c.* 800 m. towards South America; tip is 650 m. from Cape Horn and is the furthest point of Antarctic continent from the South Pole. Part of the British Antarctic Territory colony, and known in Britain as Graham Land.
Palm Island Coral group in the Coral Sea, within the Great Barrier Reef, off E coast of Queensland, Australia. Comprise *c.* 20 islands and rocks.
Palmyra Atoll comprising 55 islets in Line Islands, central Pacific.
Pamlico Sound Channel in E North Carolina, separated from the Atlantic by barrier beaches; *c.* 80 m. long, 25 m. wide.
Panama, Bay of N section of the Gulf of Panama, E Panama; 30 m. long, 75 m. wide.
Panama, Gulf of Inlet of the Pacific, E Panama, at S side of Isthmus of Panama; 115 m. wide, *c.* 100 m. long.
Panay One of the Visayan Islands, in the Philippines; 4,446 sq. m.
Panay Gulf Arm of the Sulu Sea between Panay and Negros, in the Philippines; *c.* 50 m. N-S, *c.* 55 m. E-W.
Panguil Bay SW arm of Iligan Bay, N Mindanao, in the Philippines; 25 m. long, 2–6 m. wide.
Pangutaran Group Coral island group in the Sulu Archipelago of the Philippines; largest is Pangutaran Island (36.7 sq. m.).
Pantar (also Pandai) One of the Alor Islands, Lesser Sundas, Indonesia; 281 sq. m.
Papagayo Gulf Inlet of the Pacific on Costa Rica-Nicaragua border; 25 m. wide, 15 m. long.
Papua, Gulf of Indentation of SE New Guinea, on the Coral Sea; 225 m. E-W, 95 m. N-S.

Paracel Islands Group of low coral islands and reefs in the South China Sea, forming part of Kwangtung province, China.
Paraguaná Peninsula NW Venezuela, between the Caribbean and the Gulf of Venezuela; *c.* 40 m. long, 33 m. wide.
Paramushir Island Third largest of the main group of the Kurile Islands; 954 sq. m.
Paranagua Bay Inlet of the Atlantic in SE Brazil; 30 m. long, 15 m. wide.
Paria, Gulf of Inlet of the Caribbean between Trinidad and Venezuela, separated from the Caribbean by Paria Peninsula and linked with it by Dragon's Mouths; linked with the Atlantic by Serpent's Mouth; *c.* 100 m. long, *c.* 40 m. wide.
Paria Peninsula NE Venezuela, on the Caribbean, N of Gulf of Paria; 75 m. long, 3–14 m. wide.
Pariñas Point Westernmost point of South America, Piura department, NW Peru.
Parita Gulf W section of the Gulf of Panama, central Panama; 10 m. long, 20 m. wide.
Passamaquoddy Bay Inlet of the Bay of Fundy, between NE Maine and SW New Brunswick; 30 m. long, 20 m. wide at entrance.
Pastol Bay W Alaska, on S Norton Sound, E of Yukon River delta; 50 m. wide.
Patmos Island in the Dodecanese; 13 sq. m. According to tradition, St John wrote the Book of Revelation here.
Patras, Gulf of Inlet of the Ionian Sea between the Peloponnesus and central Greece; 25 m. wide, 10 m. long.
Patrek Fjord Inlet of Denmark Strait, NW Iceland; 20 m. long.
Patti, Gulf of Inlet of Tyrrhenian Sea, NE Sicily; 18 m. long, 8 m. wide.
Pavlof Bay Inlet of N Pacific, SW Alaska; 21 m. long, 10 m. wide at mouth.
Pavlof Islands Group off SW Alaska Peninsula, at entrance of Pavlof Bay; comprise 7 islands, of which largest is Dolgoi Island (10 m. long, 7 m. wide).
Peard Bay Inlet of Chukchi Sea, NW Alaska; 18 m. long, 8 m. wide.
Pearl Islands Group in the Gulf of Panama, *c.* 40 m. SE of Panama city. There are 183 islands altogether, 39 of them fairly large; they have important pearl fisheries.
Pearl Lagoon E Nicaragua; *c.* 30 m. long, *c.* 5 m. wide. Separated from Caribbean Sea by swampy isthmus.
Peary Channel Arm of the Arctic Ocean Northwest Territories, between Meighen Island (N) and Ellef Ringnes and Amund Ringnes islands; 120 m. long, 60 m. wide.
Pechora Bay Inlet of Barents Sea, at mouth of Pechora River, N European USSR; 40 m. wide, 50 m. long.
Pedro Bank Shoal in the Caribbean, 45 m. S of Jamaica; *c.* 110 m. long, up to 65 m. wide.
Peel Sound Arm of the Arctic Ocean between Barrow and Franklin straits, Northwest Territories; 110 m. long, 15–50 m. wide.
Pegasus Bay Inlet of S Pacific, E South Island, New Zealand; 40 m. N-S, 15 m. E-W.
Peleng Largest island of the Banggai Archipelago, Indonesia; 929 sq. m.
Pelly Bay Inlet of the Gulf of Boothia, Northwest Territories; 75 m. long, 10–40 m. wide.

Pack ice in Scoresby Sound

Pelorus Sound Inlet of Cook Strait, NE South Island, New Zealand; 20 m. long.
Pemba Coral island in the Indian Ocean, off E coast of Africa; separated from Tanganyikan coast by 40-m.-wide Pemba Channel; 380 sq. m. including offshore islets. Part of Zanzibar protectorate. Grows cloves.
Peñas, Gulf of Inlet on S Chile coast, between Taitao Peninsula and Guayaneco Islands; 50 m. long, *c.* 40 m. wide.
Penobscot Bay Inlet of the Atlantic, S Maine, at mouth of Penobscot River; 27 m. wide, 35 m. long.
Pentecost Volcanic island in the New Hebrides, SW Pacific; *c.* 190 sq. m.
Penzhina Bay NE arm of Shelekhov Gulf of Sea of Okhotsk, NE Siberian Russian SFSR; 185 m. long, 60 m. wide at mouth.
Perekop Isthmus USSR, connecting Crimea with mainland, and separating Perekop Gulf (Black Sea) from Sivash lagoon; *c.* 20 m. long, 4–15 m. wide.
Peril Strait SE Alaska, extending *c.* 50 m. between Chichagof Island and Baranof Island.
Peron Peninsula Western Australia, between Denham Sound and Hopeless Reach; 50 m. long, 19 m. wide.
Petalion, Gulf of Inlet of the Aegean between Euboea and Attica, Greece; 30 m. long, 30 m. wide.
Peter I Island In Bellingshausen Sea, off coast of Antarctica; *c.* 100 sq. m. Dependency of Norway since 1933.
Peter the Great Bay (also Peter the Great Gulf) Inlet of Sea of Japan in SW Maritime Territory, Russian SFSR, between Tumen River mouth and Cape Povorotny; 55 m. long, 115 m. wide.
Pharos Peninsula, Egypt, at Alexandria; originally an offshore island, joined to mainland by mole in reign of Alexander the Great; site of the famous lighthouse.
Philippeville, Gulf of Inlet of the Mediterranean in NE Algeria, between Cape Bougaroun and Cap de Fer; 15 m. long, 40 m. wide.
Philippine Sea Section of the W Pacific on E coast of Philippine Islands, extending N towards coast of Japan.
Philpots Island Northwest Territories, in Baffin Bay, off E coast of Devon Island; 18 m. long, 14 m. wide.
Phuket Island, S Thailand, off W coast of Malay Peninsula, in Andaman Sea; 206 sq. m. Large tin deposits.
Phuquoc Island, S Vietnam, in the Gulf of Siam; 230 sq. m.
Piai, Tanjong Southernmost point of Asian continent, Johore, S Malaya. Also called Tanjong Bulus.
Piazzi Island Uninhabited island off S Chile coast, separated from Rennell Islands by Smyth Channel; 25 m. long, 3–12 m. wide.
Pico Island One of the Azores, in the S central part of the group, Atlantic Ocean; 167 sq. m.
Pines, Isle of Island off SW Cuba, to which it belongs; 1,182 sq. m.
Pini One of the Batu Islands, Indonesia, off the W coast of Sumatra; 23 m. long, 7 m. wide.
Pioner Island Island of Severnaya Zemlya, Arctic Ocean, in W part of the group; 636 sq. m.
Pitt Island W British Columbia, in Hecate Strait, separated from mainland by Grenville Channel and by Principe Channel from Banks Island; 528 sq. m.
Placentia Bay Inlet of the Atlantic in S Newfoundland, between Burin and Avalon peninsulas; 100 m. long, 80 m. wide at entrance.
Planet Deep 1. Ocean depth (32,112 ft) in the N Pacific, in the Mindanao Trench.
2. Ocean depth (30,103 ft) in the S Pacific, off S New Britain.
Plenty, Bay of Inlet of the S Pacific in North Island, New Zealand; *c.* 160 m. E-W.
Pojo Bay Inlet of the Gulf of Finland, SW Finland; 20 m. long, 1–3 m. wide.
Polaris Bay Inlet of Hall Basin, NW Greenland; site of winter quarters of Hall expedition (1871–72).
Policastro, Gulf of Inlet of the Tyrrhenian Sea in S Italy; *c.* 25 m. long, 15 m. wide.
Polillo Islands Group of the Philippines, in the Philippine Sea, off the E coast of Luzon; *c.* 295 sq. m. Largest is Polillo Island (234 sq. m.).
Polillo Strait Channel between Luzon and the Polillo Islands, Philippines, connecting Lamon Bay with Philippine Sea; 35 m. long, 11–25 m. wide.
Polynesia One of the 3 main divisions of the Pacific islands; includes Hawaii, Samoa, Tonga, Tokelau and Tubunai, Tuamotu, Society, Marquesas, Cook, Ellice and Easter islands.
Pomona (also Mainland) Largest of the Orkney Islands, Scotland; 25 m. long, 17 m. wide.
Ponape Volcanic island in the Senyavin group of the Caroline Islands, W Pacific; 129 sq. m.
Porcher Island W British Columbia, in Hecate Strait; 210 sq. m.
Porsang Fjord Inlet of the Barents Sea in N Norway; 80 m. long, 5–12 m. wide.
Port au Port Peninsula, SW Newfoundland, on the Gulf of St Lawrence; 30 m. long, up to 10 m. wide; extends between St George Bay and Port au Port Bay.
Portland Bay Inlet of the Indian Ocean in SW Victoria, Australia, between Point Danger and Cape Reaumur; 24 m. long, 10 m. wide.
Portland Inlet NE arm of Dixon Entrance and Chatham Sound, W British Columbia; 30 m. long, 4–8 m. wide.
Port Phillip Bay Inlet of Bass Strait, S Victoria, Australia, between Point Lonsdale and Point Nepean; 30 m. long, 25 m. wide.
Possession Islands Group of 9 islands, off NE coast of Victoria Land, Antarctica, in Ross Sea.
Prat Island S Chile, off coast of Aysén province, N of Wellington Island; 27 m. long, 12 m. wide.
Preservation Inlet Bay of the Tasman Sea, SW South Island, New Zealand; 35 m. long, 4 m. wide.
Prince Albert Peninsula NW section of Victoria Island, Northwest Territories; 150 m. long, 80–150 m. wide.
Prince Albert Sound Inlet of Amundsen Gulf in SW Victoria Island, Northwest Territories; 170 m. long, 40 m. wide.
Prince Charles Foreland Island of the Spitsbergen group, in the Arctic Ocean; 243 sq. m.
Prince Christian Sound Channel of the Atlantic, between S tip of Greenland mainland and Cape Farewell Archipelago; 40 m. long, 1 m. wide.
Prince Gustav Adolph Sea Arm of the Arctic Ocean between North and South Borden islands (W) and Ellef Ringnes Island and the Findlay Islands (E); 140 m. long, 60 m. wide.

Prince Harald Coast Part of Queen Maud Land, Antarctica, on the Indian Ocean.

Prince of Wales, Cape W extremity of North American mainland, at W end of Seward Peninsula, Alaska.

Prince of Wales Island Largest island of the Alexander Archipelago, SE Alaska, in the N Pacific; 2,231 sq. m.

Prince of Wales Strait Arm of the Arctic, extending from Viscount Melville Sound to Amundsen Gulf, Northwest Territories; 200 m. long, 10–20 wide.

Prince Olav Coast Section of Queen Maud Land, Antarctica, on the Indian Ocean.

Prince Patrick Island One of the Parry Islands, Northwest Territories, in the Arctic Ocean; 6,696 sq. m.

Prince Regent Inlet Arm of the Arctic Ocean between Lancaster Sound and Barrow Strait (N) and the Gulf of Boothia (S); 150 m. long, 40–90 m. wide.

Princess Astrid Coast Section of Queen Maud Land, Antarctica, on the Indian Ocean.

Princess Charlotte Bay Inlet of the Coral Sea, NE Queensland, Australia, between Cape Melville and Claremont Point; 38 m. long, 15 m. wide.

Princess Marie Bay Arm of Kane Basin, E Ellesmere Island, Northwest Territories; 50 m. long, 8–15 m. wide.

Princess Martha Coast Section of Queen Maud Land, Antarctica, on the Indian Ocean.

Princess Ragnhild Coast Section of Queen Maud Land, Antarctica, on the Indian Ocean.

Princess Royal Island W British Columbia, in Hecate Strait; 876 sq. m.

Prince William Sound Irregular inlet of the Gulf of Alaska, E of Kenai Peninsula, S Alaska.

Principe Channel Strait between Pitt and Banks islands, off the coast of British Columbia; 50 m. long, 3 m. wide.

Prydz Bay Inlet of the Indian Ocean in Antarctica, off Lars Christensen and Ingrid Christensen coasts; 60 m. long, 175 m. wide.

Puck Bay W arm of the Gulf of Danzig, N Poland, between the mainland and Hel Peninsula; *c.* 20 m. long, up to 10 m. wide.

Puerto Rico Trench Submarine depression in the N Atlantic, N of Puerto Rico; *c.* 220 m. long; deepest part is the Milwaukee Depth (30,246 ft).

Puget Sound Inlet of the Pacific, NW Washington, extending to Olympia from Juan de Fuca Strait; *c.* 100 m. long.

Pulu Laut (also Pulau Laut and Poelau Laoet) Island of Indonesia, off SE Borneo, in Macassar Strait; 796 sq. m. Sometimes also called Laut or Laoet.

Puná Island S Ecuador, at head of Gulf of Guayaquil; 33 m. long, *c.* 10 m. wide.

Qarajaq Ice Fjord SE arm of Umanak Fjord, W Greenland; 30 m. long, 4–8 m. wide.

Qishm (or Qeshm) Largest island in the Persian Gulf, SE Iran, in the Strait of Hormuz; 70 m. long, 7–20 m. wide. Also spelled Kishm.

Quadra Island SW British Columbia, off NE Vancouver Island, in Discovery Passage; 120 sq. m.

Quatsino Sound Inlet of the Pacific in N Vancouver Island, British Columbia; 50 m. long, 1–7 m. wide.

Queen Charlotte Sound Bay of the Pacific Ocean, between Vancouver Island and Queen Charlotte Islands; narrows to Queen Charlotte Strait (60 m. long, 16 m. wide) in N, which separates NE Vancouver Island from the mainland.

Queen Charlotte Sound Inlet of Cook Strait in NE South Island, New Zealand; *c.* 25 m. long.

Queen Mary Coast Section of Antarctica, on the Indian Ocean, W of Wilkes Land.

Queen Maud Gulf Arm of the Arctic Ocean, Northwest Territories, S of Victoria and King William islands; 140 m. long, 50–100 m. wide. Forms part of the Northwest Passage.

Rae Isthmus Land narrows at the base of Melville Peninsula, Northwest Territories; 50 m. long.

Ragay Gulf Arm of Sibuyan Sea in SE Luzon, Philippines; 60 m. long, 40 m. wide.

Raja Ampat Islands Group between Ceram Sea and the Pacific, off Vogelkop peninsula, Netherlands New Guinea. Chief islands are Waigeu and Misool. Also spelled Radja Ampat.

Raleigh Bay Arm of the Atlantic between Cape Hatteras and Cape Lookout, E North Carolina; *c.* 75 m. long.

Ralik Chain W group of the Marshalls, W central Pacific, comprising 15 atolls and 3 coral islands; sometimes spelled Ralick and sometimes called Sunset Group.

Ramree Island Lower Burma, in the Bay of Bengal, off Arakan coast; 50 m. long, 15 m. wide. Formerly spelled Ramri.

Ran Fjord Inlet of the North Sea in N central Norway; *c.* 45 m. long, 1–4 m. wide.

Rangiroa Largest of the Tuamotu Islands, French Oceania; comprises 20 islets surrounding lagoon 45 m. long, 15 m. wide. Formerly called Dean's Island.

Rangsang Island of Indonesia, in the Strait of Malacca, off the E coast of Sumatra; 38 m. long, 10 m. wide.

Raspberry Strait S Alaska, between Afognak and Raspberry islands, connecting Gulf of Alaska and Shelikof Strait; 20 m. long, 1–2 m. wide.

Ratak Chain E group of the Marshall Islands, W central Pacific, comprising 14 atolls and 2 coral islands. Sometimes called Sunrise Group.

Rat Islands Group of the Aleutians, W of the Andreanof Islands and SE of Near Islands; extend for *c.* 110 m. E-W.

Recherche Archipelago (also Archipelago of the Recherche) Indian Ocean, off S coast of Western Australia, extending *c.* 120 m. E-W.

Redonda Islands Group of 2 islands, SW British Columbia, in NE arm of Strait of Georgia; 108 sq. m.

Rennell Island Southernmost of the Solomon Islands, SW Pacific; *c.* 50 m. long, 12 m. wide. Coral formation.

Repulse Bay 1. Inlet of the Coral Sea in E Queensland, Australia, between Cape Conway and Midge Point; 15 m. long, 13 m. wide.
2. Inlet of Foxe Channel, S Melville Peninsula, Northwest Territories; 40 m. long, 19–40 m. wide.

Resadiye Peninsula SW Turkey, extending 40 m. into the Aegean between Kos and Rhodes islands; 7 m. wide.

Resolution Island Northwest Territories, at E entrance to Hudson Strait, off SE Baffin Island; 1,029 sq. m.

Revillagigedo Channel SE Alaska, in the Alexander Archipelago; *c.* 35 m. long.

Revillagigedo Island SE Alaska, in the Alexander

Archipelago, separated from mainland by Behm Channel and from Prince of Wales Island by Clarence Strait; 1,120 sq. m.
Revillagigedo Islands Archipelago in the Pacific, *c.* 450 m. off W coast of Mexico, to which they belong; 320 sq. m. Uninhabited. Also written Revilla Gigedo Islands.
Reydar Fjord (or Reydhar Fjord) Inlet of the Atlantic in E Iceland; 20 m. long, 2–3 m. wide.
Reykjanes Peninsula SW Iceland, extending between Faxa Bay and the Atlantic; 40 m. long, 10–30 m. wide.
Richard Black Coast Section of Antarctica, at the E base of Palmer Peninsula, on Weddell Sea.
Richard Collinson Inlet Arm of Viscount Melville Sound in N Victoria Island, Northwest Territories; 80 m. long, 15–30 m. wide.
Richards Island Northwest Territories, in the Beaufort Sea, at the mouth of the Mackenzie River delta; 50 m. long, 6–25 m. wide.
Riesco Island S Chile, separated from mainland by Skyring Sound; 75 m. long, 20 m. wide; mountainous.
Riga, Gulf of Arm of the Baltic Sea, bordering on Estonia and Latvia; 90 m. long, 45-80 m. wide.
Rincha Island of the Lesser Sundas, Indonesia, between Flores Sea and Sumba Strait; 18 m. long, 9 m. wide. Also spelled Rintja.
Ringkobing Fjord Inlet of the North Sea in W Jutland, Denmark; *c.* 20 m. long, 7 m. wide.
Ringvassoy Island, N Norway, in the Norwegian Sea; 253 sq. m.
Río, El (or La Ciénaga) Channel on N Yucatan coast, Mexico, between mainland and series of bars and peninsulas; *c.* 210 m. long, 1 m. wide.
Riouw Archipelago Island group of Indonesia in the South China Sea, at the entrance to the Strait of Malacca; 2,279 sq. m. Also spelled Riau.
Robert English Coast Section of Antarctica, at the W base of Palmer Peninsula.
Robertson Bay Inlet in Victoria Land, Antarctica, between capes Barrow and Adare; 22 m. long, 20 m. wide.
Robeson Channel Arm of the Arctic Ocean between NE Ellesmere Island and NW Greenland; 50 m. long, 11–18 m. wide.
Roebuck Bay Inlet of the Indian Ocean in N Western Australia, between Entrance Point and Cape Villaret; 21 m. long, 11 m. wide.
Roes Welcome Sound NW arm of Hudson Bay, Northwest Territories, between mainland and Southampton Island; 180 m. long, 15–70 m. wide.
Romanche Deep Ocean depth in the Atlantic, at the equator; deepest sounding is 25,000 ft.
Romano, Cayo Coral island off the N coast of Cuba, in Old Bahama Channel; 55 m. long, 10 m. wide. Forms part of Camagüey Archipelago.
Romsdal Fjord SE arm of Molde Fjord, W Norway; 25 m. long, 2–3 m. wide.
Ronne Bay SW entrance to George VI Sound; *c.* 131 m. long, 79 m. wide; opens off Bellingshausen Sea, between Alexander I Island and Robert English Coast.
Rooke Island Volcanic island of the Bismarck Archipelago, Territory of New Guinea, SW Pacific; 300 m. long. Also spelled Rook; also called Umboi.
Roosevelt Island E section of Ross Shelf Ice, Antarctica; 79 m. long, 35 m. wide.
Rosario Strait Passage connecting Georgia Strait with Puget Sound and Juan de Fuca Strait, NW Washington; *c.* 25 m. long.
Rossel Island Volcanic island of the Louisiade Archipelago, Territory of Papua, SW Pacific; 20 m. long, 10 m. wide.
Ross Island 1. Antarctica, in the Weddell Sea, just off NE tip of Palmer Peninsula; 34 m. long, 27 m. wide. Sometimes also called James Ross Island.
2. Island of Antarctica, in W part of Ross Sea, at outer edge of Ross Shelf Ice; 39 m. long, 37½ m. wide. On it are Mt Erebus and Mt Terror.
3. Island of central Mergui Archipelago, Lower Burma, in Andaman Sea; *c.* 45 m. in circumference.
Roti Island of Indonesia, separated from Timor by Roti Strait (10 m. wide); 50 m. long, 14 m. wide, 467 sq. m.
Royal Geographical Society Islands Northwest Territories, between S end of Victoria Strait and NE side of Queen Maud Gulf; comprise 4 small islands and many islets.
Rudolf Island Northernmost island of Franz Josef Land, in the Arctic Ocean; 15 m. long, 10 m. wide. Also spelled Rudolph Island.
Rupat (or Roepat) Island of Indonesia, in the Strait of Malacca, off E coast of Sumatra; 30 m. in diameter.
Ruppert Coast Section of Marie Byrd Land, Antarctica, W of Hobbs Coast.
Russell Island Northwest Territories, in Barrow Strait, off N Prince of Wales Island; 40 m. long, 7 m. wide.
Rybachi Peninsula Russian SFSR, at NW end of Kola Peninsula, between Barents Sea and Motovka Gulf; 35 m. long, 15 m. wide. Also spelled Rybachiy Peninsula.

Saare (also Saaremaa and Sarema) Largest island of Estonia, in the Baltic Sea, in the entrance to the Gulf of Riga; 1,046 sq. m.
Sabana Archipelago Group of keys off N central Cuba; *c.* 60 m. WNW-ESE.
Sabinal, Cayo Coral island at entrance to Old Bahama Channel, off NE Cuba; 25 m. long, *c.* 6 m. wide.
Sable, Cape Southernmost extremity of the United States mainland, S Florida; consists of swampy peninsula, *c.* 20 m. long, 5–10 m. wide.
Sabrina Coast Section of Wilkes Land, Antarctica, on the Indian Ocean.
Sado Island Japan, off N Honshu, in Sea of Japan; 330 sq. m.
Sagami Sea Inlet of the Philippine Sea in central Honshu, Japan, between Izu and Miura peninsulas; 60 m. long, 40 m. wide.
St Andrew Bay Irregular arm of the Gulf of Mexico, NW Florida; *c.* 35 m. long, with 3 arms (East, West and North bays).
St Croix Island Largest of the United States Virgin Islands; 81.93 sq. m.
St Cyprian Bay Uninhabited desert shore along coast of Río de Oro, Spanish West Africa.
St Francis Bay Inlet of the Indian Ocean in Cape Province, South Africa, 15 m. W of Port Elizabeth; 15 m. long, 35 m. wide at mouth.

St George Bay sw Newfoundland, between Cape Anguille and Cape St George; 60 m. long, 40 m. wide at entrance.
St George Channel Bismarck Archipelago, sw Pacific, between New Ireland and New Britain; 20 m. wide.
St George Fjord Inlet of Lincoln Sea in N Greenland; 60 m. long, 3–7 m. wide.
St George's Channel Sea arm connecting the Irish Sea with the Atlantic Ocean, between SE Ireland and Wales; *c.* 100 m. long, 50–95 m. wide.
St George Sound Arm of the Gulf of Mexico in NW Florida; *c.* 25 m. long, 5 m. wide.
St John Bay Inlet of the Gulf of St Lawrence in w Newfoundland; 10 m. long, 25 m. wide at entrance.
St Lucia One of the Windward Islands, West Indies, separated from Martinique by St Lucia Channel and from St Vincent by St Vincent Passage; 233. 29 sq. m.
St Lucia Channel SE West Indies, between Martinique and St Lucia; *c.* 20 m. wide.
St-Malo, Gulf of English Channel, off N coast of Brittany, w France; *c.* 20 m. long, 60 m. wide.
St Mary Bay Inlet of the Atlantic in w Nova Scotia, 5 m. SE of Digby; 35 m. long, 4–12 m. wide.
St Mary's Bay Inlet of the Atlantic in s coast of Avalon Peninsula, SE Newfoundland; 40 m. long, 25 m. wide.
St Matthew's Island s Mergui Archipelago, Lower Burma, in Andaman Sea; 20 m. long, 8 m. wide.
St Michael's Bay Inlet of the Atlantic in SE Labrador; 25 m. long, 7 m. wide.
St Vincent One of the central Windward Islands, West Indies; 133 sq. m.
St Vincent, Gulf Inlet of Indian Ocean in South Australia, between mainland and Yorke Peninsula; 90 m. long, 45 m. wide.
St Vincent Passage Channel between St Lucia and St Vincent, SE West Indies; *c.* 25 m. wide.
Sakishima Islands s group of the Ryukyu Islands, between East China and Philippine seas; 343 sq. m.
Salamis Island in Saronic Gulf of Aegean Sea, E central Greece; 39 sq. m. In the channel between Salamis and the mainland took place the defeat of the Persians under Xerxes by the Greeks under Themistocles (480 B.C.).
Salawati Island of Netherlands New Guinea, w of Vogelkop peninsula; 30 m. in diameter, roughly circular.
Salayar Island of Indonesia, separated from sw peninsula of Celebes by Salayar Strait; 259 sq. m. Also spelled Salajar and Saleijer.
Salerno, Gulf of Inlet of the Tyrrhenian Sea, s Italy; *c.* 40 m. long, 25 m. wide. Salerno (city) is on N shore.
Salisbury Island 1. Northwest Territories, off sw Baffin Island, at w entrance to Hudson Strait; 490 sq. m.
2. Central Franz Josef Land, Russian SFSR; 32 m. long, 12 m. wide.
Salsette Island India, off Bombay, in the Arabian Sea; 28 m. long, up to 15 m. wide. Has famous Kanheri cave-temples.
Salt Fjord Inlet of the North Sea in N Norway, just s of Bodo; 40 m. long, 5 m. wide at mouth, up to 1,180 ft deep.
Salut, Iles du Archipelago off coast of French Guiana; comprise Devils Island, Île Royale and St Joseph Island.
Samaná Bay Inlet of the Atlantic in NE coast of Dominican Republic; *c.* 30 m. long, 10 m. wide.
Samaná Peninsula Dominican Republic, on NE coast, between Samaná Bay and Escocesa Bay; 30 m. long, *c.* 6 m. wide.
Samar Third largest of the Philippines, in the Visayan group, between the Samar and Philippine seas; 5,050 sq. m.
Samar Sea Philippines, between Luzon, Samar, Leyte and Masbate.
Samos Greek Aegean island off Mycale peninsula of Turkey; 194 sq. m. Birthplace of Pythagoras.
Samui, Ko Island in the Gulf of Siam, s Thailand; 105 sq. m.
Sanana One of the Sula Islands, N Moluccas, Indonesia, in the Molucca Sea; 35 m. long, 10 m. wide. Sometimes called Sula Besi.
San Antonio Bay Inlet, s Texas, sheltered from the Gulf of Mexico by Matagorda Island; *c.* 19 m. long, *c.* 19 m. wide.
San Bernardino Strait Philippines, between SE tip of Luzon and NW tip of Samar; chief sea route to Manila.
San Cristobal Volcanic island of the Solomons, sw Pacific; *c.* 80 m. long, 25 m. wide. Also spelled San Cristoval.
San Cristóbal Island One of the E Galápagos Islands, Ecuador, in the Pacific; 195 sq. m. Also called Chatham Island.
Sandwich Bay Inlet in SE Labrador; 30 m. long, 10 m. wide at entrance.
Sandwip Island Easternmost island of Ganges Delta, E Pakistan, in the Bay of Bengal; 25 m. long, 3–9 m. wide.
Sangi Islands Volcanic group of Indonesia, between Celebes Sea and Molucca Passage; 314 sq. m. Largest island is Sangi or Sangihe (217 sq. m.). Sometimes spelled Sangihe and Sangir.
San Ildefonso Peninsula Central Luzon, Philippines, on the Philippine Sea, on the E coast of the island; 25 m. long, 1–5 m. wide.
San Jorge, Gulf of Inlet of the Atlantic in Argentina, between Cabo Dos Bahías and Cabo Tres Puntas; 145 m. N-S, 100 m. W-E. Also called Gulf of St George.
San José Gulf Sheltered inlet of San Matías Gulf, Argentina, bordered E and s by Valdés Peninsula; 27 m. W-E, 14 m. N-S.
San Juanico Strait Channel in the Philippines, between Samar and Leyte; 25 m. long, *c.* ½ m. wide.
San Juan Islands Archipelago of 172 islands at N end of Puget Sound, NW Washington.
San Matías Gulf Inlet of the Atlantic in Patagonia, Argentina; *c.* 65 m. long, *c.* 80 m. wide.
San Miguel Bay Inlet of the Philippine Sea in SE Luzon, Philippines; 25 m. long, 10–18 m. wide.
San Miguel Island Largest of the Pearl Islands, E Panama, in the Gulf of Panama; 17 m. long, 8 m. wide.
Sannikov Strait Arctic Ocean, joining Laptev and East Siberian seas and separating Anjou and Lyakhov groups of New Siberian Islands; 30 m. wide.
San Pedro Channel Passage between Santa Catalina Island and mainland of s California; *c.* 20 m. wide. Also called Catalina Channel.
Santa Barbara Channel Strait between s California coast and Santa Barbara Islands; *c.* 70 m. long, *c.* 20–30 m. wide.
Santa Catalina Island (or Catalina Island) One of the Santa Barbara Islands, off coast of s California; 22 m. long. Popular resort.

Santa Catarina Island Brazil, in the Atlantic Ocean, forming part of Santa Catarina state; 33 m. long, up to 10 m. wide. Linked to mainland by steel bridge at Florianópolis.

Santa Cruz Islands Volcanic group of the Solomon Islands, in the SW Pacific; 370 sq. m. Largest island is Ndeni.

Santa Inés Island Tierra del Fuego archipelago, Chile, between the Pacific and the Strait of Magellan; 75 m. long, 50 m. wide.

Santa Isabel Volcanic island of the Solomons, SW Pacific; 1,800 sq. m. Also spelled Ysabel.

Santaren Channel Strait between Cay Sal Bank and Great Bahama Bank in the West Indies, connecting the Straits of Florida and Old Bahama Channel; *c.* 125 m. long.

Santa Rosa Sound Lagoon, NW Florida, sheltered from the Gulf of Mexico by Santa Rosa Island (narrow barrier beach, *c.* 50 m. long); 35 m. long, up to 2 m. wide.

Santiago Island Central Galápagos Islands, Ecuador; 203 sq. m. Also called San Salvador Island and James Island.

Santo Antão Island Northwesternmost of the Cape Verde Islands, Atlantic Ocean; 301 sq. m.

São José Bay Inlet of the Atlantic off NE Brazil, between mainland and São Luís Island; *c.* 50 m. long.

São Luís Island N Maranhão, Brazil, between bays of São Marcos and São José; 35 m. long, 20 m. wide.

São Marcos Bay Inlet of the Atlantic off NE Brazil, between the mainland and São Luís Island; *c.* 60 m. long, up to 10 m. wide.

São Miguel Island Largest of the Azores, Atlantic Ocean, in the E part of the group; 288 sq. m. Also called St Michael Island.

São Nicolau Island One of the Cape Verde Islands, in the central part of the group; 132 sq. m. Also called St Nicholas Island.

São Sebastião Island SE Brazil, separated from mainland by narrow channel; 130 sq. m.

São Tiago Island Largest of the Cape Verde Islands, in the Leeward group; 383 sq. m. Also called Santiago Island.

Sarangani Bay Inlet of Celebes Sea in S Mindanao, Philippines; 20 m. long, 10 m. wide.

Saronic Gulf Inlet of the Aegean in central Greece, separating Attica from the Peloponnesus; 50 m. long, 30 m. wide. Also called Gulf of Aegina.

Saros, Gulf of Inlet of the Aegean in Turkey, W of Gallipoli Peninsula; 37 m. long, 22 m. wide.

Satsuma Peninsula SW Kyushu, Japan, between East China Sea and Kagoshima; 35 m. N-S, 25 m. E-W. Known for Satsuma ware (porcelain).

Savaii Volcanic island of Western Samoa; 703 sq. m. It is the largest and most westerly of the group. Formerly called Chatham Island.

Savu Islands Group of the Lesser Sundas, Indonesia, in the Savu Sea. Largest is Savu (160 sq. m.). Also spelled Sawoe.

Savu Sea (or Sawoe Sea) Section of the Indian Ocean in Indonesia; lies between Sumba, Flores and Timor islands; *c.* 170 m. wide.

Scapa Flow Area of water in the Orkneys, between Pomona, Hoy, Flotta, South Ronaldsay and Burray; 50 sq. m. Important naval anchorage.

Schlei Estuarine inlet of the Baltic, NW Germany; 25 m. long, average ½ m. wide.

Schouten Islands Archipelago off NW New Guinea, at entrance to Geelvink Bay; 1,231 sq. m. Comprise Biak, Supiori, Numfor and several small islands. Also called Misore Islands.

Sebastián Vizcaíno Bay Inlet of the Pacific on W coast of Lower California, NW Mexico; *c.* 60 m. in diameter, 40 m. wide.

Sebuku Island of Indonesia, off SE coast of Borneo, in Macassar Strait; 20 m. long, 6 m. wide. Also spelled Seboekoe.

Sechura Bay Inlet of the Pacific in Piura department, NW Peru; 15 m. long, 40 m. wide.

Seechelt Inlet SW arm of Jervis Inlet, SW British Columbia, between mainland and Seechelt Peninsula; 22 m. long, 1–2 m. wide.

Seguam Island One of the Aleutian Islands, SW Alaska; 13 m. long, 8 m. wide.

Seiland Island, N Norway, at mouth of Alta Fjord, in the Norwegian Sea; 216 sq. m.

Seine, Bay of the English Channel, on the Normandy coast, between Barfleur Point and Antifer Cape; 25 m. long, 65 m. wide. Receives Seine River.

Sejero Bay NW Zealand, Denmark; 24 m. wide.

Semangka Bay Inlet of Sunda Strait in S Sumatra, Indonesia; 40 m. long, 35 m. wide at entrance. Sometimes spelled Semangko.

Semau Coral island of Indonesia, in Savu Sea, separated from NE tip of Timor by Semau Strait; 17 m. long, 8 m. wide. Also spelled Semaoe.

Semisopochnoi Island One of the Rat group, Aleutian Islands, SW Alaska; 12 m. long, 10 m. wide. Uninhabited.

Senja Island in the Norwegian Sea, N Norway, just off the coast; 614 sq. m. Formerly Senjen.

Senyavin Islands Group of the Caroline Islands, comprising Ant, Pakin and Ponape.

Sepetiba Bay Atlantic coast of Rio de Janeiro state, Brazil; 8 m. long, 30 m. wide; Marambaia Island and a sand bar almost cut it off from the open Atlantic.

Serrano Island Aysén province, S Chile, just N of Wellington Island; *c.* 40 m. long. Also called Little Wellington Island.

Setúbal Bay Inlet of the Atlantic off W coast of Portugal, between Cape Espichel and Cape Sines; 20 m. long, 35 m. wide.

Severnaya Zemlya Archipelago to the N of Taimyr Peninsula, Russian SFSR, in the Arctic Ocean, separating Kara and Laptev seas; 14,300 sq. m.

Seward Peninsula W Alaska, between Norton Sound, Bering Strait, Chukchi Sea and Kotzebue Sound; 210 m. long, 90–140 m. wide.

Shannon Island NE Greenland, in Greenland Sea, separated from mainland by Shannon Sound (7–10 m. wide); 35 m. long, 5–15 m. wide.

Shantar Islands Russian SFSR, in SW section of Sea of Okhotsk; 965 sq. m. Comprise 4 large and 8 small islands; largest is Bolshoi Shantar Island (35 m. long, 28 m. wide).

Shark Bay Inlet of the Indian Ocean in W Western Australia; 150 m. long, 60 m. wide.

Shelekhov Gulf NE section of Sea of Okhotsk, NE Siberian Russian SFSR. Formerly called Penzhina Gulf.

Shelikof Strait S Alaska, between Alaska Peninsula and Kodiak and Afognak islands; 130 m. long, 30 m. wide.
Sherbro Island Sierra Leone, in the Atlantic, 65 m. SSE of Freetown; 30 m. long, up to 15 m. wide; separated from the mainland by Sherbro River (an arm of the Atlantic, *c.* 50 m. long) and Shebar Strait.
Shikoku Smallest of the 4 main islands of Japan; *c.* 6,860 sq. m. Lies S of Honshu, E of Kyushu, between the Inland Sea and the Philippine Sea.
Shimabara Bay NE arm of Amakusa Sea, W Kyushu, Japan; *c.* 30 m. long, 13 m. wide.
Shimabara Peninsula SE projection of Hizen Peninsula, W Kyushu, Japan, between Tachibana and Shimabara bays; 20 m. long, 11 m. wide.
Shimo-jima Largest of the Amakusa Islands, Japan, in the East China Sea; 227 sq. m. Sometimes spelled Simozima.
Shippigan Island Gulf of St Lawrence, at entrance to Chaleur Bay; 13 m. long, 8 m. wide.
Shmidt Island (or Schmidt Island) Kara Sea, 25 m. off Komsomolets Island (Severnaya Zemlya); 290 sq. m.
Shoalwater Bay Inlet of the Coral Sea in E Queensland, Australia, between Cape Townshend and Stanage Point; 26 m. long, 20 m. wide.
Shokalski Strait Between Oktyabrskaya Revolyutsiya and Bolshevik islands (Severnaya Zemlya), joining the Kara and Laptev seas of the Arctic Ocean; 100 m. long, 15–30 m. wide. Also spelled Shokal'skiy Strait.
Shortland Islands Volcanic group of the Solomon Islands, SW Pacific; *c.* 200 sq. m. Largest is Shortland Island (10 m. long, 8 m. wide).
Shumagin Islands SW Alaska, in the N Pacific, off S coast of Alaska Peninsula; there are about 20 islands and islets in the group.
Siam, Gulf of Arm of the South China Sea, NE of Malay Peninsula; 450 m. long, 300–350 m. wide.
Siangshan Bay Inlet of the East China Sea in Chekiang province, China; 40 m. long, 10 m. wide at mouth.
Siargao Island One of the Philippine Islands, off NE tip of Mindanao; 169 sq. m.
Siberut Largest of the Mentawai Islands, Indonesia, off W coast of Sumatra; 70 m. long, 25 m. wide. Also spelled Siberoet, also called Groot Fortuin.
Sibuyan Island Philippines, in Sibuyan Sea, S of Luzon; 173 sq. m.
Sibuyan Sea Central Philippines, between Luzon, Mindoro, Panay and Masbate.
Sidra, Gulf of Inlet of the Mediterranean, along the coast of Libya, between Benghazi and Misurata; 275 m. wide.
Silver Bank Shoal in the West Indies, separated from Mouchoir Bank (W) by 20-m.-wide Silver Bank Passage; *c.* 35 m. wide.
Simpson Strait Arm of the Arctic Ocean, Northwest Territories, between King William Island and Adelaide Peninsula; 40 m. long, 2–10 m. wide.
Simulue Island of Indonesia, in the Indian Ocean, off NW coast of Sumatra; 712 sq. m. Also spelled Simeuloee, Simalur and Simeulu.
Simushir Island One of the central group of the main Kurile Islands, Russian SFSR; 126 sq. m.
Singapore Strait Channel between Singapore island and the Riouw Archipelago of Indonesia; connects Strait of Malacca and South China Sea; 65 m. long, 10 m. wide.
Singitic Gulf Arm of the Aegean between Sithonia and Akte promontories of Chalcidice peninsula; 30 m. long, 51 m. wide. Also called Gulf of Hagion Oros.
Singkep Island of the Lingga Archipelago, Indonesia, in the South China Sea; *c.* 320 sq. m.
Sipora One of the Mentawai Islands, Indonesia, in the Indian Ocean, off W coast of Sumatra; 30 m. long, 12 m. wide. Also spelled Sipura and Sipoera.
Siquijor Island of the Philippines, in the Mindanao Sea, off SE coast of Negros; 130 sq. m.
Sir Edward Pellew Islands Gulf of Carpentaria, off E coast of Northern Territory, Australia; 800 sq. m. Largest is Vanderlin Island (17 m. long, 9 m. wide).
Sir Joseph Banks Islands Spencer Gulf, off SE coast of Eyre Peninsula, South Australia; consist of *c.* 20 islands, islets and rocks.
Sithonia Center prong of Chalcidice peninsula, Greece, on the Aegean Sea; 30 m. long, 11 m. wide. Also called Longos.
Sitkalidak Island S Alaska, in the Gulf of Alaska, off Kodiak Island; 23 m. long, 3–6 m. wide.
Skaga Fjord Inlet of Greenland Sea in N Iceland; 25 m. long, 7–17 m. wide.
Skjoldungen Island SE Greenland, in the Atlantic Ocean; 30 m. long, 4–8 m. wide.
Skyring Sound S Chile, between mainland, Riesco Island and Muñoz Gamero Peninsula; 60 m. long, 5–20 m. wide.
Sleat, Sound of Strait between Inverness mainland and Isle of Skye, Scotland; 23 m. long, 2–7 m. wide.
Smaalandsfarvand (or Vordingborg Bay) Strait in Denmark; extends E from the Great Belt between Zealand, Lolland, Falster and Moen islands.
Smith Bay Inlet of Beaufort Sea in N Alaska; 20 m. wide.
Smith Island One of the South Shetland Islands, off Palmer Peninsula, Antarctica; 13 m. long, 5½ m. wide.
Smith Sound Sea passage between NW Greenland and E Ellesmere Island; 55 m. long, 30–45 m. wide.
Smyrna, Gulf of Inlet of the Aegean in W Turkey, opposite Lesbos island; 35 m. long, 14 m. wide. Also called Gulf of Izmir.
Smyth Channel Arm of the Pacific, S Chile, connecting Strait of Magellan and Nelson Strait and separating Adelaide and Rennell islands from Muñoz Gamero Peninsula; 100 m. long. Sometimes spelled Smith.
Snow Hill Island Antarctica, off Palmer Peninsula, in the Weddell Sea; 17½ m. long, 5 m. wide.
Sogod Bay Inlet of Mindanao Sea in S Leyte, Philippines; 25 m. long.
Solent, The Channel between Isle of Wight and mainland of Hampshire, England, extending from the Needles to Southampton Water and Spithead; 15 m. long, ¾–5 m. wide.
Solor Islands Group of the Lesser Sundas, Indonesia, in the Flores Sea; comprise Lomblem, Adonara and Solor.
Solovetski Island Group in the White Sea, Russian SFSR, at the entrance to Onega Bay; *c.* 150 sq. m. Largest is Solovetski Island (110 sq. m.). Also spelled Solovetskiye.
Solund Islands Group in the North Sea, W Norway, at the mouth of Sogne Fjord. Formerly spelled Sulen.

Solway Firth Arm of the Irish Sea between sw Scotland and NW England; 40 m. long, 20 m. wide at mouth, narrowing to 2 m. wide at NE end.
Somerset Island Northwest Territories, in the Arctic Ocean; 9,594 sq. m.
Sondre Strom Fjord Inlet of Davis Strait in sw Greenland, on the Arctic Circle; 120 m. long, 1–5 m. wide.
Sonogi Peninsula sw projection of Hizen Peninsula, w Kyushu, Japan, between East China Sea and Omura Bay; 25 m. long, 12 m. wide. Sometimes spelled Sonoki.
Sor Fjord 1. Narrow arm of Hardanger Fjord, sw Norway.
2. Inlet of the North Sea, sw Norway; *c.* 40 m. long, 1 m. wide.
Soroy Island, N Norway, in the Norwegian Sea, 11 m. w of Hammerfest; 315 sq. m.
Sortland Sound Strait, N Norway, between Langoy and Hinnoy; 50 m. long, 1–4 m. wide.
South Aulatsivik Island NE Labrador, at entrance of Webb's Bay; 22 m. long, 12 m. wide.
South Beveland Island, sw Netherlands, bounded by Het Sloe, Western Scheldt, Eastern Scheldt and Zandkreek; 135 sq. m.
South Island Larger of the two main islands of New Zealand; 58,093 sq. m.
South Sandwich Trench Submarine depression in the South Atlantic, near the South Sandwich Islands, N of the Weddell Sea.
South Uist Island of the Outer Hebrides, Scotland, between Benbecula and Barra; 2,810 sq. m.
Spencer Gulf Inlet of the Indian Ocean in South Australia, between Eyre and Yorke peninsulas; 200 m. long, 80 m. wide. Sometimes called Spencer's Gulf.
Spithead Channel between Isle of Wight and mainland of Hampshire, England.
Squillace, Gulf of Inlet of the Ionian Sea in s Italy, between Cape Rizzuto and Cape Stilo; 45 m. long, 20 m. wide.
Sriharikota Narrow island along the E coast of Madras, India; *c.* 45 m. long.
Staten Island Argentina, 18 m. E of SE tip of main island of Tierra del Fuego, in the s Atlantic; 209 sq. m.
Steele Island Weddell Sea, off Richard Black Coast, Antarctica; 13 m. long, 7 m. wide.
Stephens Passage Channel between Admiralty Island and mainland, SE Alaska; 105 m. long.
Stewart Island One of the Tierra del Fuego islands, s Chile, between Londonderry Island and Brecknock Peninsula; 22 m. long.
Stor Fjord Inlet of North Sea, w Norway; 70 m. long.
Stromo Largest of the Faeroe Islands, in the Atlantic Ocean; 144 sq. m.
Stuart Channel Arm of the Strait of Georgia, sw British Columbia, between Vancouver Island and Gulf Islands; 30 m. long, 1–3 m. wide.
Sturge Island Largest of the Balleny Islands, Antarctica, off Victoria Land; 23½ m. long, 7 m. wide.
Suess Land Peninsula of E Greenland between Franz Josef Fjord and w arm of King Oscar Fjord; 50 m. long, 5–30 m. wide.
Suez, Gulf of NW arm of the Red Sea, E Egypt, joined to Mediterranean by Suez Canal; *c.* 180 m. long, 20 m. wide.
Suez, Isthmus of NE Egypt, between Gulf of Suez and Mediterranean, connecting Asia and Africa; 72 m. wide at narrowest part.
Sula Islands Group of the N Moluccas, Indonesia, between Celebes and the Obi Islands, in the Molucca Sea; 1,873 sq. m. Largest is Taliabu. Also spelled Soela.
Sulu Sea w Pacific, between sw Philippines and Borneo; over 400 m. E-W.
Sulzberger Bay Inlet in NW coast of Marie Byrd Land, Antarctica, between Edward VII Peninsula and Ruppert Coast; 79 m. long, 87½ m. wide.
Sumba Island of the Lesser Sundas, Indonesia, in the Indian Ocean; 4,306 sq. m. Also spelled Soemba, and formerly known as Sandalwood Island.
Sumba Strait Channel between Flores and Sumba, Indonesia; 140 m. long, 50 m. wide. Formerly called Sandalwood Strait.
Sumbawa Island of the Lesser Sundas, Indonesia, between Flores Sea and Indian Ocean; 5,965 sq. m. Also spelled Soembawa.
Sumner Strait Alexander Archipelago, SE Alaska, between Prince of Wales, Kupreanof and Kuiu islands.
Sunda Islands Group in Indonesia, comprising the w part of the Malay Archipelago, between South China Sea and Indian Ocean; divided into Greater and Lesser Sundas. Also spelled Soenda Islands.
Sunda Strait Indonesia, between Java and Sumatra, connecting Java Sea with Indian Ocean; 16–70 m. wide. Also spelled Soenda.
Sundene Strait between Ostero and Stromo, Faeroe Islands; *c.* 25 m. long, ½-2 m. wide.
Sunndals Fjord Inlet of the North Sea in w Norway; *c.* 30 m. long.
Suo Sea w section of Inland Sea, Japan, between Honshu and Kyushu; *c.* 60 m. long, 30 m. wide.
Supiori (or Soepiori) Island of the Schouten Islands, Netherlands New Guinea, at entrance to Geelvink Bay.
Surigao Strait Philippines, between Leyte and Mindanao, connecting Leyte Gulf and Mindanao Sea; *c.* 50 m. long, 10–20 m. wide.
Suruga Bay Inlet of the Philippine Sea in central Honshu, Japan; 35 m. N-S, 15–35 m. E-W.
Sverdrup Channel Arm of the Arctic Ocean, Northwest Territories, between Axel Heiberg and Meighen islands; 70 m. long, 40 m. wide.
Sverdrup Islands Archipelago, Northwest Territories, in the Arctic Ocean; they include Axel Heiberg, Ellef Ringnes, Amund Ringnes and Meighen islands as well as numerous smaller ones.
Swindle Island sw British Columbia, in Hecate Strait; 120 sq. m.

Tablas Island Philippines, just N of Panay; 265 sq. m.
Tablas Strait Philippines, between Mindoro and Tablas Island, leading from Sibuyan Sea to Sulu Sea; *c.* 30 m. wide.
Tadjoura, Gulf of Inlet of the Gulf of Aden, s of Bab el Mandeb, in Somali Republic; 50 m. long, 35 m. wide at mouth.
Tagula Largest island of the Louisiade Archipelago, Territory of Papua, in the sw Pacific; 50 m. long, 15 m. wide. Volcanic in origin.
Taigonos Peninsula Sea of Okhotsk, Russian SFSR,

separating Gizhiga and Penzhina bays; *c.* 150 m. long, *c.* 90 m. wide. Also spelled Taygonos.

Taimyr Peninsula Northernmost projection of Siberian Russian SFSR, on Kara and Laptev seas; 700 m. long. Northernmost point is Cape Chelyuskin. Also spelled Taymyr.

Taitao Peninsula S Chile, on the Pacific Ocean, S of Chonos Archipelago; *c.* 75 m. long, *c.* 70 m. wide.

Talaud Islands Group of Indonesia, in the Pacific, S of Mindanao (Philippines); 495 sq. m. Also called Talaur Islands, and sometimes spelled Talaut.

Taliabu Largest of the Sula Islands, N Moluccas, Indonesia, in the Molucca Sea; 68 m. long, 25 m. wide. Also spelled Taliaboe.

Tanega-shima Island of Japan, 20 m. S of Kyushu, between East China and Philippine seas; 176 sq. m.

Tangier Sound Passage of Chesapeake Bay, off Maryland and Virginia; *c.* 30 m. long, 3–7 m. wide.

Tanimbar Islands Group of the S Moluccas, Indonesia, in the Banda Sea; 2,172 sq. m. Also called Timorlaut (or Timorlaoet), and also spelled Tenimbar.

Tanna Volcanic island of the New Hebrides, SW Pacific; *c.* 215 sq. m.

Tañon Strait Philippines, between Cebu and Negros, linking Visayan and Mindanao seas; 100 m. long, 3–17 m. wide.

Taranto, Gulf of Arm of the Ionian Sea, S Italy, between capes Santa Maria di Leuca and Colonne; forms "instep" of Italy; 85 m. long, 85 m. wide.

Tasermiut Inlet of the Atlantic in S Greenland, extending to edge of inland icecap; 45 m. long, 1–3 m. wide.

Tasman Bay Inlet of Tasman Sea, N South Island, New Zealand; 45 m. E-W, 30 m. N-S. Sometimes called Blind Bay.

Tasman Sea Arm of the South Pacific between SE Australia, Tasmania and New Zealand.

Tatar Strait Arm of the Pacific between Sakhalin and mainland of Asia; joins Sea of Japan and Sea of Okhotsk; *c.* 350 m. long, 5–80 m. wide. Also called Gulf of Tatary.

Taveuni Volcanic island of Fiji, SW Pacific; 168 sq. m.

Tavoy Island N Mergui Archipelago, Lower Burma, in the Andaman Sea; 21 m. long, 5 m. wide.

Tawitawi Group Island group in the Sulu Archipelago of the Philippines, between Sulu and Celebes seas; largest island is Tawitawi (229 sq. m.). Also written Tawi-Tawi and Tawi Tawi.

Tayabas Bay Inlet in S Luzon, Philippines; *c.* 40 m. long, *c.* 20 m. wide.

Taya Bay Inlet of South China Sea in Kwangtung province, China, NE of Hong Kong; 15 m. long, 20 m. wide. Formerly called Bias Bay.

Taz Bay E inlet of Ob Bay, Tyumen oblast, Russian SFSR, N of the Arctic Circle; 250 m. long, 25–40 m. wide.

Tebingtinggi Island of Indonesia, off E Sumatra, in the Strait of Malacca; 45 m. long, 15 m. wide. Also called Rantau.

Tehuantepec, Gulf of Inlet of the Pacific in S Mexico; 300 m. WNW-ESE.

Tehuantepec, Isthmus of S Mexico, between Gulf of Campeche and Gulf of Tehuantepec; *c.* 125 m. N-S.

Temple Bay Inlet of the Coral Sea in NE Cape York Peninsula, N Queensland, Australia; 26 m. long, 11 m. wide.

Temryuk Gulf S inlet of Sea of Azov, Russian SFSR, just E of Kerch Strait; 15 m. long, 35 m. wide.

Ten Degree Channel Seaway between Little Andaman Island and the Nicobar Islands, linking Bay of Bengal and Andaman Sea; *c.* 90 m. wide.

Tenerife (or Teneriffe) Largest of the Canary Islands, Spain, in the Atlantic; 794½ sq. m.

Terceira Island Easternmost island of the central Azores group, in the Atlantic; 153 sq. m. Volcanic origin.

Términos, Laguna de Inlet of the Gulf of Campeche in SW Yucatan Peninsula, SE Mexico; 45 m. long, 12–15 m. wide.

Terpeniye Gulf Inlet of the Sea of Okhotsk in E coast of Sakhalin island, Russian SFSR; 85 m. wide.

Texada Island SW British Columbia, in the Strait of Georgia, separated from mainland by Malaspina Strait; 118 sq. m.

Thames, Firth of SE arm of Hauraki Gulf, N North Island, New Zealand; 22 m. long, 10 m. wide.

Thasos Island in N Aegean Sea, Greece, off mouth of Mesta River; 170 sq. m. Sometimes spelled Thassos. Noted for gold mines in ancient times.

Thistil Fjord Inlet of the Greenland Sea in NE Iceland, between Melrakkasletta and Langanes peninsulas; 25 m. long, 40 m. wide at mouth.

Thousand Islands Group of *c.* 100 coral islets of Indonesia, in Java Sea, off NW coast of Java.

Thurston Peninsula Antarctica, between Bellingshausen and Amundsen seas.

Tiburón Island Mexico, in the Gulf of California, off W coast of Sonora state; 458 sq. m.

Tiburon Peninsula SW Haiti, between Gulf of Gonaives and the Caribbean; 140 m. long.

Ticao Island Philippines, just E of Masbate island; 129 sq. m.

Timor Sea Arm of the Indian Ocean between Timor and N coast of Australia; *c.* 300 m. wide.

Todos os Santos Bay Sheltered inlet of the Atlantic, E Brazil; 25 m. long, 20 m. wide. City of Salvador stands at entrance.

Togian Islands Group of Indonesia in the Gulf of Tomini, N Celebes; largest is Batudaka (18 m. long, 8 m. wide). Sometimes called Schildpad Islands.

Tokyo Bay Inlet of the Philippine Sea in central Honshu, Japan; 30 m. long, 20 m. wide.

Tolo, Gulf of Inlet of Molucca Sea in E Celebes, Indonesia; 100 m. N-S, 10–100 m. E-W. Also called Tomori Bay.

Tomini, Gulf of Inlet of Molucca Passage in E Celebes, Indonesia; 260 m. E-W, 60–130 m. N-S. Also called Gulf of Gorontalo.

Tonga Island group in S Pacific, 2,000 m. NE of Sydney; 250 sq. m. Also called Friendly Islands.

Tongatabu Coral island group of S Tonga, in the South Pacific; includes Tongatabu island, largest of Tonga group.

Tongue of the Ocean Channel of the Atlantic in the central Bahama Islands; *c.* 100 m. long.

Tonkin, Gulf of NW arm of South China Sea; 300 m. long, 150 m. wide.

Toronaic Gulf Arm of the Aegean between Kassandra and Sithonia prongs of Chalcidice peninsula, Greece;

over 30 m. long, up to 15 m. wide. Also called Gulf of Kassandra.
Tosa Bay Inlet of Philippine Sea in s Shikoku, Japan; 75 m. long, 35 m. wide.
Totten Coast Section of Wilkes Land, Antarctica, between Sabrina and Banzare coasts.
Toyama Bay Inlet of the Sea of Japan in central Honshu, E of Noto Peninsula; 40 m. long, 40 m. wide.
Trading Bay s Alaska, on w shore of Cook Inlet; 10 m. long, 30 m. wide.
Traill Island King Oscar Archipelago, E Greenland, in Greenland Sea; 70 m. long, 25 m. wide. Also spelled Trail.
Tres Marías Islands Archipelago in the Pacific, off coast of Nayarit state, w Mexico; *c.* 100 sq. m. Also called Las Tres Marías.
Trieste, Gulf of NE inlet of the Gulf of Venice, at the head of the Adriatic; 20 m. wide.
Trinity Bay 1. Bight of the Coral Sea in NE Queensland, Australia; 65 m. wide.
2. Inlet of the Atlantic in SE Newfoundland, between Avalon Peninsula and mainland; 80 m. long, 20 m. wide at entrance.
Trinity Island Antarctica, in the s Pacific, off NW coast of Palmer Peninsula; 13 m. long, 11 m. wide.
Trinity Opening Channel of the Coral Sea, cutting through the Great Barrier Reef, off NE coast of Queensland, Australia; *c.* 30 m. long, 6–11 m. wide.
Trondheim Channel Sound of the North Sea in w Norway, between Hitra and Smola islands and the mainland; 50 m. long, 3–5 m. wide.
Trondheim Fjord Inlet of the North Sea in Norway, generally regarded as the boundary between N and s Norway; *c.* 80 m. long, 2–15 m. wide.
Tsimpsean Peninsula w British Columbia, extending into Chatham Sound; 36 m. long, 12 m. wide at base.
Tsugaru Strait Channel between Honshu and Hokkaido, Japan, connecting Sea of Japan with the Pacific; 15–25 m. wide. Sometimes Tugaru.
Tsushima Island of Japan, between Korea Strait and Tshushima Strait; 271 sq. m.
Tshushima Strait Strait connecting Sea of Japan and East China Sea; *c.* 60 m. long, 40 m. wide.
Tubuai Islands (or Austral Islands) Volcanic group in the s Pacific, belonging to French Establishments in Oceania.
Tukangbesi Islands Group in Indonesia, between Flores and Molucca seas; largest is Wangiwangi (60 sq. m.). Also spelled Toekangbesi.
Tumaco Road Inlet of the Pacific in Nariño department, sw Colombia; 22 m. long, 12 m. wide at entrance.
Tunis, Gulf of Inlet of the Mediterranean in N Tunisia, between Cape Bon Peninsula and headland of Sidi Ali el Mekki; 30 m. long, 40 m. wide.
Tunungayualuk Island Atlantic Ocean, off E coast of Labrador; 12 m. long, 11 m. wide.
Turks Island Passage Channel in the Caribbean, separating Caicos Islands from Turks Islands; *c.* 20 m. wide.
Turks Islands E group of the Turks and Caicos Islands dependency of Jamaica, West Indies; total area of Turks and Caicos groups is 201.7 sq. m.
Turnagain Arm NE arm of Cook Inlet, on N side of Kenai Peninsula, s Alaska; 50 m. long, 2–13 m. wide.
Turneffe Island British Honduras, in the Caribbean Sea; 23 m. long, 3–7 m. wide.
Tuscan Archipelago Island group in the Tyrrhenian Sea, Italy, between Corsica and Tuscany coast; *c.* 115 sq. m. Comprises Elba, Monte Cristo and others.
Tuscarora Deep Ocean depth in the N Pacific, at N end of Japan Trench, off the Kurile Islands; 27,929 ft deep.
Tys Fjord Inlet of Vest Fjord, N Norway; 30 m. long, 2–9 m. wide.

Ubekendt Island w Greenland, in inlet of Baffin Bay; 20 m. long, 3–15 m. wide. Also spelled Ubekyendt.
Uchiura Bay Inlet of the Pacific in sw Hokkaido, Japan; 35 m. long, 30 m. wide. Sometimes called Volcano Bay, and formerly Iburi Bay.
Uliaser Islands Group of the s Moluccas, Indonesia, in the Banda Sea; 193 sq. m. Also spelled Oeliaser.
Ulithi (or Uluthi) Atoll in the w Caroline Islands, w Pacific; 19 m. long, 10 m. wide.
Ultima Esperanza Strait Sound, s Chile, on Patagonian coast of Magallanes province; 40 m. long, *c.* 3 m. wide.
Umanak Fjord Inlet of Baffin Bay in w Greenland; 100 m. long, 15–30 m. wide.
Umnak Island One of the Fox group, in the Aleutian Islands, sw Alaska; 83 m. long, 2–18 m. wide.
Unalaska Island One of the Fox group, in the Aleutian Islands, sw Alaska, just E of Umnak Island; 30 m. long, 6–30 m. wide.
Unga Island Largest of the Shumagin Islands, sw Alaska; 20 m. long, 11–14 m. wide.
Ungava Bay Inlet of Hudson Strait in N Quebec; 200 m. long, 160 m. wide.
Ungava Peninsula N Quebec, between Ungava and Hudson bays; 400 m. long, 350 m. wide.
Unimak Island One of the Fox group, Aleutian Islands, sw Alaska; 70 m. long, 17–30 m. wide.
Unimak Pass Sea passage in NE Aleutian Islands, sw Alaska, between Unimak Island and Krenitzin Islands; 20–30 m. wide.
Upernavik Ice Fjord Inlet of Baffin Bay in w Greenland; 30 m. long, 3–15 m. wide. Extends to edge of inland icecap. Also spelled Upernivik.
Upernavik Island w Greenland, between Umanak Fjord and Karrats Fjord; 17 m. long, 5–17 m. wide. Also spelled Upernivik.
Upolu Volcanic island of Western Samoa, in the s Pacific; 430 sq. m.
Uraba, Gulf of Inlet of the Caribbean Sea in NW Colombia; *c.* 50 m. long, *c.* 25 m. wide at entrance.
Urup Island Fourth largest of the Kurile Islands, Russian SFSR; 581 sq. m.
Usedom Island in the Baltic, divided between Mecklenburg (East Germany) and Szczecin (Poland); 172 sq. m.
Useless Bay Inlet in w coast of main island of Tierra del Fuego; 40 m. long, 17 m. wide at mouth.
Ussuri Bay (or Ussuri Gulf) Inlet of Peter the Great Bay, Russian SFSR, E of Muravyev-Amurski Peninsula; 35 m. long, *c.* 30 m. wide at mouth.
Utupua Volcanic island of the Santa Cruz group, Solomon Islands, in the sw Pacific; 15 m. long, 10 m. wide.
Uyak Bay Inlet of Shelikof Strait, w Kodiak Island, s Alaska; 35 m. long, 1–5 m. wide.

Vaigach Island Russian SFSR, in the Arctic Ocean, between Barents Sea and Kara Sea; 1,430 sq. m. Also spelled Vaygach.

Vaigat Strait, W Greenland, extending between Baffin Bay and head of Disko Bay and separating Disko island and Nugssuak peninsula; 90 m. long, 6–15 m. wide.

Valdés Peninsula Argentina, on the Atlantic, between San Matías Gulf and Golfo Nuevo; 55 m. N-S, 35 m. E-W.

Valiente Peninsula W Panama, on the Caribbean, forming E side of Chiriquí Lagoon; 20 m. long, 4 m. wide.

Van Diemen Gulf Arm of the Timor Sea between Cobourg Peninsula, N coast of Northern Territory, and Melville Island, Australia; 90 m. long, 50 m. wide.

Vangunu Volcanic island in the New Georgia group, Solomon Islands, SW Pacific; *c.* 15 m. long, 10 m. wide.

Vanikoro Volcanic island in the Santa Cruz group of the Solomon Islands, SW Pacific; 30 m. long, 10 m. wide.

Van Mijen Fjord E arm of Bell Sound in SW West Spitsbergen, Spitsbergen group; 40 m. long, 1–10 m. wide.

Vansittart Island Northwest Territories, in Foxe Channel, just off S Melville Peninsula; 47 m. long, 6–16 m. wide.

Vanua Lava Largest of the Banks Islands, New Hebrides, in the S Pacific; 15 m. long, 10 m. wide. Volcanic origin.

Vanua Levu Second largest of the Fiji islands, in the SW Pacific; 2,137 sq. m. Volcanic origin. Formerly called Sandalwood Island.

Varanger Fjord Inlet of Barents Sea in NE Norway; 60 m. long, 3–35 m. wide.

Varmdo Island in the Baltic, E Sweden; 135 sq. m.

Vefsn Fjord Inlet of the North Sea in N central Norway; *c.* 30 m. long.

Vega Island Antarctica, off NE coast of Palmer Peninsula, in the S Pacific; 17½ m. long, 6 m. wide.

Vella Lavella Volcanic island, Solomon Islands, in the SW Pacific; 25 m. long, 10 m. wide.

Venezuela, Gulf of Inlet of the Caribbean in Venezuela and Colombia; *c.* 75 m. long, 150 m. wide at widest part. Sometimes called Gulf of Maracaibo.

Venice, Gulf of N section of the Adriatic Sea between Istria and delta of Po River; 50–60 m. wide.

Vermilion Bay Arm of the Gulf of Mexico in S Louisiana, at mouth of Vermilion River; *c.* 22 m. long, 10 m. wide.

Vesteralen Archipelago, N Norway, in the Norwegian Sea, N of the Lofoten Islands; *c.* 1,200 sq. m. Largest island is Hinnoy. Also spelled Vesteraalan.

Vestfjarda Peninsula NW Iceland, extending into Denmark Strait; 80 m. long, maximum width 90 m. (at NW end).

Vest Fjord Inlet of the North Sea in N Norway, between mainland and the Lofoten Islands; 100 m. long, 50 m. wide at mouth.

Vestvagoy One of the Lofoten Islands, N Norway, in the North Sea; 159 sq. m. Also spelled Vestvaago.

Victoria Fjord Inlet of Lincoln Sea in N Greenland; 90 m. long, 17–24 m. wide.

Victoria Sea Name sometimes given to the shallow section of the Arctic Ocean NW of Franz Josef Land; formerly Queen Victoria Sea.

Victoria Strait Arm of the Arctic Ocean between Victoria Island and King William Island, Northwest Territories; 100 m. long, 50–80 m. wide.

Vidal Island Uninhabited island off Patagonian coast of S Chile; 28 m. long.

Vineyard Sound SE Massachusetts, separating Martha's Vineyard from Elizabeth Islands and tip of Cape Cod; *c.* 20 m. long, 3–7 m. wide.

Visayan Islands Group in the Philippines, between Luzon and Mindanao; main islands of group are Bohol, Cebu, Leyte, Masbate, Negros, Panay and Samar.

Visayan Sea Philippines, between Leyte, Masbate, Panay, Negros and Cebu.

Vogelkop Peninsula forming extreme NW extension of New Guinea; *c.* 225 m. E-W, *c.* 135 m. N-S. Name comes from resemblance to shape of a bird's head. Formerly called Berau Peninsula.

Volos, Gulf of Inlet of the Aegean in Thessaly, Greece; *c.* 20 m. long, *c.* 20 m. wide.

Waddenzee Shallow section of the North Sea between West Frisian Islands and Netherlands mainland.

Waigeu Largest island of the Raja Ampat group, Netherlands New Guinea, 40 m. W of Vogelkop peninsula; 70 m. long, 30 m. wide. Also spelled Waigeo and formerly Waygiou.

Wakasa Bay Inlet of the Sea of Japan in S Honshu, Japan, between Kyoga Point and Echizen Point; 45 m. long, 20 m. wide.

Wake Island Atoll and 3 islets between Hawaii and Guam; *c.* 45 m. long, 2¼ m. wide. Fell to Japanese in 1941; recaptured by U.S. in 1945, after heavy bombing.

Walgreen Coast Section of Marie Byrd Land, Antarctica, on Amundsen Sea.

Walker Bay Inlet of the Atlantic in South Africa, 40 m. SE of Cape Town; 12 m. long, 31 m. wide at mouth.

Wandel Sea Marginal sea of the Arctic Ocean, off NE Greenland.

Watubela Islands Group of the S Moluccas, Indonesia, between Banda and Arafura seas. Largest are Kasiui (9 m. long, 2 m. wide) and Tior (6 m. long, 3 m. wide). Also spelled Watoebela.

Wellesley Islands Uninhabited group in Gulf of Carpentaria, off NW coast of Queensland, Australia; largest is Mornington Island.

Wellington Channel Arm of the Arctic Ocean, Northwest Territories, between Cornwallis and Devon islands; 120 m. long, 25–40 m. wide.

Wellington Island S Chile, separated from Madre de Dios Archipelago by Trinidad Gulf; 100 m. long, 15–25 m. wide.

Wells, Port Bay on NE shore of Kenai Peninsula, S Alaska; 35 m. long, 1–5 m. wide.

Wessel Islands Arafura Sea, extending NE from Napier Peninsula, Northern Territory, Australia, in 70-m. chain. Largest is 30 m. long, 7 m. wide.

West Australian Current Cold ocean current in the Indian Ocean, flowing N along coast of Western Australia.

West Greenland Current Cold ocean current in Labrador Sea, flowing N along SW coast of Greenland.

West Spitsbergen Largest island of the Spitsbergen group, in the Arctic Ocean; *c.* 15,000 sq. m.

Wetar Island of the S Moluccas, Indonesia, in Banda Sea, across 40-m.-wide Wetar Strait from NE Timor; 1,400 sq. m. Also spelled Wetter.

Whale Sound Inlet of Baffin Bay in NW Greenland; 40 m. long, 10–15 m. wide.
Wharton Deep Ocean depth in the Indian Ocean, SE of Cocos Islands; 21,191 ft.
Whidbey Island NW Washington, in Puget Sound; *c.* 40 m. long.
White Bay Inlet of the Atlantic in NE Newfoundland; 60 m. long, 20 m. wide at entrance.
White Island Northwest Territories, in Frozen Strait, off S Melville Peninsula; 38 m. long, 6–10 m. wide.
Whiteside Channel S extension of the Strait of Magellan, between main island of Tierra del Fuego and Dawson Island; *c.* 50 m. long.
Wiencke Island Southernmost island of Palmer Archipelago, Antarctica.
Wijde Fjord Inlet of the Arctic in West Spitsbergen; 70 m. long, 3–14 m. wide.
Wilczek Land Island in E Franz Josef Land, Russian SFSR, in the Arctic Ocean; 50 m. long, 40 m. wide.
Wilhelm II Coast Part of Antarctica, on Indian Ocean.
Wilkins Strait E Bellingshausen Sea, Antarctica, between Charcot Island and Alexander I Island; 70 m. long, *c.* 17½ m. wide.
Willaumez Peninsula N New Britain, Bismarck Archipelago; 35 m. long, 10 m. wide.
Wilson's Promontory Peninsula forming southernmost extremity of Australia; 22 m. long N-S, 8 m. wide E-W.
Windward Passage Strait in the West Indies separating Cuba from Haiti, connecting the Atlantic and the Caribbean; *c.* 50 m. wide.
Wollaston Peninsula SW section of Victoria Island, Northwest Territories, extending W into Amundsen Gulf; 140 m. long, 60–70 m. wide.
Wolstenholme Fjord Inlet of Baffin Bay in NW Greenland, extending to edge of inland icecap; 20 m. long, 5–20 m. wide.
Woodlark Island Volcanic island, Territory of Papua, SW Pacific, 175 m. SE of New Guinea; 40 m. long, 10 m. wide.
Wowoni Island of Indonesia, off SE coast of Celebes; 21 m. long, 20 m. wide.
Wrangell Island Alexander Archipelago, SE Alaska, between Etolin Island and mainland; 30 m. long, 5–14 m. wide.

Yaeyama-gunto (or Yaeyama-retto) Southernmost group of the Ryukyu Islands; 247 sq. m.
Yakobi Island SE Alaska, in Alexander Archipelago, W of Chichagof Island; 17 m. long, 7 m. wide. Also spelled Jacobi.
Yaku-shima Island of Japan, in the East China Sea, 40 m. S of Cape Sata, Kyushu; 208 sq. m.
Yakutat Bay Inlet of the Gulf of Alaska in SE Alaska; 75 m. long, 20 m. wide at mouth.
Yamal Peninsula NW Siberia, Russian SFSR, between Kara Sea and Ob Bay, N of the Arctic Circle; *c.* 400 m. long, up to 140 m. wide.
Yatsushiro Bay Inlet of the East China Sea between Kyushu and Amakusa Islands, Japan; 42 m. long, 10 m. wide.
Yawri Bay Inlet of the Atlantic in SW Sierra Leone, S of Sierra Leone Peninsula; 10 m. long, 22 m. wide.
Yenisei Gulf Kara Sea, Russian SFSR, at estuary of Yenisei River; up to 90 m. wide. Sometimes also spelled Enisei.
Ymer Island King Oscar Archipelago, E Greenland, in Franz Josef Fjord; 60 m. long, 3–28 m. wide.
Yorke Peninsula S South Australia, between Spencer Gulf and Gulf St Vincent; 160 m. long, 35 m. wide.
York Sound Inlet of Timor Sea in NE Western Australia; 20 m. long, 10 m. wide.
Young Island One of the Balleny Islands, Antarctica, off Victoria Land; 16½ m. long, *c.* 4 m. wide.
Ysabel Channel Bismarck Archipelago, SW Pacific, between Mussau and Lavongai; 50 m. wide.
Yucatan Channel Strait connecting Gulf of Mexico and Caribbean Sea between Yucatan and Cuba; 135 m. wide.
Yugorski Shar Strait, Russian SFSR, joining Barents and Kara seas between Vaigach Island and Yugor Peninsula; 25 m. long, 5 m. wide. Also spelled Yugorskiy Shar and also called Yugor Strait.

Zapata Peninsula Extension of Cienaga de Zapata marshland, SW Cuba; *c.* 60 m. long, up to 20 m. wide.
Zarembo Island SE Alaska, in Alexander Archipelago; 14 m. long, 9 m. wide.
Zealand Largest island of Denmark, between the Kattegat and the Baltic Sea; 2,709 sq. m.

Acknowledgments

For permission to reproduce copyright material, the Editor and the Publishers are grateful to: Curtis Brown Ltd and William Morrow & Co Inc, for an extract from *Growing up in New Guinea* by Margaret Mead, published by Routledge, London, 1931, and Penguin Books, Harmondsworth, Middx, 1954; John Murray Ltd and William Morrow & Co Inc, for an extract from *A Pattern of Islands* by Sir Arthur Grimble, published by John Murray Ltd, London, 1955, and by William Morrow & Co Inc as *We Chose the Islands*, New York, 1952 (copyright Sir Arthur Grimble 1952).

The color plates were supplied by: J. Allan Cash (Plates 6 and 13); the Central Office of Information (Plates 3 and 14, Crown Copyright photographs); Victor Glasstone (Plates 1 and 8); the Pictorial Press Ltd (Plates 5 and 10); W. A. Poucher, F.R.P.S. (Plates 11 and 15); Tom Weir (Plates 2, 4, 7, 12 and 16).

The monochrome photographs in the text were supplied by: the Agent General for Queensland (page 146); the Anglo-Chilean Society (page 120); the Australian News and Information Department (pages 41, 79 and 298); Anne Bolt (pages 70, 141, 169, 181 and 319); Central Press Photos Ltd (page 306); the Danish Embassy (page 77); the Deutsche Zentrale für Fremdenverkehr, Frankfurt AM (pages 136 and 155); the Exclusive News Agency Ltd (pages 68, 73, 88, 225, 296 and 321); the Finnish Travel Information Center (page 132); the French Government Tourist Office (pages 106, 215 and 310); Victor Glasstone (pages 112, 291 and 301); the Greek Government Information Office (page 218); the Greek State Tourist Office (pages 104, 118 and 258); the High Commissioner for Canada (pages 46, 123, 137, 224, 264 and 266); E. O. Hoppé (pages 36, 102 and 273); the India Information Service (page 40); the Indonesian Embassy (pages 61 and 93); the Irish Tourist Office (page 166); the Italian State Tourist Department (page 34); the Keystone Press Agency Ltd (page 185); the National Travel Association of Denmark (page 174); the Netherlands National Tourists Office (page 324); the Norway Travel Association (page 286); the Norwegian National Tourist Office (page 179); the Pictorial Press Ltd (page 57); Polar Photos (pages 55, 234 and 249); the Portuguese State Information and Tourist Office (page 52); Qantas Empire Airways Ltd (page 207); the Society for Cultural Relations with the USSR (page 64); the Swedish National Travel Association (pages 80 and 144); Tom Weir (pages 12, 128, 148 and 265).

The map used for the endpapers was supplied by the Istituto Geografico de Agóstini, Novara.

Great care has been taken to trace all the owners of copyright material used in this book. If any have been inadvertently overlooked or omitted, acknowledgment will gladly be made in any future edition.

The index was compiled by Dariel Davies.

Index

The figures in **bold type** *indicate the page numbers on which illustrations will be found*